THE NEW OUTLINE
OF
Modern Knowledge

THE ARTS AND SCIENCES OF THE
TWENTIETH CENTURY INTERPRETED AND
CLARIFIED BY TWENTY-SIX EMINENT AUTHORITIES
EDITED, WITH A PREFACE, BY

Alan Pryce-Jones

19 _ 56

SIMON AND SCHUSTER · NEW YORK

LIBRARY OF CONGRESS CATALOG CARD NUMBER: 56–11250
MANUFACTURED IN THE UNITED STATES OF AMERICA
PRINTED BY MURRAY PRINTING COMPANY,
WAKEFIELD, MASS
BOUND BY THE BOOK PRODUCTION COMPANY, INC., NEW YORK

CONTENTS

6

III. ART

IV. POLITICS AND ECONOMICS

V. LAW

PREFACE

by ALAN PRYCE-JONES

IT IS NEARLY A quarter of a century since the publication of
An Outline of Modern Knowledge, edited by Dr. William Rose. In the
intervening years so much has occurred that it did not seem feasible
simply to take the older book and bring it up to date. I have therefore been asked to supervise the preparation of an entirely new work,
attacking the problem of knowledge from a somewhat different angle.

This problem is never an easy one to solve. Even in the dawn of
the modern world, when St. Isidore of Seville tried to compress into
a single work the extent of knowledge available to his contemporaries,
it was already impossible to codify the facts into a single pattern.
And by now one of the chief difficulties which beset the researcher
in any field is that he has to spend most of his life checking what is
already known before he can hope to make any original contribution
to his subject.

The facts, therefore, become more and more diffuse, harder and
harder to connect. Subjects interlock, or dwindle into unexpected
futilities. Thus, mathematical and philosophical thought meet at
points which would have been indefinable half a century ago, just
as the study of metaphysics, after more then two thousand years of
concentrated attention, has suddenly been relegated (at least by
fashionable thinkers) to a backwater. Polymaths like Bertrand
Russell or Einstein bring the different facets of their experience into
new relationships which affect the procedures, if not the conclusions,
of workers in fields remote from their own. In brief, there has been
an extension of knowledge so vast since the year 1930 that it seemed
advisable to measure, as accurately as possible, its limits.

But how? In planning a book like this grave problems very
quickly arise. First of all, to whom is the book addressed? then,
how far is the modern world of knowledge incomprehensible without a detailed historical background? Finally, what *is* knowledge?
Must it be so widespread that it will include a reference to every
possible intellectual activity, or should it be confined to those
subjects which no one alive can totally exclude from his own
experience?

These questions cannot be separated, and the answers to all are
implicit in that to the first. This book is designed for an intelligent
public without any detailed acquaintance with much of the matter

in hand. I have imagined the kind of reader who is both delighted
and puzzled by the complexity of all he sees around him. He gets
up in the morning and remembers his dreams of the night before.
Suppose they had some strange significance; suppose they could
have been submitted to Freud? In the pages of this book he will
find Professor Zangwill's exposition of the newest facets of thought
in matters of psychology. In the morning newspaper his eye lights
on an angry letter concerning the sculpture of Henry Moore. Sir
Leigh Ashton will tell him, then, much about modern sculpture
which he did not know, and he may be imperceptibly drawn on to
read Mr. Ironside's essay on contemporary painting. And so forth.
For we all find ourselves constantly at a loss before the special
knowledge of others. We may know something about music but
absolutely nothing about genetics, and yet it is clear that the subject
of genetics ought not to be left exclusively to specialists. It affects us
all, to begin with, just as every subject affects us all. And so a book
like this may help to give us some of the magical power of a Hermes
Trismegistus—one who knew everything and wrote it down in
(I have read) 36,525 books.

If such a book be addressed to the ordinary intelligent man, he
will need no more of the historical background than is required to
make the problems of the present day intelligible. The historical
background can be examined in any public library. For the
present (which is our theme) is so packed with subjects under
inquiry that it is always trying to elbow the past out of the way,
while the future clamours insistently for all that remains of our
attention.

But here there is a trap. For obviously the division of subjects into
past, present and future can be highly misleading. Take the matter
of physics, for example. Most people over forty were taught physics
at school with a heavy emphasis on the past. Quite rightly, we were
taught the paramount importance of the Greeks in this field, and
often enough our masters were content to end the matter with a
passing reference to Newton as the herald of a modern world which
could safely be handed over to the dedicated experts. Nowadays, the
pattern has been violently changed. Small children talk about atoms
who have never heard of Archimedes. And yet the nature of matter
as a subject of study remains unchanged, however sensational this
or that discovery may be. Indeed it is questionable if anyone is ever
in a position to cry "Eureka"—since every conclusion needs to be
modified by some further discovery (or so it seems to the layman)
almost as soon as it is made.

That is why this book has been planned with a bias which can
loosely be called philosophical. Philosophy in modern English
nowadays is often divorced from any practical purpose. It is conceived rather as a system of mental hygiene—a disinterested

examination of verbal constructions. Mr. John Holloway has discussed this approach to philosophy towards the beginning of the book and for those gifted with the necessary austerity of mind the scope of philosophical inquiry can be narrowed until it becomes no more than an intellectual exercise.

Nevertheless, whatever name may be given to it, the ancient concept of philosophy as the study of the meaning of things still survives. It is easy enough to conclude that our words are often used so loosely that the convictions they assert have become meaningless by the way; all the time, the convictions persist, since failures of language need not imply failures of thought. And so the different writers in this book have tried to write not simply as specialists but also as contributors to a general art of living. That is why an essay on the meaning of belief is included in the first section of the book. For unless the modern reader feels himself capable of belief in an established field he will never be able to accept, let us say, Professor Rhine's theories in the new field of parapsychology.

It is one of the curious facts about our greatly extended range of knowledge that its effect has been to reduce the scale of the world about us. Not so very long ago it was possible to imagine a rough division of mankind into two attitudes of mind. There were the old-fashioned folk, content with an old-fashioned cosmogony, relying on ancient gods and refusing to pay more than passing attention to the outrageous possibilities of modern science. And there was a progressive attitude, which dismissed the ancient gods as so many foolish superstitions, and held out hopes of enlarging the conquest of matter to a point where the universe could be ordered, wherever it touched the life of man, in such a way as to save us, progressively, from all the consequences of our own stupidity. In the last twenty years this division has become blurred. For one thing, the realities of modern science have obtruded themselves to a point where it has become impossible to overlook them; and for another the universe becomes harder to codify in strictly rational terms the closer we look at it. In effect, therefore, a very much higher standard both of knowledge and of judgement is required of our contemporaries than ever of their forebears.

It was one of the weaknesses of nineteenth-century life—a weakness carried on until the end of the First World War—that a high degree of acquiescence was possible among those very people who might have helped to change the order of the world for the better. In every country the focal points of power were to be found among those who asked the fewest questions. Indeed, posterity may well judge the comfortable classes which assumed control of government more severely for their absence of curiosity than for any lack of balance which their existence may have introduced into the social system.

Divisions between rich and poor, jarring rivalries of conviction, ineptitude in public conduct, are bad enough. Far worse, however, is the attitude of mind which prompts those holding a privileged position to make an unadventurous use of it. And it is one of the consolations for living through an age of change like our own that a certain amount of intellectual adventure is now forced upon everyone. The long-standing reproach of the respectable British, the reproach of "cleverness", is less and less often made in a world where it is impossible simply to acquiesce in what goes on—to acquiesce because it is too much trouble to take any personal thought about beliefs or institutions.

But in order to take personal thought it is necessary to have some knowledge of facts. That is why this book is, as far as possible, strictly factual. It exists in order to help ordinary people to make up their minds about the problems which surround them; it does not try to make their minds up for them. And since it is addressed to ordinary intelligent people it does not aim to give a complete conspectus of every branch of modern knowledge: it is not, in fact, an encyclopedia. The borderline, however, between what must be known and what might be known has not always been easy to draw. How about spectroscopy, for example? how about the larger study of optics? how about—to take something entirely different— geriatrics? Ought our imaginary reader to be able to turn these subjects up in our pages as a matter of course? In planning the book I have been helped to a large extent by my own ignorance. For I have not been deflected by any special knowledge from the basic belief that a book which is confessedly an Outline ought to avoid too ponderous an insistence on detail. It will be enough if we enable our reader to situate each subsidiary subject in its proper category in order to study it, if need be, in detail elsewhere. Certain aspects of the modern world have forced themselves, however, upon the attention of all those who, at different stages, have made their contribution to the design of the book. For as we worked over the range of subjects which lay before us, we concluded that special study ought to be given, not so much to those themes which represent no more than a steady extension of knowledge, as to others which make new and insistent demands upon us. It is as though there were passive and active subjects, subjects which can quietly be worked on—like optics and geriatrics—and subjects which intrude their existence upon even the most negligent audience.

Thus, no one can live and breathe, even in the unfilled spaces of the world, without a sense that humanity, little by little, is ringing him round. The unfilled spaces get smaller, the encroaching houses which still are never enough march in on solitude, and it is impossible to visit even a comparatively empty land like Brazil or Chile without being made aware that in some foreseeable future the ratio between population and natural resources will become as disquieting as it already is in Europe. That is why we have asked Lord Boyd-Orr to set out the *données* of the problem of world resources in such a way that the ordinary citizen may pick his way through the conflict of opinion and prophecy which is forced regularly upon him. Again, we hear more and more about the possibilities of interstellar travel. Even in an Outline of knowledge, therefore, it seemed necessary to give some objective consideration to this subject; and similarly the new arts, such as television, which have come into being during the last few years, clearly required discussion at a length appropriate to their possibilities rather than to their realization so far.

In short, this book has been conceived in relation to the future as well as to the present. And I hope I have not allowed myself to be overfrightened of the fact that all the work on it will have to be done again almost as soon as the contents of this book have been assimilated by its readers. For just think for a moment of the changes which have altered the face of the world of knowledge since Dr. Rose published his original Outline in 1931. Take the atom alone. Twenty-five years ago the atom could be considered in various lights. It could be thought of in relation to a mathematical concept, to the quantum theory, to astronomy; but without the practical experiments of the last two decades it could hardly be considered an urgent aspect of everyday life. Or again, television. The word—naturally enough—does not occur in Dr. Rose's index. And yet within the last year or two we have reached a point where simply to appear in television is to gain fame of a kind; and to appear often on television is to outstrip every competitor for public attention. Television has even altered the attitude of the majority to some of the subjects treated in this book. Archaeology, for one, is no longer thought of as pre-eminently a professorial occupation. On the contrary, it has a dash about it. Every shard, every battered coin, shares in a general excitement which has been chiefly engendered by television. Is it possible that thirty years ago long queues would have gathered to gaze at the fragments of a Roman temple excavated in the city of London? I very much doubt it—for it is not so long since general apathy made it very difficult for a small band of enthusiasts to succeed in saving Stonehenge for the nation.

Again, we have learned in the last generation to popularize a sense of style in architecture—learned, indeed, so well that the ordinary public has often outstripped in discernment the experts who are supposed to further its needs. Here again television has helped a little in making better known some of the personalities who have succeeded in widening and directing the taste of exigent people. It is no longer possible to dismiss all building later than 1700 as somehow inferior to everything that went before; and even

the despised Victorians, after half a century of denigration, have
suddenly become almost alarmingly fashionable. There is no harm
in that. Indeed, taken as a symptom of the general truth that more
and more people, when they look at a building, have trained
themselves to use their eyes intelligently and for themselves, even
the exaggerated rapture of those who prefer Butterfield to Brunel-
leschi has at least the merit of freshness. And luckily, in parallel to an
architectural enthusiasm which is based on historical sentiment
rather than on contemporary needs, the old prejudice against anything "modern" has largely disappeared. The work of Gropius at
Harvard, like that of Niemeyer in Brazil, has been accepted as part
of the natural scene by the non-highbrow majority on whom, in the
last analysis, all questions of taste depend. Indeed, it is one of the
paradoxes of the age that the non-experts are often much more alive
to the differences in architecture between good and bad than those
who are actually in charge of building. It is not the unenlightened
citizen with a new confidence in his own taste who wrecks the landscape with badly-placed pylons, cat's cradles of wire, abominable
street-lighting, and flashy shop-fronts, any more than it is the
builders of suburbs who inhabit them.

For that matter, the modifications of taste which have occurred
since 1930 would alone require some re-writing of those sections of
Dr. Rose's *Outline* which cover the arts. We should not today
summarily dismiss the experiments of Schönberg and Berg with the
phrase, "I must confess to my total inability to foresee any possible
future for this kind of thing". We should not allow ourselves a
sentence like that in which Professor Morris, the critic in question,
declares—and it is almost the only occasion on which he brings
names into the discussion of modern music—that "experiments in
polytonal combination have been freely made by Stravinsky,
Milhaud, Hindemith, and others, so that everyone who is willing
to take a little trouble can judge for himself, if he feels so inclined".
A process of sifting and delimiting has been going on in each of the
arts since those words were written. Our eyes, our ears, our imaginative faculties are much better tuned to grasp the kind of things
which our contemporaries are likely to attempt in the stress of
creation. That is why the present age has been one of criticism rather
than of renewal: the sifting and delimiting has taken up most of
the creative energy which thirty years ago would have been devoted
to experiments of ever greater complexity.

It would have needed a prophet to decide, in 1930, which of the
experimental phases in the arts were likely to bear fruit. How about
James Joyce, for instance? How about the surrealists (then just
appearing over the horizon)? How about the different categories of
abstract art? How about the sudden impact of political systems like
Nazism and Communism on the artist in every sphere? These were

questions which Dr. Rose's book did not attempt to answer, and could not possibly have answered had it tried. They are, however, questions which are forced upon us today, and they are of the kind which we have tried to answer.

The task has been made no easier by the lack of perspective which has been imposed upon the modern world. Even thirty years ago, it was possible, if not easy, to see almost all phenomena against the appropriate historical background. Nowadays the foreground has a tendency to crowd out all that lies behind. In one of the best essays in Dr. Rose's book, for example, Lascelles Abercrombie discusses the principles of literary criticism. He does so in terms chiefly of Aristotle and Plato, and then swoops down the centuries as far as Manzoni and, in a passing reference, Croce. In a historical survey he is, of course, perfectly right. But in the last three decades the past has become more and more taken for granted—and not only in the field of the arts. New pundits arise who take their points of reference from a narrowing field. Inspired by a training scientific rather than humanist they constantly exaggerate the importance of recent events, of verifiable circumstances which have lately occurred near at hand. People travel less, they master fewer languages, they have less and less leisure to take their thought back to its sources; and so little by little a notion has been permitted to grow up that everything worth knowing in the practical world has been crowded into the last century: that outside this *hortus conclusus* there is a difficult territory, the plans of which have been long mislaid—a territory, however, scarcely worth exploring except from curiosity, since all the specimens in it worth preserving have already been collected by generations of experts and re-planted in a setting worthier of their virtues.

At this point I cannot forbear to quote from an essay first published in the 1920's by Ortega y Gasset:

The culture of the present day [he writes] is ruled by science, but science can only live up to its own pretensions and display its aptitude for ruling culture, if it is considered as the integral system of all knowledge. Therefore science is not a specialist activity. Yet, on the other hand, its vast extension makes it obligatory for scientific work to be carried on by means of a dispersion of specialities. So that specialism is simultaneously a need and a contradiction of science. Among all the harm which is implicit in this fact, I shall only call attention to one fact.

From each speciality there emerges one fine day a particular doctrine which directly proves of general interest. This doctrine descends, like a dogma, upon all other men of culture, including those who cultivate other specialities. Because these latter are not in a position to discuss it they are content to accept the doctrine meekly, as though it was all of one piece, sharp-edged and unshakeable. That is to say, by the transfer of the doctrine from those minds which created it to those which receive it, it loses precisely those properties which belong to science. Because, seen from within, every scientific theory, however firm, contains an element of the problematic, of mere approximation to exemplary and ultimate truth. It never excludes other possibilities which may in part be antagonistic. This weakness of all scientific theory is one of its virtues, perhaps that which best differentiates it from dogma.

Ortega, perhaps, goes a little out of his way to promote a paradox; he has, however, laid a finger on one of the chief of modern dilemmas. Here we all sit, we the general public, while the pontiffs lay down the law all round us. They have only to make a sufficient name in their own field for their views to be eagerly accepted outside it. As if aware that "science is the integral system of all knowledge", in Ortega's phrase, the general airs his views on theology, the historian on economics, and the philosopher edges his way into the sphere of metaphysics. In addition, we all have our own views on a multitude of exact subjects, and we ask nothing better than to air them. If the conversation turn to flying saucers, we are perfectly sure either that they do exist or that they don't. We are equally sure that logical positivism is an indispensable mental purgative or that it promotes a dangerous narrowing of the mind. We convince ourselves that we know all we need to of the chances of life on Mars, of the uses of N.A.T.O., and of the problems which face the international banker. Leaning across the table, we lay down the law on these matters with only the most delicate of deference to the experts, and as often as not we get away with it.

This book has also a subsidiary use—even a frivolous one—as well as the major one of informing ordinary people as precisely as possible about the questions which are to the fore at the moment. It can lead the pontiff who lurks concealed in us all a little further out of reach of error, and although it may for a moment look as though it were a valuable arsenal for the gamesman it is likely in the end to direct gamesmanship towards expertise. A great deal of time is spent, throughout life, in talk, and talk has to be about something. At the very best, most of the talk in the world will have the effect of enlarging and prolonging mistakes. Since even things written down have an extraordinary propensity for going wrong in the writing, it is scarcely surprising that things spoken frequently inhabit the realm of pure fantasy. Mistake crowds in upon mistake, and the muddle in which we all live most of the time becomes daily more complex. That is where this book comes in.

For if it is true—as children are taught—that conversation ought

to be about things rather than about people, it is obviously desirable
to know as much as possible about as many things as possible. And
above all it is necessary to bridge two of the most dangerous gaps
in the structure of modern life. The first is that between science and
what is very roughly called humanism; the second is between
humanism and the religious instinct.

The very concept of the scientist does not really bear looking
into: he is as vague of outline as the rationalist or the progressive
in the minds of most of those who talk about him. People conceive
him as a being dedicated to some difficult purpose, and wholly
single-hearted in that dedication. He is therefore excluded from
everything except his own branch of his own subject. It is taken for
granted that he is an agnostic in all other matters of belief. It is
also taken for granted that in some way he is more closely in touch
with the world of today than anyone else: science, in fact, means
being up to date. But of course it means nothing of the kind. It
means knowing about something. And in that sense Avicenna and
St. Teresa and Erasmus were all as scientific as Newton himself—
since knowing implies experience, and experience is futile without
some sense of the value of evidence. The scientist is therefore by no
means someone exclusively occupied with retorts and equations
and isotypes and the like; he is simply someone who is skilled enough
to acquire knowledge, and there is not the least reason why he
should not be a humanist as well.

Except this: that no two people agree about the precise meaning
of humanism. It is a pleasant-sounding word, and it brings with it
a graceful touch of fresh air from the Renaissance. Somehow or
other the humanist is ordinarily supposed to have gained the ability
to live by his own intellectual wits. He is a kind of ideal man—lithe
of mind, unprejudiced, unfettered by ancient rigmaroles, skilled in
his control of the whole province of man. But has there ever been
such a being? From time to time someone emerges out of the grey
crowd who looks, in a favourable light, like the hero we all might
wish to be. Sir Philip Sidney on the field of Zutphen, Shelley
lamenting Keats, Richard Strauss, in extreme old age, flaring into
a blaze of elegiac genius. But turn—in the pages of this book or
elsewhere—to consider a little the structure of the human personality as Jung or Freud have begun to chart it, and soon only a ruin
remains of any definable point of view which can truly be called
humanism. In no time at all the pride of the humanist vanishes and
he finds himself, like the most superstitious of Polynesians or the
primitives of Haiti, sharing the fringes of those dark lands of the
mind where words like propitiation and redemption still have an
unavoidable meaning.

I hope, therefore, that the essays gathered together in this book
may suggest to the reader an encouraging train of thought. I hope

it may deter him from accepting too easily the compartmentation of existence. I should like him to convince himself that the different kinds of people who inhabit the planet are not necessarily divided into mutually deterrent categories; that the man of science may easily turn out to be a metaphysician as well; that the religious man is not forced into bigotry by his beliefs; that if to be a humanist means very little, to be humane means a great deal. I conceive that these pages may give their readers plenty to argue about, and I am quite sure that experts in any sphere will wish to question both the scope and the execution of our plan. If ordinary people find it a little easier henceforth to understand the world around them, however, our time will not have been wasted.

THE NEW OUTLINE OF MODERN KNOWLEDGE

SECTION ONE

Philosophy and Metaphysics

ANALYTICAL PHILOSOPHY

by Dr. John Holloway

I. Introduction for the Non-Philosopher

I⊤ is ɴοτ ᴠᴇʀʏ easy to describe "analytical philosophy" by writing a single article, nor very easy to master it by reading one. Even the beginner, though, will find it easy to grasp several central facts from the pages which follow. In the first place, he will see that developments in modern analytical philosophy have been exciting and provocative. Secondly, he will see that they are likely to throw, and indeed have begun to throw, new light on many other fields of inquiry. Thirdly, he will notice that analytical philosophers may sometimes strive to deal with elaborate problems, but their basic methods of thinking are even so quite simple and sensible.

What *is* "analytical philosophy"? What does it analyse? The philosopher does not carry out experiments, like the scientist; he simply "sits and thinks" about the subject he has in hand. Some readers may have already asked themselves whether "sitting and thinking" is likely to be very fruitful. This is exactly the question which arises in the analyst's mind. What he wants to think about is— *thinking itself.* How far, he wants to know, can "sitting and thinking" take us? Is it always the same one kind of activity, or are there several kinds? If there are several kinds, are some useful and others useless? In what ways does thinking go wrong?—and so on.

There is one easy answer to this last question, of course. Thinking goes wrong where it is illogical, and there is a sense in which the logician, like the analyst, is thinking about thinking. But the logician deals in the main with one part of the story: with the rules, or laws, whereby one statement is an "implication" of another, or follows from it. Here, logic deals with rigid, precise thinking, and assumes that the individual ideas, or "terms", are definite and constant in meaning. But ordinary thinking is done in language, in words: and words are very far from being either definite or constant in meaning. This is the analytic philosopher's province. It is wrong to think that he asks merely about "what a word means". Craftsmen and experts of all kinds—and dictionaries—can tell us the meanings of words, save perhaps of certain specially tricky ones, and these the analyst does study. But mainly the analyst inquires whether a given word, *as it appears in a particular train of thought*, has been given one consistent meaning, or not; whether (to put it loosely) two or three words all have meaning in the same way, or in different ways; whether it is possible for a word with a well-known meaning to be used in a context which somehow deprives it of meaning—and so on. In fact, it is studying questions like these which help him in studying those few specially tricky words, mentioned above, whose meaning he cannot really leave to others. He usually reaches a solution in his inquiries by thinking about the relations not simply between single words, but between whole sentences in which the words occur: and the relation which chiefly helps him is that of "implication" or "following-from" which was mentioned just now.

The next section of this article, *The Historical Background*, shows how analytical philosophy is not a new-fangled invention, but has deep roots in the philosophy of the past; and how other branches of philosophy have always drawn from it. Sections III, *Earlier Modern Analysis*, and IV, *Misleading Language*, discuss how in the first thirty or forty years of the present century, analytical philosophers had come (partly as a result of studying difficulties in mathematics) to the point where they arrived at a scrutiny of all the kinds of words (or ideas if you prefer) which we use in our ordinary thinking. Section V discusses what seemed like an important special case of misleading language, the statements which we make about "material objects" (like chairs or tables). Up to this point the analysts had mainly used the idea of a "statement" as what they analysed, and of "implication" as the relation between statements which they gave attention to, in going through the analysis. The next two sections, *Linguistic Philosophy*, and *Moral Philosophy and Language "Uses"*, show how analytic philosophers discovered that these two ideas were not in fact enough for all the work they wished to do. The last section, *Wittgenstein's Posthumous Work*, briefly refers to the great Cambridge philosopher who largely created philosophical analysis as it is practised today.

II. *The Historical Background*

Modern analytical philosophy has pursued a brilliant and unforeseen and rapidly changing course. It has not, though, been a freak in the modern world, but something that has the typical qualities of that world. One can trace in it, clearly, the modern intellectuals' distrust of pious, fine-sounding, vague generalities, the scientists' admiration for minute and dispassionate analysis, a complexity and subtlety like that typical of all the contemporary arts, and in its later stages an emphasis on organic and functional inquiries like those of ecology or modern anthropology or economics. Such continuity with our whole contemporary culture deserves to be remembered, if only to do analytical philosophy justice: for this philosophy is far too often accused of shirking the traditional responsibilities of philosophy to man and society, and retiring into a linguistic hair-splitting isolation. As far as this has been true, it has been because philosophy has been typical of the whole intellectual climate of today—its detachment and subtlety and professionalism have been the approved intellectual qualities. But this detachment has been for a valuable purpose, and one which has always had, in the whole philosophical picture, a central place.

The analytical kind of philosophy which has been prominent in modern times is by no means an inconoclastic mushroom growth. To think this would be to make a fundamental mistake. It is necessary, therefore, to see how the principles and methods of the modern school are strongly and deeply rooted in the past. Indeed, to do this is important for two reasons. First, noticing the perennial tendency for men to direct their philosophical thinking along analytical lines is perhaps a better indication of value than any spectacular results in problems which may still be too near to be seen with real detachment. Second, the historical origin of modern analytical philosophy shows that it is in no way something super-subtle and over-intellectualized that is divorced from important matters of thought, or the main pattern of society. In Britain at least, it has for centuries been the expression of things which we prize deeply in our national life.

The "British Empiricists"—Locke, Berkeley, Hume—are often pointed to as the ancestors of the modern analytical approach. But this is only the second half of the story. The Middle Ages are important in this genealogy too; and it is vital, as a first move, to free one's mind from that simplified and unjust picture of the medieval world which existed in the minds of men who followed close after it and who were trying most urgently to break away from it. To the thinkers and scientists of the seventeenth century, medieval philosophy was dominated by Aristotle, and its staple consisted of metaphysical quibbles. But the Aristotelianism of the "Schoolmen" was a development of the later Middle Ages (thirteenth century). It had in part to make its way against an existing tradition of analytical thinking (Abelard, for example, or John of Salisbury), and it provoked a vigorous reaction along much the same lines as later empiricism, and with, in some ways, a clearly superior technical equipment.

For the analytical philosopher, this technical equipment means logic; and logic, to him, is of immense importance. Logic is itself developed through analysis; it embodies the results of past success in analysis; and thus it is of primary relevance to every fresh attempt.

By the time of William of Ockham (early fourteenth century) the distinction between the words which indicate what an assertion refers to, and the words like "not" or "if . . . then" which indicate the logical character of the assertion, had long been recognized. So had the existence of logically paradoxical sentences like "this proposition is false" (referring to itself). Ockham had in the "logic of supposition" a technique for analysing the different kinds of relation which an assertion might have to the objects about which it was an assertion, and this enabled him to distinguish, for example, a sentence like "man is a species" from one like "some man is white", much after the manner of modern philosophers. He was equipped, that is, to speak systematically about the relations between words and things; and this is a fundamental problem of analytical philosophy. The other main division of Ockham's logic, the logic of consequences, was also highly developed as an instrument of philosophical analysis. In this, Ockham was able to draw a clear distinction, much like that of modern logic, between "formal" and "material" implication—in other words, between the kind of implication which exists because of the logical relation between one proposition and another (determined by their intrinsic logical form), and the kind which exists merely in that the second proposition is never false if the first is true. This second logical relation is almost essential in the construction of formal deductive systems; but it leads to certain paradoxes, and these have much interested modern logicians. Ockham, however, was well aware of them too. Indeed, an awareness of the nature of material implication may be traced back to the later Stoic logicians like Chrysippus (third century B.C.), and to their study of the hypothetical syllogism, which was mentioned but inadequately treated by Aristotle.

Different readers will no doubt think differently of the incipient scepticism which may be traced in these later medieval logicians, and which led the Roman Church to follow, in preference to them, the teaching of Aquinas. But one vital fact emerges when we notice how much they achieved. The firm basis of their work on rigorous and difficult logic is a reminder that philosophical analysis issues not from sceptical wilfulness, but from that solemn, intense and precise concentration of the mind which is beyond question the surest road to new insight. There never has been, in fact, a contradiction between philosophical analysis and metaphysics: a new metaphysical system (as, for example, with Descartes, Spinoza or Kant) usually emerges from a new analysis of some peculiarly important kind of assertion. Certainly Ockham's logic had a relation to his wider studies. It was on the basis of his logical work that he produced his destructive analysis of the reality of relations (reaching, incidentally, just the opposite of the modern view, though employing the typically modern method of the *reductio ad absurdum*); as well as his sharp distinction between literal and figurative language; and his acutely nominalistic account of mental concepts. Universality, for him, resided solely in the act of the mind's attention; and this is a distinction which Berkeley and Hume were to revive, though—such are the paradoxes of the history of ideas—for them the term "second intention", which Ockham used to express the distinction, would have been a typical example of Scholastic verbiage.

Perhaps the chief difference between the analysts of the fourteenth century, and those in Britain of the seventeenth and eighteenth who are more often taken as the ancestors of the modern school, is that the former were a minority to whom the authorities were on the whole opposed, whereas the latter were expressing ideas and modes of thought which were coming to dominate their society. Francis Bacon, like Roger Bacon, begins his philosophical inquiries —*Advancement of Learning* (1605), *Novum Organum* (1620)—with a survey of the sources of error, sources which he calls *Idols*. This preliminary move became common in the century which followed him; and his comments on the *Idols of the Market-Place* are particularly relevant to modern analysis, for they point out, in effect, the intellectual harm done by "misleading language". It is exactly this which modern analysts have pointed to as making their work necessary. "The *Idols of the Market-Place* are the most troublesome of all . . . for men believe that their reason governs words; but it is also true that words react on the understanding." Bacon's understanding of these problems went further: he pointed out two kinds of linguistic error, errors which, in modern parlance, arise respectively from the tendency to "hypostatize" language, and the tendency not to recognize its "open texture". First, he notices that words can appear to be names of things, even when the things do not exist (his examples are Fortune, the Prime Mover, Planetary Orbits, etc.); secondly, he is aware that words can indeed refer to things, but be "hastily and irregularly" derived from them, and therefore "confused and ill-defined" in their significance. The example he discusses ("humid") is especially significant, because it shows him aware of the way in which a familiar word may have *no* definition which rigidly fixes its meaning. It is "a mark loosely and confusedly applied to denote a variety of actions which will not bear to be reduced to any constant meaning"; and to know its use fully we must turn not to definitions but—this is exactly the modern way of putting it—to the *use* of the word. "Even definitions cannot cure this evil . . . it is necessary to recur to individual instances, and those in due series and order." The germ of important twentieth-century discoveries about language is certainly to be found here.

The contributions of Hobbes, Locke, Berkeley and Hume to this long tradition of analysis are better known, and for the moment they can be left aside, for the chief problem is to see only how long-lasting and how firmly rooted the analytical tradition has been. In England, at least, it dominated the philosophical scene until the influence of Kant, the German Idealists, and (from about 1860 onwards) Hegel gave metaphysics a new impetus. But there is no necessary clash between metaphysics and philosophical analysis: Kant's system takes the logical concepts of Aristotle (in modified form) as its necessary starting-point, and contains brilliant analyses of a number of seemingly metaphysical propositions. Hegel's new logic is the foundation of his new metaphysics. F. H. Bradley's *Appearance and Reality* (1893) is an extremely elaborate piece of metaphysical thinking which issues entirely from the author's preliminary analysis of the idea of relation, and his conclusion that as ordinarily understood (i.e. that relations are no essential part of the objects they relate) this idea is self-contradictory and logically impossible.

III. Earlier Modern Analysis

Perhaps the contrast between this work of Bradley's and G. E. Moore's famous "The Refutation of Idealism", an article published in 1904, brings out better than anything else what is at the root of the modern analytical movement in philosophy. The difference is one of tone, and it is so pervasive that it is apparent even to the non-philosopher, even to a reader who cannot really follow the argument in either of these difficult pieces. If Bradley is acute and brilliantly ingenious, it is in willing pursuit of spectacular conclusions. Moore, for all his urbanity and unobtrusive wit, is almost laboriously pedestrian in the elaborate precautions that he takes against error; and he leaves his reader, besides this, with the impression that the avoidance of error is all that interests him. "The subject of this paper, therefore, is quite uninteresting. Even if I prove my points, I shall have proved nothing about the universe in general . . . I shall only try to show that certain propositions which I assert to be believed, are false." Moore's method is fairly typical of modern analytical philosophy. He concerns himself with arguments employed to prove something of seemingly enormous significance: that *the universe is spiritual*. But his ambition is limited to showing only that one small part (though a vital part) of the usual proof must be treated, by those who use it, as self-evident, since the proof which ostensibly underlies it is invalid. This is the part which purports to demonstrate Berkeley's *esse est percipi*, to be is to be perceived.

Moore's first move, here as always, is a lengthy analysis of what the proposition under discussion, or the proposition on which it logically depends, must mean. When this is done, proof or refutation can usually be brief. The result of the first part of Moore's argument is to show that Idealists must hold, jointly, two incompatible propositions: first, that (for example) "yellow" must by definition mean precisely the *same* as "experience of yellow" (or else it could not be true that yellow was inconceivable save as being experienced); and second, that on the contrary "yellow" must by definition mean something *other* than "experience of yellow" (otherwise it would mean nothing to say "yellow is a sensation"). This logical incompatibility is the crux of Moore's argument; or rather, of its first part. He goes on to consider an alternative formulation of his opponents' argument: that the object of a sensation (like "yellow") is part of the content of that sensation, and therefore inseparable from it. This formulation issues from Bradley's analysis of experience (Moore recognizes that it is an analysis), and is one further indication that analytical philosophy underlies metaphysics as much as it does anti-metaphysics. Moore's refutation now follows somewhat different lines. The expression, "A is part of the content of B", he argues, has a familiar and proper use. For example, it describes the relation between an object and the colour of that object. Quite possibly, he continues (with a touch perhaps of irony), it is true that, when I have a sensation *of* blue, that sensation actually *is* blue. But if so, it is blue by accident. "Something else is also true", which is that I am experiencing blue. I know this from introspection, and know too, so soon as I give the matter my attention, that the sensation is not related to blue as a flower is related to its colour: between a sensation and its object there exists "the simple and unique relation the existence of which alone [i.e., without further ado] justifies us in distinguishing knowledge of a thing from the thing known, indeed in distinguishing mind from matter". The form of the argument has an analogy with Hobbes's and Locke's discussions of matter and extension, which are referred to below. All three philosophers are saying that two expressions are different, that the use of both is perfectly familiar to us, and that to say they are the same is simply an obvious confusion. Moore, it will be seen, is denying the least vestige of analogy between two different kinds of expression ("this is a flower which is blue", "this is a sensation which is *of* blue"); the ground of the denial is simply that each expression has a clear and familiar use (though one, perhaps, which is not further analysable); and the final appeal is to our knowledge that things differ from each other, and that we can perfectly well see the differences even when we cannot analyse them. Here analysis is attempting to penetrate to the unanalysable bed-rock of analysis.

This celebrated article of Moore's has been discussed at length because Moore's method is a prefiguring of the most important things to come in modern analytical philosophy. Moore seems, indeed, to have had some of Wittgenstein's later insights (though not Wittgenstein's unique gift for conveying them); and it is likely that in the future his contribution will be valued even more highly than it is at present. Before pursuing later analyses of sense-experience, however, it is necessary to turn to the early work of Russell and of Wittgenstein.

This was concerned, predominantly, with an attempt to deal with those propositions which have always been the chief source of embarrassment to empiricist philosophers, the propositions of pure mathematics. The natural course for the empiricist is to divide knowledge into two fundamentally different kinds: knowledge of matters of fact, which comes exclusively from experience (*a posteriori*, synthetic knowledge), and knowledge of what follows logically from given premises when their terms are defined in this or that way (*a priori*, analytic knowledge). This distinction is made with full clarity in Hume, in Locke, and earlier still in Hobbes. But pure mathematics has always seemed peculiarly difficult to fit into the scheme, since its propositions seem at once to have the necessity and certainty of propositions which follow merely from definitions, and at the same time to provide a real, substantial and incorrigible addition to our knowledge of fact. They seem, that is, to be both *a priori* and synthetic. This was Kant's view (it is his classification of knowledge) and it made the corner-stone of his rejection of empiricism.

The *Principia Mathematica* of Russell and Whitehead (1910-12) was an attempt, on a very large scale, to resolve this difficulty once for all. It did so by attempting to show that, from a very small number of basic propositions which appeared perfectly self-evident, it was possible to deduce not only the whole of formal logic, but also the whole of mathematics. So far as *Principia Mathematica* has been successful, it has shown that mathematics, as we ordinarily understand it, combines (in many varying ways) intellectual activities of two fundamentally different kinds: operations with symbols in a formal system according to a closed set of axioms and given rules of inference, and techniques of counting or of ascertaining the measurable properties of space which really form part of the physical sciences. Wittgenstein's *Tractatus Logico-Philosophicus* (1922) covered a far wider range of problems, and (like Locke's *Essay Concerning Human Understanding*) was the kind of empiricist, analytical philosophy which depends for its fascination in part at least upon an underlying metaphysics; but it too treated mathematics as basically like formal logic, and by means of symbolic devices it showed more clearly than perhaps ever before (though it should be remembered that the technical equipment of both Russell and Wittgenstein can be found largely complete, though in a clumsier form, in the *Begriffsschrift* of Frege, 1879) how the theorems of formal logic were no more than summaries of the results obtained when given symbols were operated in accordance with given rules. Wittgenstein, in fact, was offering a still fuller and better proof of something which Hobbes had stated clearly in the *Logic*: "Every proposition, universally true, is either a definition, or part of a definition, or the evidence of it depends on definitions."

The final value of this work on mathematics is still, to some extent, in question. In the sequel, the attempt to reduce mathematics to formal logic proved to need a fuller starting-apparatus with regard to both the primitive propositions, and the rules of inference, than was evident at first; and various attempts were made to resolve these difficulties, either by adding axioms which were not self-evident, or alternatively by restricting the area of what could be regarded as significant mathematical propositions. But, although the technicalities cannot be explored fully here, it is certainly true to say that these inquiries have radically and permanently changed the picture. Mathematics no longer presents the stumbling-block to empiricism that it once did, and the division of it into formal deductive systems on the one hand, and certain rather specialized branches of physical science on the other, is likely to prove in the main a valid one.

IV. *"Misleading Language"*

As is so often the case, however, and as we have noticed with many philosophers from William of Ockham onwards, advances of a highly specialized kind in formal (or mathematical) logic are likely to equip the philosopher afresh, and to some purpose, for the analysis of wider philosophical problems. This happened with Russell's researches into the philosophy of mathematics. Russell had begun by assuming that certain mathematical terms and class-names represented genuinely existing realities which were the subject matter of mathematics. The view was traditional. But it led him, he found, into a series of paradoxes. Meeting each difficulty as it came, he tried to evade these by introducing a fresh axiom, to the effect that problems arising about members of a class (e.g. members of the class of real numbers, and so on) did not arise about the class itself. This led him to the idea of a class not a member of itself; and this, in its turn, to the idea of "the class of all classes which are not members of themselves". There, he made a major discovery: for this expression, harmless as it looks, and required as it was by his investigation, cannot possibly stand for any existing reality, since it is a concealed self-contradiction. This fact emerges as soon as one inquires whether this class is a member of itself, or not: for to say that it is not a member of itself, implies that it is, and to say that it is implies that it is not.

Russell therefore had, apparently, a perfectly clear proof that we could frame seemingly legitimate expressions which generated philosophical cruxes by not being what they seemed. The technical problem, as one in formal logic, was taken up and argued at length (for example, by Frege); but the influence of Russell's discovery was felt throughout philosophy as a whole. Philosophers interested more in ordinary thinking and in ordinary language than in mathematics began to see that this kind of problem might arise in their work too. All expressions began to appear as if under a light polarized in a fresh direction; any expression, however innocuous it looked, might now prove on testing to be a trick. Philosophers hunted everywhere for expressions which, to put it loosely (and this, in fact, often was put loosely), were proper to a fact or state of affairs of one kind, but were actually being used of another kind. The danger in such expressions was that they could lead their users to draw false conclusions without knowing it. It seemed that trivial, even frivolous examples were the best in illustrating this principle of "misleading language".[1] They were much easier to understand and learn from, because in a sense they caricatured the more elusive and subtle fallacies which were hidden in serious philosophical issues. Philosophers also had a chance to be entertaining, to descend a little from their usual austerity; and they seized this chance with alacrity and with varying success. Russell pointed out, for example, that saying it is false to assert that "The King of France is bald" seems somehow to suggest that there is a King of France: though the point of the denial is exactly that there is not. Alternatively, we might come to think that one thing of a strange kind existed, when what really existed were many things of an ordinary kind. "Unpunctuality" is not a thing, but people are sometimes late; there are no objects called tree-tops, only collections of twigs. "The defeat of Germany" seems to refer to a single event of a kind too vast to be observed in its entirety—and the notion that a State is some kind of supernatural entity easily arises from this. But really the statement refers to a miscellany of quite straightforward events; and the word "Germany" itself, which, if we analysed its meaning wrongly, might easily come to look as if it stood for an object of quite special and somehow more than human kind, is really only a collective expression for the individual citizens and their houses and the ground they lived on: which is all that really exists. Plainly, the new philosophers got back to straightforwardly serious philosophy at this point; a logical apparatus of analysis had equipped them to expose every form of supra-individualism as based on subtle technical muddles. They had something to contribute to the fundamental issues of political and social thinking.

The successful study of misleading language is not a monopoly of modern analytical philosophers. There is one seventeenth-century document, at least, which is still of real intrinsic interest and

[1] See especially G. Ryle, "Systematically Misleading Expressions" (*Mind*, 1933).

instructiveness as a discussion of how misleading language can occur and how it may be diagnosed. This is Chapter V of Hobbes's *Logic or Computation*. Hobbes begins by stating that "all things to which we give names, may be reduced to these four kinds, namely *bodies*, *accidents*, *phantasms*, and *names* themselves". There is much, even in this, which has a modern ring; and the distinction which Hobbes goes on to draw (rightly) between names of things and names of names, foreshadows the contrast between propositions about matters of fact, and propositions about other propositions (making up, as it has been called, a "meta-language"), which has been so important in modern philosophy. Hobbes's account is faulty, but by no means altogether so. Words of these four types, he argues, must be combined in an assertion with words only of their own type. Otherwise, they are combined "incoherently". He catalogues seven ways in which this may occur. A sentence like "a shadow is a body" combines, or "copulates", the name of a body with the name of a "phantasm", and is therefore illegitimate. "Colour is the object of sight, sound of hearing" combines names of accidents with names of bodies, and is again illegitimate. Hobbes also rejects such an assertion as "a body is magnitude", and his mode of argument is what a modern analyst would use: such a statement "is as if we should say, the *runner* is the *running*, or the *walk walketh*". In other words, he argues by analogy, referring to the idiom of ordinary language, and relying for his proof on a *reductio ad absurdum*. Locke in the Third Book ("Of Words") of his *Essay* employs just the same method. Against the Cartesian view that extension is the essence of matter he asserts that these are two plainly different ideas; and his proof is to perform ordinary logical operations on sentences in which the words occur, and then to point out that different results are obtained in the two cases. If they were identical in meaning, he argues, "it would be as proper, and as intelligible to say, 'the body of an extension', as the 'extension of a body' . . . if the ideas these two terms stood for were precisely the same, they might indifferently in all places be put for one another. But we see that though it be proper to say, *There is one matter of all bodies*, one cannot say, *There is one body of all matters*: we familiarly say one body is bigger than another; but it sounds harsh (and I think is never used) to say one matter is bigger than another. Whence comes this, then? Viz. from hence . . . matter and body stand for two different conceptions." The argument, at bottom, is that used by Moore. Usage gives words their meanings, and will indicate whether two words have identical meanings. If it indicates that they have not, there is an end of the matter.

V. *The Analysis of "Material-object" Propositions*

The philosophy of analysis thus tends to have two somewhat different branches: the analysis of *a priori* or analytic propositions (an important part of the analytical empiricists' position is to assert that they are the same) as represented by what Russell and Wittgenstein had to say about formal logic and mathematics; and the analysis of propositions which are expressed in words, which can occur in the ordinary layman's thinking, and which formed the starting points of Moore's essays in the field of what the philosopher calls "theory of knowledge". On the whole, modern analytical philosophy has developed most in this second field, doubtless for two reasons. In the first place, the philosophical study of mathematics rapidly became so highly technical that few were able to pursue it with profit. But besides this, another more important factor was at work. Logic and mathematics were, after all, matters of certainty. Analysis might show more plainly than before how this certainty arose, but was not expected either to increase or to reduce it. With factual propositions the situation was different. From statements about which it is only too easy to be in doubt, like "that frock is not blue but green", or "this line is longer than that one", it is easy to pass to other cases where the risk of error and the legitimacy of doubt are less obvious, but seem on reflection to be no less real. The possibility then arises of analysing the statements of ordinary language so as to locate that part (if any) of what they assert which is not open to doubt. Let us take an example. I say "there is a bright star", and point; but may be wrong, because it is not a star but a trick of my eye, or a meteor, or an aeroplane light; or there may have been a star but by now it has disintegrated. Yet although one may misinterpret one's experience in various ways and in doing so fall into error, one is indubitably having experiences of a definite kind ("having certain *sense-data*", as the philosophers put it); and statements which refer simply to them and nothing further can surely, it seems, be verified beyond risk of error. This appears to have immense importance. It seems to offer a way of making ordinary language, and ordinary thinking, as clearly organized, as free from vague penumbra, as the language of mathematics. It suggests that if one could show that other, more ambitious statements were equivalent to *collections* of these directly verifiable and therefore indubitable statements, one could extract all that was genuine and reliable from one's empirical knowledge. Whatever would be left over would be only vague, mystical, metaphysical— having no meaning at all, or at least no straightforward meaning.

Analysis was also given this more ambitious task: it was to penetrate down to the basic elements from which complex assertions were built up, and in this role it seemed to offer a thorough-going reform of all empirical knowledge. The prospect was in many ways exciting. All the various kinds of assertions could be put on a proper, rigorous, scientific basis. Metaphysical jargon could be abandoned once for all, and so could all pretended references to pseudo-entities which could never conceivably be observed, and which it was therefore only a pious pretence to think meant anything at all. This programme, which pervaded the whole period of the twenties and early thirties, was expressed in brilliant and yet popular form by A. J. Ayer in *Language, Truth and Logic* (1936). The basic principles of this book were that whatever has meaning is verifiable; and that outside logic and mathematics, "verifiable" ultimately means verifiable in the immediate way in which the reader of this page can assure himself that at the very least he sees a white patch with black marks on it (that is, "sense-data"). Much of the programme seemed like a glorious release from a superstitious, constraining professionalism. Propositions about "The Absolute" and other metaphysical assertions could not be analysed into anything at all verifiable immediately, and simply disappeared. Perplexing philosophers' inventions, concepts like "Transcendental Self" and "Material Substance", were rejected too. Assertions were to mean simply what could be verified in a business-like way. A word like "I" was to be given meaning in terms of the individual's perceptions, not of some mysterious entity called a Self, which led an occult life behind them; and an expression like "this table", given meaning in terms of all the real experience which were had or might be had of the table (this is the theory meant by "Phenomenalism"—of which there are several versions), and not as a mysterious Substance somehow propping them up from behind.

This programme, which could fairly honestly be called "Logical Positivism", was an early stage, a first rough approximation, in modern analytical philosophy. But that philosophy has changed much since then. Its techniques have become more delicate and, as the price of this, also somewhat less definite; and indeed, the change has been so great that anyone who now speaks of contemporary philosophy as "Logical Positivism" shows himself out of date by that fact alone. The early stage was beyond all question greatly significant. But it was a bold extreme that might excite philosophers and stimulate them to further explorations, yet could not satisfy them permanently. The prospect of eliminating metaphysics strongly attracted many thinkers (as of course, and in some cases precipitately, it repulsed others), but to most people the price of this elimination was extravagant. The statements which comprise religion were to prove meaningless too; moral judgements were relegated to the status of cries or outbursts taking the form of a sentence but really like snarls, purring or nudges. Many philosophers felt that even though these notions might perhaps hint at something true and important, they were, as they stood, untrue and perverse. Statements about the past, on the other hand, had to be analysed as roundabout statements about the future; and statements about other people's experiences had to be reinterpreted as if they referred only to the externally observable behaviour of other people's bodies. These assertions seemed to be out-and-out muddles, although by contrast with the former two they might be academic and harmless. Here then was the first significant difficulty about "Logical Positivism": treat it on its own terms, like a scientific hypothesis, and it had false implications, and must therefore itself be false.

The second difficulty was simply that the theory proved to be untenable on the strictest grounds of logic. Statements about our immediate experience were fondly supposed to be completely certain: on examination they proved to be dubitable like all the rest. Take the example used above, seeing the black and white of the page. There is no doubt that in confining what one says to "immediate experience"—to the black and white impressions, the "sense-data"—one does not expose oneself to error as one does in asserting that one sees a *page*, which might after all be a hallucination. But by the late 1930's philosophers began to detect possibilities of error (though more subtle ones) even here. Is what one sees really white, for example, and not pale grey or pale cream? Suppose that on looking again more attentively we decide that it is pale cream: is "pale cream" the exactly proper term, would this rather be beige, or pale ochre, or stone-colour? We notice that we are forced to rely on our language-habits or our colour-charts. But this returns us to the very fallibility we are trying to escape: habit and memory are both unreliable. These uncertainties may seem farcical to the layman—but is it not somewhat farcical to suppose that this page may be a hallucination, which was the original doubt? After all the sacrifices and contortions of the analysis, there proves to be still no bedrock of absolutely certain statements out of which to build up all the other statements. And if not, the game (we might say) is not worth the candle—it turns out to be a game with no prizes.

VI. *"Linguistic" Philosophy*

There was also a third difficulty. It was the most important one, too, in that it suggested to philosophers how they could progress further. This difficulty arose because of something quite unexpected about many analyses: something these could not escape even when perfected, and even when they were of types of sentences which clearly warranted analysis. The crucial and surprising fact was that, even when a model in every respect, analysis sometimes gave a result quite clearly different in meaning from the original, yet so little or so subtly different that one could seldom say what had been left out or put in. It gave something closer than an implication and yet more remote than an exact paraphrase. This new and un-suspected relation turned up at most of the really interesting transitions in our language. It was not simply a method, or a programme, like analysis itself; but a real, a major discovery.

This discovery diffused itself through analytical philosophy from perhaps 1930 on; and if we can talk about periods in modern philosophy, it was what constituted the second period of that movement. The initiator of this second movement was Wittgen-stein: for within a few years of writing his *Tractatus*, he appears to have undergone a radical change of view. This was not a complete change in Wittgenstein's philosophical opinions, but in method of thinking and explanation it was a change so profound that it approximated to a complete one. Wittgenstein himself preferred to disseminate his later views only by oral teaching. One reason for this was his essential concern now with the kind of incomplete equivalence of meaning referred to in the last paragraph; and of this Wittgenstein considered there was no standard model. One could only acquire a sense of it through detailed and lengthy study of a multitude of particular cases. In refusing to publish his views in tabloid form, indeed, Wittgenstein was refusing to pander to a weakness noticed by one of his forerunners in the analytical tradi-tion, Francis Bacon: "*But for that going to and fro to heterogeneous examples, by which axioms are tried as in the fire,* the intellect is altogether slow and unfit, unless it be forced thereto by severe laws and over-ruling authority." Wittgenstein's own personality secured this authority within the small circle of his pupils. But during the 1930's much of his teaching circulated in manuscript form, and it was so influential that even before the publication of his second book in 1953 (more will be said of this later) he had in effect transformed the philosophical scene twice over.

Some idea of this pervasive relation, more than implication and less than identity of meaning, may perhaps be given by a few examples—though only at the price of simplification. First, it comes to light if we analyse statements about ordinary material objects (like chairs and tables) into statements about our direct experiences of these objects. This was the analysis that received most attention in the 1930's; most philosophers were inclined to agree that what mattered in such a statement was what it implied about our experi-ence—if not about actual experiences, at least about possibilities of experience. Several different kinds of analysis were offered of which the subtlest were perhaps those of H. H. Price (*Perception,* 1932; *Hume's Theory of the External World,* 1940) and A. J. Ayer (*The Foundations of Empirical Knowledge,* 1940). The most discussed of these took the form of saying that any statement about a material object, observed or unobserved, could be translated into a large collection of statements about the experiences which one *would* have, *if* this or that or the other condition of experience were fulfilled— "Phenomenalism". Thus a statement like "there is a hen-egg on that table" was identified with a collection of hypothetical statements of the form, "If I did *this* and *this* . . . then I should see *that*"; and so on for every possible contingency of seeing, touching, tasting and so forth. All these hypothetical statements taken together constitute the equivalent of the original. The complexities were of course fantastic, but the question was a theoretical, not a practical one, and this was therefore unimportant. The *full* meaning might be beyond us, but what mattered was the kind of thing it was.

The distinctive relation, which was referred to above, presented itself in this problem as follows. Suppose I do what is required by the "if-clause" of any given unit in the translation (for example, stretch out my finger) but then *my senses deceive me* (e.g. I feel something woolly, not egg-like). Then the original sentence might be true, but one part of what is supposed to be its equivalent in meaning would have turned out false: which is self-contradictory. Now suppose that the egg is in fact a duck-egg, not a hen-egg. Only a small number of the hypothetical sentences would be different in the two analyses; in principle at least, my senses might deceive me every time I tested one of these, and I might *seem* to verify the hen-egg hypothetical statements on and on indefinitely, although duck-egg is there all the time. The original statement might be true, and some part of its alleged equivalent be false; or be false, and all parts of its alleged equivalent seem to prove true. A moment's thought will show that this is not something that any refinement in the analysis would obviate. It is intrinsic to the idea of analysing, or at least to verifying, in a world where illusions occur, the statements with which the analyses have to deal.

The second example was perhaps more important, because it led more directly to positive discoveries about language. Consider "Jane is genuinely devout" and what might well be offered as correcting such an assertion, getting nearer the truth—"Jane conforms in religion". To say that Jane is devout seems to say something about what she does, believes and feels, and about what she would do, believe and feel in various imaginary circumstances. We might try to combine all these possibilities into an analysis of the original statement "Jane is devout". But once again, the original and the proffered equivalent cannot really be equivalent, for they prove not to be always false together or true together. Some people are very devout in a very inconspicuous way; or they have strong "faith" without the strong feelings that often go with it. On the other hand, their devotions and feelings may be very conspicuous, but not seem an altogether sound sign of devoutness. One after another of the members of the set of statements alleged to be equivalent might prove true, but in the given case we should still say, "No, she's not really devout, she only conforms (or gets emotional)". Conversely, though, they might one after another prove false; and yet something about the situation as a whole, or some detail of a quite new kind, might still make us say that Jane's was a case of real devoutness. Our whole use of words proves more extempore, and more dependent on intangibles, than we had thought.

This view of language as ineradicably fluid was brilliantly illustrated in a long series of articles by John Wisdom (published in *Mind*, 1940-3) and it was generalized into a theory in articles by Dr. F. Waismann.[1] Waismann's term for this pervasive quality of language was "open texture". Put in a somewhat generalized form, the view is that the meanings of most words and expressions in common use are not precisely and exhaustively fixed, and more than this, that it would be very inconvenient if they were. They are given, by their users, just that degree of determinate meaning which fits them to do what they are needed to do: and to suppose that this can be a complete and rigid meaning would in most cases be a mistake. It is a mistake, partly, because experience is constantly bringing us minor surprises, and because what we need to get from language, as something that can be related to experience, changes too. A terminology is useful exactly *because* it is fluid at the edges, no less than because its centre is clear and definite. But unruly philosophers—those of the older school anyhow—instead of understanding and acquiescing in this two-sided character of ordinary language, used it unconsciously to create artificial perplexities. They took a word, strained it into a quite new use, created a paradox by reminding one dramatically at that point of the old use, and claimed that they were obliged to postulate some queer and unobservable entity to explain it away.[2] Alternatively they strained a word to a new sense, showed that (in the new sense) it could not be used where one had been using it quite happily (in the old sense), and claimed a startling discovery of a negative kind.[3] If the senses of words in the ordinary vocabulary would not stretch far enough, they were stretched to the limit, exchanged for technical terms, and the

[1] See I. Berlin, "Logical Translation" (*Proceedings of the Aristotelian Society*, 1950).

[2] For example, an argument to prove the existence of Material Substance: Consider a man in clothes. Are clothes essential to being a man? No. Strip them away. What is left?—a naked man. But is his particular height, colour, shape and so on, essential to being a man? No. Strip *them* away. What is left? Nothing? Not if we have been stripping away only inessentials. Something must be left. *Substance* must be left.

[3] This form of argument produces doctrines like "we have no *reason* to predict that the sun will rise tomorrow", "we don't *know* that Paris is the capital of France", etc. The italicized words are "treated" in the argument so that they exclude their own normal sense.

stretching process resumed. Philosophers with the new attitude decry every attempt to tamper with ordinary language either by adding specialist words, or by shifting the senses of ordinary words; and they can bring against metaphysics not the blunt and dogmatic technique of the Logical Positivists (a demand to reject what cannot be straightforwardly verified: itself at bottom a metaphysical principle) but a subtler and far more penetrating technique. They can, if their technique succeeds, expose the exact point at which an extended metaphor, or a plausible but dogmatic assertion that one phrase was the equivalent of another, or some other device, surreptitiously adjusted the sense of a key term, and made an apparent argument of no argument.

VII. Moral Philosophy and Language "Uses"

At one point the last paragraph contained the vaguest phrase possible: language was described as "something that can be related to experience". This vagueness was deliberate, it was induced by the second of the two great positive discoveries that modern analytical philosophers have made in the course of their attempts at analysis. While philosophers regarded themselves as studying "ultimate reality", or "knowledge", or "thought", they unconsciously tended to take one distinctive kind of language as the norm of language. Language, they assumed, was used to "refer"; it was used "about" the facts, to state what they were, to describe. As the attention of philosophers shifted from reality, to a keener scrutiny of language for its own sake, this tendency naturally weakened; and it was further weakened by another discovery about analysis. The tendentious, distorting quality of *some* attempted analyses could be blamed on "open texture" resulting from indeterminate meanings. Words like nouns, adjectives, verbs, that is, had an irrevocably fluid use. But this explanation did not always fit the case. It became clear that sometimes a quite different variation existed between what analysis began with, and what it ended with. The analysis seemed to distort its subject-matter, one might say, in another dimension; and in exploring this other dimension, philosophers began to produce another kind of analysis. The older form was an analysis of propositions, and tried to concern itself with their exact meanings. The newer kind concentrated rather on different *functions*: and these not only of assertions, propositions, but of utterances of any sort. Again, the older kind had striven to produce a fresh proposition (or more usually set of propositions) which would be identical in meaning with the proposition analysed. The newer kind went to work by tracing differences rather than equivalences. It adopted a variety of techniques: but its ultimate appeal was to the ways in which various utterances occurred in the real use of language; and it argued either that two utterances were different in meaning because one was not, as it ordinarily occurred, able to do the work of the other, or that if the two really were equivalent, there would be no meaning in some distinction or comparison or assertion in which we know that there certainly is meaning.

This newer and in reality much more fundamental kind of analysis perhaps first became important in the field of moral philosophy: which had benefited comparatively little from the kind of analysis which took factually descriptive statements as its norm. Moore had made an important contribution to the analysis of moral judgements as early as 1903, when in *Principia Ethica* he had argued that while "right" could be defined in terms of "good", goodness itself was a simple and unanalysable quality, and fundamentally different from any complex of ideas of a not strictly ethical kind: ideas such as "the object of desire", "producing pleasure", "in accordance with evolution" and so on. Moore christened the attempt to define "good", or rather to define it *away* in this manner, the "naturalistic fallacy". It was a fallacy, he argued, because if "good" simply *meant* such a complex of non-ethical qualities ("natural", as he called sensible qualities, or of any other kind) it would make no sense to ask whether the complex in question was or was not itself good. It always did, however (in Moore's opinion) make sense to ask questions such as "is it good to satisfy desire?", "is it good to produce pleasure?"—whatever the answers to these questions might be. Therefore all definitions of this kind must necessarily be fallacious. In pursuing this line of argument Moore was, as will by now be easily seen, full in the empiricist tradition. He was, in fact, protesting against something not unlike what Hume had protested against, in condemning how philosophers glided, in their arguments, from the word "is" to the very different word "ought"; and his decision to take as his epigraph the famous remark "everything is what it is, and not another thing" from Bishop Butler, the great eighteenth-century moralist, is one more reminder of this. Moore has been criticized for using this remark, on the ground that his argument would prohibit all definitions, and all discoveries that one expression was identical in meaning with another. But this is a misunderstanding of what he did. He had, in his view, simply discovered that "goodness" meant something which was not identical with any other quality or complex of qualities. This was the point of the remark.

From Moore's work two quite different lines of argument proceeded. One, represented by Sir David Ross, accepted Moore's analysis of goodness; rejected his analysis of rightness in terms of it; argued for the existence of a second simple and unanalysable quality which was called rightness or "fittingness" and which "resided" in actions; and proceeded to catalogue in a somewhat miscellaneous and *ad hoc* way the various actions in which this quality was domiciled. The other was a line of inquiry which Moore himself had indicated, though only as an obvious extravagance. He had said that the alternative to his theory was that moral statements should refer to *nothing*. This was the view developed by A. J. Ayer in *Language, Truth and Logic*: sentences of an ethical kind were not descriptive at all, but were expressions of emotion in the speaker, or (like commands) were ejaculations designed to cause the hearer to react as the speaker wanted. Something could be said for both these theories. The second, certainly, seemed odd and even outrageous; and it led to certain paradoxes: if moral judgements were like cries of emotion or commands, for example, how could two people ever be said to *disagree* about morality? But by its reference to the emotions and the desires of those who used moral terms, it certainly explained why these words are used in connexion with matters that we vitally care about, and it hinted at why we are often so anxious to express ourselves in moral terms to *others*, and persuade them to adopt our own attitudes. The former theory, straightforward as it superficially seems, is fundamentally deficient at this very point. Neither Ross, nor Moore for that matter, could explain why these simple and unanalysable qualities were of any interest to us at all. The differences in *value to us* between the natural and the "non-natural" or moral quality had to be *de fide*: which in this case at least was far from satisfactory. Extreme as it seemed, Ayer's theory actually proved the more fertile in the sequel.

In pursuing these lines of inquiry, philosophers made several discoveries. First, they recognized that the analysis of moral expressions had led them into an altogether more fluctuating and flexible region of language than that used for quasi-scientific description. Moral "judgements" might express emotions, issue commands, influence the conduct of others, describe features of actions or states of affairs; and these might be combined quite differently on different occasions, depending on the course which a conversation might take and so on the whole context of a given utterance on a given occasion. Second, it became clear that the descriptive function of these utterances, while it could almost never be their whole function, was on the other hand almost never wholly absent, and could not possibly be eradicated. In particular, it was present in the definitions of ethical terms which were always implicitly present behind the utterances, and which—here was the distinctive feature of the value-judgement—could be very considerably controlled and modified by the speaker, in the course of developing his argument and for the purpose of influencing how his hearer behaved.[1]

Thus there has developed a greater interest in, and respect for,

[1] See especially C. L. Stevenson, *Ethics and Language* (Yale University Press, 1944), and R. M. Hare, *The Language of Ethics* (Clarendon Press, 1952).

and willingness to study and analyse, the emotive and (more important) the prescriptive aspects of ethics, and necessarily therefore the same aspects of utterances which express values of other and humbler kinds (e.g. "that is a good watch", "you must *bowl the ball*", or "it is right for the lady to go in front"). One important reason for this has not yet been mentioned. It is that wuile "statement" or "describing" was assumed to be the typical serious function of language, to suggest that these emotive and prescriptive aspects were prominent in ethics naturally seemed to derogate from its importance. In recent years, however, philosophers have noticed more and more that "stating" is far from being the norm of language (or at least from being its only serious and important use); and that many kinds of utterance which they formerly supposed were statements referring to entities of a more or less recondite kind, were much better understood as doing something quite familiar and straightforward, but quite different from any kind of description. J. L. Austin, for example, pointed out[1] that to say "*I* promise to return this" is radically different in type from "*he* promises to return this". The latter may "describe" an action ("his" promising) but the essence of the former is not describing. It is doing: the utterance *is* the promise. And "I promise" is only one out of a large class of similar expressions like "I surrender", "I give", "I order" and so on—all of which primarily perform actions (Austin called them "performative" verbs). The analysis which distinguished expressions of this kind noticed for example that the word "hereby" can always be added to them, though it cannot to ordinary descriptive expressions; that they are not denied, so much as *challenged*: the proper counter to "I order you to . . ." being not "You are mistaken . . ." but "You are *not in a position* to order me to . . .". Austin also added a point of perhaps greater importance: assertions of the form "I *know* that . . ." are also not purely descriptive, but in part perform an action, because they offer a guarantee, they stake the speaker's credit; and the challenge "*How* do you know . . . ?" asks not merely for *evidence*, but sometimes also for *credentials* which prove one is qualified to "give an opinion". In other words, the descriptive function of language, and some other function, can be fused. In a similar article somewhat later, H. L. A. Hart[2] suggested that utterances like "That is mine" or "He did it" are also not plain descriptions, but function like the "defeasible" expressions in law which claim, or ascribe, rights or responsibilities. Another suggestion is that expressions like "That statement is true" do not describe some queer relation between statements and facts, but

[1] In "Other Minds", part of a Symposium in the *Aristotelian Society Proceedings, Supplementary Volume*, xx (1946).

[2] "The Ascription of Responsibilities and Rights" (*Aristotelian Society Proceedings*, 1948-9).

merely offer to confirm a statement already made by someone else.[1]

These are not simply explorations of linguistic oddities having some intrinsic interest. Their importance is rather that they throw a quite new *kind* of light on standard philosophical problems—in the four cases mentioned above, on the problems of "knowledge", "voluntary action", "property", and "truth". Peculiarities about the use of the word "know", for example, have intrigued philosophers in the past. They have taken account of such rubrics as "if I *know* I can't be wrong"; and this has led them to suppose that when (if at all) "know" is justly used, it is justified by one, or other, or both, of two things. These were, first, a mental state of conviction in the same ascending scale as suspecting, believing, believing confidently, being convinced—yet higher than any of these; or second, a "relation to an object" in the same ascending scale as (for example) glimpsing something, seeing it, seeing it quite clearly—but again higher still. Thus they believed that philosophy was discovering hitherto undiscovered realities, whether psychological states or "cognitive relations". The modern analysis is fuller and subtler, and shows that this is a mistake. "I know" is not higher in the same scale as "I am sure"; it relies on the same convictions, but by lending the speaker's credit it performs something which "I am sure" does not attempt, or even deliberately avoids. The shift, as it were to a new dimension, shows in persistent differences through a range of idioms. We ask *"Why* do you believe?", but *"How* do you know?". With bad evidence we say "You ought not to *be* sure", but "You ought not to *say* you know". We can say simply *"For my part* I am sure", and thereby indicate that we leave others to determine for themselves; but to say "I know" proffers our authority and calls for its acceptance. Recognizing that a difference between expressions may be a difference between descriptive and non-descriptive functions, not between the facts to be described, philosophers can cease populating the world with queer pseudo-entities which nobody else can detect.

VIII. *Wittgenstein's Posthumous Works*

By a strange paradox that resulted from Wittgenstein's own extreme unwillingness to publish his work, what should have been the basic text for all these inquiries appeared in book form at a later date than many articles and books which in fact derived from its teaching. Wittgenstein's *Philosophical Investigations* did not appear until 1953, soon after his death at a comparatively early age. Despite the anomaly of its late arrival on the philosophical scene, it deserves attention by itself. It contains a loose sequence of discussions (not, probably, quite in the form the author would finally

[1] P. F. Strawson (*Analysis*, June, 1949).

have given them had he lived) dealing with the many seemingly commonplace situations which involve expressions like, "I mean...", "I believe . . .", "I intend . . .", "I feel . . .", "I remember . . .", and so on. Besides this, it also examines a large number of imaginary situations in which we play what Wittgenstein called a "language-game". The language-game is something in which words are used according to some simplified model; and by coming to understand this imaginary situation (which may be giving orders for brick-building, or matching squares with letters), we come to understand what is really involved in using, or in learning the use of, the more complex, or more hybrid expressions of language as it really is.

It might be supposed that there is something trivial in these discussions of everyday idioms, or these frivolous-seeming hypothetical situations; but this would be a mistake. In his own oblique but vivid and immensely stimulating way, Wittgenstein by these seeming trivialities is (as he points out in his preface) covering the same ground as more orthodox philosophers who talk only of propositions, states of consciousness, logic, volition, belief, and so on. He is conducting philosophical analysis, not in the narrower sense of seeking expressions equivalent in descriptive meaning to a given expression, but in that he is seeking to diagnose what is going on in this or that whole situation when a given expression is uttered.

Summary here is difficult; but it would be right to say that the further such analyses are taken, and the more fully the complexities of the situation are recognized, the less does any one situation of using language look quite like any other. We may say something; read the same words from a page; recite them; read them from the page although we know them by heart; repeat them though we have forgotten (or half-forgotten) what they mean; utter them while acting in a play; utter them as prompter for a play; and so on. But—and here is the crucial point—this variety, this approach to uniqueness, brings nothing mysterious with it. There is no need, in order to explain what is going on, to have knowledge of a seemingly esoteric kind about "mental states" of which the layman is unaware. In the first place, these "states" would explain nothing even if they could be identified. "We are trying to get hold of the mental process of understanding which seems to be hidden behind [reading the words, having sensations of familiarity and being-at-ease, etc.] . . . But we do not succeed . . . for even supposing I had found something that happened in all those cases of understanding, why should *it* be the understanding? And how can the process of understanding have been hidden, when I said, 'Now I understand', *because* I understood." Secondly, to seek a recondite explanation is also (as this remark indicates) entirely superfluous. We really know the meanings of the expressions which we let puzzle us; necessarily we do, or we could not use them with perfect ease and confidence. This knowledge is not awareness of what strange mental entities they "stand for"; but expertise such as we have learnt by learning a variety of things about when to say this and when to say that.

The basic method whereby Wittgenstein tries to make his reader see these points is one of unremitting comparison. He demands that we shall never theorize about "what we mean" in this or that case of using words; but shall replace theorizing by intent and penetrating scrutiny. "Don't think, but look!" he writes. The ultimate effect of looking is constantly a process of *differentiation*. "Classes of expression", that favourite of the earlier kind of analyst, on the whole do not exist: the function, or the amalgam of functions, tends to be distinctive in each individual case. Here Wittgenstein displays the fundamental transmutation which has come over analytical philosophy. This movement began as a kind of thinking about the use of language which relied for its proof on logical matters like self-contradiction or *reductio ad absurdum*. But in turning, in recent years, from the merely descriptive to *all* the functions of language, it has become something very different, a matter largely of observation. It has become an empirical investigation into the variety of functions which language performs, and as such it constitutes a body of knowledge, and a steadily growing one, which is more or less of a scientific kind, and which is not at all susceptible of *disproof* after the manner of philosophical theories. Recent discoveries, for example, about the open texture of language, about "defeasible" concepts, "performative" words, and so on, are no more to be *disproved* than discoveries about animal behaviour (though either can of course be much modified by fuller observation).

But besides this, there is another strand in Wittgenstein's latest work, very much less prominent, yet of a quite different and in fact more dogmatic kind. Throughout his book one senses an underlying disposition to believe that his analyses would always give results of a down-to-earth, unmetaphysical kind—never of the opposite kind. "*Of course*, if the words 'language', 'experience', 'world', have a use, it must be as humble a one as that of the words 'table', 'lamp', 'door'." For the view that this is no doubt often, and perhaps always true, *Philosophical Investigations* provides, certainly, a massive body of evidence: but in the nature of the case a frequent tendency cannot be turned without dogmatism into a universal rule. It seems, in fact, reasonable to distinguish two fundamentally different trends in the modern philosophy of analysis: one, discoveries about language-use which are in themselves not necessarily connected at all with metaphysics; and the other, the deployment of these discoveries in support of empiricism, and in a series of powerful and convincing attacks on metaphysical thinking. (Among the most recent of these, Professor G. Ryle's *The Concept of Mind*, 1949, ought certainly to be mentioned.) In this connexion, though, one somewhat striking fact should be noticed: that recently, several writers who on the whole find metaphysics quite uncongenial have come to ask themselves whether, however little they perform the ambitious functions claimed for them by their sponsors, metaphysical assertions do not after all perform *some* linguistic function. Metaphysics may not have an obvious, or indeed much meaning; but perhaps it is not, they have thought, devoid of all meaning. As far as this function has been traced by the philosophers of linguistic analysis, it appears to be that of quickening the reader's or hearer's perception to see, somehow, a difference in the underlying quality of his whole experience. Vague remarks like "man is a spirit" or "nothing is certain" may perhaps make us see life as a whole in a new way, with a new eye; and they are, after all, the simple counterparts of metaphysical theories. That analysis has shown much metaphysics to have been sheer muddle is beyond dispute; but that analysis is necessarily opposed to, and destructive of, all metaphysics, has not emerged. Whether a metaphysician will ever be able really to exploit the discoveries about language which the philosophy of analysis has made in recent years, is something about which it is certainly too early, as yet, to speak.

(Parts of the preceding discussion have appeared in another form as articles in *The Hudson Review*, to the Editors of which due acknowledgement is made.)

BOOKS SUGGESTED FOR FURTHER READING

D. J. O'Connor, *Locke* (Penguin Books, 1952).

G. Warnock, *Berkeley* (Penguin Books, 1953).

G. E. Moore, *Ethics* (Home University Library, 1945).

A. G. N. Flew (ed.), *Logic and Language* (Blackwell; Series I, 1951; Series II, 1953).

W. Elton (ed.), *Aesthetics and Language* (Blackwell, 1954).

Margaret Macdonald (ed.), *Philosophy and Analysis* (Blackwell, 1954).

The last three works in this list are collections of essays by various hands.

THE PHILOSOPHY OF THEISM
by Dr. D. J. B. Hawkins

I.

DISCUSSION OF THE possibility and scope of our knowledge of God has become a live philosophical issue in the present century to an extent that it has not been since the Middle Ages. Its having ceased to be so calls for more explanation than its return to attention. For it is an obvious part of a philosopher's concern to discover what can be said of the source and principle of all being. The Greek thinkers had no doubt that they were called to speculate on the real as opposed to the apparent, on what is as opposed to what merely becomes, on the primarily real as opposed to what comes from it and depends upon it. Their answers were sufficiently various, but a tendency towards a theistic solution manifests itself in the history of Greek philosophy, culminating in the aspiring architecture of the system of Plotinus.

Far from any growth in the sciences of matter serving with some measure of plausibility to explain mind, the direction of progress in Greek thought was in the opposite sense. The Platonic Socrates hails Anaxagoras for having clearly asserted the independent being and efficacy of *nous*, and his reproach is that Anaxagoras made insufficient use of his acknowledgement. The importance of soul grows with the development of Plato's own thought. Material things participate in the Forms, but neither the Forms nor the material world can be an ultimate source of coming to be. The Forms are above the realm of change, and matter or space is by itself inert. Only soul can be a self-moving mover, a genuine origin of change and development. It is by the activity of soul that the world of space is differentiated and takes on the likeness of the Forms. Soul is immortal and, therefore, in the Greek sense, divine, for divinity and immortality are equivalent. In the *Laws* Plato attaches the chief souls, the gods in the full meaning of the word, to the heavenly bodies; in the myth of the *Timaeus* he speaks of a supreme soul, the Demiurge, as the architect of the whole cosmos. A Platonic myth is neither to be interpreted with absolute literalness nor to be dismissed as mere fancy; it expresses what seems likely to be, although for Plato it is beyond proof or exact statement.

The myth of the *Timaeus* at least shows a tendency towards monotheism.

While Aristotle speaks of unmoved movers rather than of self-moved movers, he equally means a spontaneous source of activity. There must be such unmoved movers, for otherwise movement in the world would be without an origin. Aristotle attaches them also to the heavenly spheres, and the first unmoved mover is the mover of the outermost sphere. This is pure intelligence ever contemplating itself and governing the processes of change in the universe by the attraction which it exercises as a final cause or end to which movement is directed.

The "One" of Plotinus is beyond intelligence, for Plotinus thinks of intelligence as necessarily involving a multiplicity of ideas and processes. The *nous*, the supreme intelligence, emanates from the "One" and itself gives rise to the "World-Soul" which governs the universe. All souls find fulfilment in rising through and beyond intelligence to an ineffable union with the "One".

When the historical monotheisms, Jewish, Christian and Muhammadan, came into contact with Greek thought, they found much of which they could make use in support of the more specific doctrines of their theologies. A corrected and developed Platonism or Neoplatonism or, finally, Aristotelianism yielded them a natural theology, a sum of teaching about God which they regarded as philosophically demonstrable. Doctrines like the Christian doctrine of the Trinity, which philosophy was incapable of substantiating, remained as the subject of revealed theology, theology in the full sense of the word because it was not only about God but was God's communication of himself. In the thirteenth century St. Thomas Aquinas offers the classical example of such a philosophico-theological system, in which Aristotelian metaphysics is used to demonstrate the existence and attributes of the God of religion.

That philosophy suffices to prove the existence of the one God, the Supreme Being and Creator of the Universe, continued to be generally held down to the time of Locke and Leibniz. The eighteenth century saw a change of philosophical outlook. The great development of the physical sciences made men begin to think that the world might be explained from below rather than from above, by the lesser rather than the greater, by the blind forces of matter rather than by the design of mind. Those same sciences promised to enable man to overcome for himself the evils for whose relief he had hitherto relied on powers greater than himself. In a more strictly philosophical context Hume's attack on the notion of causality necessarily compromised the central line of argument to a First Cause. Kant's partial restoration of causality as an indispensable instrument of the mind in making phenomena intelligible left its application to the real world beyond phenomena without theoretical justification. Kant himself thought that our moral ideals postulated a just and omnipotent God, but this was a new kind of approach to the question and did nothing to rehabilitate the old natural theology.

The nineteenth century continued on the lines laid down in the eighteenth. Those who placed their whole reliance on the physical sciences looked to them for the explanation of the world, and evolutionary theories seemed to many to make it easy to dispense with God. The dialectical materialism of Marx and Engels made scientific positivism into a militant creed both for theory and for practice. Those philosophers who followed Fichte, Schelling and Hegel in developing the idea of creative mind as Kant's system had left it found satisfaction in absolute idealism rather than in theism. Many believers followed Kant himself in seeking the rational justification of their faith in the region of moral aspiration rather than of metaphysics. The defenders of the old metaphysical proofs pursued a lonely course in isolation from the philosophical thinking of most of their contemporaries.

If the situation is different today, this is partly because men have become more aware of the limits of scientific explanation. It has become too clear that scientists disclaim all intention or power of giving an ultimate explanation of anything. Absolute idealism is no longer a philosophical fashion. Moral arguments were always a second best and now more than ever seem a fragile foundation for religious belief. Men are able to consider with more open minds again whether there is a valid metaphysical basis for theism.

For the closer investigation of religious experience shows how deep-seated the religious attitude is. A book like Rudolf Otto's *The Idea of the Holy* makes clear how fundamental in human consciousness is that combination of awe and fascination whose object is the numinous. Must there not be some fundamental type of awareness which is the source of so fundamental a reaction? At any rate it is reasonable to look for such an awareness and to try to discover its nature.

II.

No doubt this new openmindedness to the philosophical claims of theism is often accompanied, and sometimes submerged, by perplexity about the appropriate method to employ. It is as a striking expression of such perplexity that Professor John Wisdom's paper on "Gods", originally published in the *Proceedings of the Aristotelian Society*, 1944-5, has become celebrated.[1] The plural of the title is presumably intended to indicate complete neutrality about the question whether God or gods exist, and no conclusions are reached in the paper to upset this neutrality. Its merit is that it represents

[1] Now reprinted in *Logic and Language, First Series*, ed. A. Flew (Oxford, 1951).

with exceptional clearness on the philosophical level a perplexity which is fairly common among reflective minds of all types today.

The most frequently cited passage of this paper, the parable of the garden, might, if taken by itself, suggest that Wisdom was merely pointing out the ambiguities of the argument from design as presented by Archdeacon Paley in the eighteenth century. The world is like a garden in which there is a strange mixture of order and disorder. If one man points to all the signs of order as evidence for the activity of a gardener and another points to all the signs of disorder as evidence for his absence, who is to choose between them? They do not appear to differ about any issue to which facts are relevant. "Their different words now reflect no difference as to what they have found in the garden, no difference as to what they would find in the garden if they looked further and no difference about how fast untended gardens fall into disorder." On what, then, is their difference based?

That this is not meant simply as criticism of Paley should not obscure the truth that it is good criticism of Paley. Reference to specific instances of apparent design in the world can always be countered by reference to specific instances of apparent lack of design. But Wisdom carries the discussion on. He is not content, with the arrogance of dogmatic logical positivism, to describe the difference as one purely of emotional attitude. What he is feeling for is some analogy with making people see characteristics of a situation which are hard to discern, which cannot be simply pointed out or logically inferred, but whose acknowledgement can be assisted by hints and indirect approaches. How, for example, do you help a man to see that something is beautiful? Is perceiving the reality of the religious object like perceiving the presence of beauty?

Wisdom leaves the problem unsettled, but there is one criterion of solution which he decisively rejects. This is metaphysical inference, inference in the manner of mathematics or logic. "No doubt", he says, "dispute about God has sometimes, perhaps especially in medieval times, been carried on in this fashion. But nowadays it is not." This short and untentative statement amid so much that is tentative spurs us to ask why not. It is not altogether true as a matter of fact that no one any longer argues about the philosophy of theism in this way, and it is not sufficient to exclude the method of logical inference merely on the ground that it is unpopular. The possibility that it is valid should be kept in account as well as Wisdom's analogy with the discernment of beauty.

Contemporary differences of method may also be usefully related to the dictum of Wittgenstein: "There is indeed the inexpressible. This *shows* itself; it is the mystical."[1] What can be said is typified

---

[1] L. Wittgenstein, *Tractatus Logico-Philosophicus* (Routledge and Kegan Paul, 1922).

by the propositions of science; what cannot be said but shows itself is still accessible to the human mind although in a different way; and there might be what can be neither said nor shown. For some philosophers theism is beyond human saying or showing; for others it can be shown although it cannot be said in the manner of scientific statement; yet others regard metaphysics as a supreme science and theism as a metaphysical conclusion of thought.

III.

Those who regard theism as beyond human saying or showing might not be thought to enter our subject except in so far as mention should be made of the large body of agnostics regretful or militant. Nevertheless we may include under this heading those who hold philosophy to be of no avail in the matter and attribute all genuine knowledge of God to the communication or revelation of God himself. Such is at least the ostensible position of Kierkegaard and of contemporary theologians who follow him, such as Karl Barth.

For Kierkegaard the God of the philosophers is an abstraction and an idol of our own creation; the real God is the Creator before whom we stand in utter dependence and who makes absolute claims on us, and this is the God who reveals himself through Christ. Barth likewise insists that the God of the Old and New Testament asks us not to prove his existence but to approve ourselves to him; the majesty of the living God is beyond the scope of our petty rational discussion.

That a Christian, or for that matter a Jewish or Muhammadan, theologian should assert that his specifically religious awareness of God is greater both in quantity and in kind than any purely philosophical theism is not only intelligible but even obvious. The alternative would be to suppose that the historical religions could be swallowed up by philosophy. It does not follow, however, that a theologian is bound to deny that philosophy has any competence in the question at all. The majority of theologians have indeed, though not always to the satisfaction of their opponents, tried to show that reason was on their side as well, and St. Paul himself, who was not excessively complimentary to the human intellect, maintained that the invisible things of God from the creation of the world are clearly seen, being understood by the things that are made. Hence even the Gentiles ought to have acknowledged God.

Kierkegaard's position becomes more comprehensible historically. The official Christianity of Denmark in his day appears to have been very similar to the official Christianity of England in the eighteenth century. It was a creed and practice of scarcely evangelical moderation and decorum, and Kierkegaard might well have been greeted with words like those which were addressed to Wesley by Bishop Butler: "Sir, the pretending to extraordinary revelations and gifts of the Holy Ghost is a horrid thing, a very horrid thing." Of course the non-Danish reader of Kierkegaard has usually no other authority for there being something rotten in the state of contemporary Danish religion, and the reality may well have been less unattractive than it was painted by him, but we have to explain Kierkegaard's position by the way in which he looked at the facts. At any rate there was a sharp distinction for him between the reality of God in his religious experience and any semi-rationalized Christianity or philosophical approach to theism.

Barth also began his theological activity in a philosophical atmosphere which was either antagonistic or indifferent to theism. He proclaimed a vigorous return to the principles of the Reformation and, just as Luther had protested against what he viewed as the rationalistic approach of the medieval scholastics, so Barth protested against a more evident form of rationalism. To take a middle position and to uphold a rational theology seemed to Barth to be among the attitudes of the medieval church against which Luther had raised his voice and the true followers of Luther had still to assert their dissent. There was no solution of any religious problem without faith.

Yet Luther's conception of faith had tended to enlarge its meaning and to engulf the other members of the Pauline triad, hope and charity. The Lutheran and the Barthian insistence that genuine religious knowledge is by faith seems to demand the gloss that this means saving knowledge, the knowledge which avails to salvation. As such it belongs to a purely theological perspective and does not invalidate a philosophical approach to theism any more than does Pascal's cry that the God he needs is not a God who can be proved, the God of the philosophers, but the God of the Patriarchs and of Jesus Christ. A philosophically minded Christian will want to insist that this is a distinction not of opposition but of adequacy. Philosophy is not the complete solution of the religious problem, but it may still have something to contribute, and nothing that Kierkegaard or Barth alleges need deter us from examining what this contribution is.

IV.

The view that the truth of theism cannot strictly be said but shows itself can be appropriately attributed to those existentialists who make or tend towards the affirmation of God. Existentialism harks back to Kierkegaard, but the influence of Kierkegaard has been in the sphere of method rather than of doctrine. While Kierkegaard proclaimed the impotence of philosophy, his declared followers form what is commonly regarded as a philosophical school,

and, while the reality of God was for him a primary fact, the
existentialists arrive at it, if at all, by devious ways, or, in the case
of Sartre, make the option of atheism. Nevertheless existential
philosophy works on the whole in the direction of theism. Heidegger's conclusions are exceedingly indefinite, but Jaspers has of
later years inclined more and more towards a definite theistic
affirmation, and Marcel's affirmation is unambiguous. We may
begin with Heidegger.

Heidegger learned from Husserl as much as from Kierkegaard.
Husserl's palliative for the unceasing conflict between realism and
idealism, as between other opposed types of systematic philosophy,
was to suggest a preliminary phenomenology, an attempt to begin
by describing the contents of consciousness in neutral terms before
attacking philosophical controversies. Whether any description of
the contents of consciousness can really be neutral in relation to
different types of philosophical interpretation is doubtful, but
Husserl's initiative succeeded at least in stimulating a rather wider
range of approach to the problems of philosophy. Heidegger's
description of human consciousness in his book on Being and Time
(Sein und Zeit) emphasized the finiteness and contingency of man's
condition. Human life is a brief space of existence between original
nothingness and death, and its constant passing away and tendency
to return to non-being is the source of that fundamental anguish
whose source is precisely the threat of nothingness. In the concept
of anguish Heidegger links up with Kierkegaard, and we might
have expected him like Kierkegaard to find a counterpoise in the
reality of God, but Heidegger's distinctiveness lies in having elaborated a doctrine of contingency which leaves necessity problematic.

For Sein und Zeit, of which only the phenomenological part has
been published, was intended to continue with a new ontology or
theory of being. Why Heidegger has been unable to work out any
sequel satisfactory to himself becomes fairly clear when we read his
book on Kant and the problem of metaphysics (Kant und das Problem
der Metaphysik). For Kant only a creative knowledge, of which things
themselves were products, could be a knowledge of things as they
are in themselves; a receptive knowledge, like man's, could only be
of its own products, its constructions of things as they appear. Such
constructions were stimulated by the pressure of external things
and took place in accordance with the laws of mind, but their relation to things in themselves was in principle unknowable. Only the
self as moral agent, which was the source of its own law and activity,
could know itself and the conditions of its agency in their proper
reality.

Heidegger felt justified in enlarging the knowledge of the self
allowed by Kant. For he argued that time was not merely a subjective form of inner sensibility but the real condition of our real

existence. Heidegger's attention was held by those passages in the first-edition version of the Deduction of the Categories in which the transcendental imagination seems to be made the common root of both sensibility and understanding. Mind is not simply the receptivity of sense or the objectification of understanding but the objectifying receptivity which is here described as transcendental imagination. But, just as reproductive imagination involves a looking backward in time, so transcendental imagination involves a looking forward; it is an anticipation of experience. The whole business of our minds, therefore, is rooted in a real temporality. We know ourselves genuinely as temporal existences.

In this way Heidegger rescued the knowledge of the self from Kant's phenomenalism, but he was unable to effect a similar rescue for the knowledge of other things. The very concept of the other as other made the self into a barrier against mental communion with it. As long as we tried to justify the truth of our conceptions by their correspondence with external fact, the second term of comparison was unknowable and the problem of truth was insoluble. Real truth could only be the unhiddenness, the transparency of being (*die Unverborgenheit des Seins*). But how could being itself become ours without ceasing to be being itself?

In his comparatively recent essay on Plato's theory of truth (*Platons Lehre von der Wahrheit*) Heidegger insists that the conception of truth as the correspondence of mind with fact is the original sin of European philosophy from Plato onwards and is at the bottom of its recurrent and invincible difficulties. But how are we to escape from the predicament of being ourselves with *our* thoughts and *our* words and to find real being uninfected by subjectivity? Whatever we make an object and talk about is relative to us. But "the teaching of a thinker is that which is unsaid in what he says". If not *in*, then *through* the spoken word being may reveal itself. This power of revealing being Heidegger finds especially in the more evocative kinds of poetry; hence his preoccupation with Hölderlin. But he expressly states that this is not an epoch in the history of humanity when being reveals itself easily or fully. What being really is remains a question without an adequate answer.

By himself, therefore, Heidegger would scarcely enter into our subject, but his teaching is indispensable for an understanding of the similarities and contrasts in the philosophy of Jaspers. Jaspers's approach is even more explicitly Kantian. The sciences of classification and generalization deal with a world in which the known object is essentially relative to the knower and the knower essentially relative to the known. The notions of reality as it is in itself and of the self as it is for itself are merely limiting ideas beyond the range of scientific knowledge. The task of finding our way about this world of objects (*Weltorientierung*) belongs to the sciences. We ourselves

can be the objects of a scientific psychology in the same way as
other types of thing are the objects of the other sciences.

Experience itself, however, shows that an objective psychology
is not the whole truth about man. Man is aware of himself not only
as a type of object in the world but as individual subject, the active
source of what he is and does. From this point of view he is existence,
ex-sistentia, a constant dynamism seeking to go beyond what he has
already attained. This awareness is both fundamental and arduous.
It is fundamental because it reveals the real self as it is, and arduous
because, as soon as we become aware of anything, we perforce
begin to transform it into a mere object of thought. In order to
grasp ourselves as subjects we have, so to say, to look back over our
own shoulder and to catch ourselves in the split second before the
beginnings of awareness develop into logical thought. In this way
we know ourselves in our reality, our *Sein*.

But what about *Sein* in general, the reality which underlies the
whole world of objects of thought? A recognition that the transcendent *is* stands as a presupposition of thinking just as, for Kant,
the reality of the thing-in-itself was a presupposition of our phenomenal constructions. But just as Jaspers is not content to follow Kant
in leaving the real self as completely unknowable in the theoretical·
order, and asserts a genuine although elusive awareness of it, so he is
equally unwilling to leave the thing-in-itself entirely beyond knowledge. Being itself, which has to be envisaged as a subject and source
of reality as a whole, is even less accessible to our minds than the
finite self, but a philosophical understanding sees the world dimly
but unmistakably as sign and symbol of it.

In his early writings Jaspers speaks very vaguely of the transcendent, but more recently it has assumed for him much more of a
religious outline. The cause of this seems to be that he has reflected
on the Bible, on the ineradicable connexion between European
philosophy and Biblical revelation, and on the power of the Bible
to make one see the world as the manifestation of God. While he
repudiates the exclusive claims of any creed or any church, he has
come to regard the Jewish and Christian scriptures as a unique
source of divination, of discovering the traces of absolute being.
Hence he is able to sum up the contents of philosophical faith as
follows:

"They are:
the idea of the one God;
the realization of the absolute nature of the decision between good
and evil in finite man; love as the fundamental actualization of the
eternal in man;
the act—both inward and external—as the test of man;
types of moral world order which are always historically absolute,

although none of their manifestations is absolute or exclusive;
the incompleteness of the created world, the fact that it does not
stand by itself, the inapplicability of all types of order to
borderline cases, the experience of the extreme;
the idea that the ultimate and only refuge is with God."[1]

However Christian these conclusions may sound, it must always
be remembered that Jaspers holds them as the elements of a strictly
philosophical faith. Although they go beyond scientific knowledge,
they are to be held because they commend themselves to philosophical insight into the traces of absolute being in the world of history.
God is not to be proved, nor is any human statement about him to
be accepted without reserve, but, as man is aware of his own real
existence by an awareness behind ordinary awareness, so but with
greater difficulty he reaches fleeting glimpses of absolute reality
behind the world of appearance.

Gabriel Marcel's God is the God of Christianity, but Marcel is
equally averse from the notion of a demonstrative natural theology.
It is not altogether clear whether this is because he regards the
proofs of the existence of God as invalid or merely as useless because
meaningless to an unbeliever and unnecessary to a believer. At any
rate religious questions belong to a sphere of mystery, which must
be approached by its own specific methods, and not to the sphere of
problems which are susceptible of a logical and scientific approach.

"We stumble on this paradox: the proofs are ineffectual precisely when they would be most necessary, when, that is, it is a
question of convincing an unbeliever; conversely, when belief is
already present and when, accordingly, there is the minimum
of agreement, then they seem to serve no useful purpose.
If a man has experienced the presence of God, not only
has he no need of proofs, he may even go so far as to consider the
idea of a demonstration as a slur on what is for him a sacred
evidence. Now, from the point of view of a philosophy of existence, it is this sort of testimony which is the central and irreducible
datum."[2]

Hence Marcel uses a method of recollection which is very different
from the methods of abstract thinking and even of purely objective
contemplation. Recollection is distinguished by its full concreteness
and comprehensiveness; it is reflection in a concrete situation and
with the endeavour so to embrace all the elements of the situation

[1] K. Jaspers, *The Perennial Scope of Philosophy* (Routledge and Kegan Paul,
1950), pp. 105-6.

[2] G. Marcel, *The Mystery of Being*, vol. ii, *Faith and Reality* (Harvill Press, 1951),
p. 176.

that adequate participation of self and object is possible. By recollection man becomes aware of the solidarity of what in a philosophical sense Marcel calls by the theological names of faith, hope and charity; that is, he becomes aware of his communion and interdependence with his fellow-men and with the world and begins to see his being and the being of the world as a gift from primal being beyond the world. Then Marcel turns the tables on the atheist by asking whether it makes sense to deny this experience of finite being as the manifestation of a divine generosity. Is not all atheism really antitheism, a refusal in virtue of some partial aspect of experience to accept what is involved in the experience of finite being as a whole?

Since Marcel does not bear to any other systematic philosopher the intimate relation which Heidegger and Jaspers bear to Kant, his thought is in the end, in spite of the greater limpidity of his French in comparison with their German, even more difficult to summarize and to evaluate. From one point of view he might seem in spite of himself to be only presenting the traditional causal proof in a more concrete way. From another point of view he might seem to be discussing the psychological conditions of belief rather than its logical foundations. From either point of view he is distinguished by a refusal to separate logic and psychology, and that is perhaps a typical attitude of all the existentialist thinkers.

Heidegger, Jaspers and Marcel, for all their differences, are at one in holding that ultimate reality is not to be said, not to be proved, in scientific terms and by scientific methods but must reveal itself to a more arduous and complex sort of philosophical reflection. The positions of Heidegger and of Jaspers can be explained by their dependence on Kant, and it is not clear that Marcel is less really, although less explicitly, influenced by the results of Kant's criticism of knowledge on the whole of later philosophy. Not all philosophers, however, are either conscious or unconscious Kantians, and we have still to consider those who look on metaphysics as a science in its own right and with its own rational methods.

V.

The view that the truth of theism can be stated in rational terms, inadequately but none the less accurately, is that of traditional metaphysics typified in the Middle Ages by the system of St. Thomas Aquinas. St. Thomas thought that our philosophical knowledge of God rested on an inference from caused to uncaused being, from finite to infinite. The contemporary English reader will find his metaphysics reproduced in Étienne Gilson's *God and Philosophy* and *Being and Some Philosophers* and in Dr. E. L. Mascall's *He Who Is*;

the present writer has offered his own version of Thomist natural theology in his *Essentials of Theism*.

The stumbling-block which many find in Thomism, however, is the doctrine that philosophical theism is inferential. How can we validly infer the infinite from the finite, God from the world? Are we not grossly pretending to extract from the premisses more than is in them? No one has expressed this difficulty more forcibly than Dr. Austin Farrer in his *Finite and Infinite*.

The point is that God can be conceived only as a unique being in a unique relation to other beings. He cannot be brought under a rule or made an instance to which a generalization of thought could be applied. What we attribute to him cannot be attributed in precisely the same sense in which we attribute the same predicate to creatures. Hence, if we try to argue from the world to God, the term applied in the conclusion to God must have a different meaning from that which it had as applied to finite things in the premisses. For example, if we are attempting to demonstrate God as the First Cause, our proof would be valid only if the divine causation were an instance of causality as generalized from human experience. But the divine causation must be of a unique sort. Our syllogism will, therefore, have four terms and must be rejected. The metaphysical approach to God cannot, then, according to Farrer, be by way of logical inference.

Similar considerations lead Dr. J. Langmead Casserley to assert that "the first step in theistic philosophy must be some form of the ontological argument".[1] The kernel of the ontological argument, as propounded in the past by St. Anselm, Descartes and others, is that the idea of God is the idea of a being who necessarily exists. To suppose that such a being does not exist is, therefore, to introduce a contradiction to its very idea. Hence the idea of God involves of necessity God's real existence. Contradicted in the Middle Ages by St. Thomas Aquinas and in modern times by Kant, the ontological argument has not had many recent supporters. Kant pointed out clearly enough that existence is not a predicate which may be argued either to belong or not to belong to an identical subject. Either the subject is presupposed as existent and the question is begged, or the subject is a mere idea and its existence can only be that of a possibility entertained by the mind. It is true that, if God exists, he exists necessarily, but no verbal jugglery can ascertain whether he exists.

Those who now favour a return to the ontological argument look upon it less as an inference from idea to fact than as the making explicit of an implicit acknowledgement. In this way they hope to escape the criticisms of Aquinas and of Kant. The point of the

[1] J. Langmead Casserley, *The Christian in Philosophy* (Faber and Faber, 1949), p. 84.

ontological argument would then be that, when we reflect on what we mean by God, we see that we already really know him to exist. The affirmation of God's existence is not arrived at but comes to light when we reflect that we cannot without contradiction suppose that the necessary being does not exist. A theistic philosopher of a different school might reply that, while it is true that if anything exists, necessary being exists, the truth of the affirmation of God depends not simply on the idea of God but on the experienced fact that something does exist, and that the whole causal argument is wrapped up in the passage from the fact that something exists to the truth that necessary being exists. Here is a subject of actual controversy, and it remains that Casserley and others find the ontological argument sufficient.

Farrer's solution of his own difficulties is less radical but contains a measure of obscurity. "What we have to do is to show that in and through and with his effects our minds grasp God" and "to challenge man to recognize that, with theology and its consequences rigorously excluded, we must exclude from our account of the world things which in our thoughts and actions we cannot but assume to be there". Nevertheless we have to "jump to the cosmological intuition" on the basis of a recognition that a "given distinction in the finite acts as a splintered image of God".[1] The difficulty suggests itself that one jumps to conclusions, justifiably or unjustifiably, but one does not jump to intuitions; one simply has them. Farrer does not seem to be presenting the affirmation of God as being, like intuitions in the full sense of the word, logically independent of its psychological antecedents. On the other hand, if it is logically dependent on its antecedents, it is either an inference or a product of analysis. But he has denied the possibility of valid inference and says that "analysis of the 'idea' must show whether the hypothesis that he is apprehended through this idea is even worth considering. But it cannot establish the probability of that hypothesis."[2] It is scarcely possible to doubt that knowledge must be either immediate or mediate, i.e. inferential, but Farrer's account of our apprehension of God will not easily fit in on either side.

Others have made a bold attempt to represent the awareness of God as the result of an analysis of the datum of experience. Dom Illtyd Trethowan maintains that we do not understand what the being of a finite thing means until we have seen that it involves a relationship to pure or infinite being.

"To say that 'something is' is the same as to say 'something has being'—Being, that is, acting upon it, present to it. . . . 'Being', then, contains an implicit reference not only to this or

[1] A. Farrer, *Finite and Infinite* (Dacre Press, 1943), pp. 8, 12, 262, 263.
[2] A. Farrer, op. cit., p. 8.

that limited being but to pure Being. . . . We can only look at what 'being' stands for until it breaks into finite and Infinite."[1]

The difficulty about this view is that the plain man, and a large number of plain philosophers, would declare on reflection that, however much the finite may presuppose the infinite, it is possible to understand, to question or to assert the existence of finite things without even the most implicit reference to God. That this or that thing should exist appears to have a meaning complete in itself. Yet even Mascall is sufficiently impressed by Farrer's difficulty to write that the causal argument "consists not in a process of logical deduction but in an apprehension, namely the apprehension of finite beings as effect implying (or, better, manifesting) a transcendent cause".[2] The difficulty is, then, one which many competent thinkers regard as serious. It is questionable, however, whether their answers are clear or satisfactory.

The difficulty is essentially about argument in *analogical* terms, in terms, that is, which vary in meaning according to the subjects to which they are applied. When we say that a man is intelligent and that a dog is intelligent, we do not, in spite of the efforts of those who seek to construe human nature as merely and entirely a product of animal evolution, mean the same thing in each case. If we try to frame some mental definition of intelligence in terms, perhaps, of responsiveness to environment, we find that we have incurred two massive difficulties. In the first place we ought to recognize that there is an immense difference between the animal type of response to environment, which for want of a more expressive word we call instinctive, and the reflective and deliberate type of response which is specifically human. Secondly, the vague general notion of response to environment demands to be extended to plants, but we find it unnatural to describe plants as intelligent. Our definition obviously has ragged ends; it is not only vague but incurably vague. We find that we cannot arrive at a clear-cut notion of intelligence which applies equally to animals and to men.

Evidently this kind of difficulty applies to our talk about God. We want to say that God is mind, that God has knowledge and will, that God is good; and if we could not validly say anything of this sort we should not suppose ourselves to know anything about God. Yet we cannot pretend that concepts derived from our experience of finite being apply without difference to the Infinite. Moreover, finite experience cannot tell us wherein this difference positively consists. We are reduced to talking about God in terms whose finite content is plainly inadequate to the reality of God and which need to be amended in a way of which we are necessarily and in principle

[1] I. Trethowan, *Certainty* (Dacre Press, 1948), p. 45.

[2] E. L. Mascall, *Existence and Analogy* (Longmans, 1949), p. 89.

ignorant. Yet we have no other way of talking about God, and we have to describe him by analogy with the finite things of experience in a manner which we must admit to be inadequate but may claim not to be false.

When the Thomist maintains that a community of analogy is sufficient to enable us to frame a demonstration of the Infinite from the finite, he is put on his mettle to explain analogy in such a way as to justify this contention. The reproach that the current Thomistic accounts of analogy suffer from ambiguities and obscurities is not easily countered. The following account claims no authority but is presented as a suggestion about the line which a satisfactory doctrine of analogy ought to take.

Analogy is based upon inexact similarity. Two surfaces might show exactly the same shade of red. If, then, I said of surface B that it was exactly the same shade of red as surface A which you were seeing, there would be no ambiguity of any sort in my description. But red things of all shades are similar in being red. There is in this case no exact similarity, and it is impossible to isolate an essence of redness from the various shades of red. Redness is essentially a variable which we recognize as present in red things of all shades but which we cannot isolate and consider by itself apart from its range of specific determination. If I say simply that something is red, I am giving you genuine information about it, but it is information which is incurably ambiguous unless I can point out something else of precisely the same shade of red or until you can inspect its shade of redness for yourself.

Some of the obscurity of the notion of analogy is dispelled if it is admitted that the concepts which are usually described as analogous are only instances of this sort of ambiguity on a larger scale. The completely and utterly analogous concept is that of being, which applies to absolutely everything, but there is no isolable factor of existence which we can contemplate for its own sake and by itself. We know being as what is common to all beings, but it is inseparable even in thought from the forms which being takes. But, just as we could reason about redness in terms of anything which follows simply from being red, so we can reason about being in terms of anything which follows simply from it.

In reasoning about God we use the completely analogous concept of being and some other highly analogous concepts. Causation appears in experience in various forms as a relationship of an agent to its activity, as a relationship of conditions to what they maintain in being, as a relationship of temporal antecedents to a temporal consequent. The recognition that being which is caused in any way presupposes totally uncaused being is followed, in virtue of the analogy or elasticity of the notion of being, by the recognition that uncaused or necessary being can only be the infinite fullness of being.

To such infinite being we can analogously attribute in an inconceivable completeness such qualities as do not of their nature imply finiteness, especially the character of eternal and omniscient mind and of omnipotent will.

The Thomist, then, holds that the use of analogous concepts does not vitiate his reasoning. There is sufficient community of meaning in their different modes of instantiation to make valid inference possible. Thus, among those philosophers who uphold the scientific character of metaphysics and the need of a metaphysical approach to the existence of God, the fundamental difference is between those who accept an inferential method and those who reject it in favour of some more or less clearly defined alternative. While the present writer has not disguised his sympathies with an inferential method, he must leave the decision to the reflective reader.

VI.

Another approach to theism, which does not deserve to be forgotten although it is no longer fashionable, is that of the idealists. The greatest of nineteenth-century idealists can scarcely be described as theists. Hegel's Absolute, evolving and manifesting itself in history, is not what theists mean by God, and Bradley expressly asserted that the Absolute, to which nothing is opposed except appearance, cannot be identified with a God who stands over against the world. Other idealist thinkers, however, like J. S. Pringle-Pattison, whose *Idea of God in the Light of Recent Philosophy* earned considerable respect in a not too distant past, developed the general maxims of idealism in a theistic direction. Such writers are now little read. Their presuppositions are no longer accepted, and even their minor habits, such as a tendency to quote Wordsworth when in a tight logical corner, are a source of irritation to the contemporary mind.

Nevertheless the belated appearance of the late Professor G. F. Stout's Gifford Lectures on *God and Nature* was a reminder of a type of argument which has only just ceased to be familiar. Although Stout was a critic of idealism, his thought was obviously influenced by the idealism around him. Less expectedly, he puts forward the causal argument and the doctrine of analogy with little apparent respect for Kantian and other criticism. But his general discussion proceeds on a broad front to establish the primacy of mind over matter. Against the idealists the physical world is asserted to be real in its own right, but the idealists are ultimately justified in asserting that nothing could exist without being known by some mind. The systematic unity of the Universe can be sufficiently seen to imply a cosmic mind upon which its processes depend.

Dr. F. H. Cleobury's *God, Man and the Absolute* is a recent book which belongs more completely to the idealist tradition. As an attempt to revive an unpopular mode of thought it has attracted less attention than its intrinsic merits deserve. Cleobury maintains the self-evidence of the fundamental maxim of idealism by saying that he is "incapable of attaching any meaning to the notion of an existent or a subsistent or a real which no one, God or man, is conscious of".[1] Although Absolute Mind, as the all-embracing experience, must in some sort include finite experiences, Cleobury regards himself as able to make a sufficient distinction between the finite and the Absolute to rank as a theist rather than a pantheist. Many might think that he compromises his position by attempting to reduce similarity, complete or partial, to complete or partial identity. If this reduction were possible, it would seem difficult to deny that all being is not merely dependent on but engulfed by the Absolute. There is no doubt, however, that he argues ably, whether successfully or not, for a form of theism on an idealist basis.

Where he is certainly on strong ground is in pointing out that no theist can in fact hold that matter exists without at least the divine mind being aware of it. Classical theism maintains that it is more accurate to say that things exist because God knows (and wills) them than to say that God knows them because they exist. This begins to sound not so remote from Berkeley's view that things simply are ideas in the mind of God. Yet, of course, it is not the same; it is one thing to say that matter is altogether dependent on mind and another to say that it has no existence of its own apart from being an object of awareness. It remains possible for a theist to be a realist.

Nevertheless, even on a realistic basis, justice may still be done to the insights of idealism. Matter may still yield traces of its destination to mind, of its having been made by and for mind. The Platonic tradition is the massive historical witness for this. The Plotinian hierarchy of being arises from a direct consideration of the interrelatedness of types of thing and involves a clear affirmation that matter can come only from mind and that the supreme reality is a spiritual unity above mind as we know it in its finite manifestations. St. Augustine saw in the timelessness of truth the evidence that mind shares in an order superior and prior to the world of time and change. However remote Neoplatonism may seem from the current preoccupations of most philosophers, it is a part of human philosophical experience which it would be highly provincial to ignore.

Specifically, then, matter shows itself as capable of being thought about and of manifesting aspects to conceptual analysis and the apprehension of distinctions and similarities which are latent in its mode of being simply as matter. It achieves a fuller and more

[1] F. H. Cleobury, *God, Man and the Absolute* (Hutchinson, 1947), p. 10.

articulate reality for thought than it possesses simply for itself. It yields to mind the elements of generalizations which are valid independently of time and even of the existence of instances verifying them. Thus it points to primal existence as eternal and creative mind. This is an approach to theism which is not nowadays very familiar, but it is not on that account to be overlooked. It surely deserves to be integrated with other methods of approach.

VII.

A survey of the contemporary philosophy of theism might be considered unbalanced without a fair account of contemporary atheism. But atheism does not usually present itself as the result of a positive argument. Sartre's atheism is an option, a personal choice made in a supposedly irrational world. The more powerful atheism of the dialectical materialists aims at so explaining and moulding the world on the basis of the sciences that theism may become superfluous. The question, therefore, is whether theism itself can be rationally justified. If its grounds are enough to command our assent, there can be no suggestion that it is a superfluity. If they were not, we should have to do without it.

Nor does the ancient problem of evil lend itself to discussion in isolation. No doubt the presence and extent of evil in the world is the greatest obstacle to belief in God, but few would be rash enough to say either that a belief in God enabled them to explain evil in detail or that the evil which actually exists is incompatible with a providential design. Once again, the attitude which we take towards this problem depends on whether we accept theism, and not the other way round.

Yet, in spite of all that philosophy has to say, it might well be suggested that belief in God is usually prior to philosophy and exists independently of philosophy. Can philosophy do more than put up a dialectical defence of a belief that men already possess? In this respect the philosophy of theism is not in a different situation from other parts of philosophy. Philosophy has not an entirely new subject-matter; it is an elucidation and criticism of thinking which already occurs on the level of common sense or in the sciences.

We do not wait to have knowledge until we have studied the theory of knowledge. Common experience provides us with an elementary notion of knowledge, which we examine and try to refine upon in philosophical reflection. So, in detail, we ask how we become aware of the external world and of other minds, of what exactly we are then aware, and what is the logical status of the opinions that we entertain on such matters. The highly various answers given by philosophers to such questions, from the most uncompromising realism to a complete idealism, all presuppose the fact of our common experience of trees and rocks, tables and chairs, and other men.

Moral philosophy equally presupposes the general sense of obligation. The philosopher asks what this means, on what it is founded, and to what it should extend, but he has and needs no other starting-point than the ordinary man's conscience. At whatever type of ethical system he arrives, it claims to be an elucidation and criticism of the morality of common sense.

We are similarly placed with the philosophy of theism. Religion is a fact of history, and the religious instinct is a fact of psychology. Philosophy has to inquire into the rational basis of religion, the logical status of religious beliefs, and what exactly we are entitled by reason to affirm about the divine. In doing so it is no more begging the question than any other branch of philosophical reflection.

There is this, however, to be specially noticed, that the historical religions, Judaism, Christianity and Muhammadanism, claim to be more than human philosophical creations; they claim to be revelations made to man by God himself. As such they might be thought for their adherents to supersede any mere philosophy, and we have already seen that thinkers like Kierkegaard and Barth assert that they do. Nor are these thinkers without an ancestry. In the early Middle Ages religious men like St. Peter Damiani and St. Bernard resented the ambition of human logic to explore the divine mysteries. In the same way there was among the Jews and Muhammadans a theological reaction against their philosophers which put an end to specifically Jewish and Muhammadan philosophical speculation in later medieval times. There is, nevertheless, a respectable body of opinion on the other side, and certainly among Christians it is true that the majority of thinkers have aimed at a harmony of reason and revelation rather than the abolition of one by the other. As the Cambridge Platonist Nathaniel Culverwell put it in the seventeenth century, if the light of divine revelation is like the sun, reason is at least the candle of the Lord. Indeed, unless man had some rational knowledge of God, he would scarcely be able to recognize God revealing himself.

Historically, then, we can speak of Christian, as we can of Jewish and Muhammadan, philosophy, in the sense that this was philosophy cultivated by adherents of these creeds and intended to harmonize with them. We can go farther and admit that it was the challenge of these historical monotheisms which led philosophers to carry their reasoning on and to articulate the rational grounds for belief in a single personal God in a way to which the ancients had not attained. It is still true that such philosophy, precisely as philosophy, is held to be logically independent of the historical religions. From this point of view there is no more a Jewish, Christian or Muhammadan philosophy than there is Jewish, Christian or Muhammadan biology or arithmetic.

Moreover the historical religions do not make a philosophical approach to religion superfluous. Their understanding of their own doctrines is aided by the philosophical interpretation in which speculative theology consists. And the philosophical habit of mind is the greatest safeguard against superstition, the tendency to over-beliefs without adequate foundation which is an excess to which the witness of history shows the unsophisticated believer to be unduly prone. Genuine sanctity, doubtless, is a safeguard too; but, if neither sanctity nor philosophy is an easy course to adopt, philosophy is perhaps slightly the easier.

The Middle Ages arrived at a constructive metaphysic of theism. Later philosophy has uncovered many latent problems and found much to criticize which had not been criticized before. But religion and the religious instinct continue to be facts of human nature, and the philosopher has still to give an account of them. What sort of an account should he give in the light of all that has been thought, down to the present day? The answers, as we have seen, vary from the position that such matters are outside the scope of human knowledge to a thorough-going revival of constructive metaphysics. At any rate the philosophical basis of theism is being investigated with greater care and vigour than it was in the comparatively recent past, and to that extent philosophy is becoming once again more adequate to the facts of human experience which its perennial task is to elucidate and to criticize. It is man's privilege at least to seek truth; but it is a mistake to think that seeking is better than finding, and a theist might like to encourage the seekers with the words which Pascal seemed to hear: You would not be seeking me unless you had already found me.

BOOKS SUGGESTED FOR FURTHER READING

W. G. de Burgh, *Towards a Religious Philosophy* (Macdonald and Evans, 1937).

E. Gilson, *God and Philosophy* (Yale University Press, 1940).

D. J. B. Hawkins, *The Essentials of Theism* (Sheed and Ward, 1949).

G. Dawes Hicks, *The Philosophical Bases of Theism* (Allen and Unwin, 1949).

E. L. Mascall, *He Who Is* (Longmans, 1943).

G. F. Stout, *God and Nature* (Cambridge, 1952).

THE RELIGIOUS INSTINCT

by PROFESSOR R. C. ZAEHNER

"QUID PETIS AB Ecclesia Dei?"
"Fidem."
"Fides quid tibi praestat?"
"Vitam eternam."

"What dost thou look for from the Church of God?"
"Faith."
"What does faith assure thee?"
"Life eternal."

These words are taken from the rite of Baptism as practised by the Roman Catholic Church. What, if anything, do they mean? It will be the purpose of this essay to illuminate to some degree the devious by-ways that modern man explores in his search for faith, and to consider how he conceives of life eternal.

The twentieth century inherited from the nineteenth a touching faith in the ability of physical science to explain all things and to deliver man from the bondage to his environment. It was reared on the dogma of progress which had been falsely deduced from the immense expansion of scientific knowledge and the practical and constructive use to which that knowledge had been put. Early twentieth-century man was all too ready to equate the undoubted extension of man's control over matter with a corresponding improvement in his spiritual and moral estate. He could point to the abolition of the slave trade and of slavery, to an increased social consciousness in the British Isles at least, and to the development of democratic systems of government which were seen as the practical expression of the dogma of the equality of man—a dogma recognized by both Christians and their enemies, the heirs of the French Revolution. Faith in God had been largely superseded by faith in the perfectibility of the human species by its own unaided efforts. Without knowing it Europe was following a path traced out long ago by the Buddha. The nightmare of original sin was driven deep down into the unconscious, and man saw himself as the sole master of his destiny. "Work out your own salvation with diligence"[1]

1 *The Book of the Great Decease*, vi, 10.

had been one of the sayings of the Buddha, and this is what our optimistic forebears sought to do. Here, however, the parallel breaks down; for nineteenth-century optimism, secure in its faith in "progress", looked forward to an age when science would have perfected all things. The Buddha was less naïve: for though he preached that each individual must work out his own salvation alone, he had no illusions at all about the perfectibility of this world. How, indeed, could this world, unstable, impermanent, and in perpetual flux, this impure amalgam of dissatisfaction and pain, possibly be perfected? There could be no salvation in or for this world: that lay elsewhere.

Nineteenth-century optimism, then, is comparable to Buddhism in the emphasis it lays on individual effort in the battle for salvation, but it differs from it profoundly in that it puts all its hopes on this world. Faith, then, it had: but faith in eternal life it had not. It offered rather a substitute for this angelic state—the perfectibility of the human species on this earth. In its way this was a noble and altruistic ideal; for the partisans of progress, in theory at least, ceased to worry about personal immortality (the meaning of which they in any case misunderstood) and projected themselves into future generations of a perfected humanity.

These values were rudely shaken by the 1914-18 war and the Bolshevik Revolution in Russia which formed its sinister epilogue. The "war to end all wars" demonstrated, among other things, that science, though she had the capacity to perfect the material lot of man on earth, had also the power utterly to destroy him. Perhaps for the first time in history the parable of the third chapter of Genesis seemed to make obscure sense. The Tree of Knowledge proved a dangerous thing to play with if, at the same time, man preferred to ignore the existence of the Tree of Life. Material progress was shown, in bitter practice, to be in no sense a corollary to moral progress: it had been an absurd superstition to suppose that this could be so. One of the lessons that the first World War taught us was that revolution, both industrial and political, had cut us off from our past. We had lost our old faith, and the substitute faith had proved a silly delusion. In the parlance of C. G. Jung our roots, which should have been receiving nourishment from the "collective unconscious" of the race, were cut off. We had ceased to be religious.

The collocation of the words "religious" and the "collective unconscious" may seem surprising to those unfamiliar with the still very controversial works of Jung. It is, then, time for us to consider what religion is, or rather to make up our minds in what sense we propose to use this ambivalent word. Whether we try to find a common element which is present in all the great recognized religions of the world or whether we seek to track down this element in the modern pseudo-religions the most obvious of which was Hitlerism, we will note that there is always in it an ingredient which is the reverse of rational. Ultimately religions all start from the observed fact that man is both a finite being who is not wholly master of his fate and a rational being who obstinately refuses to be reconciled to the disturbing fact that, so far as his body at least is concerned, he comes to be and passes away and is never heard of again. This is no place to go into the complicated question of how man has sought to prolong his existence, to identify it with a larger and more permanent whole, or to "get in" on the right side of the mysterious powers that rule the universe and thwart him at every turn if he does not know the secret of how to appease them, to approach them and to please them: yet some discussion of these elements in religion is necessary if we are to understand the curious phenomena of the "secular" religions of today.

In the West we are all too prone to equate religion as such with Christianity, and in the United Kingdom at least with Protestant Christianity. The official Protestant Churches differ from Catholicism in that they have, to a greater or lesser extent, divested Christianity of the mysterious and therefore incomprehensible element which nevertheless seems to be an essential part of all living religion. As religious bodies they appear to mistrust, and are embarrassed by, the "numinous", the "*mysterium tremendum*", and all those other uncomfortable facts that Rudolf Otto conceived it his duty to bring once again to the light of day. Protestantism still tries to be comfortable in a far from comfortable world: disliking the mysterious and abhorring the "superstitious", it does little to placate those religious and irrational impulses which, nevertheless, demand to be satisfied. In Germany, these impulses, too long unsatisfied, found their outlet in Nazism, which was able to attract to itself and to utilize the three constituents of religion which I have mentioned above. In Germany, as in the rest of Europe, belief in a Personal God as omnipotent and omniscient ruler of the universe had waned: and with the collapse of the Central Powers after the first World War there seemed to be nothing to put in His place. Man was thrown back on his own resources and his own reason; and these were found wanting. Everyone is familiar with the social and economic conditions which led to the rise of Hitlerism; but the moral and spiritual conditions which ran parallel to them have received less attention than they deserve. "Man liveth not by bread alone, but by every word that proceedeth out of the mouth of God": this saying is never more true than when we consider it absurd. Thus the Germans were left in a spiritual vacuum.

The inter-war years were marked by a noticeable decline in Christian worship and Christian belief. What for the middle classes had long ceased to be a living faith and had become an inherited custom—the "respectable" thing to do—ceased to be even that. Regular attendance at church, which had previously been the outward and visible sign of middle-class respectability, gradually fell into desuetude. Social conventions, for once sensibly, no longer required that the pretence should be maintained. The working classes, on the other hand, violently uprooted as they had been during the Industrial Revolution, had already lost their roots, and with their roots, their faith. The reconversion of the working class remains the greatest problem facing all the churches today. The experiment of the worker-priests in France has received a temporary check, either because the priests concerned showed a tendency to be workers first and priests second, as the Vatican maintains, or because the Vatican itself has become alarmed at a novel and at what appears to them an unsound technique. It is far too early yet to form a balanced opinion, though it would be manifestly unjust to accuse the Vatican of being indifferent to a matter which is so clearly the paramount duty and concern of all Christians.

In England during the nineteenth century the religious uprooting was less violent than in France; for the Nonconformists, to a very large extent, filled in the vacuum. In exchange for the dry, deadly, and class-ridden formalism of the then Church of England, they offered a new evangelism in which the irrational and impulsive element in religion was not only recognized but freely conjured up. If there is any truth in Marx's dictum that "religion is the opium of the people", Nonconformity administered that opiate with remarkable success throughout the critical years of the nineteenth century: it kept the irrational religious impulse within its proper sphere and prevented it from breaking loose into the political arena where it has no rightful place. But, as is so often the case with "revivalist" sects, the original impulse seems soon to have been lost. In the pioneering days reliance had been placed in the free operation of the "Holy Spirit" or the "Inner Light" through individuals: these manifestations, however, became of increasingly rare occurrence, and the revolting and protestant sects themselves settled down to a more humdrum and more organized sectarian existence. Thus individual "inspiration" is absorbed into the more capacious frame of a "church": Nonconformity becomes respectable and is transmuted into the "Free Churches". It did, however, save Great Britain from the revolutionary convulsions that wracked nineteenth-century Europe. At a time when an uprooted proletariat was seeking salvation outside any religious organization in political action, the Nonconformists canalized man's natural violence into a form of ecstatic worship. Nonconformity provided the British proletariat with new roots.

The trouble with any religion that relies too much on personal inspiration is that you cannot keep it up. You cannot have everyone speaking with tongues without a return to Babel: this is a truth that the early Christian Church very soon recognized. So with the Nonconformist sects: they became respectable; and both they and the Church of England succumbed very largely to the secular and rationalist tide which a self-confident science brought in its wake. Two world wars cut deep into the Nonconformist roots, as they cut into the roots of older faiths.

On the Continent, and particularly in France, the Catholic Church was fatally identified with the pre-revolutionary order of things. The reaction against it was correspondingly violent. The French are usually considered to be the most logical as well as the most intellectual people in Europe; and so they are. On the other hand, we know the violence of their history since the Great Revolution, a violence that in its elemental savagery is quite unlike the disciplined, calculated and almost intellectual violence practised by the Nazis. Superficially considered the brutal savagery exhibited by French mobs seems quite inexplicable against the background of a civilization that is predominantly cerebral and formalist. No other nation has so instinctive an appreciation of clarity and form; yet no other nation has shown itself so brutally savage in its revolutionary moods. One wonders why.

Jung has written much on the individual unconscious and what he calls the "collective unconscious". He has pointed out that in order for one to achieve an integrated personality the unconscious must be wooed: it must not be thwarted. Any attempt to suppress or ignore it can only lead to disaster: and this is precisely what the intellectual endeavours to do. According to Jung each of us bears a Dionysus within him, and our Dionysus must not be neglected. "Dionysus", he pregnantly declares, "signifies the depths of the passionate dissolution of all human particularity in the animal divinity of the aboriginal soul—a *blessed*[1] and terrible experience that a humanity *strongly hedged within its culture*[1] believes it has escaped, till it succeeds once again in giving rein to a new orgy of blood about which all right-minded persons wonder, and for which they blame high finance, the armament industry, the Jews and the Freemasons."[2] If Jung is to be believed, then, the unconscious must have an outlet, and religion is its proper safety-valve. Once you do away with the traditional symbolism which is not merely a mythology in the commonly accepted sense of that word, but a dogmatic system corresponding to the actual composition of the unconscious, you cut man off from his roots. This metaphor, however, seems inadequate, for if the roots are cut, the plant itself withers and dies while the root will go on living. This is not quite what happens.

[1] The italics are mine.
[2] C. G. Jung, *The Integregation of the Human Personality* (Routledge and Kegan Paul, 1940), p. 125.

The conscious and the unconscious may rather be likened to a work-man and the machine he tends. The machine will dutifully obey the workman provided the latter knows how it works and provided he knows which knob to turn and which pedal to press and at what time. Our machine is constantly generating power; and if even safety is to be preserved, this power must be allowed to escape. This at least will ensure that the machine does no positive harm; but unless the machine was built by a madman, presumably it fulfils some useful function, and merely to render it harmless is scarcely enough. No workman would be regarded as either intelligent or efficient if he contented himself with opening all the safety-valves and made no attempt to make use of the machine. If he was interested in keeping his job, he would drive, control and make use of his machine, just as Plato's charioteer in the *Phaedrus* drives and controls his wayward steeds. Only an insane or wholly ignorant workman would close all the safety-valves and then sit calmly on his machine to see what would happen. As any competent foreman could have told him, he would be blown up—and serve him right. And this is precisely what our so-called rationalist would have us do; and blown up we have been, each time with a bigger, better and more devastating explosion.

Let us carry the metaphor of the workman and the machine a little further. In order to understand the machine and to work it, the workman must receive instruction from some qualified person. Otherwise he is liable to make silly and possibly disastrous mistakes. The machine, then, is the unconscious (collective or otherwise) and the workman is the individual consciousness. Who, then, is the qualified person or foreman? The foreman may be either an individual or an organization. If he is an individual, he will be the director of conscience, *guru*, or *shaykh*, depending on what religion we are dealing with. If it is an organization and we are speaking in a European context, it will be a church. Protestant bodies, since their tendency is to disclaim their right to guide the conscience of individual members, are necessarily inadequate foremen. The Church of Rome, on the other hand, has never had any such qualms: she has never hesitated to make the superb and preposterous claim that she alone knows the workings of the machine and that she alone is by right appointed foreman of the workshop to instruct the individual workman in the workings of the machine. This right, she claims, she has from its Maker. There may be others who have received private instruction from Him: that is strictly His affair. Her duty is simply to train efficient workmen to understand and handle the machine.

And what is the machine? Jung has called it the collective unconscious, a concept that seems to fit both the psychological and mythological evidence. For Plato it was the lower or animal part of the soul, and in this he was followed by the Muhammadan mystics who saw in this lower soul—the passionate and lustful—the source and fountainhead of all evil. They called it *nafs*, "the self", but they meant precisely what Jung has called "the animal divinity of the aboriginal soul". For them it was wholly evil, "for whether it be your servant, it is from Satan, or whether it overpowers you, Satan is within it. Everything which comes from it is deceitful, and no deed done by it is praiseworthy, or tends to the Truth. When you hope to be rid of it, it will strengthen itself, and if you neglect to examine it, you will fall under its control, and if you weaken in your struggles against it, you will be overwhelmed; and if you follow it in its desires, you will go down to Hell. The truth is not in it, nor any tendency to good. It is the source of affliction and the origin of all evil. None knows it but its Creator. It is incumbent on you to examine the *nafs* continually, and to seek to know it and to oppose it, and to fight against it in all to which it summons you."[1] That this *nafs* is really identical with what Jung calls the "collective unconscious" seems certain from the way both he and the Moslem mystics describe it. For the one it is an "animal divinity"; for Rūmī, one of the greatest of the Moslem mystics, it was identified not only with Hell and the Devil, but is likened to a cow, an ass, a snake, a hunting-dog, a ghoul, and a brigand: in short it is, precisely, an "animal divinity".

According to Jung to sink oneself into the collective unconscious is both a "blessed" and a "terrible" experience. Aldous Huxley's experiments with mescalin seem to indicate that this is true; and herein lies the interest of the experiment. He seems to have obtained a vivid enough vision of the "machine"; there is no evidence at all that he was within a million miles of the Maker of the machine; for there is no reason whatever to suppose that God and the collective unconscious are identical.

All this may sound irrelevant to our present subject. It is not: for so complex a nature has man that though it is certainly true that his strongest instinct is that of self-preservation, it is nevertheless equally true that he has also within him precisely the opposite instinct, the instinct to negate himself, a mad longing to escape from his cramping and confining ego in which he is, of necessity, forever imprisoned. This instinct was, of course, recognized in the earliest times in the Christian Church: through the powerful agency of St. Paul the doctrine of the Mystical Body of the Church took shape. Man was no longer left in miserable solitude; he became one with Christ and through Christ with God in the mystical union of the Church of which Christ was the head and individual Christians the members. Individuality is transcended in the greater unity of the Church. Among the Hindus the transcending of the ego was

[1] See Margaret Smith, *Early Mysticism in the Near and Middle East* (Sheldon Press, 1931), p. 226.

recognized as being the whole purpose of religion. Separate individuality is either merged into the infinite as a river merges with
the sea, or it actually becomes identical with the infinite. In either
case the objective is the same—the abolition of the distinction of
what is "I" and what is other than "I".

These ideas may sound strange to a contemporary rationalist.
They are nonetheless psychological and religious facts, and they go
a long way to explaining much in the modern world that cannot
otherwise be explained. Why do apparently sane and intelligent
men surrender to causes which are manifestly irrational as well as
being evil? What is it that makes a perfectly decent pig into a
Gadarene swine? *Al-nafs al-ammāra bi 'l-sū*, the Muhammadan
mystic would immediately reply: "The soul that commands to
evil." In Jungian parlance it is the collective unconscious denied its
normal outlet in symbolical religion. In one major respect, it is true,
Jung differs from his Moslem predecessors. For him the unconscious is not evil in itself; for if his phrase "animal divinity" is to be
taken literally, it follows that this power is neither moral nor im-
moral; like a dog it is a force which can be whipped into the service
of evil or coerced into co-operation with the good. It cannot be
neglected or repressed with impunity. "None knows it save its
Creator", says Muḥāsibī, thereby drawing a sharp and clear
distinction between the Deity and the collective unconscious which
less experienced persons tend to blur.

This human instinct, then, diametrically opposed as it is to the
instinct of self-preservation, seems to be nevertheless a fundamental
and constant component of human nature. It accounts for many of
the mass movements of today. By adhering to a mass movement, the
individual no longer feels alone; he is swallowed up in the mass.
He is safe; he is warm, and responsibility is blessedly lifted from his
shoulders. He is in and of the movement or party or whatever it
may be; he is part of a greater whole with which he is mysteriously
identified and through which a certain immortality can be achieved.
That some such feelings inspired the early Nazis will not, I think, be
denied by anyone who has had the misfortune to attend a Nazi
rally: these performances reeked of the "collective unconscious" in
all its horrid bestiality: here, if anywhere, was the "Soul that commands to evil".

The desire to transcend the ego would, then, seem to be present
in some form in all human beings. Complementary yet contrasted to
this is the need to worship. This is another instinct which modern
"civilization" has driven underground, but which re-emerged in
perverted form in the imbecile hero-worship of Hitler, Mussolini,
Stalin *et hoc genus omne*. Throughout the history of religions a conflict between the two tendencies—the longing to transcend individuality and to identify oneself with a greater whole and the

desire to worship a personal deity—makes itself felt. Thus, in Brahmanism we find first the old Indo-European gods making way for the impersonal abstraction of Brahman, the One which is at the same time the All, and which absorbs and negates all opposites and all individuality. This, in turn, leaves unsatisfied the instinct to worship a personal deity; and sure enough the vacuum is immediately filled by the evocation of personal gods with personal attributes. Shiva and Vishnu emerge from the collective Indian unconscious, if we may be permitted to adhere to the Jungian terminology.

Even more striking is the case of the Buddha. He appears to have rejected altogether the idea of Brahman, the impersonal Absolute; nor had he any time for a personal God. He presents us with the paradox of a religious genius who believed in neither God nor Absolute. His philosophy of nature was materialist; for he saw man as an ever-changing amalgam of "elements" (*dharmas*) which did not stay the same for a moment. Matter, however, was not a dead *hyle* directed by some external power: it was self-impelled and was shot through with "craving", the sinister power that binds spirit to matter and prevents its release. The Buddha saw the world as Heraclitus saw it; it was in perpetual motion, it was a fire ceaselessly consuming fuel and ceaselessly generating smoke. It is not without significance that no less a person than Friedrich Engels should have singled out Heraclitus among the ancients as an authentic precursor of Marx.

The Buddha, however, was far from deifying this "craving" which he saw operating everywhere in nature. On the contrary, it was *the* enemy that had to be overcome if *nirvāṇa*, the extinction of the flame of craving itself, was to ensue. In the present context the example of Buddhism is instructive in the sense that it shows that a great religion can arise from premisses utterly unlike anything we know in the West. The Buddha started on purely materialist premisses: he diagnosed the phenomenal world as one of perpetual flux, but escaped and "negatived" a dialectical materialism into which he might otherwise have fallen; for by equating the world of coming to be and passing away with "pain", he could not see in it an immanent force that forever keeps the world in being; he saw it rather as that thing from which, at all costs, release must be achieved. He demonstrated, as the success of his early missions show, that it is possible to found a religion on premisses that admit of neither God nor Absolute. His success was, however, only partial, for his religion left out of account the human instinct to worship. For the laity this path was altogether too difficult. The Buddha demanded that each individual should work out his salvation for himself, whereas the "average man" demands a higher power who will help him find the way. Here again the need was answered by what one might call the spontaneous generation of new Buddhas and Bodhisattvas, transcendental and purely mythical beings so enamoured of mankind that they were willing to postpone their own *nirvāna* until all creatures had been saved. The history of religion, then, goes to prove that both the personal saviour and the impersonal "whole" are concepts of which the human psyche has a positive need. Modern civilization tends to repress and submerge both; but so far at least it has not succeeded in destroying them. The decline of Protestantism can be directly attributed to its failure adequately to supply these needs; and the rise of Nazism was made psychologically possible by the fact that it recognized the vacuum and had no scruples in filling it in its own abominable way.

Hitler in some ways bore a strange resemblance to Muhammad. Had he succeeded as Muhammad did, it is quite possible that Hitlerism would have taken its place among the religions of the world. Just as Muhammad inspired the Arabs with the conviction that they were a chosen people entrusted with the sacred task of spreading the true faith throughout the world, so did the Germans see in Hitler the chosen instrument for the spread of the "superior" culture of the master race. Hitler was, for believing Nazis, in a very real sense an incarnate god. If he was not quite the Word made flesh, he was at least *Deutschtum* incarnate: he was the visible symbol of the whole power and dynamism of the master race. To identify oneself, heart and soul, with the Party was bliss indeed: the "religious" experience could, however, only be made whole, perfect and total when to this blessed knowledge of belonging was added the further ecstasy of worship. Christ the head, and the Church His body. Hitler the head, and the Party his body: this was surely the more authentic German way of doing things. Through the Party one could merge oneself into the greater whole: Hitler was the symbol and manifestation of the whole. The Party was Brahman, Hitler was Shiva.

Hitlerism is the classic, because it is the obvious, illustration of how fundamentally religious impulses can be diverted from their normal and proper use, and harnessed to destructive and evil purposes. It is the sort of outbreak that can be expected anywhere where organized religion, neglecting essential human psychological needs, is reduced to a rigid and perhaps illiberal moral code. Organized Protestantism is open to precisely such a charge; and the revival of ritual and the increasing strength of the Anglo-Catholic party are indications that this fact is intermittently realized within the Anglican Communion itself. Morality is a necessary part of religion, but it is not the whole of religion. If morality is taken merely to mean the avoidance of sin, it is a dead thing. If it is to have value either for the person who practises it or for the people on whose behalf it is practised, then it must spring from a faith which not only fulfils the needs of the whole personality but also stands out as supremely good in its own right. We have all had experience of morals without faith: it took Hitlerism to teach us what "faith" can do when divorced from "morals".

The very word "morality" has for many of us an unpleasant ring, for it has come to be identified with the mere performance of prescribed ethical duties for no other reason than that they are prescribed by some Church authority. It was inevitable that there would be a revolt against morality such as this, for it stands isolated and is not integrated with the performance of religious acts expressive of a religious faith which complete and perfect it. The tragedy of the twentieth century has been that the irrational religious impulses which seem to be common to all men, have become divorced from morality. The churches have failed to supply the primary religious needs of man: they have allowed the myths to die, and they can scarcely complain if new and destructive myths have been put in their place. Christian morality, in so far as it is Christian, flows from the life and example of Christ. Once the essential connexion between the myth and the cult which is the expression of the myth on the one hand and the moral code on the other is severed, both are doomed to die. Other myths will take their place which know nothing either of morality or of goodness.

Hitlerism is admittedly a "pseudo-religion"; but there is enough of genuine religion in it to show how foolish it is to assume that all manifestations of this religious and irrational spirit—the craving to "belong" and to be "absorbed", the craving to worship a higher power, and the urge to self-sacrifice—must necessarily be ultimately directed towards the same end. The irrational urges are present in all of us; there can be little doubt of this, whether we wish to call them the collective unconscious or something else. In themselves they are neither good nor bad: they become such only in accordance with the object of faith proposed to them by the conscious mind. This the Hindus had realized long ago; for we read in the *Bhagavad-Gītā*, "The faith of every individual is in accordance with his nature. Man is of the nature of his faith: *what his faith is, that is he*".[1]

The Nazis demonstrated the truth of this saying with terrifying thoroughness. They demonstrated that these religious impulses, which are not *per se* either good or bad, can be detached from their Christian moorings and thrown into the service of what, for lack of another word, we must still call the Devil. Nazism, however, despite the havoc it wrought and the unsuspected forces of primitive barbarism it unleashed, was, in the general context of contemporary history, irrelevant. Preceding it in time and vastly more significant in content another movement had come into being and is with us still—I mean, of course, international Communism.

It has often been maintained that Communism cannot be properly

---

[1] xvii, 3: cf. *Maitreya Upanishad*, "As your thought is, so do you become".

understood unless we consider it, in some sense, as a religion. On no other basis can the immense appeal it exercises and the sometimes heroic self-sacrifice it evokes be comprehended. There is much truth in this contention, and it is from the religious point of view that I would examine it here; for it is more than a purely social and political phenomenon. It is an *Umwertung aller Werte*, a radical change in all accepted values which is not to be explained exclusively in social, political or economic terms. The religious element is certainly present, and it will be the purpose of the remainder of this essay to discover what that religious element is.

Obviously if by religion we mean no more than lip-service to an established creed, conforming to a set of ethical values, and an unreasoned belief in a good God who is Father of us all, we are not going to get very far in establishing the fact that there is much in Communism that is religious in content. Let us, then, recapitulate some of the impulses or affections of the will which we have classed as religious, and which may justifiably be so classed because they are to be found in all the recognized religious systems of the world. These can be listed as follows: faith, hope, the desire to "belong" to a larger whole, and the impulse to worship. These seem to be the basic ingredients of any religious system. In themselves they are merely constituents of human nature; they are only good, bad or indifferent in so far as the object to which they are directed is such.

My meaning will become clear if we apply these categories to Roman Catholicism on the one hand and to Hitlerism on the other. To take faith first: Catholic faith is based on the Incarnation of Christ and in the continuance of that Incarnation in the life of the Church through the Sacraments and particularly in the Sacrifice and Sacrament of the Altar where the miracle of the Incarnation is ever renewed. For the Nazi faith denotes faith in the German nation as a chosen people, elected by God or History to rule and guide the world—faith too in an infallible Führer who will lead his people to salvation and victory. Hope, for the Catholic, means hope of eternal life in Heaven; for the Nazi it is hope of the establishment of the German paradise on earth. And in this the Nazis were unwittingly following a long tradition of chiliastic sects, both Christian and Moslem, according to which the appointed saviour was to come and re-establish the rule of justice on earth. Again with the desire to belong to the greater whole. The Christian point of view is best expressed by St. Paul in the twelfth chapter of the First Epistle to the Corinthians.

"A man's body is all one, though it has a number of different organs; and all this multitude of organs goes to make up one body; so it is with Christ. We too, all of us, have been baptized into a single body by the power of a single Spirit, Jews and Greeks, slaves and free men alike; we have all been given drink at a single source, the one Spirit. The body, after all, consists not of one organ but of many; if the foot should say, I am not the hand, and therefore I do not belong to the body, does it belong to the body any the less for that? If the ear should say, I am not the eye, and therefore I do not belong to the body, does it belong to the body any the less for that? Where would the power of hearing be, if the body were all eye? Or the power of smell, if the body were all ear?"

The Catholic, then, finds his larger unity in the Church, which is itself called the Mystical Body of Christ. Similarly, the Nazi found this unity in the Nazi Party into which his small ego was integrated and in which he could feel secure. So also the need to worship is fully satisfied for the Catholic in the Person of Christ, both as the historical Jesus, as the Word of God, and as the consecrated species on the altar. For the Nazi the need was met by the deified figure of the Führer. Thus the subjective ingredients of the cult are in both cases the same: but the actual object of veneration could scarcely be more different. It is a standing reproach to modern Christianity that it has, by default, made it possible for these religious impulses to be diverted from a figure supremely worthy to figures that are both evil and insane.

In the Nazi case the transfer, monstrous though it is, is comprehensible. In the case of Communism the attraction is less easy to analyse because it is very much more subtle and also claims to be based on reason. Any religious element there is in Communism must be heavily disguised; for Communism, calling itself "scientific" Socialism, claims to have banished both the gods and God from the world altogether. The historical example of Buddhism, however, shows that neither gods nor God are necessary to the existence of religion. Brahmanism and Taoism, in their "purer" forms, are also illustrative of this point. Neither Brahman nor the Tao can be described except by negatives and paradoxes. Brahman contains within itself all contradictions and transcends them all: it is unmoving, yet swifter than mind; it moves though it stands still. "It moves, and it does not move. It is far, and it is near; it is within all this, and it is outside all this."[1] It includes being, notbeing, and all becoming; yet by defining it you limit it, and ultimately you can only say of it "*neti neti*", "No, no." Similarly the Moslem mystic Abū Yazīd of Bisṭām describes the ultimate state of the mystic as *fanā 'an al-fanā*, which can be quite fairly translated as the "negation of the negation". His meaning is that first the individual has to be negated or annihilated in order to participate in the

[1] *Īśā Upanishad*, 5.

life of the whole, then this negation is again negated to bring about the final synthesis of Man as God.

Ideas such as these are certainly a far cry from orthodox Christianity as normally interpreted; but they are endemic in Oriental mysticism. In some types of Hindu mysticism no clear distinction is drawn between matter and mind, and in so-called Shāktism, Shakti, the ever-changing power of nature which is itself inseparable from Shiva, the changeless and eternal, is the sole object of the cult. Shakti bears an unmistakable likeness to the historical process of the Marxists; and it is precisely in this concept that Marxism meets religion—not indeed the formalized theism of Christianity, but the far more ancient nature mysticism of the "lower" forms of Hinduism and Buddhism.

There is no reason, of course, to think that in their formulation of the philosophy of dialectical materialism Marx and Engels were aware of the similarities between their system and certain streams in Indian thought. They were, however, aware of their debt to Hegel who himself has much in common with Indian idealism. Marx and Engels thought that they had discovered a fool-proof philosophical system which, being materialist, was to do away with God and religion for ever. They did not realize that religion has flourished from time immemorial in the East without finding it necessary to have recourse to the idea of a Creator God standing outside and above the universe. They did not realize that dialectical materialism was little more than a restatement in modern terms of a semi-materialist pantheism that has always exercised an attraction on certain minds. For these minds God is not separate from His creation: there is no distinction between God and nature: the two are one. To the idea of God no idea of goodness is necessarily attached; God is rather the force in nature through which things come to be and pass away, but which in itself is eternal. In Shaivite Hindu parlance God is Shiva, the eternal and unchanging monad; Shakti is his power manifesting itself in the universe. It is perpetual change, not purposeless as in some Hindu sects, but a purposeful, directive and progressive change operating in and through matter which is itself inconceivable without change. These are the principles of a religious sect; and it is precisely such theories as these that are set forth by Engels in his *Anti-Dühring*, and precisely such theories that form the basis of dialectical materialism today.

That dialectical materialism is no longer taken seriously by non-Marxist philosophers or scientists as a sufficient explanation of the universe, need surprise no one. No purely logical thinker has ever taken the Indian systems very seriously, because they are primarily religious systems in which reason only plays an ancillary part: and this has happened in Marxism too. The similarity of the Indian thinkers to Engels is striking. Since neither can express their true

meaning without distorting it, both resort to paradox. Both see
behind the world of change a fixed principle which guides and
directs that change. For the Hindus change is characterized by
duality, for Marx and Engels it is determined by "contradictions";
but the power behind the change is not fortuitous or blind, but
purposeful; and for the Marxist it is imperative to find out how
this purposeful power works in order that he may co-operate
with it and, if necessary, hasten the natural and inevitable process
over which it presides. "From this point of view the history of mankind no longer appeared as a wild whirl of senseless deeds of violence,
all equally condemnable at the judgement seat of mature philosophic
reason, and which are best forgotten as quickly as possible; but
as the process of evolution of man himself. It was now the task of the
intellect to follow the gradual march of this process through all its
devious ways, and to trace out the *inner law*[1] running through all its
apparently accidental phenomena."[2] Here we seem to have returned to the most primitive stages of religion: we are in fact quoting
Engels. Here is man once again in search of the mysterious power
that works in and through nature: he seeks, he thinks he has found
it, and he regulates his actions in accordance with it. Marxism
would have us believe that it is an exact science; in fact it is little
more than magic masquerading in scientific dress. Marx and
Engels thought that they had discovered the secret of the universe
in the law of contradiction and the negation of the negation. This
law, they claimed to have discovered, applied not only to history, but
to every branch of human knowledge: even the infinite fell within its
scope. "Infinity is a contradiction and is full of contradictions.
From the outset it is a contradiction that an infinity is composed of
nothing but finites, and yet this is the case. The finiteness of the
material world leads no less to contradictions than its infiniteness,
and every attempt to get over these contradictions leads . . . to
new and worse contradictions. It is just *because*[3] infinity is a contradiction that it is an infinite process, unrolling endlessly in time and
space. The removal of the contradictions would be the end of
infinity."[4] The language here is the language of neither science
nor philosophy: it is a chain of paradoxes: it is the language
of natural mysticism. Take again Engels's parable of the grain
of barley, so reminiscent, despite its authorship, of the Gospel
parable. "Let us take a grain of barley", he says. "If such a grain of
barley meets with conditions which for it are normal, if it falls on
suitable soil, then under the influence of heat and moisture a
specific change takes place, it germinates; the grain as such ceases to

[1] Italics mine.
[2] Engels, *Socialism, Utopian and Scientific* (Allen and Unwin, 1950), pp. 36-7.
[3] Engels's italics.
[4] Engels, *Anti-Dühring* (Lawrence and Wishart, 1934), p. 61.

exist, it is negated, and in its place appears the plant which has arisen from it, the negation of the grain. But what is the normal life-process of this plant? It grows, flowers, is fertilized and finally once more produces grains of barley, and as soon as these have ripened, the stalk dies, is in its turn negated. As a result of this negation of the negation we have once again the original grain of barley, but not as a single unit, but ten, twenty, or thirty fold. . . . But if we take an ornamental plant which can be modified in cultivation, for example a dahlia or an orchid: if we treat the seed and the plant which grows from it as a gardener does, we get as a result of this negation of the negation not only more seeds, but also qualitatively better seeds, which produce more beautiful flowers, and each fresh repetition of this process, each repeated negation of the negation increases this improvement."[1]

The Marxian dialectic then presents us with a philosophy of inevitable but progressive dialectic change. The senseless slaughters in nature and in human history only make sense when the negation they represent is itself negated. Through strife nature perfects herself; and the whole grand purpose, working through infinite time and an infinity of contradictions ever resolved and ever recreated, culminates in the historical mission of the proletariat which is to resolve and negate the capitalist negation. This is the proletariat's historical mission conferred on it by nature herself. To oppose it would be not only unnatural and therefore wrong; it would be suicidal.

Just as the true doctrine in India can only be "correctly" expounded by a *guru*, so for the Marxists it is only the man fully trained in the Marxian dialectic (which alone gives insight into the workings of the historical process) who is qualified to judge what is "correct" analysis and what is erroneous. Only men possessed of this esoteric knowledge, this *jñāna* or *gnosis*, are truly free, for "freedom does not consist in the dream of independence of natural laws, but in the *knowledge*[2] of these laws, and in the possibility this gives of systematically making them work towards definite ends. . . . Therefore the *freer*[3] a man's judgement is in relation to a definite question, with so much the greater *necessity*[3] is the content of this judgement determined; while the uncertainty, founded on ignorance, which seems to make an arbitrary choice among many different and conflicting possible decisions, shows by this precisely that it is not free, that it is controlled by the very object it should itself control."[4] This is the very language of Gnosis; for the gnostic always claims exclusive knowledge of an esoteric truth to which he and his sect alone hold the key. So with the Marxists: while the proletariat as a whole is nature's chosen instrument for achieving the negation that will

---

[1] Engels, *Anti-Dühring*, p. 152.   [2] Italics mine.
[3] Engels's italics.   [4] Ibid., p. 128.

negate all negations, it is only the party *élite*, as it was only the Manichaean *electi*, who hold the golden key of knowledge. They alone can read the signs, for they alone *know*; and knowing, they are free, and their freedom consists in "an existence in harmony with the established laws of nature"—laws which they alone can read "correctly".

In the Sāṁkhya system among the Hindus the Soul is said to descend into Nature which for a time holds it in her embrace but at the same time works for its release. Nature is a restricting power, but nonetheless a beneficent power which finally releases its grasp in order to let the Soul go free. So too in Marxism, Nature—one is reminded of Spinoza's *Deus sive Natura*—works all the time for the perfection of man and for the release of proletarian man from capitalist bondage. With the achievement of the proletarian revolution and the establishment of the classless society, nature's purpose will have been worked out; all possible negations will have been negated. This is the Marxian *nirvāṇa*, the resolution of all conflicts, the extinction of all "craving", since in a society from which all contradiction has fled nothing will be left for which one might legitimately crave.

Just as Christian morality derives from the Christian dogma of the Incarnation, so does Marxist morality derive from the Marxian interpretation of history and of nature. The good must necessarily be that which co-operates with nature; evil is that which opposes it. Translated into practical politics this means that all and everything is legitimate which promotes the interests of the Party and the Revolution, and that all that runs counter to them is necessarily evil. There is no such thing as absolute morality since any contemporary moral code merely reflects a given stage in the historic evolutionary process. In this light the incredible brutalities of Communist régimes, the personal perfidy of individual Communists and the acquiescence of Communist sympathizers in these things are seen, from their point of view, to be not only comprehensible but virtuous. The bourgeoisie and its supporters are so much putrescent wood encumbering the new growth; as such they must be cut away. It is meet that they should die so that the people may live. The bourgeoisie has fulfilled the function assigned to it by nature; its continued existence merely thwarts and impedes the inevitable process of nature; it is living not in accordance with nature, but against it, and man's function and freedom consist in living "in harmony with the established laws of nature". The bourgeoisie can do this only by dying quietly and without fuss.

It is now time to look once more at the four elements which we saw to be proper to religion: faith, hope, the desire to belong, and the need to worship. Each of the four needs is handsomely met by Marxian metaphysic. The third receives pride of place, and is developed on lines recalling in substance, though not in detail, some of the Indian metaphysical systems and more particularly that of the Shāktas. It is a type, though perhaps a queer type, of natural and materialistic mysticism, deifying nature, claiming to have sounded her secrets, and seeking to co-operate with her and to do her will and be identified with her. This "self-immolating" or "mystical" element in man is precisely that part of his religious organism that Christianity, and more particularly Protestant Christianity, has most neglected; and this goes at least some way to explain the immense attraction that Communism still exercises and the self-sacrifice and selfless devotion it has at times been able to evoke. Faith too it has been able to summon to its aid, and faith is essentially other than reason. When, however, faith is dressed up in the garments of reason and the hocus-pocus is glorified with the name of *scientific* Socialism, the attraction to the half-educated who still believe in the infallibility of science is irresistible. So it is that people who regard the dogmas of Christianity as being a superstitious survival from an unscientific past, are quite happy to swallow all the rigmarole of the negation of the negation and the purposeful evolution of nature, without for one moment suspecting that they are making an act of faith. Faith, however, it is. And along with this faith goes an immense hope, the hope that one will live to see the establishment of the classless society on earth, a society with which nature has been travailing from all eternity and which is the end and goal of all her striving. Thus modern man has the immense privilege of being able, under the wise guidance of the prophets of the Kremlin, to witness and to participate in this inevitable and astonishing apocalypse. Like Engels's grain of barley he must be negated that he may be born again of the negation of the negation.

Seen as a religion, Communism is of course weakest on the side of worship. During Stalin's lifetime Soviet worship of his person was encouraged, as was the veneration of the dead Lenin. Today the trend is away from the worship of these personal godlets; and here the Soviet leaders are making a psychological mistake, though they are the purer Marxists for doing so. The need for worship cannot be safely neglected, and it will be interesting to see how, in Russia, this need will ultimately be fulfilled.

In this essay on religion in the contemporary world I find that I have devoted all my space to an analysis of two "secular" religions, paying scant attention to more orthodox religious manifestations. This was, however, right, for these secular religions are what distinguish our era from all that have preceded it. Nazism, we may hope, is dead: Communism, however, is very much alive, and it is a phenomenon which concerns every one of us. As a religious phenomenon it is a fascinating study, and from this point of view it deserves to be studied with far greater attention than has hitherto been given it. It is futile to rate and rant at the evils of Communism since, evil as it is, it has in the past supplied and, despite its present naked imperialism and injustice, is still supplying human needs which are normally satisfied by religion, but which the churches have largely failed to supply. Communism threatens Christianity and all the organized religions of the world with a far greater challenge than they have ever had to face since the rise of Islam. Its danger lies not so much in its atheism—for religion and theism are far from being synonymous terms—but in the fact that of all creeds it is the most intolerant, and that whereas the older creeds have learnt from bitter experience that persecution damages the persecutor more than the persecuted, Communism has learnt no such lesson and is prepared, in the interests of what it considers to be the true reading of the laws of nature, which necessarily work for the perfection of mankind, to crush out error with a ruthlessness not before witnessed in history.

It remains to be considered what religious and spiritual forces are lined up against Communism today. There is a greater desire than has existed in the past on the part of representatives of the great religions to form a common religious front. Officially, this desire finds expression in such organizations as the World Congress of Faiths. In the purely practical field we find that Christian mission-aries are adopting a more "irenic" approach in their relations with non-Christian religions, though it cannot be said that the latter's suspicion of Christian missionary enterprise has greatly diminished. Again within the Christian body itself a greater desire to co-operate shows itself in the World Council of Churches. This desire for co-operation is wholly laudable; but this association of churches has the same weakness as does any free association of organizations or nations when faced with a "monolithic" totalitarian system. This weakness is the more apparent in the ideological sphere; for while on the purely material plane it is easy to make good deficiencies in specific material products, the same principle scarcely holds true when the commodity in question is doctrine.

In Asia we are now faced with a political renaissance the force and momentum of which would have been impossible to foresee twenty or even ten years ago. The immediate force behind this renaissance is nationalism combined with fear and hatred of the former colonial powers and what is regarded as the "new im-perialism" of the United States. It is all too easy for Communism to exploit these nationalist feelings, and it does so relentlessly and successfully. It is now time to consider what resistance the individual religions are likely to put up to Communism.

Throughout the earlier parts of this essay I have tried to show that dialectical materialism can be interpreted as a religious as well as a social and economic phenomenon, if approached from the point of view of the Oriental religions. Hinduism is interesting in that, though basically monist, it can adapt itself with equal facility to theism and to pantheism or "pamphysism". As India is politically neutral between the two great power blocks, so is she neutral between the rival creeds of theism and pantheism. If anything she has a bias in favour of the latter. Hinduism, moreover, claims that all religions are merely different paths leading to the same truth; and *a priori* there seems no reason to suppose that dialectical materialism will not be admitted as yet another such path. Ideologically, then, Hinduism is at a hopeless disadvantage as against Communism, for Hinduism carries tolerance to extreme lengths and shows the greatest reluctance to draw any hard and fast line between good and evil. In this it is in full agreement with Marxism. In the sphere of ideas, then, Hinduism can, of its very nature, only offer a feeble resistance to Communism. Its strength lies in the fact that it is the national religion of India: it is the symbol of India's new-found nationhood. Thus the Hindu's dislike of missionary activity on the part of Christians is based not on an antipathy to the content of Christian teaching, but to the fact that for him Christianity means Europe and the bad old days of imperialism.

Buddhism, too, is a profoundly syncretistic religion, and the Chinese experience would suggest that it can offer no effective resistance to Communism. The fact that, contrary to the confident predictions of Marx, Communism has in practice spread East, can be explained both on economic and on religious grounds. Buddhism, of all religions, is the least suited to resist a militant atheism. Like Hinduism it is disposed to see truth in all rival systems, and even more than Hinduism it is averse from resisting evil. It is not, then, surprising that in China this ancient faith has gone down without, apparently, even trying to defend itself.

The case of Islam is different. Islam is not only a monotheistic creed: it is a militant and aggressive one. There is nothing in dialectical materialism as a philosophy that can possibly attract a Moslem, though there are economic aspects of Communism which some naïve Moslems like to compare to the early days of Islam. As a religion, then, Islam is opposed to Communism even more than is Christianity. But Islam again is inextricably mixed up in nationalist politics. In the Middle East Sunnī Islam means Arab nationalism, Shī'a Islam means Persian nationalism. As religions both great sects are fundamentally opposed to Marxism; but as nationalist movements their animus continues to be directed against the "imperialist" West.

There remains, then, Christianity, the only religion that so far has had to face up to the full impact of secularism and materialism. In the course of this essay I have repeatedly referred to the decline of Protestantism and the reasons to which I attributed that decline.

Despite more or less spectacular revivals of the Billy Graham
variety which make their appeal to the long neglected "unconscious", Protestantism continues to decline. The conversions of such
public figures as Mr. T. S. Eliot and the late C. E. M. Joad to
Anglicanism are of no more significance than the conversions of
Mr. Graham Greene and Mr. Evelyn Waugh to Catholicism. Individual conversions do not necessarily illustrate trends.

The only religious revival, since the second World War, that is of
real significance in Europe is the immense revitalizing of the
Catholic Church itself. Spiritually the Catholic Church has never
been stronger. Of her powerful political activity displayed in the
founding of Christian Democratic parties and Christian trade unions
and, in a different sphere, in her crude anti-Communist crusade in
the United States so oddly incarnate in the person of Senator
McCarthy, this is no place to speak, except in so far as all this activity
is the outward manifestation of a new and self-confident vitality.
It is, then, obvious that the Catholic Church is the natural rallying-
point of all believers in God as opposed to those who equate Him
with nature. Yet though this is true, and though the Catholic Church
is incomparably the most cohesive, the most vital and the most
universal religious organization in the world, she nevertheless has a
capacity of attracting to herself a repugnance and sometimes a
hatred among non-Catholic bodies which makes it impossible for
them to follow her lead. This distrust and dislike which is still very
much alive among both Protestants and Orthodox is something that
the Communists have not been slow to utilize. The fact is, of course,
that secular democrats and many Protestants oppose Communism
not so much because it is atheistical as because it is anti-democratic.
They would be very loath to see any great increase in Catholic
influence as a result of the weakening of Communism, for in the
Catholic Church they see a crypto-totalitarianism which they love
not at all. For Catholics *qua* Catholics the issue is quite other than
this. Communism denies both the existence of God and the rights of
the human individual: it makes absolute claims on the part of the
State and denies all rights to the Church. There can be no compromise with it on these grounds alone. That it is undemocratic is,
for the Catholic, entirely beside the point.

Thus the "free" world, in its alignment against the new creed, is
really divided between on the one hand a free association of organizations each holding a different belief, and the most compact
religious body the world has ever seen on the other—a body held
together by one faith and acknowledging one head and one spiritual
authority as alone valid. In this body non-Catholics detect a spiritual
totalitarianism; and rightly so, for it is difficult to see how any other
form of government is possible in a society which claims to have been
founded and to be directed by God Himself.

The religious situation today, then, is conditioned by the appearance on a massive scale of a new materialistic "pantheism". Politically it is opposed by all who are interested in preserving their freedom; but on the purely religious side it can only be successfully opposed by the dogmatically theistic creeds. Pantheism is too akin to it to offer serious resistance. It is then only natural that this great battle of the faiths will be fought out between the old theistic creeds on the one hand and dialectical materialism on the other. It is the doubtful privilege of the present generation to take part in this second major instalment of the wars of religion.

BOOKS SUGGESTED FOR FURTHER READING

C. G. Jung, *Psychology and Religion* (Yale University Press, 1938).
C. G. Jung, *Answer to Job* (Routledge and Kegan Paul, 1954).
Victor White, O. P., *God and the Unconscious* (Harvill Press, 1952).
H. J. Paton, *The Modern Predicament* (George Allen and Unwin, 1955).
R. S. Lee, *Psychology and Worship* (S.C.M. Press, 1955).

METAPHYSICAL SPECULATION

by E. W. F. TOMLIN

I.

THERE ARE CERTAIN subjects with which everyone feels bound to make himself tolerably well acquainted. For purely practical reasons he must know a little mathematics, a little biology, a little economics, even a little medicine. There are other subjects, more specialized, which he is content to leave to those wiser than himself. There are still others which appear to bear so little relation to practical affairs that, so far as he is concerned, their study can be left to a few self-appointed eccentrics. Of such subjects he feels no shame in remaining permanently ignorant; for even if one or two persons in each generation succeed in becoming expert in them, the sum of wisdom is not noticeably increased, nor the happiness of mankind promoted. To most people, metaphysics is such a subject. What is the use of metaphysics? Is such an apparently obscure subject worth more than a passing thought in the course of a lifetime?

In adopting this negative and almost contemptuous attitude, the common man has not been without powerful allies among the professional thinkers themselves. Many of the latter have contended that metaphysics is an intellectual blind-alley. The adjective "metaphysical" itself has come to mean "vague", "pretentious", or "abstruse". Part of the history of thought, in other words, has consisted in the attempts by certain thinkers to confine philosophy within the sphere of what is called common sense.

In the present article, we propose to begin by inquiring how metaphysics has traditionally been defined. Secondly, we shall endeavour to understand how the various movements hostile to metaphysics have arisen. If we are able to show that metaphysical inquiry, despite its difficulty, forms a legitimate and indispensable branch of philosophical thought, then it should be possible to detect its survival even in the systems most resolutely opposed to it. We shall therefore need to study with particular care those trends in modern philosophy in which the movement against metaphysics would seem to have reached its climax. Finally, we shall attempt to isolate the distinguishing characteristics of metaphysical thought, and to estimate the chances of its restoration to the forefront of philosophical inquiry.

II.

Forms of thought which deserve to be called metaphysical antedate by many centuries and even millennia the deliberate use of the word to signify a special science. This is a circumstance to which insufficient attention has been paid. According to most textbooks of philosophy, the history of metaphysics began with the Greeks. But it is suggested that the word metaphysics came into use by a kind of accident. In classifying the numerous writings of Aristotle, a commentator, Andronicus of Rhodes, decided to place a particular treatise *after* that dealing with the problems of physical science. Thus the treatise in question came to be known as the meta-physics (μετὰ τὰ φυσικά). In other words, metaphysics was originally the title of a book rather than the name of a science. But why, after all, did the editor choose to establish this particular order? On the assumption that he was discharging his duties efficiently, it may be presumed that the treatise following that on physics was concerned with problems "going beyond" those of physical science. And this was indeed the case. Aristotle's *Metaphysics* discusses the so-called "ultimate" problems of philosophy.

The impulse to seek for the meaning of existence is as old as human nature. Man is an "interrogating" animal. In order to get anywhere he must ask the way. Experience tells him that appearances are sometimes deceptive, that some paths are blind-alleys, and that first impressions are often mistaken. According to Aristotle, metaphysics is that branch of philosophy which seeks to penetrate this unsatisfactory world of appearances. The aim is to reach a sphere in which things not merely appear but *are*. The individual sciences study particular aspects of reality, or rather they study reality from particular aspects. Rising above such limitations, metaphysics studies reality as it is in itself.

To define metaphysics in this fashion, however, raises some controversial problems. First of all, *is* there anything beyond the world of appearances—the world that we know with our senses? If there is not, metaphysics is clearly a science without any real content. If there is, how can we go beyond the reports of our senses in order to have acquaintance with such a world?

Let us examine this problem in greater detail. To maintain that we know only that which our senses perceive has seemed to many people a matter of common sense. For how can we know that which is outside our experience? Although such a conclusion seems obvious, the word "experience" remains highly ambiguous. Why should the knowledge of our senses contain the whole of our experience? Or, assuming that we define experience as "sensuous knowledge", why should there not be ways of knowing which transcend this form of experience? To identify knowledge with *sensation* is to run into a host of difficulties. An existence of pure sensations would be a jumbled succession of "experiences" without any thread of continuity. Even to call it a "succession" would be to lend it too much structural coherence. A succession of experiences must happen *to* something; and that something, oneself, must somehow survive the experiences in order that they should be able to happen to it. This reference to a "self"—an independent and judging entity existing above, or subsisting through, the stream of "experiences"—disposes of the idea that life can be a matter of pure sensations. For even if such a life were possible, we should not be in a position to grasp it. The fact that we are able to "stand back" and discuss the world we see, hear, smell, taste and touch proves that we are not imprisoned within this world, but that we can grasp our sensations objectively. Perhaps this is the chief difference between an animal and a man. The world of "things"—the world that we perceive with our five senses: in short, the *perceptual* world—cannot therefore be the only world that exists.

III.

Let us now inquire whether, on a survey of the history of thought, such a conclusion appears to be confirmed. To determine at what point systematic philosophy began is extremely difficult. Certain philosophers of the nineteenth century, notably Auguste Comte (1798-1857), argued that the developing human mind passed through a series of distinct mental stages. There was first a religious or myth-making stage. Next there was a "metaphysical" stage in which the gods, formerly regarded as glorified or magnified human beings, became abstractions or "forces". Thirdly, there was a "positivist" or truly human stage. This last stage implied the elimination of all "transcendental" ideas and the final liberation of mankind from superstition. Such a rigid classification of mental evolution is today regarded as unhistorical. The period under review is clearly too brief, even though coterminous with the whole of recorded history, to warrant such a vast generalization. That man's capacity for thought should undergo systematic progress of this order is more than doubtful. Just as man has always been an artist, and often a supremely great artist when otherwise most primitive, so he has always been a thinker. To "think in myths" is already to think. In the surviving epic poems of antiquity, there is already evidence of profound thought: witness the remarkable Sumerian poem *The Epic of Gilgamesh*, with its searching observations upon the nature of life and death. Furthermore, we possess some very early examples of pure thinking or philosophizing. In the Egyptian fragment called the "Memphite Drama", dating from the fourth millennium, we find an account of the creation of the world in terms which can only be called metaphysical. Man and nature are here defined as being the product of a creative principle or *logos*. This was long before the Greek philosopher Heraclitus wrote about a similar principle. While there is much in the fragment that we cannot understand, the complexity of the argument suggests a long tradition of theological speculation. We too often assume that the "beginnings" of history were really the beginning, instead of the "end" or limit of our historical vision. Men do not suddenly begin to talk about the *Logos* or the *Tao*. Before becoming the key to a doctrine of the origin and principle of all things, such fundamental concepts must have been the source of endless debate among those reputed for wisdom, learning and the gift of insight.

The next important school of philosophical thinking about which we have record arose in Greece and also in southern Italy around the sixth century B.C. Beginning with Thales, the so-called Ionian School endeavoured to establish the common element or "stuff" of which nature was composed. This "stuff" or element was not what we call matter; the concept of matter originated with Aristotle. The members of the Eleatic School, led by Pythagoras, were interested chiefly in questions of mathematical order, proportion and harmony. (Even this requires qualification; the Milesians were also interested in such questions.) The work of these early thinkers survives only in fragments. Of the nature and direction of their thought we know as much as we do because Plato and Aristotle, the greatest of the Greek thinkers, summarized and developed their conclusions.

IV.

To Plato (427-360 B.C.) we owe the first elaborate and full-scale metaphysical system. His disciple Aristotle (384-322 B.C.) criticized this system and outlined a new one of his own. For the sake of brevity, we may here study Plato's system in the light of Aristotle's comments. The point at which Aristotle joined issue with Plato was as follows. Between the world of ideal Forms or Ideas and the ordinary world of change, imperfection and finitudes Plato had fixed an impassable gulf. Aristotle objected to so drastic a separation between the real and the ideal. His criticism was a plausible one. If, as he argued, the ideal world is removed from the everyday world by an infinite distance, how can the latter be said to "reflect" or exemplify the former? To say that the world was created on the model of the ideal Forms is to presuppose a power intermediate between heaven and earth which performed the act of creation. Plato spoke of such a power; he called it a "demiurge".

Dispensing with such an intermediary force, Aristotle contended that the Forms were all the time at work *in* matter, giving it existence and reality. To know the constituents of the world was to be acquainted with the forms of individual things. Of matter by itself there could be no knowledge; for without the imprint of form, matter was mere possibility or "potentiality". Forms superior to the world of "things" were, with one exception, imaginative figments. The exception was the "form of forms", God. (In his later works, Plato appears to agree with Aristotle on this point. Aristotle's criticism of Plato is thus directed at his original and most colourful statement of the famous theory of Forms.)

Plato was at heart a poet or artist; Aristotle was a scientist. Hence the statement that every man is at heart either a Platonist or an Aristotelian. Whereas Plato expounded his thought in a series of lively dialogues with credible characters, Aristotle left merely the notes of his lectures. These were the concise, working notes of a scientific investigator.[1] To describe Aristotle as a scientist, however, is not to imply that his interests were confined to the natural sciences. Over and above his interest in particular scientific studies, and no doubt arising out of it, was a desire to achieve order among the sciences themselves. If investigation within a particular science was assisted by systematic classification, so the study of the relation between one science and another required the exercise of a higher classification. Moreover, just as individual species went to form a genus, so individual sciences must imply the existence of a single, unitary science dominating and embracing them all. This "science of sciences" was precisely what Aristotle meant by metaphysics.

V.

If we ask what a particular science is about, the specialist can always point to a field of study within which his interests are confined. The physicist observes the behaviour of material particles. The biologist studies the processes of organisms. The psychologist inquires into the working of the human mind. Admittedly, certain sciences appear to overlap, or to depend upon the findings of other sciences; but each scientist can usually point to a particular *concept* as that which he is engaged in clarifying. If he concentrates upon the concept of Number, he is a mathematician; if upon the concept of Animal, he is a zoologist, and so forth. In the case of the particular sciences, this is clear enough. By no means so clear is the nature of the subject-matter or content of the "science of sciences", metaphysics. If the particular sciences are concerned with a determinate sphere of reality, the general science of metaphysics must be concerned with reality prior to all "determinations". That is to

---

[1] Aristotle also wrote dialogues as a young man, but these have been lost.

say, it must be concerned with "that which is" before the latter becomes differentiated into anything in particular. Now Aristotle called "that which is" by the name of being. Metaphysics, therefore, was the science of being. To quote his own words from the *Metaphysics*: "there is a science which investigates being as being and the attributes which belong to this by virtue of its own nature. Now this is not the same as any of the so-called special sciences; for none of these others deals generally with being as being."

In this statement of Aristotle's there is a great deal which, unless carefully considered and weighed, may give rise to misunderstanding. Let us take the keyword "science". When we talk today of science, we usually mean physical science. Physical science is a term embracing the sciences of nature: physics, chemistry, biology, etc. Aristotle would call these the "special sciences". By science in general, Aristotle means simply knowledge, *scientia*. In this sense, the "science of sciences" represents not a particular subject of inquiry, but the knowledge of that which really is, the knowledge of being as such. In the history of philosophy, confusion has sometimes been caused by introducing a special "-ology" to denote the knowledge of being, namely ontology. Although he is not altogether free from this confusion, Aristotle issues a special warning against regarding the study of being as resembling that of special sciences. "As demonstration is not the principle of demonstration", he says in his treatise called the *Posterior Analytics*, "so neither is science the principle of science". Pure being is beyond and beneath every determination. Consequently, Aristotle called its study "first philosophy" as well as metaphysics. Everything in the natural world is a determinate, individual, limited and finite thing. We move about in such a world, and our inhabiting a world of "things" permits us to exercise control and domination over it. But as the poets and mystics have asserted, this is not the only world. In order that there shall be limitation, there must be something to limit. The existence of "beings" presupposes the existence of being.

Despite the apparent logic of this argument, many thinkers have questioned its soundness. Pure being, they argue, is nothing but an empty abstraction. Indeed, it is the emptiest and vaguest of all abstractions. The human mind cannot grasp that which is by definition wholly indeterminate. The very constitution of our reason, which requires order and form in its objects, shows pure being to be a figment. A simple mental operation will serve to clinch the argument. Let us "peel the onion" of being. Having successively removed every layer of determination or quality, we are left not with being in a pure state but with nothing at all. Pure being is precisely that which does not exist.

The importance of this argument in the history of metaphysics will soon become apparent. Meanwhile, Aristotle had partially

anticipated it. The knowledge of pure being, he maintained, is of a
different order from that of the special sciences. Secondly, a different
faculty is required to apprehend it. The work of the special sciences
is conducted by reason. A scientist may have "hunches", but he
must finally outline his thought in logical stages. The knowledge of
pure being is accessible not to reason but to another and higher
faculty. Aristotle calls this faculty intellect. As a supra-rational
faculty, intellect is that which operates not by logical stages but by
a direct or intuitive apprehension of its object. It does not repudiate
reason; it transcends reason. Thus in the *Posterior Analytics* Aristotle
observes that while "science and the intellect are always true (i.e.
rational), the intellect is truer than science".

This emphasis upon intellect, a faculty superior to reason but not
hostile to it, is found in philosophical traditions much older than the
Western. It forms the metaphysical principle of *Vedanta*, the culmination of Hindu philosophical theology. This system has become corrupted by efforts, not in themselves insincere, to popularize it,
so that Western thinkers have been inclined to dismiss it as a tissue
of vague mysticism. But no account of metaphysics can neglect a
tradition of thought of such grandeur and antiquity. That the
thought of Plato and Aristotle may have derived from a tradition
common to both East and West and forming a kind of "perennial
philosophy", has been frequently suggested. For Aristotle is concerned in the *Metaphysics* with more than a theoretical account of
knowledge. He is concerned with knowledge, or its attainment, as
identical with *self-realization*. And this brings him within the orbit
of the great Oriental faiths. To Aristotle, knowledge is the same as
"true experience", a state in which the knower and the known
coincide. At the highest stage of apprehension, intellect and being
are one. Translated into metaphysical terms, the mind becomes one
with its object. Since Aristotle identifies pure being with God,
the *Metaphysics* is at the same time a treatise on theology. We shall
observe how the later split between metaphysics and "philosophy"
has forced theology into an ambiguous position.

VI.

The history of the term intellect, at least in Europe, is the history
of the fortunes of metaphysics. Since it is impossible to understand
modern metaphysical theories without taking into account this
history, we propose to summarize its chief stages. The ground to
be covered is very extensive; but if we bear in mind our central
theme, we may find the survey enlightening.

(a) Scholasticism

The first Christian philosophers were the Fathers of the Church.

While Jewish in origin, the Christian faith received its theological expression in terms of the current philosophical idiom, which was Greek. (The embryonic statement of Christian theology is the opening passage of the Fourth Gospel with its references to the *Logos* "made flesh".) Owing to a series of historical accidents, however, Aristotle's works were slow to exert influence in the West. The Aristotelian manuscripts, or such of them as had survived, passed first into the hands of Oriental scholars. From Syria to Baghdad they found their way across North Africa to Cordoba. It was from this Moslem centre, alive with learning, that they came to exert an influence upon Latin Christianity. Even so, the Church imposed a ban on Aristotle in 1215; but following protests from scholars of the University of Paris, the ban was lifted in 1231. Two great figures, Albert the Great (1206-80) and his pupil Thomas Aquinas (1225-74), consolidated the victory. In his massive restatement of Christian doctrine, Aquinas integrated Aristotle's metaphysical ideas into the body of Catholic belief. Scholasticism, as his teaching came to be known, is not merely a system of reasoned theology; it is a system of which the crowning achievement is a direct and illuminating grasp of reality. The Thomist theology is as intellectual as the Hindu *Upanishads*. In view of the steady impoverishment of meaning suffered by the word "intellect", however, such lofty philosophies have tended to be represented as cold exercises in abstraction. Yet it was not of a cold intellectual that Dante spoke when he referred to Aquinas as a "flame of heavenly wisdom".

(b) Descartes

René Descartes (1596-1650), though an admirer of Aquinas, was hostile to the sterile dogmatism into which Scholasticism, left to pedants, had degenerated. In his personal life he was apparently no stranger to forms of mystical illumination; the basic ideas of his New Method came to him in a vision. Nevertheless, his famous philosophical manifesto entitled "Discourse on the Method of Observing Reason in the Sciences" (1637), was destined to initiate a movement hostile to metaphysics and theology. Henceforth reason became both the instrument and the end of philosophical inquiry. "Illuminism" was left to the poets. The word "intellect", when not identified with reason, fell gradually into disuse. The universality hitherto associated with intellect assumed a new form in association with reason. The universal nature of reason was reflected in its most powerful adjunct, mathematics. In other words, the "discursiveness" of reason was paralleled by the universal *applicability* of mathematical axioms.

(c) Kant

With Emmanuel Kant (1724-1804) we arrive at something very

like a "crisis" of reason. Strictly speaking, the crisis had been
precipitated by the Scottish philosopher David Hume. According to
Hume, the foundations of knowledge were in the last analysis
psychological. How much he asked, do we *really* know? We observe
regular patterns or successions in nature. On the basis of these
patterns, we "jump" to the idea of cause and effect or necessary
connexion. Thus habit and custom rather than "objectivity" form
the basis of knowledge and scientific explanation. To this extreme
form of scepticism, Kant saw one insuperable objection. If Hume
were right how could modern scientific thought claim to have a
rational foundation? The Newtonian view of the universe, which
Kant accepted, depended upon laws operating independently of
our volition. The recognition of these laws had nothing to do
with habit or custom. The rationality of the system was the measure
of its objectivity. In order to refute Hume's scepticism Kant set
out to discover how, assuming such laws to be valid, our minds were
able to acquire knowledge of them. This involved an inquiry into
the nature and power of our own faculties. The fruits of Kant's
speculations are contained in his *Critique of Pure Reason* (1781).

The elaborate arguments of this work, one of the greatest in
philosophy, do not concern us. We are interested chiefly in its conclusions. Scientific knowledge, Kant argued, is concerned exclusively with phenomena, that is to say, with the "outside" of things.
But phenomena cannot be directly known; they can be known only
in so far as they conform to certain laws of our own mind. Such
laws are presupposed in every act of knowledge. It is we who
"work up" into coherent objects or things the multiplicity or
"manifold" presented to our senses. But the faculty which is able
to synthesize natural phenomena cannot penetrate to the essence or
inside of things. In order to effect this penetration, another faculty
altogether must be called into play.

The world behind phenomena or beyond "physics" had been
traditionally regarded as the province of metaphysics. From this
tradition Kant departed in an interesting and original way. In
examining the scope and limits of pure reason, he was seeking to
account for the fact that metaphysics, as opposed to physical
science, had made no visible "progress". What was the underlying
cause of this apparent sterility? Kant's reflections led him to
the conclusion that metaphysics in its traditional form had been
rendered obsolete by the physical science which had successfully outrun it. His argument was briefly as follows. If the province
of metaphysics is the world of ultimate reality, metaphysical
inquiry must deal with such fundamental concepts as God, Freedom
and Immortality. Now if metaphysics is to make progress, it can
do so only on condition that it prove itself to be a science. But
science is concerned exclusively with the world of phenomena.

Therefore the ideas of God, Freedom and Immortality are inaccessible both to science and to metaphysics as newly defined. How, then, do we enjoy contact, as we surely must, with these ultimate values? What other source of certainty can we draw upon? Kant maintained that we achieve such certainty in our moral experience, particularly in our sense of obligation or duty. The "moral law in our hearts" is the ultimate law governing existence. Just as rational understanding is that which imposes its laws upon the world of phenomena, so moral sensibility is that which "underwrites" the deliverances of our reason.

In spite of his somewhat equivocal standpoint, Kant preserves one aspect of traditional metaphysics which is of particular significance for our study. Although he no longer speaks of intellect as a faculty superior to reason, he preserves intact the chief feature of intellectual knowledge, namely its direct or intuitive character. True knowledge is still the intuitive grasp of reality. The only difference is that such intuition has become a matter of moral feeling. Rousseau, whom Kant much admired in his youth, had laid emphasis upon an intuitive faculty of this order; and in later thought, intuition was nearly always regarded as belonging to the realm of sentiment. The conflict between reason and an anti-rational intuition was thereafter to make itself felt in every department of thought.

(d) Hegel

The next stage in our survey brings us to a system at once prodigious in construction and bewildering in detail. If any system of thought deserves to be labelled "metaphysical", it is surely that of Hegel (1770-1831). Consequently, the enemies of metaphysics have been disposed to dismiss Hegelianism as the product of an overcharged imagination. Such a view is extremely short-sighted. A profound student of the history of thought, Hegel took up the problem of knowledge at the point where Kant had left off. Kant had refused to grant science a knowledge of reality. Employing the word science in its original sense of ordered knowledge, Hegel maintained that science can and must grasp the truth of things. "Pure science", he wrote in his *System of Logic*, "presupposes . . . deliverance from the antithesis of consciousness and reality. . . . Its content is the absolute truth." He therefore attempted to reinstate concrete knowledge in the forefront of philosophical inquiry. Reality was to be grasped by a form of thought called Dialectic. But reality was not an external "something" which thought "comes to know". Reality was itself dialectical: that is to say, it passed through a series of logical states, each of which built upon and completed the rest. To grasp the essence of reality was to conform to its inner movement.

In expounding his thought, Hegel employed a vocabulary which has often proved a stumbling-block to students of philosophy. Not merely was his use of the word "science" radically different from that of his immediate predecessors and successors; his view of reason resembled that which we find in the ancient wisdoms. Reason for Hegel was a principle of cosmic significance, resembling the Chinese *Tao* or the Hindu *Rita*. He even spoke of the "cunning of Reason", as if it were a form of inscrutable divine providence. Intellect, which he also employed, became an abstract or analytical faculty approximating to the reason of Descartes. What lent to Hegelianism its chief significance, however, was its repudiation of the entire tradition of empiricism. The knowledge of the senses, upon which the empiricists build their systems, was for Hegel the most elementary form of cognition. All knowledge, as opposed to mere perception, was of a reality eternal and absolute. This reality, which Hegel called the Absolute Idea, was God understood in philosophical terms. There remained a fundamental difference between Hegel's Absolute and Aristotle's pure being. The Hegelian Absolute was not an empty abstraction removed from the world of "things"; it represented diversity in unity, a dynamic synthesis of opposites, containing all the phases which the understanding, by a process of abstraction, isolates into "moments". Pure being was for Hegel the same as pure emptiness. The God of Aristotle, in other words, was a notion from which all content has been evacuated.

(e) Positivism

Hegel's influence upon modern thought has been so great, not least in the reaction that set in against him, that we sometimes forget that he died as long ago as 1832. His disciples split into two groups, the Right Wing Hegelians and the Left Wing Hegelians. Of the Left Wing, the most influential member was Karl Marx (1818-83). While repudiating metaphysics as "bourgeois ideology", Marx preserved the dialectical method of Hegel. Instead of the Spirit or the Idea, however, Matter itself became an Absolute undergoing development in time and evolving a succession of social systems. The Right Wing Hegelians, on the other hand, tended towards increasing abstraction: the word "metaphysics" as signifying nebulous system-mongering gained currency chiefly as a result of their speculations. A book entitled *The Secret of Hegel* by Stirling (1865) represented perhaps the farthest point to which such obscurantism could go. Whatever the "secret" may have been, Stirling was successful in keeping it. Nevertheless, the materialism of the Left Wing Hegelians and their followers was not so much an anti-metaphysics as a form of metaphysics *à rebours*. Consequently, while the temper of nineteenth-century science was decidedly materialistic, few philosophers ventured to proclaim themselves out-and-out materialists. In his *History of Materialism*, Lange (1828-75) felt obliged to explain that he accepted materialism not as a philosophy of life but merely as a scientific method. Similarly, T. H. Huxley (1825-95) maintained that while the scientist must necessarily employ a materialistic terminology, he ought not to subscribe to materialistic beliefs, since to do so would involve the repudiation of all civilized values.

The theory most hostile to metaphysics was not so much materialism as positivism. Of the founder of positivism, Comte, we have already spoken. In their early form, Comte's theories won the admiration of the English Philosophical Radicals, particularly John Stuart Mill (1806-73); but as his thought became increasingly obscure and extravagant, it alienated the sympathy of the English positivists. For Comte proceeded to invent a new positivist religion, with temples, priests and even bishops dedicated to spreading the positivist faith. Nevertheless, the basic ideas of Comte harmonized with the spirit of an age of material and social progress. Old orthodoxies and conventions were visibly yielding before scientific scepticism and agnosticism. A tendency to identify "transcendental" beliefs with a particular social order, now in evident decay, lent plausibility to Comte's idea of the dawn of a truly scientific—or, as he called it, sociological—era, when men should construct a new society on genuinely humanist principles. The historical method of Buckle, the "synthetic philosophy" of Herbert Spencer (1820-1903), the anti-theology of Renan (1823-92), reflected a common repudiation of metaphysical ideas. As a result, the idea of knowledge itself underwent radical change. Instead of being the means whereby truth and perfection were apprehended, knowledge was identified with factual information concerning natural phenomena. Ideals of conduct and self-realization, which thinkers until the time of Spinoza had regarded as the crown of philosophical discipline, were relegated to the sphere of "private" religious belief. The sphere of reason and the sphere of sentiment hardened into two mutually exclusive "worlds".

An attempt to infuse a new vigour into philosophy, now thoroughly secularized, was made by William James (1842-1910). The term "pragmatism", though popularized by James, was invented by another American philosopher, Charles Peirce (1839-1914), whose thought has been unduly neglected. With its emphasis upon action as the key to knowledge and virtue, pragmatism defined truth as "that which worked". James owed much to a thinker otherwise very different in character, Henri Bergson (1859-1941). The thought of Bergson, expounded in exquisite prose, revealed by contrast the arid condition into which academic philosophy had fallen. Moreover, it constituted a revival, at the level of instinct and sensibility, of the idea of intuitive knowledge. The word "intellect" was likewise reintroduced, though still in the guise of abstract reason. According to Bergson, intellect shows us the outside of things; its view of the world is spatialized or diagrammatic, like that of a blue-print. Intuition, on the other hand, is the faculty whereby we penetrate to the truth of things and feel the inner pulse of reality, which is life in perpetual creative movement. In certain respects this was a parody of the traditional idea of knowledge as fused with being. The immense vogue enjoyed by Bergson testified to the need, so long unsatisfied, for a philosophy capable of affording insight into the heart of reality. But the insight was achieved at the expense of jeopardizing the authority of reason.

VII.

To survey the history of thought from the thirteenth to the twentieth century is to witness the dethronement first of intellect in favour of reason and then of reason in favour of some form of "lower mysticism". Like all surveys, this account neglects to take into consideration a number of important counter-movements and isolated deviations. The rationalism of Descartes had been opposed by aloof thinkers such as Pascal (1623-62) and Spinoza (1632-77), the one asserting the majesty of the Christian God against the "god of the philosophers" and the other preaching the "intellectual love of God". Similarly, the materialism of the nineteenth century met strenuous resistance from such men as Schopenhauer (1788-1860), Nietzsche (1844-1900) and Kierkegaard (1813-55). All these deserve to be called metaphysical thinkers, since their vision of life transcended that of the contemporary advocates of utilitarianism, positivism and pragmatism. Even Nietzsche, who preached the "transvaluation of values", must be accounted a transcendentalist. To attain to a condition "beyond value" is to assert a higher set of values. And Nietzsche looked forward to a race of Supermen in whom these values would eventually be realized. Similarly, the cosmic "Will" of Schopenhauer, however blind and negative, forms a kind of metaphysical Absolute. Like the Buddhist conception which inspired it, it is an Absolute to be apprehended by a mind divested of passion and egoism. The tortured frustration of these thinkers, leading to bitter misanthropy in the case of Schopenhauer, agonized faith in the case of Kierkegaard, and total mental collapse in the case of Nietzsche, proves that they were at issue with a movement temporarily sweeping all before it. For when the drift of ideas presses too far in one direction, the forces of opposition tend to acquire an unnatural degree of violence.

The ideas of Hume and Comte, like some powerful corrosive, had slowly eaten into established beliefs. There came a moment when the entire structure of traditional ideas seemed near to collapse. The most vigorous and damaging assault was that made by a school of neo-positivists, whose aim was to purge philosophy once for all of metaphysical elements. Logical positivism, as the system was called, originated in Vienna. An Austrian of remarkable intellectual subtlety, Wittgenstein, emigrating to Cambridge after the First World War, inaugurated an English branch of the movement. The seed was sown in ground ready to receive it; a flourishing school of critical or analytical philosophy, led by G. E. Moore (b. 1873) and Bertrand Russell (b. 1872), was already in being. The new opposition to metaphysics was based on two principles: first, that all knowledge was derived in the last resort from sense-given "particulars" (sense-data); and secondly, that statements bearing no verifiable relation to such particulars were, apart from their emotional "penumbra", totally devoid of significance. In its early form, logical positivism was thus a kind of linguistic positivism. The pseudo-significant language of metaphysics, theology and poetry was not so much refused recognition as relegated to an "emotive" sphere. Of the psychological value of such pseudo-statements Hume had given proof. After maintaining the impossibility of demonstrating the existence of both substance and mind from "a bundle or collection of different perceptions . . . in perpetual flux or movement", Hume confessed to have fallen into "philosophical melancholy and delirium". As a cure he recommended abandoning such "cold speculations" and engaging in diversions such as "making merry with my friends". Similarly while the modern positivist is apt to describe the statements of poetry and even theology as "nonsense", his use of the inverted commas suggests the validity of a "different kind of sense" from that conveyed by "scientific" philosophy. With the object likewise of banishing the idea of value (including that of truth) he employs words such as "important", "significant" and "factual". These words, together with the crucial term "verification", imply the notion of a standard or criterion of truth hovering in the background. Such admissions, however grudgingly made, serve to conjure up once more the wraith of a "metaphysical intuition" struggling to make contact with a reality not given to sense. For it is a paradox of philosophies setting out to banish fancies and illusions that they produce in turn their own "deliriums" from which escape or deliverance (to use the traditional Oriental term) becomes a desperate necessity.

VIII.

To assume that logical positivism, in all its varieties, is the sole enemy of metaphysics today would be to over-simplify. Attacks upon the traditional idea of metaphysics have come from quarters hostile to logical positivism. Of these attacks the most interesting and far-reaching was that made by R. G. Collingwood (1889-1943) in his *Essay on Metaphysics* (1943). Collingwood's aim was to show not merely that Aristotle's "science of pure being" was inadmissible, but that metaphysics, despite appearances to the contrary, had always fulfilled a different role. Collingwood posed anew the Kantian question: can metaphysics become a science? But his answer differed from that of Kant as markedly as Kant's differed from that of his predecessors. According to Collingwood, metaphysics represented a genuine form of inquiry; but it was genuine only in so far as it was engaged in solving a fundamental if recurrent problem. Every statement, he pointed out, formed the answer to a question. But no question was asked in the void. There must be a circumstance or set of circumstances in which it could be said to "arise". In short, there must be a presupposition or series of presuppositions which the questioner, in making his inquiry, was prepared to take for granted. That which was taken for granted in the last resort was an "absolute" presupposition. To study the absolute presuppositions of discourse, especially the discourse which is called "scientific thought", was to engage in a study which is by definition "beyond science". To this study, and this only, Collingwood gave the name of metaphysics. "Metaphysics is the attempt to find out what absolute presuppositions have been made by this or that person or group of persons, on this or that occasion or group of occasions, in the course of this or that piece of thinking."[1] Such an attempt forms an historical inquiry. To the question, how could metaphysics become a science, the answer was "by being history". "All metaphysical questions are historical questions."[2]

The next stage of Collingwood's argument has aroused considerable controversy. In so far as it was really absolute, a presupposition was neither true nor false. The criterion of truth and falsity applied not to a presupposition itself but to the question whether or not it was in fact presupposed. An example may render this clear. The ideas of causation as successively entertained by Newtonian physics, by nineteenth-century science, and by modern science are demonstrably different. Newton believed that some events are due to causes, while others are due to laws. Nineteenth-century physicists, abandoning the Newtonian conception of law, maintained that all events have causes. Finally, modern physicists have been disposed to abandon notion of cause altogether.[3] Which of these presuppositions—because presuppositions they are—is true? Such a question, in Collingwood's view, was a pseudo-question. Presuppositions formed frameworks or matrices within which a system of thought was constructed. One set of absolute

---

[1] *Essay on Metaphysics* (Clarendon Press, 1940), p. 47.   [2] Ibid., p. 49.
[3] Bertrand Russell, "On the Notion of Cause" (*Mysticism and Logic*, Penguin Books, 1953).

presuppositions was not *truer* than another; it was merely different. Moreover, the procedure adopted by metaphysicians, scientists and historians has tended to confirm this conclusion. In studying the thought of an epoch, men have sought to discover not so much the various assumptions of scientists and philosophers as the "ground" of these assumptions. Assumptions are "relative" presuppositions consciously adopted; but that to which they are related, being absolute, is for the most part adopted unconsciously. In forming a true estimate of the "climate of thought", the historian of science cannot be content with a mere assortment of facts; he needs to "unearth" the principles whereby these facts compose an intelligible order. The ordinary man remains unaware of the presuppositions of his thought: it is the function of the metaphysician-historian to enlighten him.

Despite the originality of this view, it gives rise to a number of puzzling questions. The most pressing of these is why absolute presuppositions, though universally accepted, should undergo change at all. Collingwood sought to answer this question in the light of his researches into history. History was a process of continuous change or "becoming". There were no static epochs. In every age, scientists—that is to say, men consciously engaged in systematic speculation and investigation—were faced with problems arising out of the solution, or attempted solution, of past problems. Consequently, the absolute presuppositions of any epoch formed a structure which remained in unstable equilibrium. The "strains" to which such a structure was subject were felt at every point. They were "taken up in various ways but never eliminated". In order to cope with such "strains", a subtle modification in the complex or constellation of absolute presuppositions was introduced. If the pressure of the "strains" was such that no accommodation could be reached, there was readjustment by violence. This was what was meant by the collapse or decline of civilization. Civilizations did not collapse as a result of physical violence, though physical violence might finally reduce to ruins what had become merely a façade. "It was not by gunpowder alone that Cortez destroyed Montezuma; it was by using gunpowder to reinforce the strains which already tended to break up Montezuma's power."[1] The notion of "strains" was the great discovery of nineteenth-century historiography. Hegel initiated it. By drawing attention to the part played by such "strains" in economic society, Marx showed himself a brilliant historian. In prophesying a society from which all strains or "contradictions" would be removed, however, he finally transformed history into mythology; for the "classless society" is another name for the New Jerusalem.

The presuppositions of an epoch not merely received but

[1] *Essay on Metaphysics*, p. 76.

deserved what Collingwood called "unquestioning acceptance". In this sense they resembled religious dogmas. Collingwood went so far as to maintain that this was precisely what they were. Aristotle's identification of metaphysics with theology was therefore justified. Once applied to *all* presuppositions or presuppositional "constellations", however, the notion of "unquestioning acceptance" gives rise to serious difficulties. That which is received without question is not so much accepted as imposed; for where there are no questions, there is no thinking. And in suggesting, as he does, that the transition from one constellation to another is the result of "unconscious thought", Collingwood betrayed an obscure recognition of this fact. Whatever "unconscious thought" may be, it is clearly not thought of a rational kind. The unconscious, as normally conceived, is the realm of emotional or instinctive stresses. Meanwhile, what has happened to knowledge? It has virtually disappeared in an abyss of relativism. If, as Collingwood maintains, "all knowledge is historical knowledge",[1] and if all historical questions are at root metaphysical, knowledge (which is the aim of all thought) resolves itself into a process indifferent to the distinction between truth and falsity—which is to deprive it of the polarity by which it lives. Finally, the very methodology employed in historical investigation, which includes inquiry into that which presupposed to any epoch, suffers the same strictures.[2] For there can be no independent assessment of experience if the basis of that experience is placed outside the reach of criticism.

IX.

Sometimes, as in the case of Kant, a thinker is aroused from his "dogmatic slumber" by the impact of the thought of another. Sometimes the convulsions of the time awaken from dogmatism an entire generation of thinkers. The last war and its antecedents undoubtedly had such a disturbing effect. That the philosophy loosely called existentialism should have arisen first on the Continent is not surprising; Europe experienced the greatest and most prolonged impact of destruction and chaos. The metaphysical implications of existentialism are of very great interest. In the first place, existentialism has restored to currency a vocabulary regarded by many philosophers as thoroughly effete. Words such as "essence", "transcendence", "being" and "not-being", removed from the basement of the philosophical mansion, have had the dust blown off them, while an entirely new set of terms, hitherto strangers to academic thought, have joined them: "anguish" and "dread", "absurdity" and "crisis", even "bad faith" and "nausea".

[1] *The Idea of History* (Clarendon Press, 1946).
[2] Cf. Editor's Preface to *The Idea of History*, p. xvii.

To what extent does existentialism imply a genuine revival of metaphysical thought? This question must be answered with some care, for it is easy to be deceived by appearances. From one point of view, existentialism forms a deliberate protest against metaphysical *speculation*. Kierkegaard, usually described as one of the parents of existentialism, was a bitter opponent of the Hegelian metaphysical tradition. Likewise, modern existentialists are only too ready to denounce idealism in all its forms. But it is not so much metaphysics that the existentialists oppose, as all systems of thought claiming an impersonal "objectivity". Their insistence upon the subjective aspect of experience contains echoes of Kant. Just as Kant called in the moral sensibility to complement the understanding of phenomena, the existentialists have shifted the centre of gravity of philosophy from phenomenal investigation, or what Jaspers calls *Weltorientierung*, to the penetration of the self and personality. It is this subjective realm which, in their view, deserves to be called *Existenz*, or true, dynamic, creative reality. "Existence", says Jaspers, "is that which cannot be reduced to mere objectivity, the fount of my thought and action, which I express in trains of thought which are not the knowledge of any object."

The thought of Karl Jaspers (b. 1883) is expressed with some subtlety; that of Martin Heidegger (b. 1889) is the more obscure in that we must wrestle with a particularly intractable vocabulary. Heidegger's philosophy, which has been expounded only in fragments, involves the repudiation of a tradition of thought accepted unquestionably by most scientists and philosophers of the Western world. This tradition is based upon the presupposition (in Collingwood's sense) that reality is at bottom *intelligible*. We owe this idea to the pre-Socratic philosophers; for it was they who arrived, no doubt with extreme difficulty, at the conception of One World. To Heidegger, on the other hand, the world is unintelligible. Why is this? Because our lives are terminated by an absurdity, death. We are "thrown" into a world which is alien and hostile to us. Having unaccountably arrived, we are obliged to fend for ourselves, to work out our destiny, to create our own freedom. In realizing that our destiny is nothingness, we are possessed with a feeling of anguish (*Angst*); yet only in so far as we experience this feeling can we be said truly to exist. This notion of alienation is developed in the work of Gabriel Marcel (b. 1889), and with particular dramatic force by Jean-Paul Sartre (b. 1905).

In his statements regarding the ineffability and inaccessibility of being (*Sein*), Heidegger appears to owe something to the metaphysical tradition of Aristotle. His essay "*What is Metaphysics?*"[1] is concerned with so-called ontological questions. But his ontology

---

[1] Included in the collection, *Existence and Being* (Vision Press, 1949), edited by Werner Brock.

is a great deal more abstruse than that of Aristotle. Of intellectual
intuition we hear nothing. The channel of knowledge is a feeling,
almost a *frisson*. "The clear courage of essential dread", says
Heidegger in language difficult to render into English, "guarantees
that most mysterious of all possibilities, the experience of being".
Here, as elsewhere, we receive the impression of a thinker trying to
say something for which he has not yet found suitable language.
It is significant that Heidegger's major work *Sein und Zeit* (*Being and
Time*), though begun many years ago, remains incomplete. The
philosophy of Jaspers is both more comprehensive and more
comprehensible. According to Jaspers, the aim of life is not so much
the knowledge of existence as the transcendence of existence. If
there is such a thing as being, there is also a being of beings (*das
Sein als Sein*), namely God. Since God is above all categories, however, He is not accessible to rational understanding. That there *is*
something beyond our understanding we recognize as a matter of
faith. Here again we detect echoes of Kant. There is also much in
Jaspers's thought that resembles Thomism on the one hand and
Oriental metaphysics on the other. "God is known through all things
and apart from all things", said Aquinas; "and he is known through
ignorance and through knowledge." Similarly, Jaspers's emphasis
on the self as that which defies definition or scientific scrutiny (a
reason which Hume had given for regarding it as a fiction)—
thereby linking it with its Creator, the supreme Person, who is to be
defined only in negative terms—resembles the definition of the
ultimate self or *Atman* in Vedanta philosophy as *Neti, neti*, a total
negation.[1] Finally, Jaspers's contention that transcendent reality is
"glimpsed" by signs and symbols (*Chiffern*), like Heidegger's claim
that being "shows itself" without being "known", calls to mind the
language of the mystics. "The blessed essences dwelling in heaven",
said Dionysius the Areopagite, "are transmitted to us as it were in
fragments and through the multiplicity of the varied symbols of the
Divine oracles."

To make general pronouncements about a movement not yet
spent is unwise. Existentialism has reached the stage at which
certain of its most famous advocates, instead of claiming the monopoly of orthodoxy, have voiced their dislike of the term existentialist
and often of the thought of their colleagues. Heidegger has dis-
owned Sartre; Marcel disowns existentialism; Jaspers moves steadily
nearer to orthodox Christianity. Taken as a whole, their work
represents a symptom of an inner crisis of philosophy rather than a
fresh stage in its progress. Existentialism may perhaps be regarded
as a late form of pragmatism. But it is no longer the eupeptic
pragmatism of William James and John Dewey; it is pragmatism
gone sour, with a guilty conscience. This intrusion of guilt-feelings

----

[1] i.e., "not this, not that".

into a basically atheistic philosophy is the more remarkable in that there is no power or authority whom the individual appears to have wronged. Similarly, the feeling of anguish would seem to lack *raison d'être*. What cause has a creature owing no allegiance outside himself to feel anxiety? To declare with Sartre and Simone de Beauvoir that "man is in an irremediably ambiguous position" is to lay claim to some measure of acquaintance with the ideals which, by a trick of fate, man is debarred from realizing. Their confident pronouncements upon human destiny ("Man is a useless passion"), which are the reverse of ambiguous, suggest that the existentialists conceal a form of metaphysics up their sleeves.

This devious return of the metaphysical impulse may well be due, as a Belgian expert on Heidegger has argued, to our fundamental dissatisfaction with the incomplete or fragmentary philosophies of the present day. "Contingency", Professor de Waelhens says, "is something which man can never at any price accept. Finiteness is unbearable. It must somehow or other be transcended." Hence the philosophers who, like Russell, endeavour to infuse life and even glamour into scientific materialism remain visibly dissatisfied with their achievement. While "Neutral Monism", the name of Russell's last recognizable system, is a philosophy which one may accept as a mental exercise, it is not a philosophy in which one can seriously believe. It transcends nothing. It offers no illumination. To believe is to cease to remain neutral. The concept of neutrality, like that of death or "not-being", is meaningless if allowed to subsist in the void. We can be neutral only as between contending ideals or ideologies. To use an expression from the sphere of politics, there can be no *troisième force* in thought, only a *troisième faiblesse*, a vacillating scepticism.

To this, the analytical and critical philosophers are ready with a reply. In their view, despite its long association with theology and metaphysics, philosophy has nothing to do with "personal" matters such as belief. The sphere of belief is the sphere of private emotion; philosophy must follow the public path of science. Now such a view, which has the support of many contemporary thinkers, represents the *reductio ad absurdum* of rational thought. For it implies an absolute distinction between man's *convictions* and his *certitudes*. On such a view, man is placed in a position in which he is convinced of what he cannot prove and certain of what he cannot "believe". Head and heart are not merely at war one with the other; they are occupied with aims incompatible with their belonging to the same person. The reference to "person" is especially significant; for the conception of personality has inevitably undergone expulsion from analytical philosophy along with that of a unitary self. It is interesting to observe that a popular branch of existentialism is known as personalism.

X.

If the recent gospel-philosophers (as we may call them) present us with a distorted and incomplete metaphysics, what are the prospects of a fully-fledged metaphysical revival? That the public is increasingly dissatisfied with anti-metaphysical philosophy seems evident. On the continent of Europe and in the Anglo-Saxon world there is evidence of a vast, unsatisfied, indeed frustrated curiosity in philosophical matters: witness the touching earnestness with which anyone with a "message", however far-fetched, is popularly greeted. It is natural, in the strict sense of that word, that men should wish to inquire into the meaning and purpose of their lives. Nor will they be convinced by those who assure them, upon some assumed authority, that such "ultimate" inquiry is futile. Man is at heart as much possessed by *metaphysical* hunger as by physical hunger. Starvation in the one case can cause death as certainly as in the other. Collingwood may well have been right to maintain that metaphysical starvation can herald the collapse of entire civilizations.

In conclusion, we may usefully ask what conditions a new metaphysical doctrine, if legitimate, ought to satisfy. The first condition may seem paradoxical. Such a metaphysics would not in reality be new at all. Its newness would consist in the novelty of its exposition rather than in its originality. For it would be the revival of what metaphysics has always been, namely the doctrine of intellectual knowledge. Metaphysics implies knowledge of that which is permanent and eternal: a permanence and eternity which, in their contrast with contingence and change, serve to make sense of the latter. It requires a mind as honest and penetrating as Hume's to realize that contingence and change, taken in themselves, do not make sense. What Hume failed to see, or what he chose not to see, was that his capacity to judge the senselessness of things must itself be exempt from the charge of senselessness. If this were not so, the "philosophy of Hume" would itself be devoid of sense. The mind is satisfied only with that which is truly intelligible. If it finds the world of discrete or "granular" sense-data unintelligible, it must seek intelligibility beyond the sphere of sense-perception. Our consciousness of change is simultaneously our consciousness of ourselves as immune from change. "*Il n'y a de temps*", said Jules Lachelier, "*que pour une intelligence qui n'est pas dans le temps*." Time is "a refreshing river", to use the phrase of Joseph Needham, only because we are able to swim in it with our heads above water instead of drowning in it.

The second prerequisite of metaphysical doctrine is that it should be impersonal. The word "impersonal" is here employed not in a sense which excludes personality but in a sense which implies universality. The neglect of metaphysics has stimulated the

mushroom-growth of a series of "one-man" philosophies. These
represent individual or private "points of view". A man claiming
to have "his own science" would be regarded as extremely eccentric,
if not insane; to have one's "own philosophy" is considered perfectly legitimate. The ease with which one such system gives place
to another, often solely on the strength of greater "attractiveness",
and the equal facility with which a variety of "points of view" can
be entertained purely as hypotheses, suggest that the whole man is
rarely engaged. A true metaphysical doctrine is metaphysical
because meta-individual. It is neither original nor new, because
truth is not a thing we invent. In a sense, we can only invent errors.
Truth is something to which, because it transcends us, we can only
aspire. Aristotle rightly called metaphysics "the divine science".
To speak of a private or individual metaphysics is to employ a
contradictio in adjecto.

Finally, and in consequence of the above, metaphysical procedure
is by nature *analogical*. This must follow from the nature of the
reality which it seeks to apprehend. There is a tendency, as we have
seen, to regard "reality" as something that we already possess,
any "higher" sphere being dismissed as nebulous or unreal. The
"realist" is in fact a kind of idealist; he idealizes the actual. This
attitude arises from the habit, long ingrained, of interpreting everything in experience from the point of view of the lowest common
factor. On this basis, the reality of love becomes carnality, the
essence of mysticism is found in neurosis, etc. As a result of this
tendency, we witness the disintegration of spiritual forms into
material elements. Nor does the process stop here. The coherence
of the materialist views of the world, once challenged, leads to the
break-up of matter itself into elements scarcely deserving the name
material, until nature consists of no more than a series of "waves of
probability". By a gradual and descending process of de-formation,
reality thins towards the unreal and the inchoate.

In order to avoid total scepticism of the kind so familiar in modern
Western philosophy and also in certain "troughs" of the Oriental
tradition, we must adopt a procedure virtually opposite in character.
Instead of the "higher" being judged in relation to the "lower",
the "lower" must be judged in relation to the "higher". An officer
derives his authority from above, not from below. The lower in
rank is "lower than", so to speak, before he is "superior to". When
philosophers set out to ask whether there is "purpose" or "direction" in the world, they base their inquiry by analogy on the fact
that men have individual "purposes". But their recognition of
purposive behaviour in others and in themselves must imply a purposiveness at the heart of reality, for otherwise how could human
acts be "lent" a purposiveness which had no higher sanction?
A bank-note derives its worth not from the paper of which it is

composed but from the value which a particular institution has decided to confer upon it. A letter "not worth the paper it is written on" is *only* worth the paper it is written on—in short, its value is that of its most material element. Reality must therefore consist of a scale of forms of which the summit is, to use Aristotle's term, a "form of forms". This may explain why the term matter has always contained the notion of subordinateness or inferiority; for matter, in its philosophical sense, is a "falling away" from form, a descent in the scale, and finally—as a limiting conception—total formal disintegration. Such a view of matter is as implicit in the thought of Aristotle as in that of Bergson.

Just as there can be no religion without a God (even Buddhism and Jainism, though nominally "atheistic" religions, depend upon an ultimate "reservoir" of divinity, *Brahman*), so there can be no metaphysics without an Absolute. The word Absolute has a somewhat forbidding ring; modern philosophers have gone out of their way to substitute a more congenial, though often more equivocal term. What needs to be stressed is that the very relativism of experience, the obvious imperfections and impermanence of human life, presuppose an *absoluteness* against which these things are given proportion and thrown into relief. The shadows on the wall of the cave, in Plato's famous simile, were real shadows; but they were also really cast by a real fire. A world of mere shadows is an absurdity. A philosophy denying coherence to the world, such as that of Heidegger and certain extreme empiricists, may be called an arrested philosophy. It arrests its speculations at a point just short of self-contradiction; for if all is incoherence, there is no logic and therefore no set of conclusions to be validly drawn. A philosophy which repudiates the possibility of a metaphysical principle or Absolute may perform valuable tasks in exposing fallacies, detecting false analogies, and maintaining verbal precision. In this respect the various schools of philosophical analysis, particularly in Britain and America, have rendered invaluable service. But such a philosophy, debarred from scrutinizing the fundamental problems, is no more than an excursion on the foothills of knowledge.

The importance of analogy in metaphysical thought derives from the fact that the Absolute, like the God of religion whose intellectual counterpart it is, is above determinations. Such an object cannot therefore be directly described.[1] It is not an accident that most metaphysical systems have received corroborative and sometimes direct expression in poetry and art. We may call to witness the *Vedas*

---

[1] The place of analogy is well brought out in D. Emmett's *Nature of Metaphysical Thinking* (Macmillan, 1945), one of the most illuminating treatises on the subject in modern times. The following remark (p. 12) is especially relevant: "If the metaphysical nature of the world should be that of the relation of finite existents to an *absolute* existent, the absolute existent would be *sui generis* and *in principle* could only be described analogically." (My italics.)

and *Upanishads*, and the great Hindu epics and even ritualistic dancing; the poetic philosophy of the pre-Socratics; Scholasticism and its poetic counterpart the *Divine Comedy* of Dante; and, in modern times, the poetry of the Romantic Movement which sustained and nourished a metaphysical impulse that had been denied conventional outlet. In our own day, likewise, the metaphysical elements in existentialism have found their most effective expression in fiction and drama rather than in academic treatises. The human desire for that which the mystics have called "unitive" knowledge cannot be dismissed as illusory, unless the constitution of a mind satisfied only with truth and permanence is nothing but a "sport" of nature, denied authentic fulfilment. Lacking insight into truth, men are constrained to pursue phantoms, yet in the very act of pursuit they testify to their nature as more than material beings. "*Toi qui es fidèle à quelque chose*", said Alain, "*tu es esprit par celà seul.*" The path of metaphysical knowledge is both steep and difficult, and the end is frequently lost to view in landscape of increasing bareness. Only concentration on essentials will bring insight and final achievement. Those who limit their view to the surface of traditional metaphysical doctrine have often remarked upon its specious simplicity. Before regarding this as evidence of superficiality, we should do well to reflect upon the words of Rémy de Gourmont, that "very simple ideas are within the reach of very complicated minds only".

BOOKS SUGGESTED FOR FURTHER READING

Aristotle, *Metaphysics*, tr. by W. D. Ross (Oxford, 1924).

St. Thomas Aquinas, *Philosophical Texts*, selected by Thomas Gilbey (Oxford, 1954).

Ernst Cassirer, *The Problem of Knowledge* (Oxford, 1950).

R. G. Collingwood, *Essay on Metaphysics* (Clarendon Press, 1940).

D. M. Emmet, *The Nature of Metaphysical Thinking* (Macmillan, 1945).

E. W. F. Tomlin, *Living and Knowing* (Faber, 1955).

110

SECTION TWO

Science

ASTRONOMY

by Sir Harold Spencer Jones

I. Early Views

THE ANCIENTS DIVIDED the celestial bodies into two classes, the fixed stars and the moving stars or planets. The planets were the bodies that changed their positions relative to each other and to the background of the fixed stars, and were seven in number—the Sun, Moon, Mercury, Venus, Mars, Jupiter and Saturn. The seven days of the week were named after these seven planets. The Earth was believed to be fixed and immovable at the centre of the Universe, and all the other bodies rotated round it; each of the planets was attached to a separate crystal sphere, while the stars were all fixed to an outermost sphere.

This view was universally held from the time of Aristotle until the middle of the sixteenth century when Copernicus argued that it was not the Earth but the Sun that was at the centre; that the Earth, in common with Mercury, Venus, Mars, Jupiter and Saturn, revolved round it, and that the Moon revolved round the Earth. He explained the diurnal motions of the celestial bodies by supposing that the Earth rotated on its axis in the course of a day, and he thereby brought the sphere of the fixed stars to rest. The revolution in ideas brought about by the Copernican theory was so great that the theory for long met with widespread opposition.

Having brought the stars to rest, there was no longer any need to suppose that they were all at the same distance. This was recognized by Copernicus, but he refused to express a definite opinion on the matter. The first explicit assertion that the stars were scattered through space at different distances was made by the English astronomer Digges in 1576. He supposed that the differences in brightness of the stars were due to differences in distance, and that as distances became greater and greater the stars at those distances appeared fainter and fainter, until at very great distances they ceased to be visible.

If the Universe was infinite it could not be said to have a centre. The wandering monk, Giordano Bruno, was burnt at the stake for

preaching, amongst other things, that the Sun was not at the centre
of the Universe and that the Universe was infinite. In 1718 Halley
proved that some of the bright stars had certainly changed their
positions since the time of Ptolemy; thus some of the "fixed" stars
were not fixed, and it was logical to assume that all the stars were in
motion. It then became quite useless to talk about the Universe
having a centre.

II. The Motions and Distances of the Stars

The motions of the few stars determined by Halley were angular
motions across the line of sight; such motions are termed *proper-
motions*. They are quite small, in general, because the stars are at
great distances. The greater the distance of a star, the smaller on
the average is its proper-motion. The star of largest known proper-
motion takes nearly 200 years to travel a distance in the sky equal
to the angular diameter of the Moon; only about a couple of hundred stars are known with proper-motions large enough to traverse
this same distance in 2,000 years.

We require to know the distances of the stars in order to convert
their proper-motions into actual velocities in miles a second, and
also to obtain information about their intrinsic brightness. Two stars
might differ in apparent brightness (as seen, for instance, by the
naked eye) because they differ in intrinsic brightness, or because
they are at different distances, or for both reasons. Many attempts
were made by astronomers to determine the distances of stars, but
without any success until 1838; the repeated failures were due to
the great distances of the stars. The method used is to determine the
change in the direction in which the star is seen, when the Earth
moves from one end of its orbit to the other—a distance of
186,000,000 miles. The change in direction, even for the nearest
known star, is so small that measures of very high accuracy are
essential for obtaining reliable results.

Because of the great distances of the stars it is convenient to
express them in terms of the *light-year* as a unit; the light-year is the
distance that light takes to travel in one year and is about six million
million miles. The nearest known star is at a distance of about four
light-years; expressed in other words, this star is seen by light
which has been travelling on through space for four years. The
distances of several thousand stars have been measured, and these
measures have been used in various ways to derive distances of
many other stars by indirect methods.

When the distance of a star is known, its angular proper-motion
can be converted into a speed in miles a second across the line of
sight. The speed along the line of sight can be directly determined
in miles a second, if the spectrum of the star is formed, which

means that the light of the star is spread into a band in the sequence of its radiations from blue to red. If the star is moving towards us the radiations from the star are compressed, or, in other words, their wave-lengths are shortened; if it is moving away, the radiations are spread out, so that their wave-lengths are lengthened. From the measures of the wave-lengths, the actual speed can be derived. Thus we can derive the velocity of the star both across and along the line of sight, and so obtain its total velocity. The velocities in general do not exceed thirty miles per second. The Sun itself has a velocity of thirteen miles per second in the direction towards a point in the Constellation of Hercules.

III. The Brightness of the Stars

The apparent brightness of a star is expressed in a scale of magnitudes, based on the system devised by the Greek astronomer Hipparchus, who selected about twenty of the brightest stars and called them first-magnitude stars. All the stars just visible to the naked eye he called sixth-magnitude stars, grading stars of intermediate brightness as being of the second, third . . . magnitude. In this rough grading it is found that a difference of five magnitudes corresponds roughly to a ratio of 100 : 1 in brightness. This system has been given precision by defining a scale of magnitude on the basis of five magnitudes being exactly equivalent to a ratio of 100 : 1 in brightness. The fainter the star the larger is its magnitude designation; stars brighter than a star of the first magnitude may have zero or negative magnitude. Thus Sirius, the brightest star, has a magnitude of $-1\cdot6$. A star of magnitude $8\cdot4$ is $10\cdot0$ magnitudes fainter than Sirius and has thus only 1/10,000th of the brightness of Sirius.

But, as already explained, we must know the distance of a star in order to obtain some information about its intrinsic brightness. If the distance of a star is doubled, it would only appear one-quarter as bright. If we imagine all stars brought to the same distance, their apparent magnitudes would be a measure also of their relative true or intrinsic brightness. The absolute magnitude of a star is defined as its magnitude when at a standard distance of $32\cdot6$ light-years. We find that the stars differ enormously in their intrinsic luminosity; some stars are more than 100,000 times brighter than the Sun, others are less than 1/10,000th as bright. Most of the stars in the vicinity of the Sun are intrinsically faint. Of the fifty nearest known stars, only three are more luminous than the Sun and most are very much less luminous.

IV. Temperatures and Colours of the Stars

Stars differ also in colour and a difference in colour indicates a difference in temperature; just as, when a bar of iron is heated, it glows at first with a dull red colour, then becomes yellow, and finally white hot. Differences in colour amongst the stars are noticeable to the naked eye. These differences are more clearly shown when the stars are photographed, for the normal photographic emulsion is very sensitive to blue light, but relatively insensitive to red light. By comparing the visual brightness with the photographic brightness the colour of the star can be measured and its temperature inferred.

A blue star may have a temperature from 30,000° up to about 100,000° (all temperatures are measured in the centigrade scale). The Sun, which is a yellow star, has a temperature of 6,000°. A red star may have a temperature of not more than 2,000° to 3,000°. To each temperature corresponds a definite brightness per unit of surface area: the higher the temperature the brighter the surface of the star. Thus we are provided with a means by which the size of a star can be deduced; for by comparing the intrinsic brightness of the star with its brightness per unit of area, we derive the surface area of the star and hence its size.

V. Sizes and Masses of the Stars

Again we find that there is an enormous difference between one star and another. Some stars are so large that their diameters are several hundreds of times greater than the Sun's; if the Sun were placed at the centre of such a star, the entire orbit of Mars would lie within the star. Such stars are called *giants*. Other stars are so small that their diameters are less than one-hundredth of the Sun's. Such stars are called *dwarfs*. Most of the dwarfs are small, cool red stars, though there is a special class of white dwarfs. The giants may be of any colour, though the brightest of them are blue.

By determining the apparent magnitude of a star, its distance and its colour we are therefore able to derive its intrinsic brightness (or absolute magnitude), its size and its temperature. The other important property of a star is its mass. The only way in which we can determine the mass of a star is through its gravitational attraction on some other body. In the case of the Sun, for instance, by comparing the period of revolution of the Earth around the Sun, under the Sun's gravitational attraction, with the period of revolution of the Moon around the Earth, under the Earth's gravitational attraction, and using Newton's law of gravitation we find that the mass of the Sun is about 332,000 times the mass of the Earth. But in the case of a single star, there is no means by which we can determine its mass.

Fortunately, however, many stars are twin systems; in such a system each of the two components revolves around the common centre of gravity under the gravitational attraction of the other. If the period of orbital revolution can be determined and the position of the centre of gravity obtained, then, when the distance of the system is known, the mass of each star in terms of the mass of the Sun as unit can be deduced. We find that the stars differ much less in mass than in other respects; the great majority of the stars have masses which lie between 10 times and 1/10th of the mass of the Sun, though there are a few with masses that exceed 50 times the Sun's mass.

When the masses of the stars, determined from the observations of the twin or binary systems, are compared with the intrinsic luminosities of the stars it is found that there is a very close correlation. The very massive stars are highly luminous; the stars of small mass are of low luminosity. This surprising result can be used to infer the masses of single stars, which cannot possibly be determined by direct measurement. We have only to obtain the luminosity of the star from the measurement of its distance and apparent magnitude, and then from the period-luminosity relationship deduce its mass.

As the range in size of the stars is very great but the range in mass is comparatively small, the stars must differ widely in their mean densities. The mean density of the substance of a great giant star is about equal to that of the air in a fairly well-exhausted vacuum; in other words, sufficient of the material to fill an average-sized room would weigh only an ounce or two. Very different are the smallest stars known—the group of white dwarfs. They can be illustrated by the brightest naked-eye star, Sirius, which is actually a double star, though the companion is so faint that a large telescope is required to see it. It sends out only 1/10,000th part as much light as Sirius and is so much the smaller that Sirius could contain about 180,000 stars of the size of its companion. Yet the masses of Sirius and its companion are not very unequal. The companion is comparable to the planets in size but to the Sun in mass; it is on the average about 50,000 times denser than water. A match-box full of the material of which Sirius is composed would weigh a couple of tons. It is thus far denser than the heaviest materials we find on the Earth. How this is possible we shall explain later.

VI. Variable Stars

The Sun, which is the nearest star, is pretty constant in its brightness. A variation in brightness would entail a variation in its output of energy in the form of heat and light. If it changed its brightness by half a magnitude in either direction all life on the Earth would come to an end; the decrease in its brightness corresponding to half a magnitude would make the Earth a frozen waste, an increase of the same amount would make the oceans boil and the Earth so hot that life would become impossible. It is possible that the warm periods and ice ages that the Earth has experienced in the past have been caused by small variations in the Sun's output of energy.

But there are many stars which vary greatly in their brightness. They are known as variable stars. One interesting class of variable stars is provided by the twin systems in which the orbital plane lies very nearly in the line of sight, so that in their orbital revolution each star eclipses the other, either totally, or partially, in turn. But these eclipsing variable stars, as they are termed, are not variable in the physical sense of varying their intrinsic brightness.

VII. New Stars

Some of the true variables behave in an entirely irregular manner, their behaviour being quite unpredictable. Amongst these are the *novae* or new stars, a name given before the invention of the telescope to a star which appeared in a part of the sky where no star had previously been seen. They are not, of course, new stars in the literal sense of the term. They are stars which blaze up suddenly, increasing in brightness from ten-thousand- to a millionfold in the course of a few days. After its outburst, a nova fades away, rapidly at first and then more slowly, returning to about its initial brightness after several months or a few years. There is a special and rare class of novae which at their outburst increase very much more in brightness than the normal nova. They have been called supernovae. A nova which appeared in 1572 became brighter than Venus and could be seen in broad daylight; its increase in brightness when it flared up was at least 900 million times. It was a supernova. Another supernova appeared in 1604, which increased in brightness at its outburst 100 million times.

No supernova has appeared in our Galaxy since 1604. One which appeared in the year A.D. 1054, and was recorded in Chinese annals, can now be identified with the Crab nebula. A number of supernovae have been observed in other galaxies. In 1885 one flared up in the Andromeda spiral nebula and is known as S Andromedae. The outburst of a nova appears to be due to some instability setting in within the star, causing an enormously increased output of energy. The star is blown up and some of its outer layers are blown off into space. The outburst of a supernova may be accompanied by the complete disintegration of the star. Some thirty novae appear on the average in our Galaxy each year, but few are near enough to become visible to the naked eye; the supernovae are much rarer and on the average there is one supernova outburst per galaxy in about 300 years.

VIII. Pulsating Stars

The stars which are termed Cepheid variables, after the type star, Delta Cephei, are of special importance, because they serve as standard beacons in space. Their variations of brightness are perfectly regular, the periods for different stars ranging from about a day to about thirty days. It has been proved that these variations are associated with a regular pulsation of the star. There is a remarkably close correlation between the intrinsic luminosity of a Cepheid variable and the period of its brightness variation. The brighter the star, the longer is its period. The great importance of these stars arises from this remarkable relationship. A Cepheid variable can be recognized by the way in which its brightness changes: the decrease from maximum to minimum light is less rapid than the subsequent increase to maximum. When a Cepheid variable has been identified, its period of variation can be determined and its intrinsic brightness then inferred. By comparing its intrinsic with its apparent brightness, its distance can be deduced. As Cepheid variables are intrinsically highly luminous, they are visible at great distances. They provide astronomers with a most powerful tool for the exploration of space.

IX. The Nature of a Star

Observation can give us information only about the outer portion of a star. We can determine its size, its surface temperature, its intrinsic luminosity, and in some cases its mass. Knowledge of the conditions in the interior of a star can be obtained only by applying mathematical principles to the general physical properties of the matter of which the stars are composed. The temperature of a star must increase rapidly inwards because of the increase of pressure; by a simple argument it can be concluded that the temperature at the centre of a star like the Sun must be about twenty million degrees. Under such high temperatures not only can no chemical compounds exist but also the atoms must be almost completely stripped of their electrons. Inside the star, therefore, there is a hurly-burly of atomic nuclei and electrons, moving about with very high speeds and continually colliding with one another.

The star is held together by its own gravitation. In opposition to this are the pressure of the gaseous matter, tending to dissipate it into space, and the pressure of the intense radiation inside the star. The radiation is being continually absorbed by some atoms and in turn re-emitted; the net effect is for it to travel outwards and in so doing to drive the atoms which absorb it outwards. The pressure of radiation becomes important at high temperatures, because it increases as the fourth power of the temperature: if the temperature is doubled the pressure of radiation is increased sixteenfold. At a temperature of twenty million degrees it amounts to three million tons per square inch.

The mathematical theory of the equilibrium of a star, in which gas pressure and radiation pressure are balanced by the star's gravitation, is known as the theory of radiative equilibrium. The theory leads to the result that the luminosity of a star depends primarily on its mass; this relationship between mass and luminosity has been closely confirmed by the data from stars whose mass can be determined. The mean molecular weight of the material enters into the relationship; by comparing the calculated and observed luminosities it can be inferred that the stars consist predominantly of hydrogen.

The fact that within the stars the atoms are almost completely stripped of their electrons explains how a star can have the extremely high density which is characteristic of the white dwarfs. In a normal atom the nucleus and electrons occupy an infinitesimal part of the total volume of the atom; the atom has, as it were, an invisible barrier and atoms cannot be squeezed together beyond the point at which these barriers are in contact. When, as in a star, these barriers have been broken down, nuclei and electrons can be squeezed together to give incredibly high densities.

X. *The Source of Stellar Energy*

A star could not continue to emit radiation for thousands of millions of years unless it had a powerful source of energy. Without an internal supply of energy the star would contract under its gravitation; the contraction would release energy, but only enough to keep the star radiating for a few score million years. The energy emitted by a star is so great that it can be maintained only by drawing upon the store of energy locked up in the atoms. In the majority of stars this energy is obtained by building up atoms of helium out of atoms of hydrogen. The atom of hydrogen has a weight of $1 \cdot 008$ (in terms of $16 \cdot 0$ for the atom of oxygen); the atom of helium has a weight of $4 \cdot 004$. Hence when four atoms of hydrogen combine to form an atom of helium there is a decrease of mass of $0 \cdot 028$ units, which is accounted for by the energy that is released. The atomic bomb depends upon the same principle, its production of energy being obtained by an atomic reaction in which there is disappearance of mass.

The building up of atoms of helium is not a direct process; it is brought about by a cyclic process, known as the carbon-nitrogen cycle, in which a series of atomic nuclear reactions takes place, the end result of which is that hydrogen disappears, the carbon and nitrogen remain unchanged, and helium is formed. The carbon and nitrogen play the part of what chemists term catalysts.

The output of energy from the Sun is such that it is losing mass at the rate of four million tons every second. Yet in the course of 2,000 million years the amount of hydrogen in the Sun which has been converted into helium will be equivalent only to two per cent. of its mass, and the loss of mass of the Sun will be only about 1/10,000th of its original mass.

Another process in which atomic nuclear energy is made available is the building up of helium atoms out of protons. This process does not require so high a temperature as the carbon-nitrogen cycle. The central temperatures of the giant stars of low mean density are about six million degrees, much too low for the carbon-nitrogen cycle to operate. The proton cycle becomes important in these stars. The giant stars of high intrinsic luminosity, with correspondingly extremely great output of energy, consume their hydrogen at such a great rate that the lifetime of these stars cannot much exceed a few million years. It follows that the birth of such stars must still be in progress, for otherwise their comparatively brief lives would have resulted long ago in their complete disappearance.

XI. The Nearest Star—the Sun

The Sun is the nearest star and is the only star whose surface we can examine. Dark spots can usually be seen on it. They were probably first seen by Galileo in 1610, being one of the earliest discoveries following the invention of the telescope. The spots appear to move across the disk of the Sun from east to west, this apparent motion being in the main due to the rotation of the Sun in about 27 days. But the Sun is a gaseous body and does not rotate like a solid body; its rate of rotation decreases from the equator to the poles: at the equator the rotation period is about $24\frac{1}{2}$ days and at the poles about 34 days.

The spots appear dark by contrast with the brighter surrounding surface of the Sun; this is a consequence of their lower temperature, though they are actually intensely hot. A sunspot is in the nature of a vortex in the outer atmosphere of the Sun, from which matter swirls upwards and outwards, being cooled in the process. Strong magnetic fields are associated with the spots; the spots have in general opposite polarities in the northern and southern hemispheres of the Sun.

The frequency of appearance of spots varies in a cycle of about 11 years. At the beginning of a cycle spots first appear in both hemispheres in middle solar latitudes. They gradually become more frequent, the belts in which they appear slowly moving towards the Sun's equator. Then, as these belts draw near to the equator, the spots become less frequent and the minimum of the cycle is at hand. Whereas at the maximum of the cycle there is never a day without sunspots, most of the days are now spotless. The beginning of the new cycle is heralded once again by the occasional appearance of a spot in middle latitudes. The individual spots are short-lived; some last for not more than a few days and few last for more than a few weeks.

The length of the sunspot cycle averages about 11 years, but is somewhat variable. There is a curious fact which suggests that the true length of the cycle is really 22 years. For, as already mentioned, the spots in the two hemispheres have opposite polarities; in consecutive 11-year cycles, however, the polarities in both hemispheres are reversed. Thus, if in one 11-year period the polarities are north in the northern hemisphere and south in the southern hemisphere, in the next period they are south in the northern hemisphere and north in the southern. Neither the cause of the sunspot cycle nor the reason for these regular changes of polarity are yet understood.

Another feature of the solar surface is provided by the prominences, enormous tongues of flame standing out from the Sun's limb and often reaching to very great heights. First observed only on the occasions of a total eclipse of the Sun, they can now be observed at any time by special techniques. They can also be seen in projection on the Sun's surface by photographing the Sun in the light of hydrogen or calcium, instead of in its integrated light. They may last in a fairly quiescent state for several months and then not infrequently break up with great rapidity, matter being often shot completely away from the Sun in the process.

The sunspot cycle and the associated solar phenomena are reflected in various terrestrial effects. When sunspots are numerous, magnetic storms on the Earth are frequent; when sunspots are few, storms are rare. But there is not an exact correspondence; a large spot may appear without a magnetic storm following, or there may be a storm without a spot. The magnet needle, on quiet days without storm disturbance, has a fairly regular diurnal movement about its mean position; the range of this diurnal movement follows closely the changing frequency of spots, so that it increases from sunspot minimum to sunspot maximum and then decreases again.

The frequency of appearance of aurorae also correlates closely with that of sunspots. It is generally held that a storm is produced by a stream of electrically charged particles shot out from a disturbed area on the Sun; when such a stream comes into the Earth's atmosphere electric currents are produced in the upper layers, which give rise to variable magnetic fields, whose effects are superimposed on the general magnetic field of the Earth. The interaction of the magnetic field of the Earth on the electrically charged particles causes them to spiral inwards towards the magnetic poles; the electrical effects in the upper atmosphere produce the appearance of the aurorae, which are much more frequent in high than in low latitudes.

The origin of a magnetic storm can sometimes be traced to a disturbance on a particular area of the Sun. In the vicinity of a large spot a violent disturbance will not infrequently occur, in which a localized region of the Sun becomes intensely bright. Coincident with this eruption or *flare*, as it is termed, there is a sudden and complete fading on short-wave radio transmissions in channels passing over the sunlit face of the Earth. The flare is short-lived, normally lasting from half an hour to an hour, after which the radio transmissions return to normal. When the flare has occurred in the central regions of the Sun, it is followed after about a day by an intense magnetic storm.

The flare is associated with a greatly increased emission of ultra-violet light from the Sun, as a result of which the ionization in the upper atmosphere is much enhanced and extends to a much lower height than the normal. The radio waves are able to travel round the curved surface of the Earth because they are reflected by the ionized layer, but, when this layer extends into the denser region of the atmosphere, the waves are absorbed instead of being reflected, and a radio fade-out occurs. At the time of the flare, particles are shot out from the Sun which, if they reach the Earth, give rise to the magnetic storm.

There is an appreciable variation through the sunspot cycle in the ultra-violet light emitted from the Sun; as a result the ionized layer is more highly ionized at sunspot maximum than at sunspot minimum. The higher ionization is more favourable for the reflection of radio waves of higher frequency and shorter wave-lengths. The most favourable wave-lengths for short-wave radio transmissions consequently change through the sunspot cycle, and the study of the phenomena is of importance for the prediction of these optimum wave-lengths.

The Sun emits radiations on radio wave-lengths of from a few centimetres to several metres, and such emissions are much enhanced during periods of sunspot activity. The effect is to cause noise in a radio receiver which can greatly distort radio transmissions and even make them incomprehensible. A solar flare produces a great increase in the normal level of the noise. This electromagnetic radiation from the Sun is greatly in excess of the amount to be expected from a perfect radiator—the so-called black body— with a temperature of 6,000°. The study of the phenomenon has become a part of the new branch of astronomy known as radio-astronomy.

XII. *The Sun's Corona*

At the time of a total solar eclipse, the Sun, when its light is completely obscured by the Moon, is seen to be surrounded by a bright *aureole*, which is called the corona. The inner portion of the corona, which is much the brightest, can be observed without an eclipse at high-altitude stations, where there are no dust particles in the atmosphere to scatter the sunlight; a special instrument called a coronagraph is used in which the direct light of the Sun is obscured by a disk, an artificial eclipse thereby being produced. The faint extensions of the corona cannot be observed, however, except at a true total eclipse.

The form of the corona changes through the sunspot cycle. At sunspot maximum, it is compact, without very long streamers, and is more or less uniformly distributed round the Sun's disk. At minimum, on the other hand, there are short tufts at each of the Sun's poles, while long curved streamers extend outwards from the equatorial regions to a distance of a couple of million miles. At other times the form of the corona is intermediate between the two types. The structure of the inner portion of the corona is very complicated, especially in the vicinity of prominences and spots near the limb, over which one or more arches may be seen.

The corona is an outward extension of the Sun's atmosphere, consisting of protons and electrons. But part of the light of the corona is sunlight scattered by small particles in the vicinity of the Sun. There is, in the neighbourhood of the Sun and extending outwards beyond the orbit of the Earth, a thin flat sheet of dust particles. This rarefied matter scatters the light from the Sun and gives rise to the appearance of the Zodiacal light, a faint hazy band of light which extends from the Sun along the ecliptic. It is best seen on a clear moonless night soon after sunset in the spring or shortly before sunrise in the autumn, when the ecliptic has its greatest inclination to the horizon. This Zodiacal light merges into the faint extensions of the corona.

When the light of the corona is analysed with a spectroscope, it is found to contain radiations which have not been observed in the laboratory. When they were first observed, and for many years afterwards, they were attributed to a hypothetical unknown element, which was named "coronium". Modern atomic theory left no room for such an element, however, and it was therefore concluded that they must be produced by some known element or elements in an unfamiliar guise. It has been proved within recent years from theoretical considerations that the radiations are produced by atoms of iron, nickel and calcium which have been stripped of a large number of their electrons. A high temperature is needed to strip the atoms in this way and it appears that the temperature of the corona is between one and two million degrees.

Information about the constitution of the Sun is derived from the analysis of its light with the spectroscope. No elements are found in the Sun which are not known on the Earth, though the gaseous element helium was discovered in 1868 in the Sun before it had been found terrestrially: hence its name, derived from the Greek word for the Sun. A few terrestrial elements have not been detected in the Sun, either because they are extremely rare or because the nature of their spectra are such that their detection is not to be expected. As in the majority of the stars, hydrogen is by far the most abundant constituent of the Sun and helium is the next most abundant. All the other elements combined amount to less than 1 per cent. of the total. The relative abundance of the elements in the Sun, with the exception of hydrogen and helium, is in close accord with their relative terrestrial abundance.

XIII. The Planets

Associated with the Sun is a family of planets. The known planets, in order of increasing distance from the Sun, are Mercury, Venus, Earth, Mars, Jupiter, Saturn, Uranus, Neptune and Pluto. With the exception of the last three, which were discovered with the telescope (Uranus in 1781, Neptune in 1846, and Pluto in 1930), they have been known from the earliest times. These planets, with the exception of Mercury, Venus and Pluto, have one or more satellites. The Earth has one, the Moon; Mars has two; Jupiter has twelve; Saturn has nine, in addition to its system of rings; Uranus has five; Neptune has two.

The solar system contains in addition some 1,600 small bodies known as minor planets or asteroids; a large number of comets; and a good deal of débris which is revealed to us as shooting stars or meteors, fireballs, meteorites and the dust that gives rise to the Zodiacal light. The orbits of the asteroids lie for the most part in the gap between the orbits of Mars and Jupiter; it has been suggested that there was once a planet in this region which for some reason disintegrated and so produced the asteroids. The four brightest are Ceres, discovered in 1801; Pallas, discovered in 1802; Juno, discovered in 1804; and Vesta, discovered in 1807. Ceres, which is the largest, has a diameter of 480 miles, but many of the faint asteroids are smaller than one mile in diameter.

The four planets, Jupiter, Saturn, Uranus and Neptune are known as the major planets, being much larger than the other planets. The sizes decrease in this order: Jupiter is much the largest, being larger than all the others combined, having a volume 1,300 times that of the Earth, and a mass 317 times that of the Earth.

The mean temperatures of the planets decrease with increasing distance from the Sun. For each planet there is a balance between the heat that it receives from the Sun and the heat that it radiates into space. Thus while the temperature of Mercury is equal to that of molten zinc, the major planets are extremely cold bodies, Jupiter, for instance, having a temperature of about $-130°C$.

XIV. Possibility of Life on Other Planets

The question whether life exists on any of the other planets is of much interest. The possibility of life seems to depend primarily on two factors, the temperature of the planet and the nature of its atmosphere. All living matter of which we have experience is built up of extremely complex molecules and it is inconceivable that living matter elsewhere in the Universe could be built up of simple molecules. These complex molecules are fragile, in the sense that they are readily broken up by moderate increase in temperature. It cannot be supposed that life would be possible on Mercury, with its high temperature. Some living matter can withstand quite low temperatures without being destroyed; but under such conditions vital activities seem to remain in suspense and it is difficult to believe that any form of life could develop under the low temperatures prevailing on the major planets. So far as temperature is concerned, all the planets seem to be ruled out except Venus, the Earth (with the Moon) and Mars.

The tendency of any gaseous atmosphere is to dissipate away into space. It is only the gravitational pull of the planet that prevents this. The stronger the gravitational pull, the more difficult it is for the atmosphere to escape. For any given planet, the tendency to escape will be greater the higher the temperature of the planet and the lighter the gaseous constituent, because the mean speed of the molecules increases with temperature and, for the same temperature, is greater the lighter the atoms. For each body there is a certain limiting velocity, called the "velocity of escape", which must be exceeded if an atom is to escape. For the Earth it is 7 miles a second; for Mars and the Moon, 1·5 miles a second; for Jupiter, 37 miles a second; for the Sun, 383 miles a second.

For any given planet, its temperature being known, and for any given constituent of its atmosphere, the rate of escape can be calculated. It is concluded that Mercury must long ago have lost all its atmosphere; the Moon, though it could retain heavy constituents now, must very rapidly have lost all its atmosphere when its temperature was higher than it is now; the Earth and Venus have lost practically all their hydrogen and helium, but have been able to retain the greater part of their heavier constituents; the major planets have retained all their initial atmospheres, which consisted predominantly of hydrogen, this being cosmically by far the most abundant element, together with helium. Mars has lost most of its atmosphere, but has been able to retain a small part of the heavier constituents.

From geophysical considerations, it can be shown that on a cooling planet, when there is a predominance of hydrogen, the final atmosphere will contain neither free oxygen nor carbon dioxide; but large amounts of ammonia and methane (marsh gas) will be present, together with water vapour, which will be frozen out when the temperatures are low, as is the case for the major planets. It is, in fact, found that marsh gas and ammonia are major constituents of their atmospheres, which must also contain hydrogen and helium; these two gases can not be directly detected, but their presence in great abundance can be inferred from the low mean densities of these planets. Even if their temperature were sufficiently high to permit of life, their poisonous atmospheres would seem to rule out all possibility of life on them.

Venus and Mars remain for consideration.

Venus is a little smaller and a little less massive than the Earth and has an atmosphere comparable in its extent. This atmosphere contains a great amount of carbon dioxide but neither water vapour nor oxygen, in marked contrast to our atmosphere, which has a great amount of oxygen but only a moderate amount of carbon dioxide. This seems to point to an absence of plant life, for plants absorb carbon dioxide and give back oxygen to the atmosphere. The absence of water vapour is a further indication that there can be no life on Venus. Its surface temperature, because of the strong greenhouse effect of carbon dioxide, must be higher than the temperature of boiling water. With so high a temperature the atmospheric circulation is much more violent than ours; dust, from its arid surface, is swirled high up into the atmosphere, which makes it impossible for any surface features on Venus ever to be seen.

Mars has a tenuous atmosphere containing a moderate amount of carbon dioxide and possibly a small amount of oxygen, below the limit that we can detect. The white polar caps, which grow in the winter and disappear in the summer, provide evidence of moisture, though there are no oceans or lakes on Mars. It is an arid planet: much of its surface is desert, which gives it the familiar ruddy colour. There are also areas which have a greenish tinge, but which change their outlines from one Martian season to another; they also show slight changes in coloration, which appear to be of a seasonal nature.

It seems quite certain that there can be no animal life on Mars. The amount of oxygen in the Martian atmosphere is certainly less than in our atmosphere at a height of 100,000 ft.—$3\frac{1}{2}$ times the height of Mount Everest, while the almost complete lack of moisture and the rapid and extreme changes of temperature are not conducive to animal life. The greenish areas appear to be areas of vegetation. The nature of the light which they reflect is similar to that reflected by the lichens and dry mosses on the Earth, showing no absorptions due to water or to chlorophyll. Lichens on the Earth are the plant forms that can survive under conditions of great aridity and of great extremes of temperature, and which are found at high altitudes near the snow line, where no other plants can exist. It thus seems that amongst the planets in the solar system there is no life outside our Earth, except for the most primitive form of plant life on Mars.

XV. Origin of the Solar System

The solar system shows so many regularities that it cannot have been formed by mere chance. The orbits of the various planets lie nearly in the same plane. The planets all revolve round the Sun in the same direction, which is also the direction of rotation of the Sun and planets. The same is true also of the satellites, with the exception of a few of the smallest. There have been many attempts to account for the system. They have been of two types—theories which attribute its origin to some cataclysmic event in the past, and theories which suppose it to have been formed through the gradual evolution of a primordial system.

A theory that was for a time much favoured was based on the hypothesis that another star passed so close to the Sun, that a great tidal bulge was produced on it, from which matter was drawn out as the star passed by; the planets condensed out of this matter. There was one serious stumbling-block to this theory; the distribution of angular momentum in the solar system is very peculiar, in that nearly all the mass of the system is centred in the Sun which, however, has only a very small portion of the angular momentum. The theory has been elaborated in various ways in order to account for this anomalous distribution, and has become more and more artificial without being able satisfactorily to meet this difficulty.

The other type of theory is consequently now generally favoured. It is supposed that the Sun passed through a dense cloud of interstellar material and, in doing so, collected an extensive envelope. The internal frictions in this envelope changed the shape of the orbits of the particles until they became nearly circular and their planes were brought nearly into the plane of the Sun's equator. In the disk-shaped envelope so produced, viscous forces slowed down the faster moving inner parts and speeded up the slower moving outer parts of the system, thus accounting for the distribution of angular momentum in the solar system. The planets condensed out of the discoid envelope. The condensation process is found to provide a mass distribution in general agreement with that of the solar system. The satellites are supposed to have been formed inside their planetary atmospheres by condensation.

The probability that other stars have systems of planets depends upon which type of theory is correct. A near approach of two stars is such a very rare event that, if the first type of theory is correct, only an extremely small percentage of the stars can have planetary systems. If the second type of theory is correct, planetary systems would be much more abundant, because of the widespread distribution of the interstellar clouds on or near the central plane of the Milky Way. But stellar distances are so great that there would be no hope of detecting a planetary system attached to the nearest known star, even if it possessed one.

XVI. *The Distribution of the Stars: the Galaxy*

The first attempt to investigate the distribution of the stars in space was made by Sir William Herschel towards the end of the eighteenth century. At that time the true nature of the Milky Way—the broad belt of hazy light which encircles the whole heavens—was undecided. Herschel, with telescopes of his own making and of better quality than any previously made, proved that it consists of innumerable stars too faint to be seen individually with the naked eye. By his method of "star gauges"—counting the stars visible in the field of view of his telescope, when it was directed to different parts of the sky—he concluded that the stellar system to which we belong is highly flattened; Herschel himself compared it to a mill-stone. The Sun was near the middle of the system and the appearance of the Milky Way is a consequence of this flattened shape.

But our Milky Way system, or Galaxy, does not consist of stars only. Strongly concentrated towards the central plane of the system there is a great deal of gaseous matter, in the form of clouds which are made luminous by the stars embedded within them. Interspersed with these luminous gas clouds or *nebulae*, as they are termed, are many dark patches, which are relatively devoid of stars. When some of these were first seen by Herschel he thought they were vacant lanes through the stars. But we now know that the appearance is caused by matter in the form of small solid particles—dust particles—which dim or even completely obscure the light of the stars that are behind them. A small amount of material, divided up into small particles, is very effective in absorbing light, as can be apparent when looking at the Sun through a cloud of smoke coming from a chimney. The dust clouds not only dim or obscure light, but they redden the light that passes through them, because they scatter blue light much more than red.

Cepheid pulsating stars are found in many of the aggregations of stars forming the Milky Way and they can be used to estimate the distances of these clouds. But here we come up against a difficulty, for the effect of the dusty matter is to make these stars appear fainter than they really are; the distances deduced by comparing their apparent brightness with their intrinsic brightness (which is inferred from their periods of brightness variation, and therefore unaffected by the dimming) will be too great.

Fortunately this difficulty can be got round and the dimensions of our Galaxy determined by the use of a special class of objects called globular clusters. They are spherical aggregations of stars, each cluster containing many thousands; the stars are strongly condensed towards the centre of a cluster, under the influence of its gravitation. About a hundred of these clusters are known, nearly all of which are in one-half of the sky. None are found in the central region of the Milky Way. Their light consequently reaches us without travelling for more than a short distance through the region in which the dusty matter is scattered. Pulsating stars are found in all these clusters and so their distances can be found with satisfactory accuracy.

They prove to outline a more or less spherical system, having a diameter of about 100,000 light-years, in which the Sun occupies a markedly excentric position at a distance of about 30,000 light-years from the centre. This excentric position of the Sun explains the peculiar distribution of the clusters in the sky. The direction from the Sun to the centre of the system is towards the constellation of Sagittarius, where the densest star clouds of the Milky Way are to be found.

When the motions of the stars in this direction and in the diametrically opposite direction are compared, it is found that those in the direction towards the centre are moving more quickly than those in the opposite direction. This is a characteristic feature of motion under the control of gravitational attraction. We can compare it with the motions of the planets in the solar system, in which the nearer the planet to the Sun the faster it moves. It is diametrically opposite to the rotation of a solid body, where the motion is more rapid the greater the distance from the centre.

We can conclude that our Galaxy is rotating. From the analysis of the proper-motions and line-of-sight velocities of stars at different distances from the Sun, it is found that the period of rotation in the neighbourhood of the Sun is about 225 million years and that the orbital speed of the Sun around the centre is about 140 miles a second. The controlling mass is found to be of the order of a hundred thousand million times the mass of the Sun. From other considerations it is concluded that about half of the total material of the system is in the form of discrete stars, the other half consisting of the gaseous matter and dust which are scattered in or near the plane of the Milky Way. This material has not yet aggregated into stars. The presence in the Milky Way of the intensely bright blue giant stars, whose lifetime is—as we have seen—relatively short, proves that stars are still forming out of this material. In addition, stars, as they move through it, continually capture some of it by their gravitational attraction. We may say that the stars are gradually sweeping space clean, but the process is very slow, because the average distance between two stars is several light-years.

Though the Sun is nearly in the plane of the Milky Way it occupies a markedly excentric position in the Galaxy, which is contrary to what Herschel concluded. The explanation is that Herschel's survey did not reach to the limits of the system in the direction towards the centre; not only was the light-grasp of his telescope inadequate but also the dimming of the stars by the dusty matter was not known to him.

XVII. The External Galaxies

Having now gained some idea of the shape and size of our Galaxy and of the position of the Sun within it, the question naturally arises whether there is anything beyond it. Forty years ago this question was still undecided. There was then much discussion about the nature of the objects that were termed "spiral nebulae", systems consisting of a central nucleus from which, at diametrically opposite points, there extended two arms which curled around the nucleus in the form of spirals. These objects are seen at all angles of inclination, some broadside on, some at an oblique angle, and some edgewise. When seen edgewise, they are much like what we have found our Galaxy to be.

Some astronomers thought that they must be island universes in space. Others thought that they must be members of our Galaxy, for their distribution in the sky seemed to be related to the Milky Way, in that none at all were found in or near the Milky Way, and the further in the sky they were from the Milky Way the more abundant they were. At that time the importance of the obscuring dusty matter in the Milky Way was not realized. The observed distribution is what would be expected if the spiral nebulae were scattered fairly uniformly in space, beyond the confines of the Milky Way, when the effect of dimming by the dusty matter is allowed for.

When the first measurements of the line-of-sight velocities of some of these objects were made, they were found to be surprisingly large—much larger than the velocities of any stars—and, with a few exceptions, the velocities were all velocities of recession. As fainter and fainter spirals were investigated, the velocities proved to be greater and greater.

It was the completion of the 100-inch telescope of the Mount Wilson Observatory that enabled the question to be solved. For with this telescope it was possible to detect discrete stars in the brighter—and presumably the nearer—of these systems. Amongst these stars some Cepheid variables were detected and also some novae. Thus it became possible to derive their distances. The brightest of the spiral systems is the Great Nebula in Andromeda, which is faintly visible to the naked eye as a hazy patch in the sky; its distance was found to be 900,000 light-years (though more recent and improved determinations give 1,500,000 light-years). It was thus certainly far beyond the limits of the Galaxy. The problem was solved: the spiral nebulae are island universes.

The distances of a number of others were derived in a similar way. For fainter and more distant systems, distances were estimated on the assumptions that these objects are by and large of the same size and the same intrinsic brightness. It was then found that there was a very close correlation between these estimated distances and the velocities of recession. The distances of still fainter objects could then be inferred on the assumption that the line-of-sight velocities of recession are proportional to the distance.

It might appear at first sight that the fact that there is this general recession of distant objects would mean that our Galaxy is at the centre of the whole system, which would give it a place of special significance. But this is not so. The whole system is expanding, and from any individual member of the system all the others would appear to be receding and with velocities increasing in proportion to their distances from it. This relationship is the basis for the theory that the whole Universe is expanding.

This interpretation of the observations is supported by theoretical considerations. When the theory of generalized relativity was applied to the problem of the Universe, it was proved by Friedman and Lemaître that a static universe would be unstable. It could not, in fact, continue to exist in a static condition, for the slightest disturbance would cause it to begin either to expand or contract.

It was mentioned above that a few of the nearer spiral systems have velocities of approach. The reason is that the individual systems have their own proper-motions of the order of 200 or 300 miles a second, which may be in any direction, and which are superposed on the velocity of recession resulting from the expansion. For the near systems, the velocity of expansion is small and may be outweighed by the proper-motion of the system. But beyond moderate distances the proper-motions are smaller than the velocity of expansion.

Having determined the distances, the dimensions of the spirals can be obtained and they prove to be comparable with those of our Galaxy. Our Galaxy is amongst the larger of the systems but it is not the largest; the Andromeda spiral certainly, and a few others probably, exceed our Galaxy in size. The rotations of several of the extra-galactic systems have been investigated and they prove to be slowly spinning round in space and to have masses of the same order as our Galaxy, about 100,000 million times the mass of the Sun.

The number of the island universes is very large. The 100-inch telescope can probe space to a distance of one thousand million light-years; from surveys made with that telescope it is estimated that within that distance there are not less than one hundred million galaxies. They are fairly uniformly distributed through space, apart from some localized clusterings, with an average distance apart of a few million light-years. There is no evidence of any thinning out towards the limits of the survey. The 200-inch Hale telescope on Mount Palomar, which has recently come into operation, can survey space out to a distance of two thousand million light-years; it will be of interest to ascertain in due course whether at that great distance there is any indication that the limits of the system are being approached.

Such immense distances balk the imagination. The light by which a faint galaxy, at the limiting distance reached by the 200-inch telescope, is photographed has been travelling on and on through space for some 2,000 million years—more than half the life-time of the Earth. During its long journey the Earth has seen many and great changes. Mountain ranges have been thrown up and worn down by the action of rain and wind; other ranges have been thrown up and in their turn worn down. Life did not appear on the Earth until the light had completed three-quarters of its long journey; evolution has carried it through its various stages; many types of animal life developed which have long since become extinct. Man himself did not appear until the light was nearing the end of the very last lap of its long journey.

XVIII. The Nature of the Universe

If we go backwards in time some 4,000 million years we reach an epoch when all the galaxies must have been congregated together into a compact space. We do not seem to be able to go further backwards in time. Lemaître has supposed that the whole of the matter in the Universe initially formed one great primeval atom, which was unstable and disintegrated. If this view is correct, there was an initial creation of the Universe at a finite epoch in the past, for we cannot suppose this primeval atom to have existed for an infinite time and then suddenly to have disintegrated. It follows also that the Universe is finite in extent.

A galaxy at a distance of about 4,000 million light-years from our Galaxy would have a velocity of recession equal to the velocity of light. We can never see any object beyond that distance, because the light from it could never reach us. The situation is analogous to that of a runner who is running a race with the finishing tape being moved away from him at a faster rate than he can run; he could never reach it. One by one the galaxies will pass beyond this observational horizon and be lost to view. After a finite time of some 10,000 million light-years all the galaxies that we can now observe will have passed beyond this horizon; we should then find ourselves apparently alone in space. It seems difficult to suppose that out of the whole eternity of time, we should find ourselves within the relatively narrow span in which millions of other galaxies can be seen.

An alternative view of the Universe has recently been proposed which avoids this difficulty. It is assumed that the Universe is infinite in extent and that it has existed for an infinite time in the past. Wherever we might be in the Universe, it would have by and large the same appearance, as the galaxies appear to be distributed with statistical uniformity. We may suppose that the same uniformity holds for all time, past, present and future, so that we do not find ourselves in any privileged position in time. It would then necessarily follow that to counterbalance the disappearance of galaxies on passing beyond the observational horizon there must be a continuous creation of matter, at such a rate that the average density of matter in the Universe remains constant.

This creation of matter is assumed to take place throughout the Universe with statistical uniformity and, from the matter so created, galaxies would be formed as a result of the aggregation of matter under its gravitational attraction. Whatever view we favour of the nature of the Universe, the galaxies we observe are believed to have condensed out from matter more or less uniformly distributed. As all galaxies older than 10,000 million years would have passed beyond the observational horizon, we could never see galaxies of greater age.

We thus appear to be faced with two alternatives; either there was an initial creation of the Universe at a finite epoch in the past, or the Universe has existed for an infinite time, throughout which creation has been taking place as a continuous process. Observation does not at present enable us to decide between these two alternatives, though it is not impossible that it may eventually succeed in doing so.

BOOKS SUGGESTED FOR FURTHER READING

G. Abetti, *The History of Astronomy* (Sidgwick and Jackson, 1954).
J. B. Sidgwick, *The Heavens Above. A Rationale of Astronomy* (Oxford, 1948).

Cecilia Payne-Gaposchkin, *Stars in the Making* (Eyre and Spottiswoode, 1953).

James C. Hickey, *Introducing the Universe* (Eyre and Spottiswoode, 1952).

H. Spencer Jones, *Life on Other Worlds* (English Universities Press, 1952).

H. Spencer Jones, *Worlds Without End* (English Universities Press, 1948).

THE CONQUEST OF SPACE

by DR. J. G. PORTER

IT IS RATHER MORE than four years since Wernher von Braun, writing in *Collier's Magazine*, gave his opinion that "development of the space station is as inevitable as the rising of the sun; man has already poked his nose into space and he is not likely to pull it back". This statement from a world authority on the subject is entitled to our respect, the more so as von Braun is only one of the many who take the same optimistic view of the future of space travel. Yet it is natural that we should inquire more closely into the possibilities of a project which has so ardently seized the popular imagination. This is no easy matter; much of the work that is being done is wrapped in secrecy, and the literature of the subject is, somewhat naturally, entirely biased in favour of the project. The articles and books which deal with space travel are written with enthusiasm. The enthusiasts are sometimes experts, but more often are not. Enthusiasm has a habit of stifling good judgement, and makes any assessment of the present position more than difficult.

Let us in the first place discount entirely the enormous popular interest in the subject, an interest which displays itself mostly in strip cartoons and science fiction, in which the intrepid heroes of the future form the crew of a great sleek monster, streamlined from stem to stern, and driven through space by powerful jets. In between their adventures, the crew perform prodigies of computation, make snap decisions and occasionally wander outside the ship in a space suit. Out there in space, where weight has no meaning, the great ship will travel at colossal speeds, covering the millions of miles to Mars in a few weeks. If this is the common idea, then it is a completely erroneous one. It seems to owe its popularity not to any real interest in the scientific problems involved, but rather to the same form of escapism as caused its owner at one time to read nothing but stories of cowboys and Indians. The freedom of the rolling prairie has given place to the freedom of space.

Let us face realities. In the first place, since space is completely empty there is not the slightest friction of any kind to the motion of the ship, and there is no need for streamlining. The ship will actually be of any shape that is convenient, and its exterior will probably bristle with derricks, aerials, reflectors, and other gadgets. The absence of friction will, of course, make it easy to drive the ship at great speeds, and it is probably this aspect of space travel that appeals to many people. Yet the outstanding difficulty remains— how are we to get the great ship off the earth? The simple answer to this question is that it will not rise from the earth at all, for it will be built out in space. In some of the latest ideas, we are to visualize a space station, a sort of artificial satellite of the earth which is to act as a landing stage for all space ships. A trip to the planets will then consist of several steps; first a flight in a rocket ship from the earth's surface to the space station, followed by transfer from the rocket to the station, and thence aboard a space ship. This will move off on its trip to Mars, where the process will be reversed. The space ship will come alongside a suitable satellite (possibly the little moon Deimos will serve the purpose) and from this point a rocket ship will take the passengers down to the surface of Mars.

Thus before space can really be conquered we have to make a rocket capable of reaching outer space, taking with it enough material to begin the construction of the space station. This is clearly the goal of modern research on high-altitude rockets; and once the space station is built, the way to the planets is clear. Further trips will bring material for the space ships, and after the necessary explorations have been made it will be possible to build further space stations and more ships, transporting men and materials as required. The size of the job staggers the imagination but it is treated in some books as though it were already past the blueprint stage, and tomorrow's papers would carry banner headlines announcing man's latest achievement. But how much have we really accomplished to date?

To be quite frank, very little; but let us make no mistake about one thing—the whole theory and practice of space flight are taken very seriously indeed in the highest circles of many countries. Much of the work is naturally on the secret list, but occasionally the veil lifts long enough to give us a glimpse of what is being done. The rocket is clearly the only possible means of propulsion in space, and it is, in fact, more efficient in a vacuum than when acting in the earth's atmosphere. The development of the V-2 rocket during World War II showed that rocket flight is a possibility, and its extension since that time has made it clear that man's age-old dream of a flight to the moon is no longer a whimsy, but is actually on the way to become a reality. Admittedly the plans for space travel are mainly on paper, their minute detail dealing with every conceivable aspect of the problem; but money is spent in studying rocket flight and the phenomena of the upper atmosphere in quite a lavish manner.

It is sometimes implied that the sole obstacle to progress in making space flight possible is the shortage of money. This seems absurd, for the figure of 4,000,000,000 dollars, which has been quoted as the cost of building the first space station, would be spread over ten years of experiment, and is but a small fraction of the cost of present national programmes on guided missiles, nuclear energy and the like. It can hardly be doubted that if experiments show the practicability of building a space station, then its military significance will quickly be realized and any number of millions will be forthcoming. For the present, however, the practical work is concerned mainly with the engineering problems involved, with research on the adaptability of human beings to space conditions, and to furthering any form of research which will reveal the secrets of the upper atmosphere and what lies beyond.

From the theoretical point of view we have to change all our preconceived ideas about flying through space, and regard the problem as an astronomical one. A space ship behaves exactly like a planet going round the sun; the space station is a satellite to the earth, just like the moon, and the speeds in both cases are astronomical speeds. The earth, for example, revolves about the sun at an average rate of $18\frac{1}{2}$ miles a second, which is 1,100 miles a minute or 66,000 miles an hour. This is the sort of speed that we have to think about. The 600 miles an hour of a jet plane is a mere crawl in comparison, and the contrast is even greater when we realize that no force is needed to drive the earth round the sun. The earth is in the natural state of "free fall", which means exactly what it says. The earth is falling all the time towards the sun, but its rapid motion provides a centrifugal force which exactly balances the attraction of the sun. In this respect the earth (or any other object in space) behaves like a stone which is being whirled on the end of a string, the force of tension in the string preventing the stone from flying off at a tangent. Although in this simple case the stone moves in a circle, the same principle holds in space whatever the shape of the orbit in which the object moves. No driving power is necessary; the difficulty is simply one of getting the right conditions at the start, which means getting the right speed at the right place and at the right time. This may be achieved by firing a projectile from a gun, in which case the speed with which the shell leaves the muzzle is the speed that matters.

Jules Verne used this idea in his *Voyage from the Earth to the Moon*. A giant projectile containing a crew was fired in the right direction, and at the right speed and time, so as to circle the moon and return to the earth. But no instruments, and certainly no human beings, could possibly survive the tremendous shock of the explosion which discharged the shell from its giant gun. The speed must clearly be built up more slowly, but at the same time the need for economy in fuel makes it essential that the acceleration be high. This is the basis of the present ideas, in which the speed is built up from a standing start by means of rockets, the rapid acceleration acting only for a short period of time. From that moment, many miles above the earth's surface, the rocket is in a state of free fall, the nature of its path being controlled entirely by its speed and the angle at which it is moving, and no further driving force is necessary until such time as it is necessary to change course. It is rather interesting to remember that in our mechanics lessons at school we were taught that the path of a bullet (or of a stone thrown into the air) is a parabola. This is another erroneous idea, based in this case on the assumption that the surface of the earth is flat. This is good enough for short distances; but in longer flights the earth must be treated as a sphere, and the path is then seen to be an ellipse, one focus of which is at the centre of attraction, which is the centre of the earth.

In all the experiments which have so far been carried out, the speed is only sufficient to force the rocket into quite a small ellipse, which meets the earth's surface again after a few hundred miles. A greater velocity will allow the rocket to travel farther, and if it is great enough it would enable the rocket to circle right round the earth to return to its firing point. Increase the speed still more, and the ellipse becomes big enough to reach to the moon, but the rocket will still return to its starting point if its motion is not disturbed in any way. In such orbits as this the centre of attraction lies at the centre of the earth, but exactly the same arguments apply to orbits about the sun. The shape and size of an orbit of this kind, in which a space ship would have to travel to reach the other planets, is still controlled only by the original speed and the angle at which the ship sets out on its journey. A space ship cannot travel in a straight line, whether it is driven or not. There are no straight lines in space.

At the present time the round-the-world orbits naturally attract most attention, and of these the most important are the circular ones, in which a rocket would revolve for ever about the earth in a period which depends on the distance from the earth's centre. At 1,075 miles from the surface (5,040 miles from the centre) the time for one revolution would be just two hours, while at 22,000 miles above the surface, the period of revolution would be twenty-four hours. In order to enter such an orbit, the rocket would have to be fired from a point in the orbit itself, or else, if fired from the earth, would have to change course when it reached the right height. The point is of great importance in planning the creation of an artificial satellite of the earth—for this is just what a rocket of this type would become. The difficulties of making a severe change of course would be very great and would call for a considerable consumption of fuel; the most economical procedure is to arrange that the rocket reach the required distance at the top of its flight, and that it should then be travelling in the right direction. The rocket would need to be fired horizontally with exactly the right amount of power to give it the calculated velocity. Its path would take it half-way round the world, its most distant point (say 22,000 miles above the surface for the twenty-four-hour orbit) being on the opposite side of the earth from its firing point. Having reached the required distance, a short burst of power would then give it sufficient extra speed to maintain it for ever in the satellite orbit. Unfortunately this idea is quite impracticable, because it entails far too long a journey through the earth's atmosphere. A rocket is more efficient in a vacuum, and the sooner it gets out of the dense air near the earth's surface the better, quite apart from the extra friction to its motion which the air provides. Moreover, for reasons of economy it is best to give the rocket a short sharp burst of power, giving it a high acceleration for a short period. It is for this reason that we have to adjust our ideas to think of a rocket firing for only a short period of a minute or so, rising vertically to a height many miles above the earth, and then turning over into its proper orbit.

This behaviour of modern rockets was first exploited by the Germans. In the years after 1929 the German Society for Spaceship Travel (*Verein für Raumschiffahrt*) had made great strides in the design of small rockets, and the impetus given by World War II brought this research to a tremendous climax in the bombardment of south-eastern England by V-2 rockets. Those of us who lived in that area in those days have our own thoughts about the V-2, but the fact remains that it was a remarkable technical achievement. Weighing about 12 tons, it could carry a ton of instruments (or explosives) to a height of over a hundred miles, reaching speeds of the order of 3,500 miles an hour. It is not a cheap rocket, but it has certainly set the pace for future research. Many experiments have been conducted by the U.S. Army and Navy technicians with this rocket and with others of even better performance, and reports of similar work behind the Iron Curtain sometimes reach us. It is one of the outstanding features of the modern interest in this subject that so many governments, Universities, engineering firms and Rocket Societies should all be working to the same end: the perfection of the rocket. Naturally, the utmost secrecy is preserved, but details of the larger rockets are occasionally published, particularly in the United States.

Of these, the Viking seems to have been one of the most successful. The Viking No. 4, which in 1950 reached a height of 105 miles, was 45 feet long, 32 inches in diameter, and weighed about 5 tons. A later model, the Viking No. 7, had modified dimensions and an improved performance, and reached a height of 135 miles, which is believed to be a record for a single rocket. It is interesting to notice that the firing time for the Viking is about 75 seconds, at the end of which period the rocket has reached a height of 30 miles and is travelling at more than 4,000 miles an hour. The greatest height so far reached—and this is a measure of how far man has poked his nose into space—is 250 miles, achieved by a U.S. Army WAC Corporal rocket fitted to the nose of a V-2 on February 24th, 1949. The mere cataloguing of such figures gives no idea of the vast amount of information that is gained by such experiments, or of the very considerable ingenuity which has been exercised in fitting the rockets for their long flights. The payload on such flights consists of instruments which are used to record the performance of the rocket and to make scientific measurements of the upper atmosphere. Since the chance of recovering the complete set of instruments at the end of the flight is somewhat remote, the details are radioed back to earth continuously, transmissions being made on a large number of wavelengths.

The actual payload that can be carried by even a large rocket is very small, in comparison with the total weight, and it appears that the ratio of payload to total weight becomes even smaller with extremely high velocities. Thus we are told that a rocket using present-day chemical fuels could carry a payload of a hundred pounds to the satellite orbit in a rocket weighing 25 tons; but a very much larger rocket would be needed to take the same payload out into interplanetary space. The greater part of this total weight is due to the enormous amounts of fuel that have to be carried, but the performance can be improved by making use of the step principle. In this design the rocket is made in steps, each of which is employed merely as a boost for the steps in front of it, and is dropped away as soon as its fuel is exhausted. The combination of a V-2 and the WAC Corporal which reached 250 miles was a two-stage rocket of this kind. Among the many designs for a manned rocket to reach outer space, that of von Braun may be mentioned as being exceptionally detailed and carefully planned. A three-stage rocket is planned to take a crew out to the two-hour orbit. The payload amounts to 36 tons, while the rocket weighs 7,000 tons, of which over 6,000 tons are accounted for by fuel alone. Each stage as it uses its fuel supply becomes detached and is parachuted back to earth, to be used again in further flights. This ambitious scheme is stated to be well within the capabilities of modern engineers.

It is almost certainly a practicable proposition to send an unmanned multi-stage rocket to circumnavigate the moon and return to the earth, but opinion seems to have hardened to the view that no such rocket could carry a crew of human beings to the moon using the present chemical fuels. Such a moon rocket would weigh many thousands of tons, and most of this load would be fuel which would be expended in the difficult manoeuvres of rising through the earth's atmosphere, and of retarding the rocket on its return. This consideration has led to designs of a more efficient method of supplying the ship with fuel. The proposal is to refuel the rocket ship *en route*, and although this sounds difficult it obviously has many advantages. Instead of an attempt being made to lift a 20,000 ton rocket from the earth in one stage, three rockets of 7,000 tons would go up to the satellite orbit, where one of them would be refuelled from the others and proceed on its way. In this way it would even be possible to arrange for trips to Mars making use of modern fuels, and von Braun has given particulars of an exploration of that planet, allowing 100 men to stay for a year. The amount of fuel consumed on such a trip, however, is quite fantastic, and it is very obvious that something better than chemical fuels is necessary before interplanetary travel can become a workable proposition.

It is for this reason that modern interest in the subject has become concentrated on the more simple schemes for building a satellite vehicle. In its simplest form this will consist of a rocket carrying instruments which can be made to find its way automatically into one of the various satellite orbits. This robot vehicle would be used to make scientific measurements and to radio the results to earth, although how its inventors propose to service the thing if it goes wrong is not explained. In fact throughout the plans that are presented to us, it seems to be assumed that nothing ever will go wrong! But a rocket of this kind would be merely a first step to building a larger satellite vehicle, in which a crew of human beings could give all the necessary maintenance as well as make the observations. From the many schemes that have been put forward for the construction of such a space station, we may select once more that of von Braun, who visualizes a hollow ring, 250 feet in diameter, revolving about the earth in the two-hour orbit. The space station will be built in space, the parts for its construction forming the major part of the payload of numerous three-stage rockets that will bring the material up to the orbit. Once in that orbit, the material will be thrown into space, where it will continue to float alongside the rocket. The crew, clad in suitable space suits, will then assemble the parts and eventually take possession of their new home.

Not a very comfortable home by any standard! However well it may be air-conditioned and thermostatically controlled, the absence of gravity must be a source of confusion and difficulty. The station will be in a state of free fall; and its crew, sharing in its motion of nearly 16,000 miles an hour, will have no sensation of weight whatever. This is only one of the difficulties which the first explorers of space will have to face, but it is useless to argue about such things to the real enthusiast of space travel. To him, the advantages to be gained are far more important, and it is rather curious that many of the advantages that are given are not of a kind that will arouse enthusiasm in others. Thus we are assured that a powerful telescope on such a space station will reveal everything that is happening on earth, no part of the globe being able to escape its searching eye. There is a familiar ring about these words: did we not hear something similar in connexion with enemy bombers during the war? The argument in this case is just as speculative, for what is implied is, of course, that concentrations of troops and shipping could not hope to escape observation. That is, presumably, a matter of opinion, but it is indeed significant that the space station already wears a military aspect. Even the orbit in which von Braun's space station travels is designed for this same purpose: for it carries the vehicle along a north-south line, so that as it revolves every two hours, and the earth turns beneath it, every part of the surface will be visible in turn.

Out of the infinite number of orbits that are available, this one seems to have been chosen for this particular purpose. For purely scientific purposes, almost any of the others would be better. It is true that such an orbit, carrying the space station above the poles, would be able to collect invaluable information about the movements of cloud masses. Thus meteorology would gain enormously and it might even be possible to make accurate forecasts of weather in such countries as England, where the word *climate* has no real meaning. But the more important orbits will be those that lie in or near the plane of the earth's equator. Space stations in such orbits could be used to relay radio and television programmes, the whole of the inhabited earth being completely covered by three such transmitters. If, in the more distant future, it should be necessary to use space stations as landing stages or refuelling points for the interplanetary space ships, then these would need to revolve in orbits that lie close to the plane of the earth's orbit. The picture that presents itself is one of a sky full of space stations, moving with incredible speeds in different directions in a series of interlaced orbits. But this is an unnecessarily alarmist view, for not one of these objects would be visible to the naked eye and even a powerful telescope would find it difficult to spot one and keep it in the field of view. The sky, thank goodness, would still be blue.

The advantages that will acrue to science from observations made in a space station are very obvious. The earth's atmosphere is of great benefit to mankind, but it interferes badly with astronomical observations and it filters out many parts of the sun's radiation which we should like to study. Out in space these difficulties would be removed, and it would then be possible to measure in great detail the ultra-violet and X-ray portions of the solar spectrum and to study cosmic rays; while the over-all improvements in astronomical research might well be outstanding. Since all objects in free fall are weightless, it would be possible to construct enormous telescopes with very light material, not as part of a space station, but floating alone in space, and controlled by radio from a space station at some distance. Yet the very fact that empty space offers so many advantages to the scientist is more than compensated by the perils that will await the first space travellers. There is a fine optimism in all the literature of this subject; and although this is a very worthy gesture, there is no excuse for treating these matters lightly. The fact remains that we have no idea whatever of the real dangers that abound in space. We are protected on this earth, since the atmosphere shields us from the harmful effects of meteors, cosmic rays and the more dangerous of the sun's radiations; while we have no knowledge at all of how to deal with the perfect vacuum of space or with the unshielded light and heat of the sun.

The weakness in all these plans for space travel is the human element. We simply do not know how man will react to space conditions. Adaptable as he is, can he exist for any length of time under conditions of no-gravity? We have seen photographs of mice which formed part of the payload of a high-altitude rocket, and which for a few brief seconds were suspended in the nose of the rocket in free fall. The mice "seemed to be quite happy", but how would they have behaved if they had been under the same conditions for days on end? These experiments give no idea at all of the effect of such conditions on a human being, whose sense of balance and of up-and-down is maintained by the delicately adjusted mechanism of the inner ear. We are assured by the medical experts that no great dangers are to be expected, but to be on the safe side most of the plans for space stations make some provision for the addition of a form of artificial gravity. This may be simply the use of magnetized boots (as in the film, *Destination Moon*), but more generally a slow rotation of the whole ship is proposed. The centrifugal force which this would cause, although much smaller than the force of gravity to which man is accustomed on the surface of the earth, would at least give some sense of up-and-down, even if "up" means towards the centre of the ship, and "down" means towards the outside. At the centre itself there would still be no gravity, but in the outer parts of the ship some feeling of weight would be apparent; and it is for this reason that the space station is designed as a hollow ring.

This design clearly overcomes the difficulties which writers of science fiction have made familiar—the awkward drifting along the corridors, the necessity of drinking liquids through a straw, the senseless floating of any object that is not fastened down, and the unhappy consequences of any sudden involuntary movement. With some measure of weight, these unnatural tendencies are lessened, and even the unhappy victim of an involuntary sneeze may be able to prevent himself from crashing backwards against a bulkhead. But it must not be imagined that these perils of the future are being studied only from the theoretical point of view. The practical study

of the problems that arise in all forms of rocket flight and of exposure
to the unusual conditions of outer space already forms part of the
programme of the U.S. Air Force School of Aviation Medicine.
Here, for example, in the Department of Space Medicine, the
reactions of the human body to the conditions of rapid acceleration
that will exist in the first stages of rocket flight can be studied by
simulating these conditions in an enormous centrifuge. Seated in a
rapidly whirling gondola, a volunteer is subjected to forces which
range up to many times that of gravity, while his pulse, muscular
reactions, rate of breathing and other factors are measured, and
photographs taken during the experiment. In this way it has been
shown that a subject who is in every way physically fit can endure
forces several times that of gravity without ill effects. At five times
the acceleration of gravity, breathing becomes difficult and after a
few seconds the subject loses consciousness if sitting upright. When
lying down, the body is better able to endure these conditions, and
selected individuals are recorded as having suffered forces up to
more than ten times gravity for two or three minutes in this position.
These experiments are usually conducted with constant forces, but
in a multi-stage rocket the accelerations will always be of a rapidly
increasing type, and they will be repeated as each stage drops away.
Thus one cannot avoid the conclusion that the prospects at the
moment for any ordinary person to indulge in space travel are
rather remote. It looks as though only the fittest will survive.

Unfortunately it is not yet possible to imitate conditions of no-
gravity in laboratory experiments, yet it is known that pilots have
flown at such speeds that for a short time they must have been in a
state of free fall. Thus the U.S. Navy's Douglas *Skyrocket*, which is
a rocket aircraft launched from a B-29, has flown at heights of over
80,000 feet and at speeds in excess of 1,300 miles an hour; and it is
reasonable to assume that for some portion of its flight at maximum
speed the pilot was subjected to all the conditions of free fall. In this
way, therefore, it may be possible to accumulate sufficient data to
assist in future experiments. Meanwhile every possible method is
being used to explore the upper atmosphere, about which we know
practically nothing. At a height of over 15 miles, the pilot of the
Skyrocket had 98 per cent. of the earth's atmosphere beneath his
feet, but the high-altitude rockets can go right outside the atmosphere, and their instruments have already recorded radiations
which never reach the earth's surface. Of these, the shorter wave-
lengths of sunlight (ultra-violet and X-ray) and cosmic rays are of
the utmost importance because of their effects on the human body.
The atmosphere is sufficiently dense to filter out most of these
radiations, yet the effect of prolonged exposure of the skin to sunlight is well known. Sun-bathing enthusiasts will think only of its
beneficial effects; but it is generally agreed that, in the absence of a

modifying atmosphere, these short-wave radiations will be definitely harmful, and some form of protection will be necessary. This will probably take the form of special glasses to protect the eyes, the normal clothing (or perhaps a space suit) protecting the rest of the body. Even the windows of a space station would need to be glazed with special glass, although this does raise the question as to whether windows are desirable in this vehicle. Considering that it will be rotating once every half-minute or so, and revolving about the earth every two hours, the view of the sky obtained from the window would be somewhat confusing, even if one could bear the terrible contrast of unmitigated sunshine and bright starlight against the black sky. It seems strange to consider that the crew of this vessel, floating in what must surely be the most wonderful view imaginable, may have to spend their lives entirely in artificial light.

Far more serious problems than these will confront the space traveller. Within the space station itself, air-conditioning and temperature control will at least make life bearable, but every bit of that air will have to be carried up from the earth below, together with food, water and every other necessity of life. Plans have been made for the recovery of water, the disposal of waste, and the continual purification of the air supply; but however carefully these plans are made, replenishments will obviously be necessary. Thus the actual building of the space station is not enough. Once the station has been erected it must be possible to send up a continuous supply of stores, and such a ferry service must be planned parallel with the main scheme for building the station. Its power supply will already be available in the heat of the sun, which can be concentrated by means of reflectors on to tubes containing mercury. The boiling mercury can be used in its turn to generate power for lighting, heating, cooking, radio and other electrical machinery. The mercury vapour can be condensed (and other forms of refrigeration applied) on the shady side of the ship, where, away from the sun's rays, the temperature will be extremely low. This contrast of temperatures will set many problems to the designers of the space station, but these are not incapable of solution. A more troublesome difficulty is likely to be in the design of a suitable space suit in which members of the crew can venture out into space to undertake repairs, or, in the first place, to build the space station itself. The temperature and humidity inside such a garment are matters of supreme importance; and even when these factors are controlled, the first user of a space suit will need to be a very brave man. To hang suspended and virtually helpless in space may well be a terrifying experience. If a sudden movement inside a rocket in free fall is liable to be dangerous, what will happen out there in space? What will happen to the man in space who starts to drive home a rivet, or tighten a nut with a heavy spanner? The answer is clearly that new

methods of construction will have to be devised, new engineering
techniques developed, and a complete drill of space-movements
planned for the crew. Even the small jet pistol which, in the illustrations, is used by the space-man to propel himself backwards, may
only be used in a definite manner. A slight error in the angle at
which the jet is pointed would clearly result in the unfortunate
individual's spinning over and over, instead of moving backwards
through space.

These trips in a space suit form one of the standard topics of the
writers of space fiction, and although in theory we know how to
make things air-tight, the absolute vacuum of outer space is something entirely outside our experience. The best vacuum that we have
ever made on earth is far from being the perfect vacuum of space,
and the last traces of gas can only be removed from small sealed
vessels, such as TV tubes, X-ray bulbs and the like, by chemical
means. The purely engineering problem of maintaining a good
vacuum in a large piece of apparatus is always troublesome, and it is
quite surprising how many leaks can develop in the most awkward
places. In the 250-foot space station, which is much larger than any
vessel that has yet been evacuated, there will be the additional
necessity of preserving every trace of the air that has been brought
so laboriously from the earth. In one design the station is made of
plastic materials, which can be inflated with air to form a number of
separate sections, each complete in itself. A thin metal hull would
hold the whole structure together, for no great strength is needed
where there is no weight. Even so, the possibility of leakage must be
faced, and the most obvious cause of such leaks would be the possible
penetration of the structure by meteors.

The word *meteor* is often used as though it were a synonym for a
shooting star, but it means rather more than this. A shooting star
is certainly a meteor, but only the larger and brighter ones are
visible to the eye, while in daylight hours or under cloudy conditions
no shooting stars are seen, although meteors are falling all the time.
It is estimated that in twenty-four hours, many thousands of millions
of meteors fall on the earth. They consist simply of small grains of
dust which are travelling in paths about the sun, and which therefore have speeds which are comparable with those of the planets.
If these dust particles come sufficiently close to the earth they are
attracted and forced into a new orbit about the earth. If this orbit
happens to cut through the atmosphere, the resistance to the motion
of the particle is great enough to convert its energy into heat, and
all but the largest stones become completely vaporized. The
luminous track of the hot gases gives the appearance known as a
shooting star, and such tracks are formed fifty to eighty miles above
the surface of the earth. Evidently the very thin air above that
height is quite sufficient to destroy these particles; but in outer space

there will be no such protection, and these meteors become a really formidable problem. Travelling at speeds up to twenty-five miles a second, and in all directions, meteors may meet the space station with speeds varying from six miles a second if they overtake, to more than forty miles a second if the collision is head-on. At such speeds even a grain of sand can penetrate armour plate.

In recent years there has been a great revival of interest in the study of meteors, and with radar methods it is possible to measure their characteristics in daylight hours or through thick cloud, and even to detect those which are much too faint to leave a track visible to the naked eye. Improvements in optics have also made a useful contribution, and the Harvard Meteor Programme makes considerable use of highly efficient Schmidt cameras in the photography of meteors, from which it is hoped to obtain a better understanding of the meteorology of the upper atmosphere. As a result of such research it has become clear that the meteors which intercept the earth are essentially a part of the solar system, the grains of dust travelling about the sun like miniature planets. Most of these orbits are small ones, which suggests that the number of meteors would increase as we travel towards the sun; but as we can only detect the meteors which happen to cut the earth's annual path round the sun, we have no knowledge whatever of the meteors in other parts of the solar system: we can only assume that space is filled with these wandering grains of dust. For the most part these grains maintain an individual existence; but quite a number of swarms of meteors are known, and these are, in some cases, known to be travelling in orbits which are practically identical with those of known comets. Presumably these swarms consist of the debris of worn-out comets, but it does not follow that all meteors have arisen in the same way. When such a swarm encounters the earth the number of shooting stars increases enormously, and on occasions can only be described as meteor storms when the shooting stars seem to fall as thick as snow-flakes.

Such conditions offer a further hazard to the space traveller, although statistical investigations show that the probability of a space station (or of a space ship) being hit by a meteor is very small. But the danger is a very real one, and is being taken quite seriously by the designers. One of the simplest forms of protection, suggested by Whipple, the Harvard meteor authority, is to provide a meteor bumper, which is simply a false metal skin to the space station. A meteor which penetrates this sheet of metal would have so much of its energy destroyed that it would be unlikely to penetrate the actual body of the ship itself. Nevertheless, it has been thought necessary to design further methods for detecting and sealing small leaks; and however feasible these may be, it is important to remember that they deal only with *small* leaks. The chance of collision with a larger body is quite small, but large stones have been known to fall to the earth, having passed right through the atmosphere without being destroyed. Such stones, generally called meteorites, may even weigh many tons, and are known to have caused great damage in the course of their fall, but there is no apparent correlation between these bodies and the known meteor swarms. The space traveller would have no warning of their approach and could take no evasive action. The radar methods which are used to detect meteors on earth, make use of the fact that the luminous track of a meteor will reflect radio waves; in space there would be no such track, and the speed of approach of such a large body would make radar methods useless. This is just another risk that will have to be taken.

At the other end of the scale of sizes come cosmic rays, presenting a danger about which we know very little. These atomic nuclei, coming from somewhere in outer space, have very small mass, but their speeds are many thousands of times as great as those of meteors —almost as great as that of light. These cosmic rays are absorbed for the most part in the upper atmosphere, but their bombardment of the atoms of the gases of the air gives rise to secondary radiations, some of which are capable of penetrating deeply into solid objects. Since every collision gives rise to further radiations, there is a cascade effect, and no method of protection from cosmic rays appears to be possible. We know something of the effects of the radiation-sickness which is suffered by human beings exposed to radioactive materials, but nothing is known of the physiological effects of cosmic rays. It is agreed that exposure to these rays for short periods is not likely to be harmful, but the effect is probably cumulative, while the space traveller will be subject to the full effect of the primary cosmic rays which will easily penetrate the thin walls of the space station. Intense research on this subject is going on in every country in the world, but it seems likely that the most useful results will be obtained from measurements made by high-altitude rockets of the cosmic radiation in outer space.

Taking one thing with another, it looks as though life in a space station will be something of a hazardous undertaking. Whatever advantages this vehicle may have, there must be some limit to the endurance of the men who form its crew; and from the scientific point of view there is every reason to look further afield for a better base from which to explore the universe. For this reason a good deal of thought has been given to the establishment of a colony on the moon. Here, with solid ground beneath their feet, with a respectable amount of gravity, and with traces of an atmosphere which, however thin by earthly standards, will at least form some protection against meteors, a team of scientists could live under much better conditions than those of a space station. The moon may be a waterless desert, and every item of food, air and water may still have to be carried there, but these are scarcely more than the normal difficulties of an exploring party on the earth—once we have solved the difficulty of getting there. Yet it is there, rather than in a satellite orbit, that the giant telescopes of the future will be built. On the slowly turning moon, where the stars are always visible in the dark sky, and the sun is hidden for a fortnight at a time, there will be adequate opportunity for studying the faintest galactic nebulae and of mapping in greater detail the surfaces of the planets which will be the goal of future expeditions. Such telescopes will be guided by servo-mechanisms, the principles of which are already known and used in some of our observatories today. The inhabitants of the lunar base may well find the use of some of the smaller instruments rather difficult, since all observations in the open will have to be done while wearing a space suit. Under these conditions even a theodolite would be a troublesome thing to use, but these are minor technical difficulties which will, no doubt, be readily overcome. The survey of the moon's surface will be a matter of intense interest to astronomers and geologists. Are the craters really volcanic, or were they caused by the impact of meteors? Are the level plains really solidified lava, or are they just dust bowls, the level surface disguising a great depth of fine dust which will be a trap for man and machine? These and a thousand other questions are waiting for an answer; new problems in science will present themselves with the study of the moon's geological structure and its magnetic field. There will be a new set of scientific terms to be learned—clearly the word "geology" will be the first to be replaced! Perhaps we may find some further clues to the age-old mystery of the formation of the solar system.

The exploration of the moon seems to set an upper limit to the detailed plans of the present day; and although we are assured that man could send an expedition there within the next twenty-five years, it seems more likely that any such exploration of space must await the arrival of more economical sources of energy. The general principles of such trips, in which the space ship is in a state of free fall, are well understood. For the trip to the moon, for example, the space ship will take aboard its passengers and fuel while it is moored alongside the satellite vehicle. In the two-hour orbit, this will have a speed of 15,840 miles an hour, and a short burst of power at the right moment will give it a speed of 22,100 miles an hour, which is sufficient to carry it to the moon. Only a slight increase in this speed will take the ship on a longer path to the planets, and these paths will need to be tangential to the earth's orbit at one end, and to the planet's orbit at the other. Thus the time required for the journey is just one-half of the period of a body revolving about the sun in such a tangential ellipse. In the case of a trip to Mars, for example, the ship will set off with a speed of 74,000 miles an hour in the direction of the earth's motion round the sun. Of this speed, the earth's motion contributes nearly 67,000 miles an hour, and the satellite vehicle adds a further quota; yet it is still necessary for the space ship to get away from the attraction of the earth, and such figures do not give a complete picture of the amount of energy that is necessary to give the ship sufficient speed. But this problem of designing suitable paths for interplanetary travel is a fascinating one, and it has led to a spate of papers on the subject, most of them based on these elementary ideas. Such articles, however plentifully they may be sprinkled with differential equations, do little more than give a general picture of certain orbits in space. The problem is not a static one. It is a dynamic problem of great complexity, and as yet there is no simple solution to the very difficult task of forecasting the initial speed and direction of a ship, taking into account the attractions of all the other planets. All that has been done is to suggest suitable conditions under which a ship in free fall could pass (at certain rare intervals) from the earth to another planet. It is rather like the problem of calculating the shortest route for sailing from New York to Liverpool. Nobody would doubt the accuracy of the answer, but no ship would (or could) ever follow that route. In the same way the space ships of the future will set off at almost any time, and find their way to their destination, not by following a free-fall path, but by choosing a suitable path which is corrected as necessary on instructions from the navigator.

It follows that if fuel is to be used in changing course in this way, the ultimate solution is to use fuel all the time, and although this is out of the question at the present time, it seems likely that the release of atomic energy will supply the answer. Of the various schemes that have been suggested the simplest would appear to be that of Spitzer, in which charged particles of suitable gases are electrically accelerated to give the high exhaust velocities which are required. The method would require only moderate voltages, and quite small thrusts would be produced; this, however is a matter of small importance, for with a constant drive of this kind the acceleration required in space need only be very small. Thus we can imagine the great ship moving off quite slowly, so that it travels only six inches in the first second. This represents a very small acceleration (that of gravity on the earth is thirty-two times as great), yet the ship will have covered 1,220 miles at the end of an hour, and will then be moving at 2,450 miles an hour. If the same driving force is maintained, the speed at the end of twenty-four hours will be 59,000 miles an hour, and the ship will then be 700,000 miles from its starting point. These figures assume a standing start, but in fact the ship will always begin its journey from the satellite orbit, and will have a considerable initial speed. Thus it is possible to think of trips to the moon in four hours, and to Mars in a week or two.

The simplicity of this method is most attractive, and much smaller accelerations than this would give all the speeds necessary. They would also remove the embarrassments of no-gravity, since even the smallest continuous acceleration would give the sensation of weight. It would no longer be necessary to rotate the ship and, it might even be possible to dispense with those magnetic boots. If the ship is to start from a space station it will still be necessary to use rocket ships and efficient chemical fuels to climb up from the earth's surface. Even this expedient may in time be avoided, for, with the coming of cheap atomic power, it should prove possible to use high-velocity gases to propel the ship from the earth's surface with quite small accelerations. This is clearly the ultimate goal at which space travel must aim, for the convenience and comfort of passengers and crew must always be an important incentive to progress. Man is so adaptable to his surroundings that we may accept this estimate of the ordeal before him, and of the way in which it will be overcome, with some confidence. Yet there remain many problems which most writers gloss over as if they were of no importance. Foremost among these must be reckoned the psychological effect upon the crew of their sense of utter isolation. The earth will be merely a bright star in the dark sky, remote and inaccessible; and, in the space ship, no night or day, no changes of any kind will break the monotony of a sense of detachment from the rest of the living universe.

It is taken for granted in many books that the navigator of a space ship will always know how fast he is travelling, and in what direction. But how is he to know these things? We on this earth are travelling on an enormous space ship, but the methods of determining its speed and which way it is going are by no means simple, and there is no possible way of reading the answer from a dial. It will be just the same for the navigator; he will have no sense of movement whatever, and no nearby objects to mark his progress. It is true that at moderate distances from the earth (or some other planet) he will be able to use radar methods, but these do not promise to give results of the required accuracy.

Constant and accurate navigation would seem to be the only solution to this difficulty, but space navigation is no easy matter. On earth, observations of the stars are referred to the horizon, and two such observations will fix one's position on the earth's surface. If no horizon is available, a comparable reference line may be used— a plumb-line or the bubble of a bubble sextant. But out in space there is no gravity, no up or down, no plumb-line, no bubble. Move as we may about the solar system, the fixed stars remain in the same relative positions, and the only objects that can provide any means of fixing our position are the sun and the planets. Simultaneous observations of three of these will give us some idea of our position, but the errors are likely to be considerable. This is not the place to discuss these difficulties; but it must be said that the navigation methods which have so far been suggested are all too crude or too laborious for use, mainly because they have been based on the methods that are useful on earth. If we get right away from these ideas, it is not difficult to find other approaches to the problem. Thus, in the neighbourhood of the earth, radar methods will give us the distance from the earth and from the moon. It is not an easy proposition, but U.S. Army engineers have already shown that radar signals can be detected from the moon's surface. It would be even more simple to measure these distances by just measuring the apparent angular diameters of the earth and moon, the ordinary accuracy of a sextant being quite good enough for the purpose.

Following this idea to its logical conclusion, it could be used for navigation in any part of the solar system. The sun instead of the earth would be used; the ship's distance would be found by measuring the apparent diameter of the sun. This would be done, of course, by photography, so that an accurate measurement could be carried out on the plate. The longitude and latitude of the sun (and therefore of the ship) would be obtained by measuring the position of the sun among the stars on the plate. The difficulty of photographing sun and stars simultaneously is quite possible of solution; there is already at the U.S. Naval Observatory a type of moon camera which takes such photographs of the moon and surrounding stars for the purpose of measuring accurately the moon's position. The brilliance of the moon's image is reduced by means of suitable filters, and the same method could be used for the sun. The distance of the ship from the sun, together with its latitude and longitude, fix its position in space; and this simple method offers a solution when we are travelling near enough to the sun. The problem takes on another aspect altogether, however, if we venture out as far as Jupiter (five times as far away as the earth), where the sun is reduced to a small bright disk, and the planets are too near the sun to be useful to the navigator. The farther out into space the ship goes, the more difficult become the problems of navigation; and the whole subject is in need of serious study.

Another form of trouble arises when the navigator, having found his position, needs to correct his course. It is too often assumed that a space ship that is sent off in the right direction and with the right speed will reach its destination without fail; and although this is true, it is not always appreciated that the course followed by the ship is extraordinarily sensitive to errors in the initial direction and speed. It must also be remembered that every planet in the solar system will have some effect on the travelling space ship, and these effects, constantly varying in force and direction, can build up to an astonishing extent. It has been suggested that all these effects can be allowed for at the start, the elaborate calculations being worked on electronic machines either before the journey begins or, more optimistically, during the actual flight if the ship is suitably equipped. Yet no such calculations are of any value if the conditions are wrong at the start. To take a simple example, the initial speed required for a projectile to reach the moon (240,000 miles away) from the earth's surface may be taken as 6·92 miles per second. If this is increased to 6·95—a change of only a thirtieth of a mile per second—the projectile will go on for ever into space and will not return. The case is probably not important; clearly if the ship comes near enough to the moon, it can make use of the moon's gravitational force and can make a safe landing. The case becomes much worse if the trip is to Mars or some more distant planet. Here the starting conditions must be controlled with considerable accuracy, the speed within a thousandth of a mile per second, and the direction of take-off to about a three-hundredth of a degree, if the ship is to come within 50,000 miles of Mars in a free-fall orbit. These are impossible conditions, and the first few seconds of flight of the ship will be the most important of the whole trip. A trained and experienced crew would be able to extricate their ship from a difficult situation, but one is left to wonder how these matters would be dealt with in the unmanned ship which we are assured will first be sent to blaze the trail.

Even if the space ship is manned, the task of changing course will not be easy. There are no straight lines in space—the motion of the ship, whether fast or slow, in free fall or driven, is always a curve. At any point on that curve, the ship will have a speed controlled only by the distance of the ship from the sun and the shape and size of the curve. If we picture two ships travelling in the same orbit, one behind the other, it will be impossible for the ship at the rear to catch up with the one in front *and remain in the same orbit* simply by increasing speed. The effect will be to throw it into a larger orbit, a different curve altogether. The amount of manoeuvring that will be necessary to pass from one point to another is quite astonishing in its complexities. This is not a case of steering right or left, up or down. A space ship, like any other planetary body, behaves like a gyroscope, whose axis will never move in the direction in which it is pushed; but some means or other will have to be found to apply the right forces in the right direction for the right length of time. And first of all some method is needed of fixing quite accurately the direction in which the ship is moving in space. When fuel and energy become plentiful, these problems will cease to be serious, and it will be possible to steer the ship like a liner, to set out at will at any time and to reach the distant planet without fail. But those days are not yet. For the moment we are just paddling on the edge of the unknown sea, and our plans are rather too full of the dangers behind us; there are others ahead.

We are told that the country which first builds a space station will have an overwhelming advantage over all others. The space station is a vantage point, an observation platform, from which every part of the world can be surveyed in the course of a few hours. Nothing can be hidden, no warlike preparations can go undetected —and the speeding platform is itself an ideal place from which to fire guided missiles that can conquer the world. This may be true, but we have heard it all before. There have always been nations that have invented unbeatable weapons, but we are still here. No weapon that the mind of man has conceived has really proved unbeatable—there is nothing that the mind of man can invent that the mind of man cannot counter. And the extreme vulnerability of a space station, and its need for constant supplies, will not be lost on the other inhabitants of the planet.

Here, perhaps, lies the greatest danger. Man's knowledge of science has long outstripped his common sense. We live in a world which is willing to spend millions on atomic bombs and precious little on the development of science. Atomic power is ours for the asking—abundant energy to drive all the world's machinery, to drive man if need be to the distant planets. Yet our time is wasted, and our minds are occupied, with the hydrogen bomb. Will there be no end to it? One is left with the uneasy feeling that the first space ship to land on Mars will plant a flag in the name of this or that country, causing the whole silly business of interracial feuds to start again. Perhaps this is the philosophy of despair; science should rise above such things. Let us at least hope that before man is able to conquer space, he may be able to conquer his own weaknesses.

BOOKS SUGGESTED FOR FURTHER READING

C. Bonestell and W. Ley, *The Conquest of Space* (Sidgwick and Jackson, 1950).

A. C. Clarke, *Interplanetary Flight* (Temple Press, 1950).

A. C. Clarke, *The Exploration of Space* (Temple Press, 1951).

H. Haber, *Man in Space* (Sidgwick and Jackson, 1953).

W. Ley, *Rockets, Missiles and Space Travel* (Chapman and Hall, 1951).

C. Ryan (ed.), *Across the Space Frontier* (Sidgwick and Jackson, 1952).

PHYSICS AND THE ATOMIC AGE

by DR. HENRY SELIGMAN

DURING THE LAST twenty years, man has learned a lot about the origin of matter. Physicists have found ways of handling atoms. Although they are much too small to be seen with the finest microscope, we have learned to weigh atoms, to study their physical behaviour and even to transform them. We shall see how a few fundamental discoveries, followed by technological developments, have given us the Atomic Age. Some discoveries have only theoretical interest and the ordinary person never hears about them. Two important discoveries, in 1932 and 1939, however, had unforeseen consequences which will affect mankind, and to some extent have done so already.

In 1932 a particle was discovered which had a small mass and no electric charge—it was electrically neutral and therefore called neutron. Other particles had been discovered before, but whilst the other discoveries helped to clarify the origin of matter, this new particle was born under a lucky star. Seven years later, in 1939, one found that by taking this particle as ammunition and shooting it at the heaviest element known—uranium—something quite unexpected happened. The uranium decomposed in bits. Similar shooting at other atoms with this particle, or any other known particle, never had this result. Usually the particle got caught inside the atom and changed the target somehow, but always without splitting it, so this splitting of the atom was something quite new. Scientists had known for a long time that vast amounts of energy are held in the heart of atoms. By splitting the heart one had a chance of recovering some of this energy.

To understand the progress achieved, we shall first have to discuss the consistency of matter. Any material which we use in our daily life is of complex composition. We may compare it with a city made up of many houses (called molecules); each house consists of a number of rooms (called atoms); and each room is built by bricks (atomic nuclei). These atomic nuclei consist in the main of two different types of bricks, say red ones (protons), and white ones (neutrons). The red bricks, the protons, consist of mass and have in addition an electric charge; the white ones have no charge, they are electrically neutral. The number of charged particles, the red bricks (protons) in each nucleus, is an important figure. It tells us what element we have. If there are, say, 78 protons, we have platinum; 79 would give us gold; and 80, mercury. And in addition we have our white bricks, the neutrons. The more we have of these, the heavier our element becomes. Normal silver, for instance, consists of two types of atoms, some having 60 white bricks, others 62: the only difference is in their weight. We therefore say that silver consists of two isotopes. We see that we can thus change the number of neutrons at will, but the element will still remain the same element, it will only change its weight. The simplest atom we know is hydrogen which, in its natural state, consists of one proton only and has no neutrons at all. We can add some neutrons to this nucleus, thereby making it heavier, as, for example, in "heavy hydrogen". We see that what in former days the chemists used to do by fiddling about with molecules to make different molecules and thereby different materials, the physicists do now by playing about with the inside of the atom, thereby changing isotopes at will. In fact the dream of the alchemists has come true; we can make every element artificially, although to change appreciable amounts is usually very costly.

How can we get energy from atoms, or better, how can we get it from the nuclei? Well, energy from atoms we get every day. We burn coal or oil and transform the carbon atom, for example, into compounds of carbon dioxide, thereby releasing a certain amount of energy. How can we obtain energy when an atom is split? When the split occurs, then the two parts into which the uranium atom has decomposed together weigh slightly less than the original uranium atom, and this loss of mass is, as one learns from Einstein, equivalent to energy. Now it was only the question of finding the right conditions under which one could have continuous splitting of the uranium atoms in a given controllable system and at the same time extract the energy thus created. This did not prove to be too difficult; the first thing was to find the reaction which, once initiated, would repeat or sustain itself automatically—a chain reaction. Here we were again lucky. If a neutron hits a certain uranium atom, the uranium is split and at the same time two or three new neutrons are born. If an arrangement can be made whereby one of these two or three new neutrons would hit another uranium atom and cause that in turn to split, we should have such a chain reaction. The only thing which remains to do is to extract the created energy which occurs as heat. Assemblies which can do this were first developed during the war and are called piles, or more correctly, nuclear reactors.

Such nuclear reactors consist of uranium, which is the fuel, arranged in such a way that more than one of the newly created

neutrons are hitting a uranium atom. At the present time technicians, engineers and physicists are endeavouring to find the best
conditions for such nuclear reactors in order to obtain the maximum
amount of heat with the minimum amount of fuel and processing
cost. There are an enormous number of possibilities as to how a
reactor may be built, and one of the achievements of the next
decade will be to find a reasonably economical reactor which is
easy to maintain and operate. To understand why there are so
many possibilities we have to know a bit more about our fuel, the
uranium.

As we already know, most of the chemical elements like iron or
silver consist of a variety of different nuclei; they only differ in
their weight, they do not differ in their electric charge, which, as
we discussed, specifies the element. The silver which we use in our
everyday life is a mixture of two kinds of silver, roughly half
of which weigh two per cent. less than the other half. It may be
regarded as normal that the elements as we know them are such
mixtures, and only a very small proportion consist of the same kind
of nuclei. Natural uranium as we get it from our ores consists of
three such isotopes, which means that we have three different
uranium nuclei which differ only in their weight. The percentage of
one of them is, however, extremely small. The majority of uranium
has the weight 238, and under one per cent. consists of uranium-235.
Unfortunately, it is this uranium with the weight 235, and of which
we have less than one per cent. available, which has the property
of splitting so conveniently when hit by a slow neutron. One of the
tasks of recent years was to concentrate this very useful isotope by
separating it from the not-so-useful uranium-238. Engineers and
scientists had to use their ingenuity to effect such a separation on a
large scale; the main difficulties to be overcome were again of a
technological nature. One method of achieving this separation was
by using an enormous magnet. Uranium atoms would then be
accelerated within the magnet. It is obvious that the heavier the
object, the more difficulty it has in changing its straight path once
it is in motion. Therefore, by having the atom mixture accelerated
within the magnet, one can separate the two kinds of uranium atoms;
the uranium-235, being lighter than the uranium-238, will be more
easily deflected from its straight flight. But there are other methods
of doing the same thing. If one lets gases diffuse through small
holes, the lighter atoms will come first as they move faster. In this
case one had to synthesize a gaseous compound of our uranium
mixture and then use the diffusion process to separate the two
isotopes in question. This may sound easy, but in practice it turned
out to be one of the more difficult technical problems which had to
be solved. First, one had to find a reasonable gaseous compound,
and there is only a small selection in this case. The gas turned out

to be corrosive. In addition, each step brought very small enrichment and it was necessary to install more than a thousand such stages in order to get the pure uranium-235 one wanted. Today, the bigger countries have either pure uranium-235 or at least a mixture in which the uranium-235 has been enriched over its original natural occurrence.

From this we see that, during the last decade, the advances in pure physics are perhaps of less importance than the developments in technology. One still has to measure new nuclear data and has to acquaint oneself with the chemistry of relatively new substances, but the immediate questions to be answered are technological ones. For example, we must find a metal that will stand up to the terrific heat generated in an atomic reactor. We must find an efficient cooling system which can withstand the fabulous conditions of radiation which occur in such reactors. And all this without reducing the operating power or influencing too much the chain reaction which is the essence of the running of the machine.

To some extent these problems have been solved; the first real power plant using uranium as a fuel will be in operation very soon. This will be an orthodox power station. The only difference is that the part where normally the combustion of the coal or oil takes place will be replaced by an "atomic reactor" which is delivering the heat. Many more of these reactors will be built in the near future. In the United Kingdom alone we hope in twenty years' time to generate 40 per cent. of all our electricity by atomic power stations.

It is no wonder that all countries are so interested in this method of power generation. We must remember that, weight by weight, the right kind of uranium fuel will give ten million times more energy than a piece of coal.

There are also some disadvantages; the fuel used has to be processed from time to time in order to extract substances which are formed by the uranium "splitting" or fission process. If this were not done, these uranium-splitting products, or fission products as they are called, would, by their presence, dilute our original uranium. Some of them, and there are many dozens, would also hinder our chain reaction by eating too many of the neutrons which we need to keep our chain reaction going.

These chemical operations are rather awkward to perform. The uranium "fuel" and its created fission products, when withdrawn from an atomic reactor, are highly radioactive. This means radiation is being emitted and some of the radiation is very penetrating; it will penetrate, for example, a foot of concrete. Therefore all these chemical operations will have to be done behind thick lead or concrete walls with remote handling devices. Should anything go wrong in such a processing plant, it would be very difficult to put it right owing to the very damaging effect of these radiations.

When the processing is finished and we have separated the uranium from all the other substances, we are still left with the fission products. Being highly radioactive they cannot be thrown away, again for health reasons, so they have to be stored. Some of them will lose their activity fairly quickly, say within months; others, however, will be active for a very long time. In a later section we shall see that there may be, however, very good uses for these "long-lived fission products". But before using them, we should have to concentrate and perhaps separate them and put them into a solid form.

The first atomic power station may be compared to the first steam engine; in the year 2000, less than fifty years hence, such a plant will probably look very bulky and as outmoded as Stephenson's Rocket does beside the most modern of our railway engines. But however funny it may look, it will have produced the first nuclear energy at reasonable cost.

Let us see what different types of reactors we could build today. Before we can establish this we have to take account of another physical fact: the neutrons which are emitted from uranium when it splits have a high speed and a high energy, but the uranium-235, however, can capture one of these neutrons, in order to keep the chain reaction going, only if these neutrons are not of such high energy and are not moving too fast. After all, it is easier to catch a rabbit that is moving slowly, and this is exactly the same with atoms. But there are some substances which do not mind catching neutrons that move very fast. They have a special physical property which we can perhaps compare with traps set for rabbits. Therefore, when we use energetic fast neutrons or less energetic slow ones, scientists talk of fast and slow reactors, meaning that in the first case the neutrons need not be slowed down after they are born from uranium fission, whilst, in the other, one must have some device which reduces their speed. This reduction of speed is done by collisions, usually against other light nuclei. These atoms must be well-behaved, they must not be greedy and eat up neutrons which we still need for the chain reaction. There are very few substances which can be used for this slowing-down process. There is carbon in pure form, or water which, instead of the normal hydrogen, has the "heavy" hydrogen atom in its molecule. These substances are called moderators, as they are moderating the neutrons.

Fast reactors need no moderator. Such a power station would consist only of the fuel, the cooling material and the regulating mechanism for the reactor. There are quite a number of possibilities for building these reactors and the near future should give us at least one that is economical to run and does not have too many technical problems.

There is one amusing thing which should be mentioned. By cleverly arranging the building of a reactor, one can manage to have some of the kind of uranium which does not split so easily—the uranium-238—converted into the very useful plutonium, a new element which itself can split and give off energy. This may be compared to a furnace which burns coal, giving hot water, but at the same time produces wood from, say, some stones which are in the coal. Scientists have great hopes that in the future reactors can be built which will produce fuel while they burn, and even perhaps more fuel than the reactor consumes. This would again reduce the cost of power and make it even more economical.

So far we have spoken only of big atomic power stations. There is no doubt that such energy-generating systems can also be used as smaller units, although most likely less economically. One problem in the case of smaller reactors is the heavy shielding necessary against the radiations of the atomic power unit. If used for propulsion of an aeroplane, for example, the power unit would be very heavy and bulky. The same applies to motor cars. In addition there is also the much increased health hazard in case of accidents. One must never forget that even in a relatively small reactor of the kind described above, we have all the radiations of the fission products!

But we not only hope and believe that the future will bring streamlined power-generating units of the type described: we might also be able to build power stations of an entirely different type, without the disadvantages described above; they will not create effluent of a radioactive nature with its attendant difficulties of handling and storing. It has long been known that certain nuclear reactions would release even more energy than the uranium fission process if one could get the nuclei near enough to each other to produce the reaction. All nuclei are positively charged and two such bodies having the same electricity will repel each other. These repulsing forces get stronger the nearer we try to bring the nuclei. The best way of getting the nuclei near enough to each other is by heating them; the higher the temperature, the nearer they can come. If the temperature is very high indeed, say 20 million degrees, then there is a very good chance that light nuclei will come so near to each other that they will react and release a great amount of energy. This process is called fusion. The energy comes again from mass. The two nuclei which fuse will weigh separately a little bit more than the product into which they become transformed.

In the past, it was not possible to generate the very high temperatures necessary for the fusion reaction, but now, having uranium "bombs", or let us call them detonators, we have a source which can create high temperatures and thus perhaps set off the fusion reactions. It has been suggested by Peierls[1] that the so-called hydrogen bomb could be constructed by having a uranium bomb surrounded by material which will undergo fusion at the very high temperature created by the neutron reaction on uranium.

The materials which can be used for fusion are light elements. In these cases there is no splitting into other radioactive materials; these are the ideal material to burn in any generating station, and light elements are abundantly available, but first we must find the way to master the technology. This is not a simple matter. For use at high temperatures, metallurgists will have to create materials which will stand up to the terrific heat or the engineers will have to design these futuristic reactors in such a way that the materials are cooled before they reach any metal in the power stations. The extraction of heat is also a very difficult task. The problem seems a very tough one to solve. Different predictions have been made on possibilities of future fusion reactors. Some scientists think the problem might be solved in ten years' time, others think after a much longer period, or perhaps never!

One very big fusion reactor is quite well-known to us; it is our sun. For quite some time it was known that the sun could only radiate at the present rate, without losing measurable amounts of energy from year to year, if the radiation emitted is exactly balanced with some nuclear reaction which gives the power. Helium has been found to be the reaction product. It cannot be produced by collision of a number of elementary particles, as multiple collisions are very unlikely to occur. Therefore, both Bethe and Von Weizsäcker suggested a different reaction which takes account of a cycle and at the same time is so calculated as to give the right amount of energy. The cycle starts with a normal carbon atom being hit by a hydrogen nucleus, called a proton. The carbon is converted into nitrogen with a mass 13, which itself decomposes, because it is not stable, into carbon with a mass 13. Carbon-13 is then hit by another proton, giving oxygen-15, which decomposes automatically into nitrogen-15. This being hit by still another proton gives helium and again the carbon-13, which then can be used for another such cycle. The result of these reactions is a total consumption of four hydrogen nuclei or protons, and the production of helium. Such a reaction releases vast amounts of energy.

Incidentally, we should never forget how fortunate we are in having the sun for hundreds of millions of years at this temperature and at this distance. Only so was it possible to have the right temperature on this earth for organic life to develop. There are, of course, a number of other important factors which are pre-requisites to organic development, but the right temperature condition is certainly a fundamental one.

[1] R. E. Peierls, *The Laws of Nature* (Allen and Unwin, 1955), p. 253.

One of the great mysteries in nuclear physics is still the amazing fact that nuclei can exist when some of the bricks have positive electricity only, which, according to the simple laws of physics as mentioned before, should repel one another. For a long time scientists tried to get more information on the mechanism of the binding of these protons in the nucleus by studying cosmic rays. Cosmic rays had been observed for a long time and it was known that their radiation could penetrate deep into the seas and lakes. But cosmic rays, when entering the earth's air space, will hit all the elements that exist in our atmosphere. Only by carrying out research at very high altitudes can the fundamental particles which enter the atmosphere be studied. High-flying balloons, and more recently rockets, have contributed a lot to this research. Better detection systems for cosmic rays have been devised by developing special photographic emulsions which record these radiations, from which scientists can even deduce the type of particle which hits the photographic plate. Also electronic devices have been improved, but the results of all the investigations on cosmic rays have been surprising and have certainly posed more questions as new particles were discovered.

A new type of particle, created by cosmic rays, was discovered, and called meson because its weight lies between the lighter electrons and the heavier protons. Then an entirely different type with a different mass and different mean life became known, and more recently many more types of mesons have been discovered: charged particles, neutral particles, bigger and smaller particles, mesons with longer and shorter lives. None of these five newly discovered mesons, designated by the Greek letters, λ, θ, κ, τ and χ, have helped to clear the situation. On the contrary, they have made life for the scientists much more difficult. One assumes today that the greater part of cosmic radiation entering the earth's atmosphere consists of protons, and the moment they hit some part of our outer atmosphere certain mesons are formed which disintegrate into other mesons. But it is not known where the radiation comes from, and in fact everything is so much out of place that the scientist hopes for some clever discovery that will settle the unanswered questions of cosmic rays, as well as the cohesive mechanism that holds our nuclei together.

In October 1955 it was announced in Berkley, California, that a new particle had been discovered which was named "antiproton". What does this mean, and in which way does this affect our knowledge of the nuclei?

Here, as so often before, the experimentalists have found what theoreticians predicted long ago. The experimentalists built an "atom smashing machine" which is so calculated as to give particles such an energy that they can produce this evasive new particle.

The existence of anti-protons was predicted from the fact that according to modern theory proton waves would have a fantastic behaviour unless these anti-protons existed with the same mass as the proton but having negative electricity. It was assumed that the proton and anti-proton would annihilate each other.

There are good reasons why one did not observe anti-protons in the past. If they exist in cosmic rays they will decay when they hit other nuclei, most likely into mesons. In the laboratory, even the strongest accelerating machine did not give protons sufficient energy that when hitting other particles they might have enough energy to create this new particle. Though, in fact, one could exactly calculate what energies one had to give protons so that they could produce this anti-proton. Scientists knew that the new Berkley machine would be able to do this, if that particle existed.

The production process is the following:

The original proton, by being given enormous energy, can form a "proton pair" when it hits another particle. This experiment shows the reverse case from creation of energy from mass which we discussed in the splitting of uranium atoms. The "proton pair" is formed from energy, or energy has been converted into mass.

The proof of the anti-proton's existence has shown that we are on the right path to penetrate further into the forces of the nuclei.

Discussing recent advances in physics, we have to mention an entirely different field. It is the development of machines which can produce particles with high energies, like the one used at Berkley. The first such machine was built by Cockcroft and Walton in 1932. Since then a number of different machines have been developed, like Van der Graaf's, and particle-accelerating machines like cyclotrons and linear accelerators. The reason for this development was to create particles with very high energies which can then be used as ammunition to shoot at other nuclei. This is the other approach. The study of cosmic rays was one; here we try to learn about some nuclear laws by making cosmic rays in the laboratory. It is of the greatest interest to study the interaction of these very high-energy particles with other nuclei. As bigger particle-accelerating machines are built so our chances will increase of getting to know more about the nuclear laws of nature.

Such machines can be used to make materials radioactive, but by far the cheaper and more convenient way is to use atomic research reactors for this purpose, where one can expose materials to the neutron radiation. As more than a million × million × million neutrons are created each second in a small reactor, it is no wonder that material put into such a reactor has a very good chance of being hit by the neutrons, although the atoms are very small indeed. When they are hit, they will still be the same element as before but, as already shown, they will be slightly heavier. In many cases we find that the atom is not too fond of this neutron increase in its inside. The nucleus cannot get rid of the neutron as such, it can only get into a more comfortable and stable state by emitting radiation. This radiation usually consists of either beta particles, which is negative electricity, or gamma-rays (photons or short-wave X-rays).

Why is it interesting to make materials radioactive by exposing them to neutrons in a reactor? There are quite a number of reasons for this. First, one can detect theoretically every emission of radiation, which means each disintegration of an atom that was radioactive. Practically, this means that one is now able to detect some elements a hundred million times better than before when using orthodox methods of analysis. As with the discovery of the microscope, a new world has been opened up. We suddenly see much farther. Radioactive materials are most important tools of research.

The second reason for the usefulness of the radiation of these radioactive materials is that one can make radiation visible without changing the system. Every chemist knows that when he makes an analysis he usually destroys or changes the sample, and therefore with such methods one cannot locate the place of the material to be analysed, one can only measure the quantity. By making these radiations visible, for example on a photographic film, one can not only measure them but can also locate them.

The third reason for the importance of radioactive materials is that one can make good use of the radiations themselves. They penetrate materials in the same way as conventional X-rays; they make ordinary air conductive for electricity, and their reflections can be used to give information on physical properties. There is today not an industry which has failed to benefit in some way by the development of atomic reactors, as a result of using these radioactive materials produced in them.

Perhaps the greatest advances in scientific research have been made in biology and biochemistry. Only by using radio-isotopes can one label or mark a compound, and by this method it is then possible to follow up metabolism in the body, or to follow atoms contained in food, or learn about the reaction of a drug in the body. By labelling animals, inheritance deductions can be made. The method is really an astounding one if one remembers that the radiation from the active isotopes can be measured in most cases without disturbing the system. Today, very few metabolism studies would be possible without the use of radioactive material.

Agriculture has also derived great benefit from these new tools of science. The first extensive studies were in the fertilizer field. In the past, it was difficult to find the best conditions for fertilizing. It was necessary to carry out considerable research and wait for the results. Today, accurate measurements can be achieved by making the atoms of the fertilizers radioactive, that means one "labels" the fertilizer. It is thus possible to distinguish between the nourishment the plant gets from the fertilizer and the nourishment which is taken out of the soil.

Radiation also affects seeds. In some cases it might cause mutations, and scientists all over the world are now investigating mutations created by radiation. Already wheat has been grown bearing two heads, and new forms of leaves in different plants have been observed.

The most obvious impact of radioactive materials has been in the field of medicine. There is hardly a major hospital today which does not use radioactive materials for research, diagnosis and therapy. The working of certain glands, the blood volume in the body, can both be measured with a very small dose of radioactive material, harmless to the patient. Blood-circulation tests give immediate answer in locating blockages. Radio-phosphorus is sometimes applied for the treatment of some blood diseases. Radio-isotopes of iron and chromium have recently been used for a number of important medical investigations. The destruction of tumorous tissue and the reduction of certain over-large glands is done by the use of radioactive material. In some cases the treatment is simple and eliminates the use of the surgeon's knife. For certain diseases of the thyroid the patient may drink a glass of water containing the radioactive material, which concentrates in that gland. By its action it will destroy certain tissue and so reduce the gland to the right size. Radioactive sheets, wires, seeds, colloidal or clear solutions, radioactive materials incorporated into a foil or plastic, are all used in the daily routine to treat tumours. In each case, the main point is to get the radiation to the tumorous tissue, if possible without damage to healthy tissue, and for this purpose the medical profession has devised a number of ingenious methods. Radioactive particles are even made to measure in such a form that they are caught by the diseased organ only. External application of radiation is also of importance. Very small but strong sources have been prepared for this purpose and within a few years many hospitals will be equipped with such machines. Scientists are working at present on the detection of brain tumours with radioactive materials, which constitutes a very difficult problem. Ingenious techniques have been tried and to some extent progress has been made.

Industry, too, has taken up the use of radioactive materials. The fact that small amounts can be measured is being used to solve mixing problems. Where small quantities of vitamins are to be mixed with large amounts of food, this mixing can be controlled by adding the radioactive material to the vitamin. This active material will be so chosen that the activity decays quickly, and the substance is, of course, some normal one as, for instance, common salt.

The motor industry makes use of the easy detection by measuring wear of engine parts: this could not be done so accurately by other methods and would also take many months to complete.

In the dyeing industry radio-isotopes help in making better products, as with their aid one can easily control impurities carried over from other dye baths.

Problems of leaks occurring underground in pressurized cables, water mains, or oil pipe-lines can all be solved by the use of radio-active materials. The radioactive solutions are introduced into the pipes and, by the use of ingenious devices that have been developed, the leaks can be located in a very short time by tracing the radiation that penetrates the leaks.

In the production of metal parts, X-rays are used widely in factories. With their help one finds flaws in metals and can check welds. In many cases X-ray sets are now being replaced by small radioactive isotopes emitting the right wave-length of X-rays for the metal to be investigated. The advantages are obvious. There is no maintenance cost, the material usually has a long, useful life, and the price is a fraction of that of a conventional X-ray set.

Nature was kind because she gave us isotopes with the right gamma energies, enabling us to make radioactive materials that can be used for X-raying anything from a thin light alloy to a seven-inch steel wall.

Today thousands of small pieces of radioactive material with different properties are being used for industrial purposes. If a pipe-line is built far from civilization, it is obviously much more convenient to use radioactive material enclosed in a portable lead pot for checking the welds.

Other radioactive materials are used in factories which manufacture products like wool, nylon or paper. During the manufacturing process all these products become charged with electricity and then constitute a great fire risk. The best way of getting rid of this disturbing electricity is by making the surrounding air conductive for it, so providing a path for the electricity to go to earth. Radioactive materials do just that. In this case, one would use a radioactive source in the form of a foil placed near the site where the electricity is being formed and the radiation from that foil would discharge the electricity, thus making many industrial processes safer and even, in some cases, increasing production as the machines would then run faster.

But perhaps one of the greatest uses for radioactive materials in industry today is in instruments designed for process control. Any materials which have to be rolled during the manufacturing process, like steel sheet, paper or rubber, can be gauged with radio-isotopes. In this case one makes use of the fact that some of the radiation will be absorbed when it goes through the material.

Corrosion of pipes can now be measured from the outside. This means that an industrial process does not have to be stopped any more for checking pipes. The use of radioactive isotopes for this purpose will save this country alone hundreds of thousands of pounds each year. Many packages are tested before they leave the factory with equipment containing radio-isotopes—the toothpaste you buy in the shops might have been examined by one of these little atoms in order to see that the tube was properly filled.

Even in drilling for oil, isotopes are used to find out the brine level underground. One can also analyse the strata which surround the bore-holes. Building materials are investigated with active material to find out how far moisture is penetrating, say in solid bricks. There are many more of these applications, all developed as a result of atomic energy progress during the last few years.

As mentioned before, in twenty years' time forty per cent. of the electricity supply of this country will most likely be generated by atomic power plants. Each power plant, however, which is based on the splitting of uranium, will leave the fission products as a residue. As we saw, these fission products are highly radioactive; some of them will lose their activity within a very short time, in a matter of weeks or months. Others, however, will be radioactive for many years, even hundreds of years. The short-lived fission products constitute no serious effluent problem: one can just let them rest until they have lost their activity and then dispose of them. The tons of long-lived fission products, however, which constitute an enormous amount of radiation, will have to be stored. This would be an embarrassment to all countries producing atomic power. Scientists are at present at work to find a use for these relatively long-lived products of nuclear fission. They are trying to turn a handicap into an asset. It is hoped that by separating the long-lived fission products and then putting them in the right form as relatively small solid sources of massive radiation, this radiation can be put to good use. Already there are indications that it will do a number of useful jobs. Gazing into the future, we may even venture to make a few predictions. Certain perishable food-stuffs, after irradiation, are found to have a longer storage life. If this can be achieved without damaging the food in any way, and without creating toxic compounds, it will be a very great asset indeed. A number of drugs, penicillin for instance, are difficult to sterilize by conventional methods without destroying their efficacy; but it may be that sterilization can be carried out by the use of the radiation of these so-called "waste materials" of atomic energy plants.

It has been established already that certain plastics change their properties after irradiation. Some become more elastic, or harder, or do not melt so easily as before irradiation. But not only physical changes occur, certain chemical changes may be induced by these radiations. Compounds which are expensive to synthesize by orthodox methods, it is hoped to produce more easily and cheaply under irradiation. There are indications that, by irradiating certain materials, it will be possible to carry out syntheses which are at present only done at high temperatures and with high pressure.

Medicine, too, may profit by these sources. Therapy units which are used for the irradiation of patients may switch to utilizing these cheaper substances which will be readily available. In fact, it is highly probable that these fission products, which now are considered a nuisance and a waste product of power production, may have great significance in medicine and industry tomorrow. It has been predicted that the applications of radiations, irrespective of whether they come from a material made specially radioactive in the atomic pile or from these "waste products", may easily, in the long run, be of far greater importance to mankind than the production of atomic energy.

We have seen that two fundamental inventions were of unforeseen importance. The technological progress which followed was so speedy that the generation of power from the atom became a fact within fifteen years. There is no doubt that, as conventional fuels run short, and as industry, the standard of living—and with these, power consumption in the world—expand, nuclear fuel will slowly replace the conventional fuels, certainly for big power stations. When relatively cheap electricity becomes available, it will make Britain a cleaner country. Fast electric trains, no more smoking chimneys, and therefore no air pollution, will be the benefits of the atomic developments for the next generation.

Materials made radioactive in atomic reactors are already playing an important part in science, medicine, agriculture and industry. All this is due to the interaction of nuclear particles. The irony is that many problems of the atomic nucleus are still unsolved. We use materials which we still do not quite understand.

BOOKS SUGGESTED FOR FURTHER READING

O. R. Frisch, *Meet the Atoms* (Sigma Books, 1947).

Sir George Thomson, *The Atom* (Oxford, 1955).

H. S. W. Massey, *Atoms and Energy* (Elek Books, 1953).

R. E. Peierls, *The Laws of Nature* (Allen and Unwin, 1955).

W. J. Whitehouse and J. L. Putman, *Radioactive Isotopes* (Oxford, 1951).

K. E. B. Jay, *Atomic Energy Research at Harwell* (Butterworth's Scientific Publications, 1955).

PSYCHOLOGY

by Professor O. L. Zangwill

I. Introductory

The traditional idea of psychology as the science of mind is today in process of revolution. As Ryle has argued, this idea is deeply rooted in the Cartesian dualism, out of which grew the programme —or dream—of psychology as the "counterpart science to Newtonian physics".[1] Although nearly a century has elapsed since psychology first took shape as an experimental science, this dream shows little sign of coming true. Experimental psychology has produced many facts, a few generalizations, and even an occasional "law". But it has so far failed to produce anything resembling a coherent and generally accepted body of scientific theory. Why is this so?

The first reason that springs to mind is scientific immaturity: certainly psychology, in its experimental aspects at least, has a short history, but so also have biochemistry and genetics, in both of which progress has been astonishingly rapid over the past fifty years. A second reason, advanced by a leading psychological historian,[2] is that psychology has yet to discover its own man of genius. Although this may well be true, it seems hardly sufficient to account for the meagre outcome of the toil of innumerable lesser men. More fundamental, perhaps, is the reason put forward by Ryle.[3] Psychology, he suggests, has been founded on the assumption that there exists a distinct order of phenomena—mental events—open to study by the methods of natural science. This assumption he believes to be wholly gratuitous. Although Ryle's position is based largely on philosophical considerations, there would seem no doubt that many psychologists have independently come to recognize its strength. As Ryle himself has said, the Cartesian picture left no place for Mendel or Darwin, and psychology as we know it today finds its main inspiration in the biological sciences. During the past fifty years, indeed, there has been a steady shift of interest

---

[1] Gilbert Ryle, *The Concept of Mind* (Hutchinson, 1949), pp. 319-27.

[2] E. G. Boring, *A History of Experimental Psychology* (Appleton-Century-Crofts, 1929), p. 660.

[3] Ryle, op. cit., p. 320.

within psychology from the traditional analysis of mind to the broader study of the behaviour of organisms in their relations with the environment. No longer does psychology aspire to become the science complementary to physics; it is content to claim modest recognition as one of the many disciplines of which modern biology is composed.

Although the concept of mind is no longer central in present-day psychology, it cannot be said that the earlier concern with introspective analysis has altogether vanished from the scene. Vestiges of the earlier systematic psychology, as represented in the writings of such men as Ward, Stout and McDougall, still persist to confuse the beginner and enrage the Pavlovian purist. Further, conflict exists between those who seek an experimental basis for the subject and those who hold, with Freud and Jung, that the realities of human conduct are seldom, if ever, open to laboratory control. Psychology, then, is a subject whose very foundations are in process of flux. No longer is it the study of mind; not yet has it evolved into a fully objective science of behaviour. As Ryle has well said, modern psychology is most appropriately conceived as a "partly fortuitous federation of inquiries and techniques" which neither has, nor needs, a logically trim statement of programme.[1] The practising psychologist is perforce constrained to wander far and wide in search of method and to borrow freely from his colleagues in related spheres of biological inquiry. Unsatisfactory as this state of affairs may appear, it must be borne in mind that every biological science has shown comparable variety and confusion in the earliest stages of its growth.[2] In science, there are no short cuts; in psychology there is no royal road.

In the present essay, a selection will be given from among the many loosely-related "inquiries and techniques" which together compose modern psychology. This selection makes no claim to be authoritative, nor even wholly representative of present-day interests and preoccupations. It is governed first, by the relevance of the studies described to a biological conception of conduct; secondly, by their probable significance as "growing-points" for future research; and thirdly, by the personal interest which they happen to hold for the writer. At the present time, every psychologist has perforce to create his own psychology, and the view of the subject presented here may well prove unacceptable to many who, with equal right, hold themselves competent to survey the contemporary scene. In particular, the scant reference made to applications of psychology in the fields of industry, education and medicine will strike many as wholly out of key with the modern spirit. This

[1] Ryle, op. cit., p. 323.

[2] An apposite parallel between physiology yesterday and psychology today is provided by Sherrington in *The Endeavour of Jean Fernel* (Cambridge, 1946).

neglect is intentional. In the first place, several excellent accounts of applied psychology are already available.[1] And in the second place, it is the author's view that much that passes for applied psychology is no more than the application of certain well-tried scientific techniques to particular practical problems. Important as this work may prove for the welfare both of the individual and society, it cannot properly be viewed as the application of established scientific knowledge. In psychology, indeed, there is little knowledge sufficiently well-founded to merit confident application. It follows, then, that applied psychology cannot be said to constitute "knowledge" in the accepted sense of the term. For this reason it is excluded from our survey.

II. Studies of Animal Behaviour

The study of animal behaviour has for long been dominated by two opposing dogmas. The first, commonly called *mechanism*, has sought to account for all behaviour in terms of the quasi-automatic activities of the central nervous system. Its units have been the tropism, the reflex and, more recently, the conditioned reflex. The second, commonly called *vitalism*, has sought to explain behaviour in terms of non-material principles, commonly equated with life or mind. This dichotomy has obviously sprung from the traditional dualism of mind and matter and betrays all the gloomier tints of the Cartesian picture. It has provoked vigorous polemics, dictated by prejudice rather than by evidence, but no agreed method of resolving the dilemma.[2] In quite recent years, however, a fresh point of view has gradually been evolved by behaviour students. This is bound up with the emergence of a new type of behaviour study which endeavours to combine the rigours of scientific materialism with genuine understanding of the ways of animals. This branch of study, which is associated especially with the names of K. Lorenz and N. Tinbergen, has been christened *ethology*.[3] Although it has arisen under the auspices of zoology rather than of psychology, its obvious importance would seem to justify some short account in the present context.

Ethology is concerned with field-observations of behaviour and

[1] For an adequate account of the major fields of applied psychology see *Current Trends in British Psychology* (Methuen, 1953), edited by C. A. Mace and P. E. Vernon.

[2] The opposing viewpoints have been hotly debated by J. B. Watson and W. McDougall in *The Battle of Behaviourism* (Kegan Paul, Trench, Trubner, 1928). This battle clearly resulted in a stalemate.

[3] This term was originally introduced by John Stuart Mill to denote what he was pleased to call the "science of character". Its present-day usage is entirely confined to the study of animal behaviour as it is observed in the natural state. A full account of modern ethological work is given by Tinbergen in his book on *The Study of Instinct* (Clarendon Press, 1951).

their systematic interpretation. Special attention has been paid to the study of inborn (instinctive) behaviour patterns in the lower vertebrates and a serious theoretical attempt made to relate them to the activity of preformed nervous mechanisms. Although it has not yet proved possible to isolate the latter from a strictly neurological point of view, it has already become clear that instinctive behaviour cannot be reduced to a simple combination of reflexes and chain-reflexes of the kind so beloved of an earlier generation of animal psychologists. It is probable, indeed, that reflex action in the traditional sense plays but a small and insignificant part in instinctive activity and that the latter is predominantly subserved by nervous mechanisms of a non-reflex type. At all events, ethologists favour a view of instinct regarded not as a complex reflex system but as a hierarchy of directed activities, motivated from within, and susceptible to priming and release at a variety of levels.[1] Although this conception is open to objection, and is by no means generally accepted by scientists, it provides a convenient framework within which to group the observed facts.

Some of the most interesting work carried out by the ethologists is concerned with the external factors, or stimuli, that provoke instinctive responses in the lower animals. As McDougall clearly saw, effective action presupposes effective recognition, and if the action is unlearnt so also must be the recognition.[2] But McDougall undertook no systematic analysis of the perceptual factors which evoke innate behaviour and it is only in quite recent years that a genuine start has been made. In the first place, it is clear that the effective stimulus to any particular response is by no means necessarily the "biologically appropriate object", as McDougall supposed. For instance, gulls "instinctively" retrieve their eggs if they are removed a short distance from the nest. But they will also retrieve pebbles, potatoes and billiard balls. Hence it cannot be the egg *as such* that elicits the response but some aspect of it common to all objects within a certain range of size, shape and brightness. In the same way, a male robin will attack not only another male intruding into its territory but also a small tuft of red feathers mounted on a wire.[3] In this case, it is the stimulus of the red breast with which the bird's aggressive responses are innately linked. It would therefore appear that the instinctive behaviour is set off by the perception of a limited feature of the environment which acts as a signal to the immediate performance of appropriate action. To these signals the name *sign-stimuli* has been given. Their significance must clearly depend in some way not yet understood upon inborn constitution.

[1] Tinbergen, op. cit., p. 112.
[2] W. McDougall, *An Outline of Psychology* (Methuen, 1923), p. 110.
[3] David Lack, *The Life of the Robin* (M. F. and G. Wetherby, 1946), p. 154.

An amusing observation which has been made in certain birds is that the "sign-stimulus" which evokes a particular action in the natural state is not always optimal for this purpose. Thus the oyster-catcher actually prefers to incubate a model egg very much larger than its own and if given a choice of several eggs of varying size will always select the largest.[1] It is possible that the tenderness shown by many birds towards the cuckoo at the expense of their own young is likewise due to the "supernormal" stimulus value of the lusty intruder.

Another class of actions to which ethologists have drawn attention are those known as *displacement activities*. It is not uncommonly observed that an animal will pause while performing some coherent sequence of actions and do something totally at variance with the actual needs of the moment. "For instance, fighting domestic cocks may suddenly pick at the ground, as if they were feeding. Fighting European starlings may vigorously preen their feathers. . . . Herring-gulls, while engaged in deadly combat, may all at once pluck nesting material."[2] These activities occur principally under two types of condition. First, when there is an element of conflict in the situation confronting the animal; and secondly, when there is a "surplus of motivation". As an example of the first type may be mentioned "displacement sand-digging" in the stickleback, studied by Tinbergen. When male sticklebacks meet on the border of their respective breeding territories, one or both of them may be observed to "stand on its head". This posture is in fact part of the nesting pattern, and is normally adopted to dig a pit for the nest. Under present circumstances, however, it is seen as the outcome of a conflict between the tendency to attack, activated by the presence of a male within the territory, and a tendency to flee, evoked by the presence of a male outside the territory. One may suppose that this conflict becomes acute at the territorial border and issues in a response which ordinarily forms part of an entirely different behaviour pattern. Interestingly enough, Tinbergen has been able to show that certain displacement activities may come to acquire fresh significance in the course of evolution.[3] Thus "displacement sand-digging" in the stickleback appears to possess the secondary significance of a threat. This further evolution of a displacement activity is known as "ritualization" and would well repay more detailed study.

The second type of situation under which displacement activities may arise are those in which a highly motivated animal is unable to undertake the appropriate consummatory response. In many species, for instance, the male is unable to perform coition until the necessary sign-stimulus is displayed by the female. If for any reason she should fail to do so, displacement activities derived from a

---

[1] Tinbergen, op. cit., p. 45.   [2] Tinbergen, op. cit., pp. 113-14.
[3] Tinbergen, op. cit., pp. 191-3.

variety of non-sexual behaviour patterns may be observed. It would appear, then, that displacement activity is in general a response either to conflict or frustration. Although it has been studied in detail only in the lower vertebrates, it almost certainly occurs in the mammals as well, and possibly even in man. In particular, striking parallels have been drawn between displacement activities of the kind described and many non-adjustive human actions, more especially those studied by the psychopathologist.[1] Although inferences from animal behaviour to that of man are always somewhat risky, it is at least possible that closer studies of the innate activities of animals will throw light on the vexed question of instinct in man.

III. Physiological Psychology

The history of physiology shows how activities ascribed to "vital forces" by one generation have been resolved into "mechanical activities" by the next. In psychology, we may discern a somewhat similar trend: Activities ascribed to "mental forces" by one generation are interpreted in terms of neural mechanisms by its successor. Although this does not necessarily mean that mental processes can be identified with brain processes, it does suggest that many aspects of behaviour formerly attributed to mind may now be more profitably viewed as the outcome of nervous integration. At all events, a body of knowledge is steadily being assembled which relates the facts of behaviour to the nervous and glandular activities of the body. To this body of knowledge the term "physiological psychology" is commonly applied. In the present section, some illustrative recent work based principally on animal experiment will be briefly considered. Evidence from human neurological study will be reviewed in the following section.

A very old problem in psychology is that of the perception of spatial relationships. Is this function innate? Or is it, on the other hand, a skill acquired by experience? This issue has been debated at very great length by philosophers and psychologists, but their arguments have failed to produce a clear-cut solution.[2] Recently, however, important light has been thrown on the question by the experiments of Sperry and his co-workers at Chicago.[3] These research workers, approaching the problem from the anatomical standpoint, have been able to show that in amphibians such as the

---

[1] D. Russell Davis, "Some Applications of Behaviour Theory in Psychopathology", *British Journal of Medical Psychology* (1954), vol. xxvii, pp. 216-23.

[2] A good account of this celebrated controversy is given by W. McDougall, op. cit., pp. 235-50.

[3] For an introductory account of Sperry's work, see J. S. Wilkie, *The Science of Brain and Mind* (Hutchinson, 1953), pp. 44-9. For an advanced review, see R. W. Sperry on "Mechanisms of Neural Maturation" in the *Handbook of Experimental Psychology* (Chapman and Hall, 1951), ed. S. S. Stevens.

frog or newt it is entirely possible to rotate the eye on its optic axis through 180 degrees, leaving the optic nerve intact. The eye heals readily in its new position but the animal thereafter shows *a complete reversal of all its visual responses*. In attempting to catch a fly, the animal will invariably strike at a point in the visual field diametrically opposite to the actual position of its prey. A similar result is obtained if rotation of the eye is actually combined with section of the optic nerve. Although the severed nerve fibres regenerate, the new connexions preserve the old spatial relationships so that there is again systematic reversal of visual-motor reaction. These reversals, moreover, *never undergo correction*. It may be concluded, then, that in the amphibian at least accuracy of visual localization depends upon inborn nervous arrangements. Individual experience would appear to play a negligible role.

In a further series of experiments, Sperry has shown that localization on the skin is likewise governed by considerations of anatomical pattern. If skin-flaps with their original innervation intact are transplanted across the mid-line of the frog's back, the animal is found to misdirect its reaction to the opposite side of the body. If, for instance, a point on the transplanted areas is gently touched, the frog will perform a "wiping reaction" with the hind-limb falsely aimed at the *original* site of the skin-flap. Even more striking, perhaps, is the following experiment: The sensory roots of the nerves serving the hind limbs of a tadpole are severed and cross-connected to the opposite sides of the spinal cord. After metamorphosis, a touch applied to (say) the *left* hind foot of the animal is found to produce reflex withdrawal of the *right* hind limb—i.e. the "wrong" foot is withdrawn. As in the case of vision, these maladaptive actions are never corrected. Although it would be unwise to generalize too freely from these admittedly artificial preparations, it is at least clear that control of adaptive behaviour is very largely vested in preformed nervous arrangements. To this extent, at least, Sperry's findings lend support to nativist theories of space perception.

The physiological psychologist has also given much attention to the bodily factors governing instinctive activity. Whereas the ethologist, as we have seen, is principally engaged in defining the external factors, or sign-stimuli, upon which such activity depends, the psychologist has concentrated his research mainly on the internal conditions necessary for its display. Of these, the most essential are of course the nervous system and certain chemical substances (hormones) secreted into the blood by the endocrine glands. As a rule, though not invariably, nervous and chemical factors co-operate closely in the control of innate behaviour. In the case of fear and rage, for instance, the hormone adrenalin, released through the activity of the sympathetic nervous system, works closely in "sympathy" with the latter to promote effective bodily action. In the case of sex, testicular hormones in the male and ovarian hormones in the female appear essential to mating behaviour in all classes of vertebrates below the level of the primates. Although the precise mode of action of hormones in relation to behaviour is not clearly understood, it is at least clear that no theory of instinct which fails to take account of their significance can be regarded as complete.

The nervous mechanisms subserving certain forms of instinctive activity, in particular those concerned with reproduction, have been closely studied in recent years and a clearer conception of their nature is beginning to emerge.[1] It has already become evident that the sequence of actions composing an instinctive response, despite its apparently unitary character, results from the integration of activities organized at very different levels in the central nervous system. In the male frog, for example, the "sexual clasp" is a spinal reflex; the spawning movements are controlled by the mid-brain; whereas release of the female by the male depends on the posterior areas of the forebrain. It follows that at least three component mechanisms, governed by the spinal cord, the mid-brain and the forebrain respectively, are concerned in the total mating pattern. From the neurological point of view, therefore, the simplicity and coherence of the total pattern is somewhat deceptive. As knowledge advances, one may hope that the descriptive schemes of instinct based on the observations of the ethologists will be brought into fruitful relation with the data of direct neurological study.

There is good evidence that the part played by the higher brain centres in instinctive activity becomes progressively more important as we ascend the phylogenetic scale. This is shown first by the progressive liberation of sexual behaviour from the strict control which, in the lowlier animals, is exercised by the sex hormones; and secondly, by the ever-increasing responsibility of the cerebral cortex for the control of sexual activity. In the male, especially, the cortex comes to play a most important part in governing sexual responsiveness. In the male rat, sexual activity is markedly depressed by extensive cortical injury. In the female, on the other hand, mating behaviour survives total decortication. In male cats, sexual activity is even more disrupted by cortical injury than in the rat, but here again the female may continue to mate after extensive injury to the forebrain. It is not yet known whether a sex difference of this kind is likewise characteristic of the primates. It is possible, however, that sexual arousal in the female primate is less dependent on the cortex than is the case in the male. Apart from these sex differences, however, it may be said that sexual mechanisms which, in the

---

[1] Recent advances in this field are largely due to the work of F. A. Beach and his colleagues at Yale. See C. S. Ford and F. A. Beach, *Patterns of Sexual Behaviour* (Eyre and Spottiswoode, 1952), for an over-all review of modern work.

lower animals, are subserved by subcortical nervous mechanisms, are represented in the cerebral cortex in the higher mammals and man.

Beach has further shown that parental behaviour in mammals depends on the integrity of the cerebral cortex. In the rat, cortical injury disrupts all aspects of maternal behaviour, the degree of deterioration being roughly proportional to the extent of the injury. Thus normal females begin nest-building several days before the birth of the litter. Animals on whom the operation has been performed, on the other hand, may delay this essential duty until just before the young are born; if the injury is severe, indeed, no nest at all may be constructed. Care of the young is likewise affected by cerebral injuries: thus removal of more than 30 per cent. of the cortex renders the mother unable to collect and clean her young in an efficient fashion, and she may fail to retrieve them should they stray from the nest. Although no single element of the maternal behaviour pattern is completely lost, the over-all efficiency of the latter is gravely reduced. It is probable, then, that the coherence of maternal behaviour reflects the integrative activity of the cerebral cortex.

The effects of cortical lesions upon inborn and acquired behaviour patterns are by no means wholly dissimilar. In a long series of admirable researches, K. S. Lashley[1] has shown that maze-habits and kindred skills acquired by training in the rat are significantly impaired by cortical lesions, the degree of impairment being broadly proportional to the extent of the lesion and independent of its locality. Again, we find that no specific component of the behaviour sequence is totally lost, but the various reactions involved become harder to evoke and their over-all integration is significantly weakened. It is also notable that the more complex the habit, the greater the impairment produced by a cortical lesion of given extent. The results of these experiments have led Lashley to the view that complex behaviour patterns, whether inborn or acquired, are not laid down in any very specific fashion in the brain cortex, e.g. in the form of anatomically discrete "traces" or systems of neuronal connexions, but in some more generalized fashion involving large areas, if not the whole, of the cerebral cortex.

Although no very precise localization of function appears to exist in the cortex of the lower mammals (except with regard to the central representation of the special sense fields), it is likely that a greater degree of cortical segregation occurs in the primates and man. In monkeys, there is good evidence to suggest that skills

[1] K. S. Lashley's earlier work is reported in *Brain Mechanisms and Intelligence* (University of Chicago, 1929). For more recent work in this field, see C. T. Morgan and Eliot Stellar, *Physiological Psychology* (McGraw-Hill, Second Edition, 1950).

depending upon immediate memory for their execution are selectively impaired by lesions of the frontal lobes. On the other hand, skills involving fine discrimination, visual or tactual, are affected solely by lesions involving the posterior areas of the brain cortex. In man, as we shall see below, there is evidence that intellectual activity, though in some respects dependent on the cortex as a whole, is almost certainly bound up in its more specialized aspects with the integrity of particular regions of the brain. This task of unravelling the functions of the brain, which a distinguished physicist has dubbed as "not only one of the tasks, but *the* task, of science", is of course still in its infancy. Yet it may be hoped that the physiological psychologist, along with his colleagues in neurology and neurophysiology, biochemistry and genetics, will play a not unworthy part in its eventual elucidation.

IV. Human Neurological Studies

The general plan of the central nervous system undergoes no fundamental change as we ascend the vertebrate scale. It follows, therefore, that much information derived from experimental work on animals, especially the higher primates, throws light on the functions of the human brain. In experimental physiology, much use has been made of techniques of electrical stimulation, especially in the study of movement, and the results of this work have taught us a great deal about the organization of motor function in the human cerebral cortex. At the same time, it is often perilous to base theories of human behaviour upon the results of animal experiment. The extraordinary development of the human intellect creates at least a *prima facie* case for a corresponding advance in human cerebral organization, even if the factors upon which it depends are invisible under the microscope. The only method open to us, therefore, is to turn directly to the human nervous system and to inquire whether it has yielded up any of its secrets to the probes of the neurologist.

Neurological inquiry in man cannot, by its very nature, be prosecuted by strictly experimental methods of study. Its place lies within medicine, its *raison d'être* being the relief of nervous afflictions. The experiments with which it is concerned are experiments of nature, unplanned and undesired, but none the less an incidental source of invaluable scientific evidence. In recent years, it is noteworthy that neurologists and neurosurgeons have not only concerned themselves increasingly with the scientific implications of their work but have given constant encouragement to the psychologist to associate himself with their inquiries. It is indeed not too much to suggest that the neurology of today may well provide the psychology of tomorrow with its basic principles.

Among the many lines of neurological inquiry at the present day few have attracted more widespread interest than the experiments of Penfield on the direct electrical stimulation of the human brain cortex.[1] This procedure is of course carried out only in the course of essential brain operations, where it is often of great value in the location of abnormal cerebral tissue. But in view of the fact that the patient is conscious, suffers no pain, and can report freely on his experiences when his brain is stimulated, the method obviously holds great promise as a method of psychological research.

The first important result of this work has been to confirm, in man, the existence of discrete areas of the cortex, stimulation of which produces either discrete movements of the various muscle groups (e.g. fingers, wrist, elbow, shoulder, neck, eyelids) or specific sensations referred to particular regions of the body surface. Although the cortical areas devoted to sensation and motion respectively overlap to a very considerable extent, the general pattern of representation agrees closely with that established in sub-human primates by purely physiological methods. The sensations evoked by cortical stimulation are often described by the patient himself as a numbness, tingling or "feeling of electricity". Rarely is the sensory experience identified with a particular modality of sensation, e.g. heat, pain or touch. It is also noteworthy that patients may on occasion report a sense of movement in a particular part of the body without the latter being actually observed to move. Occasionally, too, the "desire to move" an arm or leg may be reported, again without actual movement taking place. Very rarely, the patient may report a sense of inability to carry out a particular movement. In all these experiments, however, the phenomena induced by stimulation have a distinctly "intrusive" character. When movements occur, they are experienced as coerced rather than as the outcome of the patient's own intention. Although these phenomena are of great interest, it must be borne in mind that they represent extremely crude and unorganized responses. In Penfield's own words, the movements produced by cortical stimulation "... are not more complicated than those the newborn infant is able to perform".

A second finding of great interest is Penfield's recent success in inducing both *vocalization* and *arrest of speech* by cortical stimulation.[2] The vocalization is usually a vowel sound and bears more resemblance to the cry of an infant than to true speech. This cry may be intermittent or continuous, depending on the region stimulated, and is often associated with some involuntary lip-movement. Arrest of speech may be regarded as the negative counterpart of

[1] W. Penfield and T. Rasmussen, *The Cerebral Cortex of Man: A Clinical Study of Localization of Function* (Macmillan, 1950).

[2] Penfield and Rasmussen, op. cit., pp. 87-108.

vocalization. It is generally evoked by stimulation within the same regions as produce vocalization and is clearly an inhibitory phenomenon. If, for instance, the patient is instructed to count, application of the stimulus causes his counting first to slow down and then to cease altogether. If it is applied before counting begins, the patient is unable to start and is apt to say that he could not think of the numbers. On tests of naming objects, stimulation may provoke temporary forgetfulness of the required names and even some confusion of words, closely parallel to what is often observed in cases of aphasia. Although these phenomena of vocalization and its arrest are evidently primitive, it may be hoped that their further elucidation will throw important light on the neurological basis of language.

Among other interesting findings reported by Penfield are crude visual and auditory phenomena evoked by stimulation of the occipital and temporal areas respectively. The visual effects are generally described as whirling lights, balls of colour, or crudely coloured forms—never, be it noted, as formed visual experiences. Their localization in the visual field is not very precise, but does appear to bear some relation to the area of cortex stimulated. It is also noteworthy that colours are more frequently seen when the stimulus is applied to the primary visual cortex rather than to its immediate vicinity. As regards auditory phenomena, these are likewise crude—being generally described as buzzing or whistling noises. They are usually referred to the contralateral ear. No case of elaborate auditory hallucination has been reported to follow stimulation of the particular area of the temporal lobe from which these crude auditory responses may be evoked.

The most dramatic effects of cortical stimulation are to be seen in certain cases of epilepsy in which the pathological disturbance involves the temporal lobe. In these cases, the epileptic seizure typically consists in a curious alteration of consciousness, in which the patient is liable to experience feelings of misplaced familiarity (*déjà vu*), apparent changes in visual or auditory experience, and occasionally dream-like trains of visual imagery. Now in cases in which surgical treatment is expedient in relieving the symptoms, electrical exploration of the brain cortex is often carried out prior to operation. In such cases, Penfield has been able to show that *the characteristic mental features of the seizure pattern can be duplicated, in part or in whole, by direct stimulation of the temporal cortex.* Perceptual illusions, *déjà vu*, alterations in mood, elaborate memory images, and even fragments of dreams, have all been artificially evoked by stimulation in fully conscious subjects. Sometimes, too, elements of past experience which do not normally form part of the seizure pattern are similarly revived. These remarkable findings have led Penfield to the view that "memory patterns" are actually "stored in the temporal lobes and are reactivated by the electrical stimulus".[1] At the same time, it must be borne in mind that such phenomena have been elicited only in cases of temporal lobe epilepsy and no comparable evidence exists regarding the location of "memory patterns" in the healthy individual. None the less, Penfield's brilliant work has given fresh hope to those who seek the basis of perception, memory and thought in the physical machinery of the human brain.

A complementary approach to the study of cerebral function in man is by way of the changes brought about by injury, disease or surgical removal of circumscribed areas of the brain. The advent of neurosurgery has made possible the study of a large number of human beings who have undergone extensive removals of brain tissue, and careful study of the resulting psychological deficits (if any) might be expected to throw valuable light on the functions of the parts removed at operation. Unfortunately, this type of study is less easy than is often supposed. No two patients, no two brains, and no two operations are exactly alike. Further, the effects of a brain operation on mental capacity depend upon many factors other than the precise locus and extent of the removal. The age of the patient, the nature of the pathological condition, and the time that has elapsed since operation all play an important part in determining the final picture. None the less, the psychological study of neurosurgical cases is an interesting and provocative field and a number of important psycho-physical correlations have already been established.

It has been found by neurologists that lesions of the frontal lobes, if severe, are liable to produce some impairment of thought in its conceptual aspects, often accompanied by deterioration of character. In some cases, however, unilateral removal of a frontal lobe (lobectomy) gives rise to surprisingly little alteration in the psychological sphere. Lesions of the parietal lobes commonly cause a variety of defects in perception and orientation which are of great interest to the psychologist. Difficulties in spatial judgement, in fine manipulation, in route finding and topographical memory, and in awareness of certain aspects of one's own body, are often prominent and have been subjected to detailed analysis.[2] Lesions involving certain regions of the frontal and temporal lobes of the left hemisphere commonly cause the disorder of language known as *aphasia*, in which speech may be disturbed in its expressive aspects, its receptive aspects, or in both. Reading and writing may also be affected, though not always in association with speech disorders. Although these various conditions have been known to neurologists

[1] W. Penfield, "Memory mechanisms", *Archives of Neurology and Psychiatry* (1952), vol. lxvii, pp. 178-98.

[2] An exhaustive account of these syndromes is given by MacDonald Critchley, *The Parietal Lobes* (Edward Arnold, 1953).

for many years, it is only quite recently that attempts have been made to subject them to more refined methods of psychological examination. Thus the methods of mental testing have made possible a quantitative assessment of intellectual deterioration that is often of value to the neurologist. More refined tests of spatial judgement and mechanical skill are proving of great value in analysing the effects of brain injury, more especially of the parietal lobes. Tests of scholastic attainment are useful in the study of aphasia and kindred disorders of language. Although test methods have to be adapted with some care for use in neurology, and despite certain limitations which they carry in the clinical setting, it may be said that the analysis of brain damage is rapidly becoming a major concern of modern experimental psychology.

It may be objected that neurological study in man has given us no new theory regarding the relation of body and mind. While it remains true that this essential gap in our knowledge remains as large as ever, it may none the less be argued that we are approaching a view of the brain envisaged as the instrument of behaviour rather than as the "seat of the soul". Hence the body-mind problem in its traditional form ceases to exercise us. By analysis of the modes of breakdown of human psychological performance, data essential to a proper understanding of its structure and development are beginning to emerge. To give but one example: It is clear from the findings of neurology that human orientation in space is a complex affair dependent above all upon the integrity of the parietal lobes. No theory of orientation which neglects the role of parietal mechanisms is likely to meet with enduring success. In consequence, theories based solely upon observations of behaviour in healthy individuals are unlikely to prove acceptable to the neurologist. The study of neurological symptoms is thus no mere psychological sideline: it is an essential method, comparable to the ablation method of the physiologist, without which data indispensable to psychological theory will be for ever wanting. The neurological approach, while no royal road to psychological truth, is at least a well-worn track not wholly destitute of sign-posts.

V. Experimental Psychology

The idea of experiment as a method of systematic exploration of human reactions grew up in Germany in the latter half of the nineteenth century. By observing human behaviour under conditions open to systematic variation and control, it was hoped to establish more or less exact relationships between physical stimuli and at least the simpler forms of human experience and reaction. In the sphere of sensation, for example, it proved possible to establish a fairly constant relationship between the intensity of a physical stimulus and the increment necessary for a just perceptible difference in sensation to result. This relationship, known as the Weber-Fechner law, has proved to be an empirical generalization of some value in the study of the human senses. In the sphere of reaction, systematic attempts were made to measure the time required for movements of various types to occur in response to sensory signals of varying complexity. The "reaction times" thus determined were of some importance in relation to our understanding of movement and its central control and proved relevant to a variety of practical issues involving speedy decision and action. In the field of memory, a large number of experiments were performed on the learning, retention and forgetting of material memorized under set conditions. This led to the formulation of the "curve of forgetting" and other empirical generalizations concerning memory. Attempts were even made to study thought processes experimentally but the outcome in the opinion of many was meagre. Although it is often said that nothing of the first importance emerged from experimental psychology, it at least set an example of method hitherto unknown in mental science. The pioneers of experimental psychology made it their business to evolve standards of evidence and control in no way inferior to those prevailing in the established sciences. Every student of psychology today stands in their debt.[1]

It has already been pointed out that experimental psychology has not wholly justified the earlier confidence placed in it as a department of science. It soon becomes apparent that human reactions are influenced by internal no less than by external circumstances, and that experimental control of the former is difficult, if not impossible, to achieve. Thus although the stimulus applied to an individual may be controlled with the utmost precision, we cannot so readily control or determine the mental attitude which he brings to its interpretation. It follows that an attempt to make psychology fully objective is unlikely to succeed unless we confine ourselves wholly to the study of behaviour. This, of course, is the answer of the Behaviourists, but it has failed to appeal to those whose interest lies in experience rather than in conduct. In consequence, psychologists who wished to preserve experiment, but at the same time to study experience, have been obliged to reconsider the whole structure of their science. Some, like Bartlett, have taken the position that it is folly for the psychologist to stick to the ideal of constant objective conditions and have attempted to introduce a less rigid conception of experiment in psychology.[2] Others, like the Gestalt-psychologists, have limited their studies to aspects of experience in

[1] The aims and methods of experimental psychology have been well described by C. S. Myers, *Textbook of Experimental Psychology* (Cambridge, Third Edition, 1925). See also R. S. Woodworth, *Experimental Psychology* (Holt, 1938).

[2] F. C. Bartlett, *Remembering* (Cambridge, 1932), and other works.

regard to which variations in mental attitude are of minor importance.[1] Although both approaches have proved fertile, it remains
true that the whole conception of experiment in psychology awaits
clarification.

The contemporary use of experiment in human psychology is
perhaps best illustrated by reference to two lines of inquiry which
have developed independently within recent years. The first, which
we owe almost exclusively to Michotte, of Louvain, has endeavoured
to define the conditions under which various types of causal connexion occur in visual experience. The second, associated especially
with Sir Frederic Bartlett, of Cambridge, has been concerned with
the experimental analysis of human skills and their breakdown
under conditions of stress. Although no really satisfactory theoretical
system has evolved from either set of findings, the results well bring
out the gain to psychology of an experimental approach to its
problems.

Michotte's work has been principally concerned with the conditions under which particular constellations of sensory events give
rise to experiences (or implicit judgements) of causal relationship.[2]
In a series of elegant experiments, Michotte has been able to show
that *mere proximity* of two objects may, under certain specified conditions, be sufficient to produce the impression of a causal relationship. For instance, a disk A may be arranged to move horizontally
towards a second disk B, and to remain in contact with it for about
half a second. If, then, B is independently set in motion at about
the same speed as A, the observer unfailingly reports that *its motion
has been caused by the impact of A*. This propulsion effect is reported by
all subjects and is considered by Michotte to be largely, if not
wholly, independent of past experience. He regards it as a primary
phenomenon narrowly bound up with the time-relations and other
intrinsic conditions of the experimental setting. If, for instance, the
period of contact between the disks is too long, or their respective
sizes and speeds too diverse, the impression is partly or wholly lost.
Variations in direction of motion may also modify the effect. The
regularity of "apparent propulsion" and its close dependence upon
spatio-temporal aspects of the visual field have led Michotte to the
view that the impression of causation is given in, or coerced by,
the objective conditions of stimulation. Although this strongly
nativistic interpretation has been disputed, the empirical value of
Michotte's observations is evidently considerable.

In a second series of experiments, Michotte endeavoured to
specify the physical conditions that determine our impressions of

[1] K. Koffka, *Principles of Gestalt Psychology* (Kegan Paul, 1935).

[2] A. Michotte, *La Perception de la Causalité* (Louvain, 1946). A summary of this
work, and related inquiries, is given by M. D. Vernon, *A Further Study of Visual
Perception* (Cambridge, 1952), pp. 183-99.

the permanence and reality of perceived objects. His results indicate that there is a strong tendency for a perceived object to retain its identity even under conditions in which, objectively regarded, it ceases to exist. If, for instance, a rectangular patch of light is moved horizontally on a plain ground towards a large black square, and is then caused to shorten as soon as contact is made, the observer invariably perceives it as *sliding behind* the black square. If, then, the rectangle is reconstituted on the opposite side of the latter, the observer perceives it as if emerging from a tunnel. Thus the patch of light appears to preserve its identity whilst concealed from view. From these and many other ingenious experiments Michotte concludes that the normal appearance of objects as real and permanent can be related to the objective structure of the stimulus field. The orderly character of the perceptual world depends less, he believes, upon inference and judgement than upon certain preformed perceptual reactions to particular constellations of sensory events. In particular, the role of past experience in perceptual organization may be somewhat less central than is often supposed. Although Michotte's interpretations are both tentative and controversial, his work holds great promise for the fuller understanding of the origins of experience.

The work of Bartlett and his school has been predominantly concerned with the analysis of skill in highly trained adult personnel. This work differs principally from earlier studies in so far as the skills under inquiry are relatively complex and studied under conditions as lifelike as laboratory conditions permit. Thus some of the factors involved in flying an aeroplane were investigated by constructing a dummy cockpit in which all the instruments responded to controls in very much the same way as they do in a real machine and all movements made by the pilot were systematically recorded. In this way, "instrument flying" over a period of several hours could be intensively studied. In other experiments, the conditions obtaining in a variety of industrial skills have been systematically duplicated in the laboratory. Although it can be objected that such experiments must inevitably be artificial, it is none the less true that they permit the study of a great many factors which cannot be isolated under natural conditions of performance. At the sensori-motor level, at least, the propriety of this form of human experiment has been abundantly justified by results.[1]

In the Cambridge experiments, particular attention has been given to the breakdown of skilled performance under conditions of

---

[1] An outline of this line of work has been given by R. C. Oldfield, "The Analysis of Human Skill", *New Biology* (1952), vol. xiii, pp. 49-60. For more detailed accounts, see F. C. Bartlett, "The Measurement of Human Skill", *British Medical Journal* (1947), vol. i, pp. 835, 877; A. T. Welford, *Skill and Age* (Nuffield Foundation, 1951); N. H. Mackworth, "Researches on the Measurement of Human Performance" (1950), *Medical Research Council Special Report Series*, no. 268.

stress and fatigue. In the first place, it is commonly found that well-established skills display a remarkable resistance to adverse conditions and may be sustained without appreciable loss over a wide range of variation in the environment. If, however, the range specific to any particular skill is exceeded, performance rapidly deteriorates. For instance, Mackworth[1] has shown that the skills involved in wireless telegraphy are maintained without significant change if the room temperature is increased from a dry bulb/wet bulb reading of 85°/75° to one of 100°/90°. A further increase to 105°/95°, however, leads to an enormous increase in mistakes, particularly marked among the less skilled operators. It is therefore probable that every skill displays a certain "range of tolerance" to adverse conditions, depending both on the nature of the skill itself and the proficiency with which it is executed. The neurological basis of this "tolerance range" is at present unknown.

Secondly, it has been shown that the breakdown of skill is seldom a matter of simple muscular fatigue. It is above all an affair of defective sensori-motor co-ordination. In the cockpit experiment, for instance, the fatigued operator tends to make more—and less appropriate—movements, to time his movements less precisely, to react to unduly limited aspects of his perceptual field (e.g. the information conveyed by a single instrument), and to become increasingly irritable and dissatisfied with his performance. It is clear that some of these indications of breakdown arise from failure of interpretation, others from a narrowed capacity to co-ordinate the incoming pattern of signals with effective action. Yet others may reflect temperamental changes. Here again, an analysis of these fatigue effects from the neurological standpoint may be awaited with lively anticipation.

An interesting·development of this work on skill is the link that is being forged with the general field of self-regulating machines and with the concept of the operator as an element in a control system. This line of thinking, which arose in part from the work of the late K. J. W. Craik at Cambridge,[2] is at present being widely developed both in this country and in America. Although the relation of psychology to engineering might appear somewhat tenuous, it is likely that the subject has much to gain from exposure to the fresh ideas recently marshalled under the banner of Cybernetics.[3]

In conclusion, it may be said that the idea of experiment is firmly established in psychology, although its use is no longer

---

[1] Mackworth, op. cit., pp. 134-41.

[2] The posthumous papers of K. J. W. Craik on "The Theory of the Human Operator in Control Systems" were published in the *British Journal of Psychology* (1947), vol. xxxviii, pp. 56, 142. See also W. E. Hick and J. A. V. Bates, "The Human Operator of Control Mechanisms", *Ministry of Supply Monograph No. 17,204* (1950).

[3] Norbert Wiener, *Cybernetics* (John Wiley, 1952).

restricted to the study of human consciousness. Apart from its application to the study of animal behaviour, and to the nervous mechanisms whereby it is sustained, experiment has a valuable part to play in specifying the conditions of human experience and behaviour. In the hands of Michotte, experimental psychology may be said to have thrown light on some thorny problems in the theory of knowledge. In the hands of Bartlett, experimental psychology has helped us to master, in a manner loyal to scientific evidence, the technological demands with which modern man is increasingly confronted. Although we have far to go before the outcome of human experimental psychology can be linked with the simpler nervous reactions discussed in earlier sections, its place in scientific endeavour is already secure.

VI. *Psychoanalysis*

Only a few years ago it was commonly said that psychoanalysis is *par excellence* the "new psychology". This is no longer true today. Although there has been no more recent development in the subject of comparable interest and importance, medical psychologists are nowadays more concerned with the limitations of Freud's work than with the undeniable magnitude of his achievement. It should be clearly understood that the methods of psychoanalysis, which have now been on trial for more than fifty years, have proved distinctly limited in their field of successful application. The belief, once widely entertained, that these methods offer new hope in the treatment of the psychoses (insanities) has been grievously disappointed. Even in the treatment of neurosis, for which the Freudian method was specifically designed, psychoanalysis is now seldom regarded as the therapy of choice, except in a small minority of cases. This is not of course tantamount to saying that the method is of no value; indeed many neurotic sufferers have gained fresh understanding and lasting relief from their symptoms after a course of psycho-analytic treatment. In psychiatry as a whole, however, psycho-analysis as a therapeutic weapon has failed to justify its early promise. Excessive devotion to its claims is hence no longer in key with the spirit of modern inquiry.

The comparative failure of psychoanalysis as a method of treatment must not of course be taken to mean that Freud made no contribution of lasting value. Indeed it is hard to over-estimate the debt which modern science owes to this remarkable man. Almost alone, he broke down the sterile psychological systems of the nineteenth century, putting in their·place a scheme of the human mind which does more adequate justice to the sombre realities of human experience and conduct. Controversial as are many of his theories, his work was illumined by a genius seldom outshone in the long history of psychological speculation. Indeed it is Freud above all who is responsible for what little intellectual distinction modern psychology may fairly claim. Although the earlier enthusiasm kindled by Freudian theory is giving place to a more cautious appraisal of its value, the influence of psychoanalysis upon current psychological thought remains very considerable indeed. We may therefore inquire briefly into recent developments in psychology directly inspired by Freud's outlook.

It may be argued that the most important development in psychoanalytical inquiry is concerned with the study of normal behaviour in early childhood. Freud, it will be remembered, placed overwhelming stress upon the early years of life in forming character and in governing predisposition to nervous disorder in later life. He did not himself, however, undertake any systematic inquiry into the psychology of childhood and was in general content to accept a theoretical reconstruction based upon the analysis of adult patients. It has been left to others to ascertain how far this reconstruction tallies with the actual facts of observation. Direct observations of young children, especially of their play, have multiplied rapidly in recent years; and it is slowly becoming possible to base empirical generalizations of some validity upon the results obtained. Although not all these studies bear the marks of truly objective inquiry, the extent to which Freud's inferences have been borne out by the findings is truly remarkable. In particular, one may call attention to the evidence bearing on infantile sexuality presented by Susan Isaacs and her co-workers,[1] the evidence relating some forms of juvenile delinquency to early deprivation of maternal care adduced by Bowlby,[2] and the evidence relating character, upbringing and cultural pattern assembled by Kardiner.[3] Despite the objection of bias in interpretation commonly brought against these studies, it is impossible to remain wholly unimpressed by the results which they have given. Indeed it is hardly too much to say that the existence of unconscious mechanisms and relationships in infancy, of the kind surmised by Freud, may nowadays be taken as established.

A second notable development in psychoanalysis is an increasing concern with the problem of *character*, normal no less than abnormal. In the earlier years of psychoanalysis, attention was principally directed to the study of those unconscious processes presumed to underlie and determine neurotic manifestations. Not unnaturally,

[1] Susan Isaacs, *Childhood and After* (Routledge and Kegan Paul, 1948). See also *Developments in Psycho-Analysis* (Hogarth Press, 1952), by Melanie Klein, Paula Heimann, Susan Isaacs and Joan Riviere.

[2] John Bowlby, *Maternal Care and Mental Health* (World Health Organization, 1951).

[3] A. Kardiner, *Psychological Frontiers of Society* (Columbia University Press, 1950).

the patient's symptoms were the main focus of interest, and less attention was given to the nature of the personality which constituted their setting. In the figurative language of Freud, analysis was concerned not with the Ego but with the Id. Today, on the other hand, it is the Ego that has usurped the principal role.[1] Indeed "character analysis" is often practised on individuals who present no explicit neurotic disabilities. The various mechanisms and subterfuges employed by the Ego in accommodating to his uneasy bedfellows—the Superego and the Id—have been elucidated in some detail—particularly by Anna Freud[2] —and a broad picture of the "character of character" is beginning to emerge. When more complete, this picture may well represent many facets of normal personality hitherto obscure. In particular, the development of moral sense, the structure of belief and prejudice, and the acquisition of social roles may all find some measure of elucidation in terms of the intensive study of individual character. Although the Freudian nomenclature appears fanciful to many, the facts behind words are a great deal less shadowy than is often supposed. These facts, one may hope, will eventually find their place within a more adequate framework of scientific explanation.

A third aspect of psychoanalysis to attract wide interest in recent years is its relationship to the social sciences. In the first place, the development of group-methods in psychotherapy (so-called Group Therapy) has given the opportunity to observe, in a relatively natural social milieu, the interplay of roles and tensions hitherto confined to the austere setting of the consulting room. Indeed more than one analyst has attempted to erect a science of human relations upon observations of this character.[3] In the second place, there has been a marked endeavour to bring the theories of psychoanalysis to bear upon the material assembled by anthropologists in their studies of primitive societies. Broadly, the position taken is that the personality of an adult will reflect the type of upbringing and family relationship conventional in the society into which he is born. In view of the great importance attached by Freud to early infancy as the formative period in individual development, many features of adult personality in different societies may be linked with differing parental and social conventions. Thus there is already evidence that children brought up under conditions in which affection is traditionally withheld develop into aggressive and mistrustful adults. These qualities may indeed be regarded as typical of

[1] This shift of interest is clearly foreshadowed in Freud's later writings. See particularly *The Ego and the Id* (Hogarth Press, 1927), and *Group Psychology and the Analysis of the Ego* (Hogarth Press, 1922).

[2] Anna Freud, *The Ego and the Mechanisms of Defence* (Hogarth Press, 1937).

[3] See, e.g., W. R. Bion, "Experiences in Groups", *Human Relations* (1948), vol. i, pp. 314-20, 487-96; (1949) vol. ii, pp. 13-22, 295-303; (1950) vol. iii, pp. 3-13.

normal personality in the particular culture concerned and are commonly mirrored in its social institutions. Equally, a society in which children are reared with solicitude and open display of maternal affection is liable to produce adults who, though secure, are typically lacking in drive and·ambition.[1] Although the relations between upbringing, character and cultural pattern are obviously complex, and unlikely to be wholly elucidated in terms of a single discipline, this whole field of study holds promise of an important advance in our understanding of the psychological basis of society.

It is a curious accident of history that the recent developments in psychoanalysis which have been outlined have taken place not in medicine but in psychology and the social sciences. In medicine, as had been said, the scope of psychoanalysis is limited both by inherent considerations of technique and by the stubborn refusal of its practitioners to countenance the role of physical factors in mental illness. It would now appear that the data typically brought to light by analysis are in no way peculiar to the neurotic and that their recognition by the patient is in no sense a guarantee of cure. Indeed it may be doubted whether the biographical evidence extracted by the analytical technique bears any essential relationship to the aetiology of neurotic illness. None the less, psychoanalysis has permitted inferences of great value regarding unconscious mechanisms, the nature and growth of character, and the interplay between the individual and his society. If Freud has failed as an innovator in medicine, at least he has forged one of the most powerful tools ever known to psychological science and put forward a speculative body of theory which has had an unparalleled influence upon modern thought. Every psychologist worthy of the name stands in his debt.

VII. Intelligence and Mental Measurement

It has been said that intellectual testing is "a technology whose theoretical foundations are distinctly insecure".[2] This remark, which has been warmly challenged,[3] is not intended to imply that mental testing is not carried out in accordance with the dictates of scientific method. Indeed scientific procedures of some complexity have been evolved to deal with the construction, standardization and validation of mental tests.[4] What is meant, however, is that no

[1] See Kardiner, op. cit., for a systematic treatment of these relationships. Also Margaret Mead, *Sex and Temperament in Three Primitive Societies* (Routledge, 1935).

[2] O. L. Zangwill, *An Introduction to Modern Psychology* (Methuen, 1950), p. 141.

[3] C. Burt and C. Banks, "Statistical Analysis in Educational Psychology", in Mace and Vernon, op. cit., p. 152.

[4] See P. E. Vernon, *The Structure of Human Abilities* (Methuen, 1950).

established and generally accepted body of scientific theory exists which can form a firm basis for applied intellectual testing. Although a statistical rationale underlies many of the psychological tests in current use, it is doubtful whether this can be identified with a genuine scientific understanding of the mental processes governing test performance. Our understanding of the mental and physiological determinants of intelligence is still too embryonic, and too closely bound up with cultural considerations, to justify our regarding intellectual test procedures as other than arbitrary. None the less, an enormous amount of work on psychometric methods has been undertaken by psychologists during the past fifty years and a considerable controversy has grown up around their use—particularly in the field of education. Some brief mention of the aims and limitations of mental testing is therefore in place.

The use of mental tests for purposes of scholastic or occupational selection is abundantly justified on purely empirical grounds. If, for instance, it is found that children who score below a certain level on a standard intelligence test do not in general profit from normal schooling, a *prima facie* case exists for using the test in the detection of the educationally subnormal child. In the same way, if it is found that the results given by a particular test, say of mechanical skill, correlate highly with success in a particular occupation, say electrical engineering, there is no good reason why the test should not be given to would-be entrants into this trade. Indeed the use of tests may be strongly defended in reducing human wastage and in promoting optimal satisfaction in work. None the less, it is important that the limitations of the test method should be firmly borne in mind. In the first place, it would appear that test performance is more greatly affected by environment and training than was formerly supposed. In the second place, temperamental factors may greatly affect test performance and give rise to a deceptive impression of intellectual level. And in the third place, many aspects of skill and judgement, particularly in the more highly creative aspects of intellectual life, cannot with propriety be assessed by the test methods in current use.[1] "Beyond all reasonable doubt", wrote a pioneer of intelligence testing, "the tests do proffer such a potent aid to life that their renunciation would be suicidal. But on the other hand, the very fact of their potency should be a warning to handle them with circumspection."[2] It may be hoped that this warning will be heeded by all who make use of tests in an educational or industrial capacity.

[1] These, and other, limitations of psychometric methods have been well discussed by Dr. A. W. Heim in her recent book on *The Appraisal of Intelligence* (Methuen, 1954).

[2] C. Spearman and Ll. Wynn Jones, *Human Ability* (Macmillan, 1950).

VIII. Social Psychology

The development of social psychology is one of the most striking features of the contemporary scene. Although the scope of the subject is still somewhat vague, and its methods poorly defined, there are good grounds for supposing that the study of man in society will increasingly supplant the study of man as an isolated laboratory subject. Among the many lines of contemporary inquiry may be mentioned the systematic study of groups, the study of qualities of intellect and character and their social determination, and the measurement of social attitudes and public opinion.[1] Although no systematic theoretical framework yet exists within which the diverse, and often discrepant, facts of observation may be co-ordinated, there are signs of an increasing concern with the conceptual apparatus of social science. In particular, the "field theory" of Lewin and his associates, originally inspired by considerations of Gestalt psychology, has provided a fresh, if limited, body of concepts for handling observations of human social behaviour.[2] Inspiration, too, has been forthcoming from psychoanalytical sources, and a recent important study of social relations in industry goes far to justify this approach.[3] Although it has not proved possible to apply Freudian theory in any precise way to the problems of social science, it has at least become clear that fuller understanding of the unconscious origins of much human behaviour is an essential prerequisite for their solution.

It is probable that advances of some magnitude will be made in the study of human social behaviour in the coming years. At the same time, it is most doubtful whether the findings of psychology will permit more than a very limited increase in the rational control of human affairs. As in the case of nuclear physics, scientists cannot necessarily expect their discoveries to be applied wholly or exclusively in the interests of human welfare. Psychology is not magic; psychological knowledge does not necessarily spell wisdom.

[1] An adequate review of the field is given by W. H. J. Sprott, *Social Psychology* (Methuen, 1952).

[2] K. Lewin, *Field Theory in Social Science* (Tavistock Publications, 1952).

[3] E. Jaques, *The Changing Culture of a Factory* (Tavistock Publications, 1951).

BOOKS SUGGESTED FOR FURTHER READING

F. C. Bartlett, *The Mind at Work and Play* (Allen and Unwin, 1951).

S. Freud, *Introductory Lectures on Psychoanalysis* (Allen and Unwin, 1922).

O. L. Zangwill, *An Introduction to Modern Psychology* (Methuen, 1950).

192

M. Klein, P. Heimann, S. Isaacs and J. Riviere, *Developments in Psycho-Analysis* (The Hogarth Press, 1952).

G. Ryle, *The Concept of Mind* (Hutchinson, 1949).

R. S. Woodworth and M. Schlosberg, *Experimental Psychology* (Methuen, 1954).

PARAPSYCHOLOGY

by PROFESSOR J. B. RHINE

PARAPSYCHOLOGY, the science of psi (or "psychic") phenomena, is a newly established branch of inquiry. It is so new that in some quarters there is still controversy over whether or not it *is* a science. Probably no other subject of study, however, has been given more widespread human interest. It is largely this lay interest that has been sustaining the investigation of psi phenomena while scientific recognition has slowly been catching up.

In fact, the very feature of psi phenomena that makes them seem important to the world at large offers a special challenge to the conservative orthodox scientist. Certainly if any psi phenomena at all occur, the prevailing scientific concepts of the nature of man and the universe to which he belongs are much too narrow and inadequate and will have to be vastly extended. This new science, then, is also a revolutionary one.

Parapsychology is technically a division of psychology, which is the general study of personality in men and animals. Psi phenomena, like all psychological occurrences, belong to one of two general types: they are either subjective experiences or objective effects. On the subjective side all the psi phenomena that have been as yet studied scientifically come under the heading of extrasensory perception (ESP), the awareness of (or response to) something outside one's self, without the use of the sensory channels. It includes *clairvoyance*, the extrasensory perception of an object or objective event, and *telepathy*, the awareness of the thought or mental state of another person. There may be ESP not only of events in the present but of those in the future as well. If the future is involved, the phenomenon is called precognitive ESP or *precognition*.

On the side of objective effects the manifestations are known as *psychokinesis* or PK. In this type of phenomenon the individual produces an effect upon some object in his environment without the use of his own motor system. Thus psychokinesis is the direct action of mind on matter. It has much the same relation to ESP as muscular action has to sensory perception. Psi as a whole would appear to be the direct interoperation of subject and object; that is, interoperation without the intermediation of the sensori-motor system of the individual. It is man's contact with his environment by a method more direct than those of sense and muscle.

What is it that is so radically new in psi phenomena? It is the fact that there is nothing at all in present-day science that can begin to explain them. They are beyond the senses; and the senses have, of course, been the very foundation of all the physical sciences. Indeed, the entire physical picture of the universe, as man has come to think of it, consists of generalizations and inferences from sensory modes of experience. Accordingly, all Nature has come to be regarded as a system of *physical* forces. When occurrences and experiences have been encountered that do not seem to belong to the world of matter, they have either been ignored or have been relegated to the world of the supernatural. They do not fit into the universe as science has envisaged it.

Parapsychology, having now brought such apparently non-physical occurrences under careful scientific study, has found some of them to be natural and lawful and has experimentally confirmed their occurrence. Although the first reaction of the majority of fellow-scientists was one of rejection, that attitude is giving way to gradual acceptance, and attention is being directed now to inquiries into the nature of psi capacity.

The field of parapsychology proper had best be regarded as limited to its more controlled experimental studies. It may well have something in common with religious groups such as the spiritualists, with practices such as dowsing, and with numerous other associations. But the name may easily be borrowed too freely and its meaning much confused unless it be designated to identify what has now become the established problem area of psi phenomena. Let it then expand as its experimentally radiating results are extended to wider areas of problems.

The field is known, too, by other designations. If, as seems likely, those who use older terms like "Psychical Research" and "Metapsychic" or "Psychic Science" will concur in the specification of problem-area just given, these expressions may be used interchangeably with parapsychology.

Parapsychology owes its initial stimulus to instances in which psi occurred spontaneously. These occurrences, popularly called psychic experiences, are familiar in every culture and are recorded in the literature of all peoples. Across the cultural and historic divisions, the essential character of the experiences seems much the same.

The general pattern of the psychic experience accordingly needs no illustration. One of the most common types is that which conveys to a person some awareness of a significant event, more often than not a tragic one, occurring to a loved one, often in some far-away area of the globe. Sometimes the experience suggests that there has been a telepathic transfer of thought from one individual to the other. In other cases it seems as if there had been some clairvoyant perspective of the distant scene that enabled the event to be perceived in spite of long distance or other barriers.

As often as not the experience occurs in a dream; or, if the percipient is awake, he may experience a hallucination of the far-away event much as if it were in a dream. In many instances, however, the experience may be only a premonition, an intuitive feeling, a mere compulsion to act in a way that turns out to be significant in the light of an actual related event. For example, a mother may leave a party and hurry home to find her child in a critical state, perhaps not knowing until she arrives why she had to come. But whether or not she is conscious of the reason for such a guiding or compelling impulse, she feels that in some way which she cannot explain she did make contact with the critical situation. In other words, she did have knowledge not secured by sensory means.

Spontaneous psi experiences have been taken more or less seriously in every civilization. They have played an important part in the making of all the religions, a part which appears to have been an essential one. With the development of sciences based upon the sensori-motor contact of man with reality, these experiences were, in the nature of the case, ruled out as having no basis in reality. Reality had to be defined in terms of the principles of nature filtered through the sensori-motor system, and that of course was physical. This situation led to the state of affairs in the last quarter of the nineteenth century that produced the first investigations of psi phenomena. The clash between supernatural religion and the materialistic philosophy of natural science produced a crisis in the minds of thinking men. Most of the more scientific either abandoned their supernatural religion or came to a settled compromise by which they allowed the best of religion and science to occupy distinct mental compartments. A few, however, decided to have a closer look at Nature to see whether there were not in Nature itself evidence of reality that transcended physical explanation.

These early inquirers became known as psychical researchers and in the last quarter of the century they founded psychical research societies in many countries of Europe and America. They began by collecting and classifying spontaneous cases of telepathy, because apparent contact of mind with mind across the reach of space in such cases seemed to suggest a transcendence of the material order by the human mind. It suggested a spiritual, as against a physical, type of operation. But in spite of the best efforts to collect and authenticate these experiences of telepathy, it proved impossible to make from them a case so sound that it would refute the engagingly simplifying concept of Nature that the natural sciences had universally favoured. It became clear that it would take something more impressive than anecdotal material to establish a case for a transcendent or spiritual element in man. Then it was that experiments in telepathy began to spring up in various countries.

An experiment as it was conducted in the eighties and nineties can readily enough be criticized today: for example, the experimenters did not even take the trouble to exclude the possibility that clairvoyance rather than telepathy might operate in the test. The sender was asked to concentrate on a playing card, a number, or a drawing, while the receiver, usually seated in the same room with his back turned toward the sender, was asked to identify the target upon which the sender was concentrating. In such a setup, of course, clairvoyant perception of the object itself was as much a possibility as telepathy.

The main purpose of the experiment was served, however, even though by present standards the experimental design was not perfect. The tests gave evidence that something beyond mere chance had been in operation, and the experimenters themselves were satisfied that the results could not be accounted for by any existing theory. Their reports, published in the *Proceedings of the Society for Psychical Research*, as most of them were, and in various books of the day, presented a new claim on the intelligent interest of mankind, a challenge to the current mechanistic thinking on the nature of man. Some of the pioneers in these experiments were themselves distinguished physicists, such as Sir Oliver Lodge, Sir William Crookes and Sir William Barrett. And later an occasional psychologist of distinction would give his attention to the problem, although in the main the profession of psychology, itself still new, held aloof. Among these pioneers were Professors William James, G. Heymans and William McDougall. The net effect of the experimental work was to build a strong case for the continued investigation of telepathy. It is true, the experimental work carried out in such psychology laboratories as those of Harvard, Groningen and Stanford during the first quarter of the twentieth century turned out to be short-lived; for the reactions from the psychology profession as a whole were such as thoroughly to discourage further investigation. The results obtained had, however, been encouraging, whether or not they were acceptably conclusive; and their existence made it easier for a more enduring and systematic centre of investigation to be established later.

Under the sponsorship and guidance of Professor McDougall, research in ESP was begun at Duke University in 1930. A series of psi investigations led to the development of a research centre there which, in the course of a few years, took the identifying title of The Parapsychology Laboratory of Duke University. In 1934 a monograph summarizing the results of the first three years of its work was published under the title *Extrasensory Perception*, and in 1937 the *Journal of Parapsychology* was started with Professor McDougall as one of the founding editors. Twenty-five years later this laboratory is still the only one of its kind in which a staff of full-time investigators is maintained for the study of parapsychology.

One of the main developments in parapsychology in the thirties consisted of the devising of methods. There was great need of standardized procedures that could easily be repeated by different experimenters. A special pack of cards was designed for the investigation of ESP. It consisted of twenty-five cards, each having one of five geometric designs that had been selected for distinctiveness—star, square, waves, circle and cross. The pack might be made up in either of two ways: It might have an equal number of cards of each symbol (closed pack) or it might be made up from a larger collection (or by using random numbers) and thus would have unequal numbers of the five symbols. Thus, in the proper use of the cards it could be taken for granted that an average score of five per twenty-five, or a 20 per cent. rate of success, was to be expected from chance alone.

In the testing of telepathy an effort was made to exclude the possibility of clairvoyance by not giving the sender any object (card) to look at during the test. He would not even record the symbol of which he was thinking until after the signal indicated that the receiver had already made a record of his response. Thus there was no physical target object involved in the sender's part of the test, nothing except the functioning of his nervous (or neuro-muscular) system. For that stage of the investigation (the mid-thirties), this condition was considered adequate for a test of pure telepathy; it was at least an improvement on the older type of telepathy test, which would now be considered rather as a test of general or undifferentiated ESP.

In a clairvoyance test the cards were shuffled and cut and kept face downward by the experimenter during the test. They had, of course, to be kept out of the subject's view and if the ordinary or closed pack was used, the subject was told his score only at the end of the run.

Later developments made it necessary to modify both the test procedure for clairvoyance and that for telepathy, for it turned out that the safeguards against telepathy in the clairvoyance test and against clairvoyance in the telepathy test were not so good as they had been supposed at this early stage to be. In this brief review it will not be possible to trace these developments through their subsequent stages but the full story can be found in the original publications in the *Journal of Parapsychology* (see especially volumes for 1945 and 1946), or in my book, *The Reach of the Mind*. Those who follow the story through will be surprised to discover that although telepathy was the first type of psi phenomenon to be systematically investigated, it turned out to be the type in which it was most difficult to rule out conclusively the possibility of the operation of other types of psi.

Once methods of standardizing the testing of ESP had been developed, the logical next step was to design an experiment that would be crucial and so take the question of the occurrence of psi out of the realm of debatability. For the Duke investigators this milestone was reached in 1933 when the Pearce-Pratt series of experiments was completed. The first part of this series, which was designed as an adequate test, has been reported in the monograph already mentioned. This series will suffice to illustrate here the method and general character of this stage of the research in extra-sensory perception.

The standard pack of ESP test-cards was used. The cards were handled by J. G. Pratt, then a graduate student in psychology and my assistant in the ESP research. Located in another building one hundred yards away, Hubert Pearce, a Divinity School student, attempted to identify the cards as Pratt isolated them one by one, as it had been arranged with Pearce that he would do. The two men had synchronized their watches. One minute was given to each card. Two runs through the pack were made each day for six days, duplicate copies of the records were made, and before they met to check the number of successes each man sealed up one copy to be handed over to me. In the total of 300 trials that were made in the series the number expected on a theory of chance was 60, or twenty per cent. Actually, 119 hits, or approximately 40 per cent., were made by Pearce. Such a result could hardly be thought of as explainable by chance, for it would not be expected once in more than a trillion of such experiments. Even the possibility that the two men might have entered into a conspiracy to produce the scores fraudulently was ruled out by later experiments at which I was present and watched the operation where Pearce was being tested. Nothing then but ESP could explain the results.

Satisfied as the experimenters were that the occurrence of ESP was now established, their interest then turned logically to the question of the nature of the process; though naturally the evidence of ESP went on accumulating, even faster than before. While not every experimenter obtained confirmatory results, the majority of them did. Many of these repetitions were carried out under well-controlled conditions, some even with improvements over the Pearce-Pratt stage of method-development. If space allowed, there should be an account given of the elaborately controlled work of Dr. S. G.

Soal of Queen Mary College, London, and his associates. Starting a repetition of the Duke experiments in a mood of professed scepticism regarding them, Soal had his attention directed to evidence of ESP overlooked in his analyses as he was about to report negative results. He (with Mrs. K. M. Goldney) then set out to repeat his experiment under much improved conditions, and they reaped an impressive harvest of ESP evidence as a result.

In response to criticism by psychologists, an elaborately controlled series of ESP tests was conducted in 1939 at Duke by two psychologists, Dr. Pratt and (now Dr.) J. L. Woodruff. It was probably the most completely controlled experiment ever carried out in a psychology laboratory. It yielded significant evidence of ESP even though the procedure was burdened with complicated precautions. For detailed accounts of these later experiments the reader may turn to the bibliography at the end of this review.

While the flow of research continued to gather more and more evidence of ESP, the Duke inquiries were extended to include other questions. How was this ESP effect to be classified, first of all with regard to physics? Could it be that even though no obvious explanation based on known physical processes could account for the Pearce-Pratt results, there might still be a physical explanation for them? This question of whether ESP was a physical process led to a series of more advanced experiments. The first of these bore on the question of distance and ESP.

One point that had stood out in the Pearce-Pratt results was that the average score Pearce had made when he was 100 yards distant from the card, was not below that which he had made in experiments in which shorter distances were involved, and even those in which the cards were on the table in front of him. This and other work that followed gave rise to the suggestion that in this kind of test distance was not an important factor, a suggestion that had already been given by earlier work and by the large collection of spontaneous cases in which the persons concerned had been, in many instances, hundreds and even thousands of miles away from the events they clairvoyantly or telepathically perceived.

The suggestion that ESP was not related to the distance over which it operated raised another question. It seemed to follow logically that if *space* is not a limiting condition, ESP should be independent of *time* also. It seemed reasonable to attempt next to discover whether the subject in ESP tests could identify a future order of cards in the pack as well as an immediate order. On this point, too, the collection of spontaneous material offered very definite and clear-cut support. In the Duke collection of spontaneous material begun in 1945 by Dr. Louisa E. Rhine, almost half of the items reported are instances of prophetic or precognitive awareness, most of them premonitory dreams, but many of them waking visions in which some scene was perceived in advance of its actual occurrence.

On the level of actual testing the project seemed feasible, at least on an exploratory basis. It was necessary only to arouse interest in the subject to see whether he could direct his ESP capacity to the future card order instead of the present. He was then asked to predict the sequence of symbols, not as it was at the time but as it would be after the cards had been rearranged by a special shuffling treatment. As had been logically anticipated, this shift from the present to the future in the ESP tests was successful at the scoring level the subject had been able to attain on immediate card order. Significant extra-chance scoring was produced and the first actual experimental testing of the old claim of prophecy became a matter of record in the Parapsychology Laboratory in December, 1933.

As in the case of telepathy, however, there was a long development between the exploratory stage in precognition and the definitive experiment. The story involved is fascinating to those who appreciate the adventure of discovery. Several times the experimenters carried through an investigation, obtaining evidence that appeared to justify the conclusion that precognitive ESP had been operating, only to find when alternative interpretations were pushed to their extreme limits that it was at least possible, if not entirely reasonable, that the results could have been produced by something other than precognition. Research advances in other problems also turned up new alternatives that changed the picture. So long as a reasonable alternative could be imagined, the experimental design had to be altered and new experiments conducted. For example, the first exploratory step based on hand shuffling gave way to mechanical methods of rearranging the cards. That method, in turn, was found inadequate; it did not eliminate the possibility of a psychokinetic factor in the rearrangement.

Even today the state of the precognition research is still a fluid one. The present case for the occurrence of precognition rests on experiments in which the packs of target cards, in addition to being shuffled mechanically in a routine way, were then cut in accordance with a design involving the use of temperature readings published in a specified newspaper on a designated date. The purpose of this complicated ritual by which the target order was arrived at was to exclude any alternative possibility by which significant scoring might be secured; if the results were significantly different from chance, and the design was sufficiently sound, the case for precognition would be confirmed.

Evidence of precognition has been obtained in the Duke Laboratory under the conditions described, first by myself and then in a confirmatory series by Dr. Betty M. Humphrey and myself. No other systematic effort, however, has been made to investigate precognition except in the Duke Laboratory, but even at Duke there is not complete satisfaction that the case is watertight. The reason for this extreme open-mindedness to alternatives to precognition is the fact that precognition probably represents the most revolutionary hypothesis ever raised in science. It challenges the whole concept of seriality in causation as nothing has ever done. For that reason some investigators are tempted to emphasize the possibility that a psychokinetic factor might enter into the manipulation of the thermometer or that some other alternative to precognition might have played a part in influencing the weather or the meteorologist who recorded its data. Perhaps this state of hyper-intellectual anxiety illustrates as well as anything could do the difficult atmosphere in which experiments in parapsychology must be carried out.

In any case, more experiments in precognition are needed, and those which are in process have already been additionally safe-guarded. In determining the random target order—now a calculation too complicated for the unaided human mind—an electric computing machine has been introduced. This is intended to provide security against any alternative except direct precognition. It is too early to say anything conclusive, but as of the moment the indications are that the new addition is not going to weaken the case for precognition. It is safe, perhaps, for the inquirer in parapsychology now to direct his efforts toward the great mystery of *how* precognition can operate. For this study there is not only great need and great challenge, but the methods are ready and they would be usable even by comparative amateurs.

Soon after the beginning had been made on precognition came the problem of psychokinesis. The early experiments in PK began, in fact, only a few months after the initial testing in precognitive card calling. The reason for this spread of interest was not that there was any feeling that now the case for precognition had been settled once and for all. Rather, in the first flush of satisfaction over the fact that the precognition experiment had confirmed the logical prediction, made on the basis of the distance tests of ESP and the spontaneous cases of precognition, there was encouragement to use the same predictive logic to ascertain what else might be inferred from past results that would indicate further areas to explore.

The argument for PK was this: In the ESP test the subject responded to the card object in a way that made it appear that the object produced some effect upon him. In all natural science it has long been supposed that the law of reaction holds good universally; i.e. to every action there is a reaction. In this case, then, there should be supposed to be some reaction upon the object or upon something which the object produces or influences. But what possible reaction could there be upon the object? Nothing at least had been discovered that could be registered on the cards so far as known measurements were concerned. Obviously some other kind of test was necessary if any hypothetical effect of the subjective state of the individual on the object was to be measured. If the capacity operating as ESP had been found to function, it was necessary to devise a measure that would capture a very light and erratic effect. In this case, however, the effect would be physical; for the hypothesis was that a psycho-physical interaction between subject and object was taking place by some other channel than the motor system of the individual.

In February, 1934, the suggestion was made by a gambler that we take note of the fact that many people believe they can influence the fall of dice by direct action of the will. This suggestion was just what was needed. Here was a method that could be adapted to the purpose of the experiment. The game-like character of the test would enable the subject to experience an easy conviction that he was able to influence the dice. Methods of handling the dice could be introduced that eliminated the possibility of manual skills. The test could be so designed that any possible error introduced by inequalities in the structure of the dice could not introduce an error into the interpretation of results. The methods, necessarily simple at first, had, of course, to be developed as the research progressed: the sophisticated controls that become necessary at certain later stages are quite out of place and unjustified in the exploratory steps of a new programme of inquiry.

After eight years of investigation in which many different individual experimenters took part, the time came when conclusions could safely be drawn. The staff of the Parapsychology Laboratory had arrived at a crucial type of demonstration of the case for the occurrence of a psychokinetic effect in the dice-throwing experiments: a demonstration that was independent of any single experimental method. The development of this conclusive case led then to the first publication in 1943 of the results on psychokinesis.

The nature of the original case for PK can at least be outlined. It rests on the analysis of a large body of experimental records assembled over the eight-year period mentioned. The one fact common to all of this group of experiments was that the subjects attempted to influence falling dice.

These records were the results of eighteen different research series representing different experimenters and different subjects, although there was some overlapping. In general, too, in the various series there were differences in the way the dice were handled, whether thrown from cups or released and allowed to roll by gravity or rotated in electrically driven cages; there was even one series in which they were thrown by hand. In some cases different numbers of dice were thrown at a time, in many series the dice were of different sizes, and different types of record sheets were used. Again, the target face or combination of faces which the subject tried to reproduce with each throw of the dice was determined by different procedures or systems from one series to another. The point is, these were all exploratory experiments, some of them conducted by university psychologists, some by students, and some by others of the university community and its friends. They had served their purpose of helping the experimenter to decide whether the dice-throwing technique of testing PK was promising enough to justify further interest.

In 1942, however, my assistant Miss Betty M. Humphrey and I decided to look into the records of all these experiments for certain declines of scoring rates that had proved to be fairly persistent in the records of the experiments in ESP. We discovered that there was a tendency on the record sheet, no matter what the method or target face or number of dice per throw, to show a falling off in percentage of hits from left to right across the page and from top to bottom down the column. It was a simple matter then to take all of the homogeneous pages, quarter them equally, and compare the percentage of successes. A strong accumulative effect was found as we went from series to series, showing that the upper left-hand quarter showed the highest, and the lower right the lowest scoring on the page. It was necessary only to evaluate the difference between these two quarters, the first and fourth, series by series and for the entire eighteen series, to see that here was something not reasonably attributable to chance.

For the total cumulative difference the odds were of the order of a million to one that such a result would not be produceable from a chance series. Here was an effect that could only be psychological. The dice were the same and the methods of throwing and recording were the same throughout the page. Yet here, as in the ESP records, was evidence of this curious falling off of scoring rate which had become a kind of earmark of the functioning of psi under test conditions.

Fortunately it was possible to do an independent test of this principle, as on the record sheets in twelve of the eighteen series there were smaller units within the page total which were called sets. The sets were quartered as the total page had been and were found to show the same decline from the first to the fourth quarter, with even a more striking rate of difference. Again, even though fewer data were involved in this analysis, the odds were a million to one against our obtaining such a difference by chance.

This test appeared so crucial and, with its confirmation based on the analysis of the set, so conclusive, that it seemed advisable to anticipate the inevitable last resort of the sceptic that there must be something wrong with the analyses. In publishing the reports of the quarter-distribution analyses, we announced, therefore, that the records were open to any qualified committee or representative of an investigating committee who wished to repeat the analyses. And to satisfy ourselves that we were, indeed, prepared for any such independent investigation, we invited a former member of the Laboratory staff who had been dissociated from the investigations of psychokinesis, Dr. J. G. Pratt, to make a special investigation as though representing an outside agency. He found and reported one error which was not of serious import. The case for PK, based on these analyses, therefore remains as yet unchallenged.

As in the case of research in ESP, the conclusion regarding PK reached at the Duke Laboratory has been confirmed by results obtained elsewhere. This confirmation has occurred many times over and with certain angles of improved design added to the experimental procedure. For example, Dr. R. H. Thouless, in a series of dice-throwing tests in which he himself was the subject as well as the experimenter, introduced a method of selecting the target face by a complicated design based on the Latin Square method that eliminated the possibility that he used precognition of the way the dice were going to fall in selecting the most favourable target face for a given series of throws.

Dr. Robert A. McConnell of the University of Pittsburgh, using apparatus borrowed from the Parapsychology Laboratory, conducted a series of PK tests in which the dice were handled completely mechanically and a photographic record was taken of the way in which they fell. His results showed the same type of decline towards the right and downward which previous work had shown, and they produced an internal difference of statistical significance that justified the conclusion that PK was a factor.

Just as we came from the distance experiment in clairvoyant perception to an experiment in precognition and obtained confirmatory evidence of the prediction; so by similar logic and subsequent experiments we made the jump from the same clairvoyance experiment to the test of psychokinesis, and the predicted reaction of subject upon object was demonstrated. The whole rational network illustrated by these two cases has given to the findings in parapsychology a highly integrated interrelationship. A rationale has emerged that, to the inquiring scientific mind, is the most reassuring aspect of the research. This growing concept of relations led to the hypothesis that in the psi functions we are dealing with one basic subject-object interaction, reversible in type and broad in its range of application, independent of space, time and mass, but lawful and orderly in its own way of operation.

dark introspectively as the subject was, there was bound to be a considerable hit-or-miss quality to his responses even though he possessed some ESP capacity. If he had known when he was right or wrong, he could, of course, have designated for record only those trials that he knew to be correct. His score would have approximated perfection and he would have eliminated the necessity of using statistical method.

Again, if a subject knew when he was right or knew definitely when he was wrong, there would be a possibility of learning and, accordingly, of improving the scoring rate, of discovering the conditions of more effective performance, and of putting the whole research on a basis of efficiency that is not even now attainable.

Many other curious effects that have been found in the researches are now less puzzling: as, for example, the decline in scoring-rate as a subject continues through a long sequence of trials. It is much easier to see how this decline in scoring-rate could come about once it is recognized that the subject was using an elusive, unconscious function. Similarly with the tendency shown by some subjects to displace in their responses and make a practice of aiming at the card ahead or lagging one card behind as they went through the run of trials in the tests. These and other unconscious twists in the operation of the psi function were robbed of at least part of their mystery by the recognition of the failure of introspective consciousness to get any glimpse of the real process.

During this same period, the forties, the effort was made by a number of psychologists to find a correlation between psi capacity and some of the more familiar personality states and traits. There has, of course, always been quite a range of beliefs among various peoples that certain groups are more "psychic" than others. To begin with, there have been racial and national linkages of this sort in the popular mind, as, for example, the association of second-sight with the Scots. During the period of experimental work in parapsychology, too, there have been many suggestions made that perhaps some special selection of subjects such as identical twins, persons who are blind, or some other grouping, might show outstanding psi capacity of one kind or another.

Without attempting here to summarize the experimental data, I can say that none of these general impressions or specific suggestions has thus far received any experimental support. Rather, as the evidence has accumulated from various parts of the world and from various cross-sections of humanity, a quite different impression has taken the place of these more popular concepts; namely, that it is probable that everyone has psi capacity but that there are individual and even group differences in the way in which the capacity is regarded and, to some extent, the readiness with which it may be allowed to function. Even while a subject exercises psi in any form he is, of course, a whole personality with many other functions and operations going on at the same time. Some of these may favour his exercise of psi in a test situation, whereas others may hinder it. The late Dr. C. E. Stuart of the Duke Laboratory pioneered in the study of these associated personality states; and others, particularly Dr. Gertrude Schmeidler and Dr. Betty Humphrey, considerably extended the range of personality correlates included in the programme of research. Findings of immediate practical value both in the research itself and in the understanding of the way psi works in a test situation came out of this broad programme of inquiry; but it left the impression, nevertheless, that psi itself is a more basic and more deeply embedded function of the organism than had been supposed and is as broad as humanity itself, if not extended even further. Certainly no single human group has a monopoly on it.

In consequence of this survey of personality correlates, along with recognition of the fact that psi is unconscious, the hypothesis of a pre-human origin for psi gradually developed. In support of this there had been, along with the spontaneous human experiences of psi, an occasional report of animal behaviour that suggested capacities in other species similar to those called psi in human beings. By the early fifties the accumulated psychological findings concerning the nature of psi pointed so strongly to the necessity of a biological study that such a project was initiated. Preliminary surveys of animal behaviour that seemed most to suggest the possibility of the presence of a psi factor pointed to the dog, cat, and pigeon as perhaps the best species to use as starting points for exploratory investigation. The collection of anecdotal material on exceptional feats of homing in these three species gave about as strong a case as such material taken alone can do. Instances of particular interest were found in which the animal was reported actually to have followed and found its human companion in territory completely new to the animal and over distances as great as hundreds of miles.

Exploratory tests with cats got under way first, since this species proved to be a more feasible one·with which to work. As a result Dr. Karlis Osis and his associates at the Duke Laboratory have now obtained experimental evidence of the operation of psi in the domestic cat. Experiments with the other two species are under way and may be characterized as at least promising, although still inconclusive.

A word on historical perspective should be given before closing, and also a note on the prospect ahead. Beginning about seventy-five years ago with a study of loosely identified puzzling phenomena, the study of parapsychology has come through certain phases of definition and organization. The nature of its problems has been clarified: namely, as dealing with the essential question of whether in human life or all life there are operations that transcend the boundaries of what is called physical. It is true that the distinction between the physical and the non-physical is not likely to prove in the long run to be a profound one. Most of the efforts to divide nature into nice curricular classifications have eventually given way to the essential unity of nature. But just now, in times when it is important to discover what is distinctive about personality and life, this difference is very important to the study of man. Human institutions have been founded on a concept of man as non-physical: a conception progressively challenged by the physicalism emerging from the sciences. Ideologies are now gaining the ascendency in human civilization that derive largely from materialism and the cerebrocentric concept of man. Parapsychology has at least made a beginning and opened a way toward the scientific solution of this great basic question of the nature of man.

The establishment of any kind of psi phenomena as having occurred however fleetingly in any individual breaks the bondage of human thought to the mechanistic philosophy of man. The discovery of the types of psi phenomena, the conditions under which they function, the various types of lawful operation and interrelation that have been discovered all furnish the reassurance required by the rational mind in recognizing this area as a domain of the reality of nature. And there is consistency: first, the finding over a wide range of experiments of the consistently non-physical nature of psi; and secondly the equally consistent relationship found between psi functions and mental processes other than the sensori-motor functions (which of course represent contact with the physical environment). This consistency affords a convincing conclusiveness to the inquirer whose study permits him to gain the perspective needed to appreciate it.

Plausibly enough, there is no reason known to science why at this point, any more than at an earlier stage in the history of science, the mind of man should stop moving forward to new areas of exploration. Why, indeed, should we suppose there could be no kind of energy beyond those that are known? Why should it be assumed that all the energies of nature, like those that are already familiar, should be subject to time and space and mass relationships or interceptible by the sensory organs of man? We know, as a matter of fact, that much of the energetic activity of nature is quite beyond the sensory range; and now and then we are reminded by the physicist that he himself cannot find definite measurable relations with time, space and mass for all his phenomena. It would be witless, indeed, for us to close the gates to new hypotheses concerning energetics so long as our whole range of subjective experience is still so completely unexplained as to have almost nothing in common with the known laws of physical nature. The psi investigations are calling attention to the fact that, as in PK, energetic effects can be produced without the usual familiar criteria of physics being present. That is an opening that both the psychophysicists and the psychologists will some day want to use.

There is a wide zone of unfinished labour just outside the area of experimentally cultivated parapsychology. On the side of practical affairs there are many areas of application to which throughout the history of man psi capacities have been applied or it has been attempted to apply them. The attempt to divine the future, to obtain knowledge of far-away events, of the military secrets of a potential enemy, the nature or prognosis of disease, the location of lost or underground objects and substances ranging from water to uranium are all examples. The very fact that no reliable art or practice has developed based on psi capacity indicates that present knowledge and present endowments of the human race are not enough. If any reliable practice is possible, it will have to be brought about by acquiring new knowledge. That, of course, has been the history of technological advance in general. This whole range of practical application is an area for future research, important enough in itself but secondary to the other implications and bearings of the psi investigations.

On the broad front of religion and its affiliates parapsychology has its major significance. All that is needed, to see something of this significance, is to recognize that, in a universe in which it were clearly established that only physical forces exist, religion, morality, democracy, freedom and many other functions that make life meaningful would have no place or reality. It is not necessary to say more at this point concerning the significance of parapsychology for religion than to point to its experimental refutation of a physical theory of man. In my book, *New World of the Mind*, I have developed the significance of psi for religion, for mental health, and for the conduct of life to a somewhat speculative extent. For the present, however, it is enough to say that if mankind is going to continue to make use of concepts of value in human life, if man is going to continue to take his own subjective experience seriously and try to integrate it with natural science, if human beings are going to try to understand each other and survive in an age as explosive as ours has become, we shall need to follow up the leads that the psi researches have given—in the direction of principles representing a reality that, while neither physical nor supernatural, is the proper domain of the natural science of the mind.

BOOKS SUGGESTED FOR FURTHER READING

J. G. Pratt, J. B. Rhine, B. M. Smith, C. E. Stuart and J. A. Greenwood, *Extrasensory Perception After Sixty Years* (Holt, 1940).
J. B. Rhine, *The Reach of the Mind* (Faber, 1948).
J. B. Rhine, *New World of the Mind* (Faber, 1954).
S. G. Soal and F. Bateman, *Modern Experiments in Telepathy* (Faber, 1954).
G. N. M. Tyrrell, *Science and Psychical Phenomena* (Methuen, 1938).
D. J. West, *Psychical Research Today* (Duckworth, 1954).

MEDICINE

by LORD AMULREE

THE TWENTIETH CENTURY has been a time when the great discoveries of the nineteenth century have been developed and expanded. The changes have not, perhaps, been so exciting as those that followed the long, almost stagnant period from Galen to Sydenham and Harvey: they are, nevertheless, sufficiently dramatic.

The pattern of medicine is gradually changing, as it will always change. Diseases common to one generation become unknown to the next, and others, equally unknown to the earlier, take their place. During the last fifty years there has also been a remarkable change of attitude: the emphasis of medicine has changed from cure to prevention. For this, however, medicine has to thank not one of its own members, but a great lay administrator of the nineteenth century, Sir Edwin Chadwick. It was Chadwick who, realizing how much of disease was caused by dirt and overcrowding, urged on an unwilling world the adoption of sanitary reform. He saw that in the polluted water and inadequate sewage disposal of our great towns lay the seeds of much preventable disease. From Chadwick's work grew up the doctrine of environmental hygiene which insisted that human beings should be born into and live in decent, wholesome surroundings. Largely as a result of this work the expectation of life of a child born today is twenty years longer than it was in 1900. Little change has been made, however, in the over-all prolongation of life, and the expectation of life of a man or woman of sixty-five has hardly increased at all. The great killing diseases of infancy, scarlet fever, diphtheria and a number of respiratory and gastrointestinal infections seem to have been brought under control. There are many reasons for this, but among the most important is the general improvement in housing and living conditions. The deplorable standard of living of many of the poorer working-class people has been greatly improved, and as a result these diseases, which spread so easily and fatally when masses of people lived huddled together in overcrowded squalid tenements, are now in retreat. It would be inadvisable, however, to assume that their defeat is permanent; for, if similar living conditions were to reappear, we have no grounds for assuming that these diseases would not resume their toll of infant life. At the same time, the growing practice of immunizing potential patients against diphtheria has contributed much to the lowered incidence and death-rate from this disease.

The feeding of infants has been studied with care and detail, and the great developments in pediatrics have resulted in many a child surviving the storms of childhood who, fifty years ago, would inevitably have perished. Hopkins's discovery of vitamins has greatly assisted in the knowledge of what is the proper diet for infants, and such deficiency diseases as rickets are slowly vanishing. The knowledge that a sick or undernourished child may die from dehydration, or lack of fluid alone, has assisted medical treatment. Blood transfusion or the replacement of fluid by other means has helped to reduce the mortality of infants and young children. Premature babies are now cared for in incubators and kept free from outside dangers of infection. This, combined with a better appreciation of their dietetic requirements, has greatly improved their expectation of life. Infant and child welfare services are available in most civilized countries, and pediatrics and the care of children is becoming more and more a preventive service.

But adolescents no less than children have benefited from the improvements in environmental hygiene. Although part of the fall in the death-rate from pulmonary and other forms of tuberculosis must be attributed to improvements in diagnosis and treatment, yet improved housing and working conditions have led to a noticeable fall in the incidence of this disease.

Dodds's discovery of the sulphonamides and Fleming's and Florey's of the antibiotics, notably penicillin, have from the curative and treatment angle done more than any other single discovery to reduce mortality from infective disease of all sorts, in young and old alike. No longer does one see in hospital young, strong adults battling, too often hopelessly, with a lobar pneumonia, while both young children and elderly patients recover, as if by magic, from an attack of broncho-pneumonia which would have inevitably proved fatal twenty years ago. The great improvement in the result of the treatment of wounds in the second world war compared with the first world war must very largely be attributed to these discoveries.

Cancer still remains one of the great killing diseases of mankind, but, while the general picture remains confused, considerable progress has been made in the treatment of cancer of various organs. Cancer, it should be realized, is a disease of individual organs, and responds to treatment quite differently in each one of these. The causes of a cancer developing in an organ are twofold. It is now becoming generally accepted that there is some general bodily condition which makes a person liable to develop cancer, and that there is also a local factor which determines in which organ that cancer shall appear. Of the first of these causes we know but little; of the second, a large amount of knowledge has been accumulated and more is being added each year. For example, the incidence of cancer of the lip has been greatly reduced by the disappearance of the clay pipe. Better dentistry and the adequate treatment of syphilis have together led to a reduction in the incidence of cancer of the mouth and tongue. The cancer of the scrotum associated with mule-spinners in Lancashire is now, since preventive measures have been taken, almost unknown. Among the Indians it has been shown that cancer of the skin is associated with the use of kangri heaters applied to the abdomen, while that of the mouth is associated with chewing of the betel nut. But there are many curious and unexplained facts. For example, among men who are circumcised at birth cancer of the penis is unknown; cancer of the neck of the womb is more common in women who have borne children than among those who have not. It might be argued, therefore, that improvement in midwifery methods and general post-natal care will reduce the local causative factors. Cancer of the breast, however, is commoner in women who have not borne children and seems, therefore, to be associated with a lack of a physiological factor in function. Cancer of the stomach is common among the higher social classes and cancer of the rectum among the lower. Why this should be is unknown. The fact that the incidence of cancer of the oesophagus is proportionately and significantly commoner in Holland than in England is interesting but inexplainable: it looks as if a difference in the diet of the two countries should give the answer, but up to the present there is no evidence of what that will be.

Much attention has recently been given to the spectacular increase in the deaths from cancer of the lung, especially among males, since the beginning of the century. When this increase was first noticed, thirty or forty years ago, it was thought that it might be attributed to improvements in diagnosis. X-rays were in more general use, and it was found that there was a slow reduction in the number of deaths certified as from rather vague chest conditions. But the increase has now become so great that it is accepted that there must be a real increase in the incidence of this disease. Some observers have claimed that this increase is the result of heavy smoking, and formidable arrays of figures have been produced towards this end. While, however, there does seem to be evidence that there is some connexion between excessive cigarette smoking and the incidence of lung cancer, what that connexion is is not clear: it does not seem to be a direct one of cause and effect. The tobacco companies in U.K. and U.S.A. propose to spend large sums of money in extensive research into this problem, and we must wait for the results of this research before we can answer the problem.

When considering the question of any general increase in the incidence of cancer, it must not be forgotten that one of the results of an ageing population is an increase in the number of patients who suffer from cancer. This does not mean that there is a real increase in the cause or in the incidence of the disease; but, as cancer is, in the main, a disease of the second half of life, more cancer will develop as the lives of more people are prolonged into this period. This is well shown when the steady rise in the crude death-rate from cancer is compared with the death-rate standard-ized to meet the changing age and sex constitution of the popula-tion, for then the increase is seen to be more apparent than real.

From what has been said it is clear that to talk of a "cure for cancer" is to err on the side of too great a generalization. It is unlikely that any one cure for all the cancers of the body will ever be made available. But when one considers the treatment and cure of cancer of certain organs, the outlook becomes more encouraging. It is true that treatment has, up to the present, not progressed much beyond that by surgery or by radiotherapy. Radical surgery is, after all, nothing more than a form of mutilation; and although a large number of people live for many years, free from disease, after such treatment, some more satisfactory method must still be sought. But, even so, surgery does give a good hope of cure for many sufferers. Radiotherapy, either by means of radium or deep X-rays, offers good hopes of cure of cancer at certain sites. But, and this must be emphasized very strongly, it is the delay of patients in seeking treat-ment when they have first noticed "something wrong" that is one of the great handicaps to obtaining more successful results. A good example of the importance and effect of this delay can be seen in the results of an investigation into the treatment of cancer of the neck of the womb that has been carried out for many years under the auspices of the health section of the former League of Nations. The histories of 73,600 patients from approved hospitals were recorded, and it was found that, among those patients who first attended for treatment when the cancer was at an early stage, 60 per cent. were alive and well at the end of five years after treatment. Yet of patients attending for treatment only 19 per cent. were seen at an early enough stage to come into this first category. The remainder were seen at stages when the percentage of "cures" fell to 41 per cent. and then to 6 per cent. As long as this state of affairs continues, progress will be slow. But by means of intensive propaganda carried out in the State of Massachusetts, the period of delay for patients attending with cancer of the breast has been reduced from nine months to six months. Recent work in nuclear physics has given new hope of the use of radioactive isotopes in the treatment of cancer: for example, radioactive cobalt is a useful, and cheaper, substitute for radium, while radioactive iodine shows encouraging results in the treatment of cancer of the thyroid. So far, these are among the few civil advantages that have been derived from all the work carried out on atomic energy. The use of super voltage X-rays, too, has shown encouraging results in the treatment of cancer of some organs, especially cancer of the brain. Chemical treatment has had a limited success in the use of stilboesterol for cancer of the prostate. This drug does, apparently, have some success in certain types of cancer of the breast in elderly women. But for cancer of many organs, and among these are two of the commonest sites, stomach and lung, treatment is only possible in a small proportion of cases, and even for these few the results are not encouraging. In view of the variability in the results of similar forms of treatment on what appear to be comparable types of the disease, a considerable amount of research has been carried out to discover why this should be so. As a result it is being found possible to come to some prognostic decision from a study of the microscopic appearance of sections of diseased tissue. Cancer seems to run a more active and malignant course in a young patient compared with an old, and disappointment can be caused by a failure to realize this. At the same time pathologists are now able to diagnose the disease, by finding malignant cells in various body fluids and excreta—e.g. malignant cells can be found in the sputum of those suffering from cancer of the lung, and in the urine where cancer of the renal tract is present.

When radium was first discovered by the Curies in 1897, it was thought that the cure of all cancer had been discovered, and the remedy was used indiscriminately by many ill-trained and ignorant persons. Because of this, early results of treatment were not satisfactory, and in addition many patients suffered considerably from the effects of ill-planned and ill-regulated dosage. Accordingly, treatment by means of radium became widely discredited, and it is only within the past thirty years that, as a result of much patient and laborious work, proper conditions of dosage and protection have been worked out. Many hitherto unsuspected dangers have been discovered, and it is now realized that all forms of radiotherapy should only be given by highly trained and skilled persons. As a result of this work, radiotherapy is now able to take its rightful place in medicine. It may be appropriate to refer here to the similar fate which has befallen the drug cortizone. When this powerful drug was first discovered in 1948, it was thought to be the long-sought answer to the treatment of rheumatoid arthritis and other rheumatic diseases. Many people only waited for its production on a wide and an economic scale to see these painful and crippling diseases controlled for ever. But prolonged administration of cortizone has not only been followed by unexpected and distressing ill effects but its value as a therapeutic agent was found to have been based on too high claims, so that it has fallen from the high favour in which it stood at first. It is realized that its therapeutic value remains high; but, such are the hazards involved, it can obviously never be used on the wide and generous scale that was at first contemplated. In time, therefore, the enthusiasms and claims will have settled down again, and this drug will assume its rightful if limited place in the therapeutic armamentarium. It has been shown that the treatment of rheumatoid arthritis with cortizone or with aspirin leads to almost similar results. It is so with so many new forms of treatment: on their discovery they are regarded almost as a panacea: when these hopes are proved false they fall in public favour and repute. But at the same time their effects and value are carefully investigated, and in time they emerge with their true value known. Experience has shown that there are limitations even to the use of penicillin: some organisms are found to be resistant from the start, and others develop a resistance in time. Further, repeated small doses taken for trifling complaints will result in a patient becoming insensitive to the drug when suffering from serious illness. Luckily, the range of the anti-biotics is large, and, as further samples are discovered, the indications for use, with proper safeguards, tend to increase. There seems no reason to fear that their use is likely to be restricted by the development of resistant patients or bacteria in the immediate future.

For other diseases, certain killers in the past, treatments have been discovered which, while not exactly cures, have enabled patients to live a normal life until old age is reached or death supervenes by reason of some intercurrent complaint. Insulin, discovered by Banting and Best in 1920, has changed the whole outlook of the management of diabetes. By its proper use the diabetic can now look forward to a life as normal and useful as that of any ordinary human being. The disease is not, it is true, cured, for the sufferers frequently have to take insulin for the rest of their lives. The disease, therefore, still appears on a death certificate as among the causes of death: this gives great joy to the anti-vivisectionists. But the sufferer, by conforming to certain rules, can look forward to many years of useful life, instead of living a few precarious years and being at the mercy of any mild infection or accident. Similarly, pernicious anaemia was a disease which, although subject to long remissions, led inevitably to a fatal conclusion. In 1928 Minot and Murphy discovered that the presentation of raw liver or liver extract to the sufferer maintained normal health until death ensued, again either from old age or from some intercurrent disease. Because the sufferers have to remain under continuous treatment they cannot be said to be cured, but they do maintain a normal, active life. The use of prostigmine in the treatment of myasthenia gravis and of the extract of thyroid and of its synthetic substitute thyroxin in the treatment of diseases of the thyroid, are further examples of the way in which modern therapy can overcome hitherto irremediable diseases.

Other deficiency diseases have been remedied by treatment with appropriate vitamins discovered, as has already been mentioned, by Gowland Hopkins in 1912. Scurvy, beri-beri, rickets and other such complaints are now rare and can easily be treated. Recent work on vitamins has shown that their range and use is even wider than was at first suspected, and a great variety of pathological conditions can now be successfully treated by administration of the appropriate vitamin.

The range of surgery has been extended to include extensive operations on the central nervous system, the lungs and the heart. Many of the congenital malformations of the latter organ can now be remedied, while the crippling effects of juvenile rheumatism on the valves of the heart can often be compensated by skilful surgery.

Improvements in the technique of anaesthesia and in the preparation of patients for operation have reduced the mortality in many surgical operations and have made surgery possible for diseases of hitherto inaccessible organs and for patients in the higher age-groups. Intravenous anaesthesia has removed much of the unpleasantness formerly associated with inhalation anaesthesia, with all its terror and dread, howbeit unwarranted, of suffocation. By these new methods the post-operative distress of nausea and vomiting has been almost entirely abolished.

The importance of maintaining the blood-volume and the blood-pressure in major operations, particularly on elderly patients, has led to much careful attention being paid to the patient before operation. Blood transfusions and other necessary treatments designed to keep the blood chemistry of these patients normal have greatly reduced the shock formerly associated with severe operations. With the use of these methods it is found that elderly patients can be submitted, if necessary, to severe operations with none of the worry and apprehension of former years. Further advances in anaesthesia by means of freezing methods have also extended the scope of surgery. Lowering of the body temperature slows all metabolic processes and enables operations to be performed on the heart and other organs with greater ease and success than was possible before this new method was introduced.

It has become general practice now after surgical operations to get the patient out of bed as soon as is possible, and not to insist on a long, quiescent period. This greatly shortens both the patient's stay in hospital and convalescence after discharge. For the weakness formerly associated with a long stay in bed after an operation is prevented, and various post-operative risks eliminated. Similarly this early ambulation, coupled with the reduction in the use of irritant anaesthetics, has lessened the onset of respiratory infections and other post-operative complications. The same principle is applied by orthopaedic surgeons to fractures of the lower limbs; and, what is particularly applicable to elderly patients, fresh lines of treatment, notably by pinning the fragments together, in the management of fractures of the neck of the femur have made it possible for many more patients suffering from this disability to walk again. Pinning of the broken fragments, followed by what would formerly have been considered dangerously early ambulation, has greatly reduced the mortality and permanent disability following this type of accident in elderly patients.

The experience of two wars has shown the value of accessory methods of rehabilitation of injured and other patients. Physiotherapy, once considered to be concerned only with lamps and massage, now covers a whole range of movement of injured or enfeebled limbs. And it is quickly being recognized that for many conditions active movements carried out by the patients themselves are of more value and importance in their rehabilitation than passive movements carried out by a physiotherapist. Occupational therapy has also greatly expanded its field of use. Starting as a means of restoring damaged or crippled limbs to some useful activity, it is now found to be of equal value as a diversional therapy; and, by overcoming some of the boredom which must of necessity be associated with a prolonged stay in hospital, it keeps the patient's brain active and thus encourages the will to get better.

Medical practice with elderly patients has also greatly changed during the last fifty years. Although it has always been recognized that many patients, although well advanced in years, responded to treatment as well as their younger contemporaries, yet formerly many elderly patients, particularly those who were suffering from degenerative diseases associated with old age, were thought to be almost untreatable and were therefore condemned to pass many years in bed and were regarded as "chronic" sick. But recent work has shown that these elderly patients will respond to treatment well; and although some of the illnesses from which they suffer may in the strict sense of the word be held to be incurable, this does not mean that they are necessarily irremediable. Although a complete restoration of function may not be possible, enough rehabilitation can often be done to enable a patient to "potter around" rather than be confined permanently to bed or even to a chair.

But there has been a great change in the whole concept of the medical care of elderly patients: it has arisen as a result of the last war. The size of families had been falling in many countries, over a number of years, and at the same time the expectation of life had increased by over twenty years since the beginning of the century. Although more people are living into old age, there is no question of the life-span in general becoming greatly prolonged. The reasons for this have already been discussed, and we must now consider some of the effects. Small families do not produce the requisite numbers of daughters and nieces who, remaining unmarried, are prepared to give up their lives to the care of some elderly relative. At the same time the demand for labour, combined with an economic pressure due to a high cost of living, makes it both easy and essential for more young people to obtain employment than before, and for more married women and middle-aged persons to remain in employment. It is necessary, therefore, that as many of the elderly as is possible shall remain in good health and thus be able to lead normal and independent lives for as long as possible. Hence the rapid development of a new branch of medicine, geriatrics, which can briefly be defined as a comprehensive medical and welfare service for the elderly.

Many elderly sick people have always been treated and have recovered in much the same way as their younger contemporaries. But a number, and particularly among the poorer classes, have been, when ill, taken care of in municipal hospitals where there was little or no skilled medical care available for them. They were well fed and nursed by kind, untrained women, and lived a life which in time became almost animal in its quality for many years. But now physicians are becoming interested in their welfare, and they are being given the same facilities for diagnosis and skilled treatment as younger patients. And the result can be quite startling. Given this medical and nursing care, many of these patients can be restored to such a degree that they can once more resume a normal and independent life in their own home or, if this is impracticable because of their frailty, in a communal home. This is undoubtedly what all but a very few, no matter what their age, would prefer, and not only is it much better for them to live like this, but it is also a far more economical way of taking care of them than any other. Close co-operation between the hospital, the general practitioner, the municipal authority and voluntary organizations is essential if a geriatric service is to be a success. So much can now be provided by way of meals, home helps and district-nursing services, that many elderly persons, whom it would have been impossible formerly to have returned to their homes, can now resume their life at the point where it was broken by their collapse, and often in very much better health.

Geriatrics should not be regarded as a new medical speciality, and it is to be hoped that its medical side will soon be absorbed in the work of the general consultant or practitioner in medicine. The principles of treatment do not vary according to age, and it is the realization of this that has brought happiness to many old people. In a well organized geriatric service a high death-rate in hospital must be expected, for many patients are admitted with fatal illnesses, but it will be found that over 8o per cent. of the patients admitted will either be dead or discharged within two months of their admission, while the number who need to remain in hospital for over six months is remarkably small, something in the nature of 5 per cent. There are few new medical techniques involved in this approach; the good results from a proper geriatric practice derive more from an attitude of mind than from the introduction of new measures. But a preventive approach is required here as in most other branches of medicine. It is found that many old people become sick, both mentally and physically, because they are bored and lonely. These two states of mind lead, very soon, to a neglect of the body which is expressed by malnutrition and dirt; and once an elderly person has started to deteriorate in this way the fall is rapid, and within a short space of time he becomes seriously ill. It is not, of course, possible always to prevent this, but much can be done with success for many people. Work, interest and company are needed. Regular, friendly visiting by a voluntary visitor will do a lot to correct the feeling of loneliness and unwantedness that is so distressing, while membership of an old people's club will help greatly to restore the elderly person to a right and proper place in society. But if it is possible for an old person to continue in, or return to, regular, gainful employment, this type of treatment will probably prove the best of all. It has been shown that elderly folk who remain at work do not suffer from senile confusion as much as do those who have no occupation, while a recent experiment has given some evidence that treatment in the occupational-therapy department of a hospital, of patients suffering from senile confusion at an early stage, does make them more suitable for living at home with their families than when they had nothing to do all day and yet needed some care and attention.

Patients suffering from senile dementia in its early stages respond to treatment in much the same way as elderly patients suffering from degenerative and other diseases of old age. Good feeding, the possibility that a high protein diet will prove beneficial, should always be investigated; company and a limited amount of discipline play their part in successful treatment; and about 40 per cent. of these patients can be discharged improved enough to take their place in a normal household at the end of six months, a similar proportion will probably die, while the remainder will show further deterioration and will need to be cared for until they die.

It is felt wrong that these patients, suffering only from a degeneration associated with their age, should be admitted to mental hospitals with the genuinely insane, and that they should be subjected to the formality of certification as insane. This latter carries with it not only a considerable stigma, but certain inconveniences for relatives who wish either to emigrate or to insure their lives. The right place for the irremediable senile dement is in special wards attached to a "geriatric unit". They must be cared for in separate wards from patients suffering from other physical diseases, because they are frequently noisy and are distressing to other patients by reason of their anti-social habits.

Medical treatment is, on the whole, unsatisfactory. Varying results have been obtained from the use of vitamins; nicotinic acid and, on the theory that the confusion is increased by a shortage of oxygen within the brain, priscol and other vaso-dilators have been used without any definite improvement in the patient's condition being noticed. Others have used hexamine with glucose and vitamin B, but this treatment, again, does not seem to be generally applicable.

The nineteenth century saw the great developments of environmental hygiene, and now this has become so universally accepted that the need for a wholesome water supply and an adequate sewage-disposal system is taken as a matter of course in all urban and most rural communities. Bad housing, with lack of ventilation, dampness and overcrowding, is accepted as being the cause of many of the ills of mankind. The place of man in his environment is now being given some study, and the branch of social medicine is developing in many places. Surveys and inquiries covering many fields have been undertaken, and much useful information has been collected. For example, it was known that a high incidence of pulmonary tuberculosis existed among the shoemakers of Northampton, and it was for long thought that there was some unknown occupational hazard in this trade. But a careful inquiry by a team from the school of Social Medicine at Oxford showed that it was rather the sheltered nature of the occupation, which attracted a not very physically strong type of worker, that was the cause of the high incidence; in other words, it was the susceptible worker who went to the trade rather than the healthy worker who was risking an abnormal industrial hazard.

Industrial medicine has made great progress during the past half-century. Medical inspectors of factories were appointed over 100 years ago, and more industrial processes have recently been recognized as constituting a danger to the health of employees than were so considered in the past. Factory doctors have the right of entry to premises where a trade subject to supervision is being carried out or where juveniles are employed. In addition to requirements which concern health in general, cleanliness, ventilation, reasonable space and temperature, etc., special requirements can be made to prevent certain recognizable disease hazards. The use of lead is controlled to ensure that no worker suffers from lead poisoning. Silicosis, a progressive and often fatal disease of the lungs, can be prevented by prohibition of the use of certain dangerous materials and the suppression and removal of dust when using others. Protective clothing, a protective ointment or the use of masks all play their part and because of this strict control these diseases, with the exception of industrial dermatitis, form a relatively minor part of everyday industrial health. Lung disease, due to the inhalation of dust from quarries or asbestos mines, can be prevented either by proper ventilation or by wearing a mask. Cancer of the lung was long known to be more common than usual among workers in the uranium mines of Schneeberg and Joachimstaal, while the nose and upper respiratory tract were affected in chromium and nickel works. Proper ventilation or the wearing of masks can go a long way to prevent the development of these cancers. Henry's work on cancer of the scrotum among the mule-spinners of Lancashire has led to the prohibition of the use of certain mineral oils, and there are diseases of the skin which are well-known concomitants of certain employments, and can be prevented by ensuring that appropriate precautions are taken by all workers. Arrangements are, therefore, made by means of legislation and careful inspection to minimize these evil effects, and to ensure that no worker shall be unnecessarily exposed to danger at his work.

The field of radiation, be it from radium, X-rays or nuclear physics, has led to other health hazards. Fatal illness can often result from ill-regulated exposure to these powerful rays, the best known example being the deaths, from various ill effects of radiation, of a number of young girls who, while painting instrument dials with luminous, radioactive paint during the first world war, were in the habit of moistening their brushes with their tongues and thus absorbing a certain amount of radioactive material. Special attention is paid to the ventilation of the rooms where this work is carried out, and the health of the staff and the condition of their blood are supervised; for an intractable anaemia is one common result of exposure to these rays, observed by frequent tests. Regular holidays and the prohibition of eating, smoking or even of using make-up in these laboratories reduce the chances of accidental contamination to a minimum.

In the field of psychological medicine great changes have occurred. The work of Freud in his analysis of dreams and in the establishment of the fact that sex is the fundamental motive for all human actions and reactions has led to a greater understanding of the complex mental processes that go to make up even normal men. Although Freud's theories are not now, perhaps, accepted with quite the authority they were accorded twenty years ago, yet his work has done more to ensure a more reasonable approach to the complex psychological factors that determine human acts than that of any other man. But as so often happens, much of his work has become the hunting-ground of people whose standard of work and integrity has not been up to that of the master. A result of this can be seen in the large number of patients who are unnecessarily submitted to psychoanalysis at the hands of inexpert practitioners.

The greater understanding of psychiatric matters and the importance of assessing the psychology of persons before undertaking their employment in tasks requiring an abnormal degree of understanding and skill is now recognized. Unfortunately, modern methods of psychological testing and investigation have not proved as successful as was at first hoped and indeed claimed. Assessors are therefore being thrown back once more upon the older-fashioned methods, based on insight and experience, which had been used for centuries and which are showing themselves now to be not entirely devoid of value. That the state of the body does depend upon the mind is now widely accepted, and it is found that the old adage *mens sana in corpore sano* is capable of a wider interpretation than had been suspected. The proof that the body does react to mental processes in various predictable ways has been given by Freud and his followers: but the fact had been realized for many generations in a confused and unintelligent way.

What is called psychosomatic medicine derives from the full realization of this fact. Duodenal ulcer is now known to be prevalent more among thin, anxious men, than among other, sturdier types, and the colon to respond unpleasantly to changes of mood in another type of worried and harrassed patient. The association of the onset of thyrotoxicosis or of diabetes with some mental shock or disturbance has been recognized for some while, but the actual connexion remains uncertain. Rheumatoid arthritis develops, although not exclusively, in a type of woman with a well-recognized mental approach to life. There is always a danger, however, of confusing the cause with the effect, and care must still be taken not to attribute too many physical diseases to mental upsets or peculiarities when, in fact, the sequence of events may be the reverse.

Following this record of diseases successfully treated or understood must come the other side of the picture. Cancer has already been referred to as a potent cause of death and ill health, but there are two other diseases whose incidence has increased greatly during the period under review. Coronary thrombosis, or blockage of the main artery supplying blood to the muscles of the heart itself, has advanced during the period under review from a rare disease to one of the commoner complaints. Although it occurs more frequently in middle and late life, it can attack people in their thirties and forties, and these often with fatal results. Old patients seem to survive this illness better than younger ones, but in all age-groups the mortality is high, and a long period of convalescence is necessary for sufferers. The reasons for the increase in the incidence of this condition are unknown: the growing, grinding stress of modern life is

a common attribution, but no definite evidence is available. Others
hold that it is the sedentary worker who is more liable to be attacked
than the active. Some half-suspected dietary factor has also been
suggested, but no real proof is yet available.

Infantile paralysis, or anterier-poliomyelitis, has greatly increased
in incidence during the past few years, and, contrary to what was
the case in former times, is found to be just as liable to attack
young or even middle-aged adults as young children. It frequently
assumes epidemic proportions, but in most epidemics the proportion
of victims who are left with a residual paralysis is lower than
might be expected, though death in the acute stages is not
uncommon, especially among healthy young adults. The cause of
this disease is known to be a virus which is particularly liable to
attack when the victim is tired. Its origin, however, is uncertain,
and opinion varies between a respiratory and an intestinal source.
The fact that the incidence of poliomyelitis has increased so greatly
at a time when the incidence and virulence of other infectious
diseases has so noticably fallen makes a good object-lesson of the
fact that there will never be an end to these medical problems.
As one disease is mastered, another rises up to take its place; and
this, so far as can be seen, will continue until the end of time.

Typhoid fever, which killed more men during the South African
War than did the enemy, is now controlled by a preventive inoculation. Cholera, some of the dysenteries and other tropical and sub-
tropical diseases can be rendered harmless to any contact by means
of a preventive inoculation. It is true that the effect of this will wear
off in a short time, and so the inoculation should be repeated before
each potential contact. Attempts are now being made to provide a
preventive inoculation against poliomyelitis, either by means of a
vaccine or by the injection of some other preventive agent. Medicine
has accomplished much in this way to clear the world of noxious
diseases and to open up vast new areas to cultivation and habitation.
Malaria, spread by mosquitoes, can be controlled by quinine or its
synthetic substitute, and at the same time the mosquitoes themselves can be destroyed by D.D.T. and their breeding places
removed by proper drainage of marshy land.

The present tendency for medicine is to regard the work of the
doctor, or hospital, as unfinished until the patient has been completely rehabilitated, has returned home and is back to work again.
Too often in the past the doctor, especially if attached to a hospital,
had felt that his work was finished with the discharge of the patient.
But that rather harsh attitude is now coming to be regarded as a
thing of the past. An almoner service, which cares for the private life
of the patient, is now held to be an essential part of hospital practice,
and more and more hospitals are finding how valuable almoners can
be. Not only can an almoner relieve a patient's anxiety about his

family and job while he is sick, and therefore expedite his recovery, but he can arrange for any necessary service to be made available to the patient on discharge from hospital, and in this way the patient can often be discharged sooner than would otherwise have been possible, and his bed made available for another sufferer. The fact that so many patients are covered by various measures of social-security, both official and voluntary, contributes to this rapid return to normal in no small measure. In fact the whole modern tendency is to curtail the amount of time a patient needs to spend in hospital. Thus the stay in hospital becomes a less important incident in the patient's life than before, with the result that there is less dislocation of his life than would otherwise be expected. This transition, from normal life to hospital and from hospital back to normal life, can be greatly facilitated if there is a good liaison between the hospital, the local authority, the general practitioner and the voluntary organizations, and towards this liaison an efficient almoner can be of enormous assistance.

At the same time doctors are taking more interest in the final results of their work. Patients are now asked to attend the hospital from time to time for a "follow up", and the doctor can thus see how successful treatment has been over a number of years. For some diseases, such as cancer, this "follow up" is made as complete as possible, and is maintained for a period of five years. In a good clinic under 1 per cent. of patients will be lost sight of, and a very complete picture of the natural history of disease and of the effects of treatment can be obtained. This information is found to be of great value in the treatment of future patients.

Medicine in many countries is developing on a regional basis. In the United Kingdom, the university hospitals, with their closely connected laboratories and scientific departments, make the centre of a region. Instead of each hospital in a region competing with its neighbour in establishing some department for a comparatively rare technique, such as neurosurgery and chest surgery, these specialities are centralized at one hospital, or possibly two, in the region. The consultants from these centres visit the other hospitals in the area, either as a routine or on request, and patients requiring these specialized treatments or investigations are transferred to the specialized centres to receive them. In this way full advantage is taken of the known fact that a doctor who sees many patients suffering from any one disease in a year is more likely to show greater skill in dealing with this disease than one who only sees one or very few. There is nothing derogatory to the second doctor in this approach, but greater experience is important.

To sum up, medicine has made considerable progress during the past fifty years both in a curative field and in a preventive field. This is reflected in the greatly increased expectation of life that faces a new-born child today. This, in its turn, brings its own problems, and it is to the solution of these—to the control, for instance, of cancer and the cardiovascular diseases—that medicine must now turn its attention. The enormous advances in the science of nuclear physics bring with them great medical problems: it will be interesting to watch what progress is made in solving them during the next fifty years. That new and unanticipated difficulties will arise during this period is certain; that these will in their turn be solved can be confidently expected.

BOOKS SUGGESTED FOR FURTHER READING

I. Berenblum, *Science Versus Cancer* (Sigma Books, 1946).

Lord Horder, *Fifty Years of Medicine* (Duckworth, 1953).

Lord Amulree, *Adding Life to Years* (National Council of Social Service, 1951).

Douglas Guthrie, *History of Medicine* (Nelson, 1945).

Report of the Committee on Nutrition, 1950 (B.M.A.).

S. E. Finer, *The Life and Times of Sir Edwin Chadwick* (Methuen, 1952).

GENETICS

by Professor C. H. Waddington

I.

In all branches of science one of the major objectives is to discover the nature of the basic units or elements out of which the material under investigation is made up. In the study of living things —the great department of science collectively known as biology— there have been, indeed there still are, difficulties in carrying this endeavour through to the end. There has never been much doubt, however, about one of the most promising directions in which to look. During its lifetime an animal or plant undergoes great changes in its degree of complexity. The body of the adult may contain many different organs, each with a very complex structure. But each individual begins life in a much simpler form, as a fertilized egg-cell or seed; and this is just as truly John Smith the human being, or Pluto the bulldog, as the adult creature which will eventually develop out of it. If there are any elementary constituents out of which the living being is constructed they must all be present in the newly fertilized egg, and we may reasonably hope that they will there be combined with one another in a less elaborate and a more easily analysed way than they are in the fully developed adult.

The fertilized egg arises from the union of the reproductive cells of the two sexes—the egg and the sperm. It comprises the material which the new individual inherits from its parents. One of the ways of investigating the nature of the fertilized egg is therefore the study of the processes of biological inheritance, or heredity. The science concerned with these problems is known as "Genetics". It has, as we shall see, actually revealed to us a whole category of elementary biological constituents which are certainly amongst the most important basic units out of which living things are made. We shall have to discuss later, however, whether they are the only units of this kind, or whether, at least, they are so much the most important that any other constituents of living organisms can be regarded as only subservient to them.

Genetics is a comparative newcomer among the biological sciences. No real progress in understanding biological inheritance

occurred until about the beginning of this century. The fundamental discovery was actually made some forty years earlier by the
Czech monk, Mendel; but the significance of his work was not
appreciated at the time, and it was not until about 1900 that his
ideas fell on fertile soil and stimulated the growth of the new
science. Once it had got under way, however, genetics matured
extremely quickly. Within about forty years it had become one of
the major aspects of biology, with a theoretical structure which was
more coherent, precise and closely argued, and which at the same
time penetrated more deeply into the ultimate nature of living things,
than any other branch of the subject.

In its first years, up to about the time of the First World War,
genetics had, in the hands of men such as Bateson and Correns,
dealt only with biological inheritance in the straightforward and
comparatively narrow sense; that is to say, the passing on from
parent to offspring of particular features such as hair colour, eye
colour, the shape of a leaf or other organ, etc. During the years of
the war and in the early twenties, our knowledge of these phenomena took an enormous stride forward, chiefly owing to the work of
Morgan and a group of American geneticists, of whom Muller,
Bridges and Sturtevant are the best known. At this time a beginning
was made in linking up our understanding of the rules of inheritance
with our knowledge of the material structure of cells. The thirties
saw a very thorough synthesis of these two branches of biology—
genetics, the science of inheritance, and cytology, the science of cell
structure. They became so intimately fused (particularly by the
work of Darlington) that the two are often referred to together by
the common name of cytogenetics.

At the same time the first steps were taken towards showing how
genetical ideas open up new lines of approach into other fundamental biological sciences. Authors such as Goldschmidt began to
explore the ways in which the factors which an organism inherits
from its parents operate to determine the characters which it will
develop as it grows into an adult. Thus genetics gradually became
one of the essential parts of the science of embryology. It proved
equally illuminating in relation to the study of evolution. The earliest
geneticists, such as Bateson, had been very well aware that the new
science they were developing was destined to fill up one of the
major gaps in the theory of evolution. This gap, as Darwin himself
acknowledged, was its inadequate treatment of the problem of
biological heredity. It was not, however, till about the thirties that
a solid foundation was laid for the application of genetics to evolution, in the theoretical works of authors such as Haldane, Sewall
Wright and Fisher.

By the beginning of the Second World War genetics had reached
a condition which can justly be regarded as marking the end of a

first major phase in its historical development. It was a body of doctrine almost as closely knit and coherent as the atomic theory of chemistry had been in the early years of the century, and, like it, gave a plausible account of nearly all the phenomena within its field. The first half of this essay on genetics will be devoted to expounding the solid structure of what we may call "classical genetics". But, as the use of this epithet implies, present-day genetics has already advanced well beyond this point. No scientific theory yet has ever given a completely satisfactory account of everything coming under its view, and classical genetics left enough unaccounted for to give it possibilities for further growth.

There were, on the one hand, some aspects of heredity which classical genetics only dealt with in summary outline. Recent genetics has tried to expand this into a more thorough treatment. The fields of evolutionary genetics, and of the artificial breeding of livestock and crop plants, are the two most important examples. Then again, during and since the war there have been great developments in the application of genetics to the most lowly types of organisms, such as the single-celled animals (protozoa), bacteria, yeasts and viruses. Finally, classical genetics had been strongest in explaining how hereditary factors are passed on from one generation to the next, but weakest in describing how they operate to produce their effects on the new developing individual. This problem of the functioning, as opposed to the transmission, of the hereditary elements is still little understood, but is increasingly becoming the central point around which genetical interest is focused. It looks as though it may hold the key even to problems which at first sight seem very different from it, such as those of evolution or artificial breeding.

II. The Theory of Classical Genetics

The basic idea of genetics, which was originally propounded by Mendel in 1865, then forgotten, and rediscovered again at the beginning of this century, is quite a simple one. It is an idea about the kind of thing which is passed on from one generation to the next in biological inheritance. Before Mendel (and unfortunately even today in unenlightened circles) it was thought that an animal inherited from each parent something which was without structure and of the nature of a quality. It was often referred to as "blood". One said, for instance, that such and such a racehorse had much of the "blood" of a certain line of winners. The word "blood" here, of course, did not mean the actual fluid which coursed in the veins of an ancestral animal and which went into the grave with it. It did indicate, however, that people thought of whatever it is that is inherited as having qualities like those of a fluid, so that the

hereditary contributions from the mother and father could be completely mixed together and mingled in the offspring, losing their
own identity, as the gin and the vermouth do when mixed together
in the Martini. The essential idea of genetics is a denial of this.
It says that we inherit from each parent a certain number of definite
and distinct factors, each of which retains its own nature through
many generations. In a newly-fertilized egg, they are mixed together
only in the sense in which the pieces of apple, pear, peach, orange,
etc., are mingled in a fruit salad, and it is easy to imagine them
being sorted out again as one could never sort out the constituents
of a cocktail.

The central feature of classical genetics is the account it gives of
the way in which hereditary factors are passed on in biological
inheritance. Every individual receives from each of its parents a
large number of these factors. Each factor is a separate entity in its
own right, quite distinct from all other factors. We need not at
present consider exactly what a factor consists of, but we must think
of it as something which endows the new organism with certain
potentialities, which will be realized to a greater or lesser degree as
development proceeds gradually towards the adult state.

One of the great triumphs of classical genetics was the discovery
of the structures on which these factors lie. Animals and plants are
made up of cells, each cell being a small lump of·living substance
(or protoplasm). Within each cell is another smaller lump known as
the nucleus, and within the nucleus again are still smaller structures
which have the property of staining deeply in certain dyes and are
called chromosomes. During the life of the cell the chromosomes
change their shape considerably. At the stage at which they are
most easily seen they are short and thick, but careful observation
shows that these short forms consist of a long, thin fibre which has
become closely coiled. When a chromosome is untangled and fully
spread out it is, in fact, seen to consist of a thread. It is on these
threads that the genetic factors lie. After this point was proved, and
hereditary factors shown to be parts of a material structure, people
began to refer to them not by the rather vague term "factor", but
instead by the particular technical name of "gene". We see, then,
that the genes lie along the length of the thin, thread-like chromosomes.

The inheritance of genes can be studied in two different ways. We
can breed animals of different types together and follow how their
potentialities are handed on to their offspring. Alternatively, we can
observe how the chromosomes behave during the processes of
reproduction and from this deduce what should happen to the
genes. Both methods give the same answers. It is perhaps easiest
to explain them in terms of the behaviour of the chromosomes.

The first point is that in most animals and plants the nucleus of every cell contains several different kinds of chromosomes (some long, for instance, and some short), and always two of each kind (Fig. 1). As we shall see, one of each pair has come from the male parent and the other from the female parent. Having two of each kind of chromosome, each cell naturally contains two of each kind of gene. These two representatives of the gene may not, however, be exactly identical. They belong to the same family but may be different members of it. Geneticists speak of the whole family of genes which occur at a given place on a certain chromosome as occupying a "locus". The different members of the family are the "alleles" of the locus. (The word "locus" is the Latin word meaning place, and refers to the position on the chromosome. Its plural is "loci".)

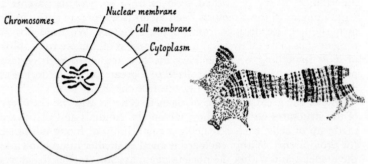

Fig. 1. On the left is a diagram of a cell, showing the nucleus, in which are a set of chromosomes, of which there are two of each kind. On the right is a pair of giant chromosomes, lying side by side, in a nucleus of a salivary gland cell in a fly. The pair shown corresponds to the small dot-like chromosomes in the other figure.

In any individual organism, then, the paired chromosomes in its nuclei may contain different alleles at certain loci along their length, while at other loci both chromosomes may have the same allele.

During the growth of the individual the cells grow and eventually divide in two, then grow again and divide once more, and so on. If one observes the behaviour of the chromosomes during this process it is found that very careful arrangements are made to ensure that when the cell divides each daughter cell obtains exactly the same complement of chromosomes. Before the cell division takes place each chromosome thread splits longitudinally in two: or perhaps it is better to say that a new chromosome thread appears, lying closely side by side with the old one. During the process of division these closely associated pairs of threads lie in the plane along which the cell is being split into two, and they then move apart from each other so that one sister thread gets into each of the two new cells which are being formed. In this way the new cells get exactly the same equipment of chromosomes and of genes as the original. We may say that every potentiality in the original cell is inherited by the daughter cells.

When the organism becomes adult and sexual reproduction occurs, something different from this simple process has got to happen. If it did not, and eggs and sperm were produced in exactly the same way as all other cells, then each egg and each sperm would contain two of each kind of chromosome. When they came together in fertilization the offspring would contain four of each kind; and a similar multiplication by two would go on in every generation. If things are to be kept stable it is clear that sexual reproduction must involve some process of halving the number of chromosomes, so as to compensate for the doubling that occurs when the egg and sperm fuse. In point of fact this is done by a rather subtle modification of the normal process of cell division. We have seen that in ordinary division the chromosomes split (or a new one appears beside the old) shortly before the division occurs. However, in one special division which takes place in the cells from which the eggs and sperm will be formed the process is different (Fig. 2).

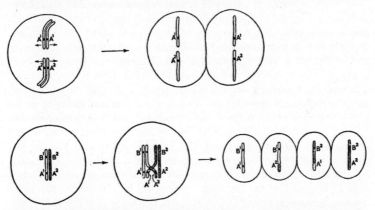

Fig. 2. Above is a diagram of the normal division ("mitosis") of a body-cell; only one pair of chromosomes is shown. Below is the special type of division ("reduction division" or "meiosis") which occurs in the formation of the germ-cells. In this the two like chromosomes first come to lie closely side by side, then each divides, and the four threads fall apart two by two except where they are held together by the breakage and rejoining of the threads. Two successive cell-divisions sort out the threads into separate cells. In some of these there has been a "crossing-over", giving new combinations of genes (A^1B^2 and A^2B^1).

The two chromosomes of each pair come together and lie closely side by side before each one has split into halves. The split occurs a little later and thus gives rise to a group of four sister threads. This group of four almost immediately starts to fall apart again into two groups of two. However, these two groups do not usually succeed in separating completely from each other, because they are held together by places where the threads have broken and rejoined. Suppose, for instance, that threads 1 and 2 are tending to separate as a group from threads 3 and 4. They would succeed in doing so were it not for the odd fact that it is quite common to find that threads 2 and 3 have both broken at the same place, and joined up again so that the near end of thread 2 is joined to the far end of thread 3 and vice versa. The consequence of this is that when the cell eventually divides the two daughters do not contain exactly the same chromosomes. One, in the example we have given, contains thread 1 and the near end of thread 2 with the far end of thread 3, while the other contains the near end of thread 3 with the far end of thread 2, together with thread 4. The same sort of thing happens with all the other pairs of chromosomes. The breakage and rejoining of the threads which causes this difference in the chromosomes going to the two daughter cells is known as "crossing over". We shall see later not only what its consequences are in heredity, but why it is that animals and plants have evolved such peculiar mechanism.

To continue with the story of sexual reproduction. The daughter cells formed by the first special division which has just been described are already provided with pairs of closely associated chromosome threads (e.g. a pair consisting of thread 1 associated with the near end of thread 2 joined to the far end of thread 3). It is therefore perhaps not unexpected to find that the first division is very quickly followed by a second one, in which the two threads of each pair become separated from one another, one sister thread going to each of the two new nuclei formed. As a result of these two divisions a set of four cells is formed, each of which contains only one of each chromosome instead of, as usual, a pair of them; and moreover, some of these chromosomes have been formed by the breakage and rejoining of the original chromosomes in new combinations. These four cells give rise to the eggs or sperm. In the male, all four usually become sperms; but in the female, three of them chosen at random degenerate and it is only one out of the four which becomes a functional egg. Since, however, quite a large number of cells undergo these divisions, in the long run all the possible types of eggs are formed in the right proportions.

Now consider what results this process will have on the inheritance of genes. Suppose we have an animal and that in one of its pairs of chromosomes there are two different alleles, A_1 and A_2, at one of the loci. When the germ cells are about to be formed the two chromosomes will come together so that A_1 lies beside A_2, Then each chromosome will split and we shall have a group of four alleles, A_1, A_1, A_2, A_2. The two special reduction divisions will sort these out into a group of four cells, two of which will contain A_1, and two A_2. What would happen if we crossed two such individuals: say a male, half of whose sperm carried A_1, the other half A_2, and a female, half of whose eggs were A_1 and the other half A_2? Clearly the A_1 sperm would have a fifty-fifty chance of uniting with an A_1 egg or an A_2 egg, and would thus give rise to equal numbers of offspring of the constitution A_1, A_1 and A_1, A_2. Similarly the A_2 sperm would give equal numbers of A_1, A_2 and A_2, A_2 offspring. Thus we should finish up with offspring in the proportion: one, A_1, A_1; two A_1, A_2, and one, A_2, A_2. One can work out the results of other sorts of crosses in a similar way. The ratios of the numbers of different types of offspring in some of the simpler cases are known as the Mendelian ratios, and it was their discovery by Mendel in his breeding experiments with peas which opened the door to the whole subsequent development of genetics.

We have still not seen the consequences or the point of the peculiar breakage and rejoining of threads which was described above. Its effects can only be detected when we are dealing with pairs of different alleles at two loci in the same chromosome. Suppose that the original animal had the alleles A_1 and B_1 at two loci in one of its chromosomes, and the alleles A_2 and B_2 at the corresponding loci in the other chromosome of the pair. At the stage when there are four threads, these will at first be two of A_1, B_1 and two of A_2, B_2; but if two of them break and rejoin at some position between the A and B loci, we shall finish up with a set of four which consists of one A_1, B_1, one A_1, B_2, one A_2, B_1, one A_2, B_2. Thus in the germ cells which are formed there will be combinations of genes such as A_1, B_2, which were not present in the original parent. If the loci A and B lie close together on the chromosome it is rather unlikely that the breakage and rejoining will happen to occur between them, and most of the germ cells formed will have the original combinations A_1, B_1 or A_2, B_2. We can, in fact, estimate how far apart A and B lie by determining the proportions in which the new cross-over combinations A_1, B_2 and A_2, B_1 turn up (Fig. 3).

It was evidence of this kind which gave the first hint that the genes lie in a row along some material thread-like structure. By making suitable crosses and detecting the new combinations of genes, people estimated the frequency of crossing-over between two loci, A and B, and thus the distance between them; and then did the same thing with loci B and C and finally with A and C. It was found that what we may call the crossing-over distance between A and C is roughly equal to the sum of the distances between A and B and B and C. This is just what one would expect if A, B and C were all points on a material thread. All sorts of other evidence soon accumulated to show that this is really the case. For instance, unusual breakages and rejoinings of chromosomes sometimes occur.

We may sometimes find that part of a chromosome containing gene C, which normally belongs with A and B, has been broken off and joined up with some other chromosome containing, perhaps, genes P and Q. When this happens the other genes which originally lay in the immediate neighbourhood of C go along with it, and are now

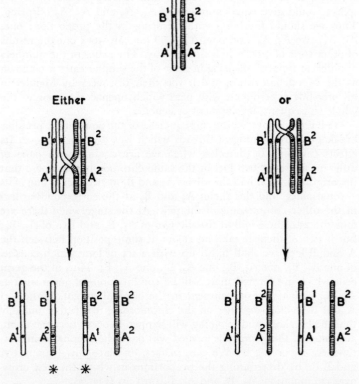

Fig. 3. The diagram shows what happens when the eggs and sperm are found in an animal which has different alleles at two different loci in one pair of chromosomes (A^1B^1 and A^2B^2). A breakage—and—rejoining (crossing-over) may occur between the two loci, giving new combinations (at asterisks on left), or it may happen in some other position (on right). The distance between the loci can be estimated from the frequency of the cross-over types.

also found attached to P and Q. Again, if we have a long chromosome with a number of genes A, B, C, D, E, F, G, H, sometimes a section gets broken out and joined in again in a reverse order, making up a new chromosome A, B, F, E, D, C, G, H. Again we find that the genes which belong together, such as C, D, E, F, are changed around in a coherent group. It is quite easy to understand these phenomena if the genes are parts of a material thread, and almost impossible to give a plausible explanation of them in any other way.

Chromosomes are very small bodies only visible with fairly high powers of the microscope. Each one may contain anything from a few hundreds to a few thousands of genes. It is therefore usually impossible to see in the chromosomes any structure sufficiently fine-grained to correspond to the exceedingly minute genes. There are, however, a few special cases where this can be done. In some special cells, particularly in the tissues of certain flies, the chromosome threads are completely uncoiled and have multiplied in number so that there are a large number of them lying side by side, thus making up a body thick enough to be examined in detail. These chromosomes (which are often known as salivary gland chromosomes, after the organ of the fly in which they are best seen) show a structure consisting of a large number of cross striations in the form of darkly staining and lightly staining bands. Fortunately, these chromosomes are beautifully developed in the fruit-fly *Drosophila*, which is the favourite laboratory subject for breeding experiments and in which a very large number of genes are known. It has therefore been possible to study the sequence of bands in the chromosomes in cells in which a group of genes (such as the C, D, E, F above) has been broken out and reinserted in inverted order or joined on to some other chromosome. It is found that the chromosome structures are absolutely consistent with what one can deduce from the results of breeding; in fact in certain cases particular genes can be precisely located and proved to lie in a certain specific band. The proof that the genes lie in a single series along the thread-like chromosomes is complete.

It is now time to turn to some of the general biological consequences of this peculiar mechanism by which genes are passed on from one generation to the next. Some of the most important of these consequences stem from a fact that has not yet been mentioned. We have pointed out that in most organisms the cells contain two of each type of chromosome and thus may contain two different alleles at each locus. For instance we mentioned animals which contain genes A_1 and A_2. Now it is very frequently found that in such cases the animal with A_1 and A_2 appears exactly the same either as that with two A_1's or that with two A_2's. If it is like the A_1, A_1, we say that the A_1 gene is dominant over the A_2, which is said to be recessive. We have to suppose in such cases that the presence of one example of the dominant gene produces an effect on development which is strong enough for the full development of the character involved; so that even if there are two dominant genes, no further effect is produced. The general importance of this phenomenon is that it provides Nature with an easy way of keeping some of her tricks up her sleeve. Some of the genetic factors may remain hidden;

by looking at an animal one cannot tell whether it contains two dominant genes (A_1, A_1) or one dominant gene and the corresponding recessive (A_1, A_2). But if two such animals mate with each other, the two hidden recessive genes may come together and produce a new type; as we have seen, they will do so actually in a quarter of the offspring. From this it follows that we can *never* be certain how an animal will breed or what characters it will pass on to its offspring if all we know about it is how it appears.

The consequences of this are legion. For instance, in human heredity one cannot tell by looking at a man or woman whether they contain hidden recessive factors which might have very harmful effects on an individual who did not contain the corresponding dominant. If two people each containing the same hidden recessive gene marry and have children, a quarter of these children will be expected to show the recessive character. Fortunately, as we shall see, very harmful recessives are rare. It is only very seldom that both partners to a marriage contain the same one. This is rather more likely to occur if the husband and wife share a common ancestor (for instance, if they are cousins); for if the ancestor contained a recessive, it may have been passed down the lines of descent, remaining hidden all the time, until it reaches the two people who are now getting married. Equally, of course, cousins are more likely than people picked at random out of a population both to possess one example of a valuable recessive, in which case their family will be genetically better than average. But valuable recessives are probably somewhat rarer than harmful ones, and their beneficial results probably do not deviate so much above the average as the effects of harmful recessives fall below it. Thus from the purely genetic point of view, which is of course by no means the only one of importance in this connexion, marriage between cousins is a slight gamble, though by no means an outlandishly risky one.

Recessive genes, because they remain hidden when combined with the corresponding dominant, are very difficult to get rid of from a population. It has often been suggested that one could improve the human race by making it difficult or impossible for some of the less admirable individuals to reproduce. This is not the place to discuss the thorny question of how one could decide who should be rated as "less admirable", or who should be charged with the responsibility of such decisions. Even if this problem could be solved, we should not be much further ahead as regards all those characters which depend on recessive genes. We could only detect these genes in individuals which contain two of them and thus show their harmful effects; but if the genes are fairly rare, the greater proportion of them will be carried by people who also contain a corresponding dominant, and will therefore be undetectable. The reason for this can easily be seen. Consider a person who contains two of the recessives. If the gene is harmful enough for its elimination to seem a worth-while objective, people showing its effects will obviously be fairly rare. It is very unlikely that one of them will marry another person showing the same defect. It is much more likely that the person will marry someone who is normal in respect to this gene and contains two of the dominant, though if the gene is not too rare there is a slight chance that he will marry a person who contains both a dominant and a recessive. In the first, commonest, case the genes which were visible in the original person will disappear in his offspring, being covered up by the dominants derived from the other partner to the marriage. One can put the argument in a more precise form. Consider, for the whole population in question, all the eggs and sperm which are going to unite to form the next generation. Suppose a small proportion of them, which we may call U, contained a harmful recessive gene, while the remainder of them, $1-U$, contained a dominant. When they unite in fertilization the chances of two recessive genes coming together will be $U \times U = U^2$, while two dominants will come together in the proportion $(1-U)^2$, and dominant will be combined with recessive in the proportion $U(1-U)$. Now if U is a small fraction, U^2 is extremely small and much smaller than $U(1-U)$. Thus the combination of dominant and recessive will be much more frequent than the co-existence of two recessives; most of the recessive genes will be hidden and it will therefore be impossible to weed them out.

The principles which apply to human genetics also operate in populations of wild animals, and provide the basis for a new understanding of evolution. They are, in fact, much more easily investigated in animals which one can breed together experimentally than in men, where one can at best observe what has happened without being able to control it.

The first impact of classical genetics on the theory of evolution was to clear up a long-standing puzzle. Darwin admitted that he, like everyone else at his time, knew very little about the process of heredity. He tentatively adopted the current view that parents passed on to their offspring something which behaved rather like a fluid, the contribution from the two parents blending in the offspring. The difficulty that arises for the theory of evolution is this. Darwin supposed that evolution occurred because certain organisms had hereditary qualities which enabled them to leave more offspring than their contemporaries, with the result that the valuable hereditary characteristics were passed on to an ever-increasing proportion of the population. That is the process of natural selection. But if heredity involves the blending of the characteristics from the two parents, then the valuable hereditary qualities will gradually become blurred out of existence by mingling with less valuable ones. Darwin considered this one of the weakest points of his theory, and he could see no way round the difficulty. Very soon after Mendel's work was rediscovered and the science of genetics had been born, it was realized, for instance by Bateson, that the new knowledge had cleared the matter up. Hereditary qualities do not blend in the offspring, even if they seem to disappear and show no signs of their presence. The gene concerned (a recessive one, for instance) is still present and can be passed on to further generations and will emerge again into the light of day when two similar recessive genes come together. There is no danger that the mere process of crossing and interbreeding will change the amount of essential heritable variation available for natural selection to work on, and reduce all individuals to a drab uniformity.

In fact it follows from our present genetical knowledge that a population of animals usually contains much more heritable variation, which can serve as a basis for evolutionary change, than would appear at first sight. If one collects a large number of wild animals of some particular species, say mice or flies, a vast majority of them usually look extremely alike and there are only one or two aberrant or peculiar individuals. One might think that, if conditions changed so that the species had to evolve into some new form adapted to the new situation, there would only be very few variants from which natural selection could pick a new form more suitable than the old one. However, as we have seen, a great many of the apparently normal individuals may really contain quite a number of recessive genes, each present in only one chromosome of a pair and therefore showing no effect. This constitutes a reserve of hereditary variation much larger than one would guess from the small number of actually atypical individuals; and this reserve can be called upon if the species has to make some adjustment to fit into a changed environment.

It was not till about the beginning of the thirties that these problems of evolutionary genetics were taken up in earnest. At that time a number of authors, particularly Sewall Wright, Haldane and Fisher, started to develop the mathematical theory of how the frequency of particular genes would be increased or decreased within a population under the influence of natural selection. Other workers, such as Timofeeff-Ressovsky and Dobzhansky, began the more laborious but equally important task of investigating natural populations of animals to find out how great a range of different alleles they contain, and what actually happens to them under natural conditions.

Both the theoreticians and the practical experimentalists soon came up against a point which had already presented itself to those concerned with a particular kind of man-made evolution, namely the breeding of live-stock and crop plants. The qualities which distinguish a useful variety from a poor one, or which enable one

individual to leave more offspring than another, are only rarely
dependent on single genes with clear-cut effects. Much the most
convenient materials for ordinary genetical experiments are genes
which produce definite and easily-recognizable effects whose
transmission from parent to offspring can be easily followed. But in
animals living in a state of nature, where natural selection has
already picked out the most effective type, any clear-cut change
from the norm is almost certain to be harmful. The slightly-better-
than-average animals which natural selection will favour are those
which are only a little stronger, a little faster, or a little larger, than
their fellows.

These slight and more or less impalpable variations from the
average show a type of hereditary behaviour which is rather different
from that of strong, well-defined characteristics. In the first place,
in a character like size, say, we usually find that there is a continuous
gradation between the largest and the smallest individuals in a
population. There will be a low proportion of very small individuals,
rather more which are a bit bigger, the majority of the population
at intermediate sizes near the average, then again a moderate
number of rather oversized ones, and a very few extremely large.
But there will be no sharp distinction between a group of smalls, a
group of medium and a group of large, such as we would expect
if there is only one pair of alleles concerned in determining the
size.

If we breed such animals, crossing large with large or large with
small, we find two things. Firstly, an individual does not affect its
offspring to the extent that one might have expected from looking
at it. Thus if two very large animals are crossed they do not necessarily produce offspring as large as themselves. Some of the variation
in size, in fact, is due to the particular kind of environmental circumstances in which the animal grew up—whether it had an
unusually large amount of food or other favourable circumstances,
for instance. Variation produced in this way is not hereditary and is
not passed on to the offspring. One of the most important things to
determine in drawing up a programme for breeding livestock for
increased size or increased milk production and similar characters,
is the degree to which the available variation in the character is
hereditary. If it is all environmental, no amount of selecting the
best animals will improve the qualities of the offspring; while if the
variation is all capable of being transmitted, later generations can
be rapidly improved. Geneticists used the term "heritability" to
indicate the degree to which the character they are interested in is
transmitted from parent to offspring in the population they are
studying.

The second point about variation of this kind is that its heredity
seems at first sight to behave rather as one would expect on the old

theories of blending inheritance. That is to say, if one crosses the large and small animals out of a population their offspring are usually intermediate in size, as though the hereditary characters had blended. But if one goes on to the next generation, by crossing the intermediate-sized hybrids with each other, the blending type of theory begins to break down. It is true that in the second generation one does not get any clear-cut separation into a definite ratio of small, medium and large. There is still a continuous gradation in size. But the important point emerges that the range of this gradation is wider than in the first generation of hybrids; the smallest of the second generation are smaller than any in the first, and the largest larger. This could not happen if the hereditary characters had really blended. On the other hand, it can be shown that the continuous gradation, the formation of an intermediate population of first-generation hybrids, and the widening of the range of variation in the second generation, are exactly what one would expect for a character which was affected not by a single pair of alleles but by a large number of different pairs, each of which had a small effect which was added to or subtracted from the effects of all the others.

Thus practical animal and plant breeders have to deal with the heredity of characters which are influenced by whole batteries of genes. This point was first recognized back in the days of the First World War, but it was hardly realized at that time how difficult the situation is to deal with. We have still made little progress towards either a comprehensive theory of it, or confidence in handling it in practice.

Students of evolution are confronted with much the same situation. Characters which render an animal well adapted are similar to those favoured by the animal breeder in depending on many pairs of genes rather than on only one or two. Fortunately for the evolutionist, he is not so pressingly interested as the breeder in exactly how fast the hereditary improvement of his animals proceed. There is plenty of time for Nature to evolve; a dairy farmer wanting to improve his output of milk is more impatient. But the evolutionist is up against still another complexity. An animal to be a success in nature, must be an all-rounder. It is no use improving one character, such as size, unless some other, such as strength, keeps pace with it. Thus evolutionary advance does not depend merely on collecting a large number of genes, each with a small positive effect on the improvement of a particular character, but rather on getting just the right complex combination of genes which affects a number of characters in a well-balanced and harmonious way.

There is no obvious reason why such harmonious combinations of genes should arise spontaneously. So far we have discussed how variation, dependent on different alleles at particular gene loci, is passed on from generation to generation. We have not dealt with the question of how it comes into being in the first place. The answer to this is that genes, although they are extremely stable, do not blend with one another, and are passed on unchanged from individual to individual through very many generations, are nevertheless not *absolutely* stable. A given gene will occasionally change into another allele of the locus. The process of change is called mutation, and occurs with frequencies ranging from one in a thousand to one in a few million lifetimes (there are a few genes known which mutate more frequently, but there may be something rather abnormal about these). These frequencies sound very low, but they mean that in a large population there is a continual appearance of new alleles. Many of these, of course, are harmful in their effects and are eliminated by natural selection just as fast as they are formed. This does not mean that the population will be quite free of the harmful recessive. In each generation a certain number of new mutations will occur, and to keep the situation constant an equal number of such genes must be eliminated by natural selection against the unfortunate individuals which carry two of them and show their effects. This "normalizing" activity, by which natural selection keeps control of the newly-arising mutations, is one of its most important functions.

It is a function which natural selection may have to exert with considerable vigour on the human race in the future if we allow things to get out of hand. The rate of mutation can be speeded up by any form of very penetrating radiation which can carry energy through the outer parts of the cell to the nucleus where the chromosomes reside. X-rays can have this effect, and so can the extremely intense radiation associated with an atomic explosion. The perils of this appalling weapon are not over for those who survive the immediate holocaust. It can cause the production of a whole crop of new mutations in the reproductive cells of those within range of some of its radiations; and if these individuals have children, the harmful genes will be passed on in a hidden form through many generations before two of them eventually come together in a single individual, when they can at last be eliminated from the human inheritance, but only at the cost of the suffering of the person who shows their effects.

But to return to the scientific side of genetics. Although it is twenty years since H. J. Muller discovered how to stimulate the production of new mutations by the use of X-rays we are still quite unable to control the process so as to produce mutations which make the organism more useful to us or better adapted to the life it has to lead. Mutations, both those which are artificially induced and those which occur naturally, are "random". A gene changes into another allele, but one cannot tell beforehand which gene is going to change or exactly what it will change into. Thus populations in a state of nature will always contain a number of less usual alleles which give it a reserve of variation to call on when an evolutionary advance is called for; but it will be variation in all directions. Useful changes will depend, as we have seen, on picking out, from this haphazard and multifarious collection of slightly unusual possibilities, certain particular combinations which fit together to give a harmonious individual better adapted to the new circumstances than was the original type. It will obviously be advantageous to a race of animals or plants if there is some way of shuffling around the new genes, so that all the various combinations of them can be tried out.

This gets us back to the point at which we started this exposition of classical genetics: namely, the two peculiar divisions by which the pairs of similar chromosomes in the body cells of an organism are reduced to a single chromosome of each kind in the eggs and sperm. When the events of these divisions are considered from this point of view it will be realized that they are an efficient and subtle shuffling mechanism. They make possible the whole process of sexual reproduction, in which an animal which carries, say, an abnormal allele A^1 can mate with another which carries an unusual allele at some other locus, say B^1. If A^1 and B^1 lie in different chromosomes there is nothing to prevent them being passed on together in some of the reproductive cells of the offspring. Even if they lie in chromosomes belonging to the same pair they will sometimes be brought together if a breakage and rejoining (crossing-over) occurs between them. The tying together of genes into groups by attaching them to one another to form long, thread-like chromosomes, which, however, sometimes break and rejoin, provides the opportunity for a nice balance between the advantages of continual shuffling and those of preserving a valuable combination.

Within the whole range of animals and plants one can find considerable variety in the degree to which the shuffling or the preservative functions of sexual reproduction are developed. It is clear that rather different types of evolutionary machinery will be at work, according as one or the other is preponderant. It was primarily the English cytologist, C. D. Darlington, who pointed this out and showed that during the history of life there must have been an evolution of evolutionary mechanisms—a gradual formation of a process which gives the best balance between flexibility and conservation. By propounding this idea he rounded off very prettily into one coherent whole the many diverse and complicated items of knowledge which genetics had accumulated during the first phase of its history. We came to understand not only what the mechanism of heredity is, but why it is so.

III. Genetics: The Second Phase

The second phase in the development of genetics may be said to have begun about the time of the Second World War. There was no very sharp and clear-cut break between it and the earlier phase; but a fairly considerable reorientation of interest took place within a few years, and a range of new problems was taken up, which gives the genetics of recent years a rather different flavour from that of the earlier period. Roughly speaking, one can say that people became less interested in the sheer mechanics of inheritance and devoted more attention to trying to discover the nature of the gene and the mode in which it operates. But there was, of course, a considerable carry-over into the new period of problems which had been in the forefront of interest earlier on.

In particular, the old problem of selection—both artificial selection in the breeding of plants and livestock, and natural selection in the evolutionary processes going on in nature—has continued to be a major pre-occupation. A general theoretical account of what might be expected on the basis of classical genetical theory had been provided, particularly by Sewall Wright. The major endeavour in recent years has been to conduct experiments to find out what actually happens in practice. Both those interested in artificial breeding and the students of evolution have come up against phenomena which seem to be forcing them to turn their attention towards the dynamic activities of genes; that is to say, towards the main direction of interest of other geneticists in recent times. One thing which has tended in this direction is the discovery of the importance of inter-actions between genes at different loci. Evolutionists, for instance, are discovering that in wild populations all the genes have been selected in such a way as to give harmonious combinations with one another. They envisage a population which persists through many generations as possessing a certain pool of genes out of which the gene complement of any particular individual is drawn; and they emphasize that the genes in the pool are "co-adapted"; that is to say, selected so that any group which is drawn out of it to equip an individual is likely to produce a well-balanced and efficient creature. Such a concept emphasizes the importance of the ways in which genes interact with one another.

It is also becoming recognized that one of the most important problems requiring genetical analysis is the evolutionary significance of the effects which different environments produce on animals developing within them. It is over-simple to consider evolution only in terms of genes which produce efficient animals. One has instead to think of genes which cause an animal developing under the influence of a certain environment to be efficient in dealing with that environment. Once again we find that we have to consider the dynamic actions of the genes and the way in which they are modified by the environmental factors. The concepts of classical genetics, which were content to think of a given gene as inevitably correlated with a particular character in the adult, were adequate enough when we were merely trying to discover how genes are passed on from parent to offspring, but were too abstract to enable us to solve the more complex problems of evolution or selective breeding.

The study of the process of mutation is another problem, the investigation of which began in the classical phase of genetics but has been very actively and fairly successfully continued in more recent times. It has been mentioned above that Muller showed that ionizing radiation, such as X-rays, could cause mutations. During the war Auerbach and Robson found that similar effects could be produced by certain chemicals, such as mustard gas. Since then a large number of "mutagenic" substances have been discovered. The effect of all of them, like that of X-rays, is to increase the frequency of mutations in general; none of them specifically produces any one particular step in mutation. They must act then to disturb the stability of genes and make them change more frequently than they would naturally do. The unspecificness of this behaviour, and the very different nature of the substances which are capable of exerting it, makes it difficult to understand in chemical terms just what these mutagenic substances are doing.

The chemistry of genes is, in fact, an exceedingly difficult field. It has been possible to obtain at least a rough idea of the size of an individual gene. It turns out to be considerably larger than any known well-defined chemical molecule. It is about as large as some of the virus particles, which are often considered to be the simplest types of living things. In such an entity, which on the scale appropriate to chemistry is of enormous size, there is room for a very great deal of complexity. Genes seem to be made up of a combination of two of the most complex types of substance known. One of these is protein, the basic substance in the flesh of all animals or the sap of all plants. The other is nucleic acid, a substance built up out of sugar, phosphates and certain bases, which are bound together to form complexes which seem to be almost as elaborate and complicated as the proteins themselves. These two types of substance, proteins and nucleic acids, are essential parts not only of the gene but of the whole substance of the cell. The character of any particular cell (whether it is a nerve or muscle cell, a human, a dog or a fish cell) certainly depends to quite a large extent on the type of proteins it contains not only in its nucleus but in its whole substance. When genes control the development of an egg, and cause it to develop into a particular type of adult with certain characters, they must do this quite largely by determining the types of proteins which are formed in it. Thus one of the major problems for modern genetics is the relation between the protein constituents of the genes in the nucleus and the proteins which are being formed in the rest of the cell.

The nucleic acids, also, are not confined to the genes. But the nucleic acid in the genes belongs to a rather different category from that in the rest of the cell. The greater part at least of the gene nucleic acid contains one particular type of sugar, whereas the nucleic acid in the rest of the cell tends to contain another. It is not quite certain how far these non-genic nucleic acids differ in the cells of different tissues of different species. Perhaps they, like the proteins, are one of the major diagnostic features of the cell; but opinion seems on the whole to be that their function is to help determine the type of protein which the cell produces rather than themselves to endow the cell with its particular character.

Genetics has also found itself transported out of its original interest in the modes of inheritance into these new fields of physiological and bio-chemical inquiry by another set of recent inquiries which at first sight did not seem likely to produce this result. The rules of classical genetics covered a very wide range of organism, from quite simple plants to the most complicated animals. In recent years a great deal of attention has been paid to genetics in organisms at the very lowest end of the evolutionary scale.

The first group of this type to be extensively studied was the fungi, a family of lowly plants in which, on the whole, inheritance follows the classical rules. Indeed, for a greater part of their lifetime these organisms are in a state corresponding to the reproductive cells in higher animals and plants, containing only one of each kind of chromosome. This means that the rules of classical genetics operate in a way which at first sight seems unfamiliar, but which is really simpler than that which we are used to. The major contribution of the fungi to genetics was that the peculiarities of their life history made it particularly easy to discover genes which affect the biochemical capacities of the organism. In the mould *Neurospora* a vast array of genes was found in this way, each of them controlling the ability of the plant to carry out one particular step of the processes by which the nutrient materials it takes in are converted into the normal living substance. Mutations of this kind were, in the first place, of very great value to the science of biochemistry, since they provided a new tool for investigating the exact ways in which substance A becomes converted through the intermediates B, C, D, E, etc., into a final product—say, G. But from the point of view of genetics they brought us up once more against the fundamental problem of recent years—what exactly is a gene doing when it deprives the organism of the capacity to turn A into B? In many cases in fungi we know the exact chemical nature of A and B, and therefore seem to have some hopes of getting to grips with the problem. Unfortunately, however, its solution still eludes us. It was at first thought that a gene which prevented the conversion of A into B did so by inhibiting the formation of the particular enzyme (biological catalyst) which normally carries out this conversion, but in one or two cases at least it is now known that the explanation is not so simple; the enzyme may be present even in a cell which fails to carry out the job.

The genetic exploration of the lower forms of life did not stop with the fungi. Recent investigators have turned to the simplest one-cell organisms, the protozoa; to bacteria, which are smaller still and which, until recently, were thought not to possess anything corresponding to a nucleus; and finally to viruses, which are even smaller than bacteria and so (relatively) simple that some of them can form crystals as though they were chemical substances. The genetics of bacteria and viruses, it must be confessed, is still obscure, but it is one of the recent triumphs to prove that they have a genetics at all. In both it has been proved, much to everyone's surprise, that two individuals can come together and exchange hereditary material in some way which, though still not fully understood, must be more or less comparable to sexual reproduction in higher organisms.

In the other class of primitive being, the protozoa, we have been able to go considerably further. These have a visible nucleus; in fact, many of them have a highly complicated nuclear apparatus. Within the nucleus they contain a battery of genes which, on the whole, behave in the ways with which classical genetics has made us familiar. The most important new element which has been brought into the picture by protozoa (and by yeasts, which are primitive plants of a rather similar degree of complexity) is evidence for the existence of hereditary factors not associated with the chromosomes, but lying outside the nucleus in the rest of the cell. Some indications of the existence of such factors had already been found in higher plants and, in a very few cases, in higher animals. It has, however, been easier to investigate them thoroughly in protozoa and yeasts. At first geneticists tended to welcome the appearance of such factors with great enthusiasm. They were known as "plasmagenes", and many people thought that they were probably quite common constituents of cells. The rarity with which they show any evidence of their presence in breeding experiments was supposed to be due to their great stability, so that when two higher animals are crossed they normally contain the same plasmagenes, which thus remain undetectable. But it was supposed that, as an egg develops, the cells in the different regions come to contain different plasmagenes, and that it is these bodies which determine whether the cell will be a muscle cell, a nerve cell and so on.

More recently, however, second thoughts have begun to arise.

Some of the plasmagenes, both in protozoa and in higher animals, for which the evidence was most impressive, have begun to appear not as natural constituents of the cell but rather as foreign invaders, perhaps of the nature of virus particles. If this is so, they cannot be taken as evidence that normal cells contain hereditary particles not associated with the chromosomes. There is considerable controversy about this at the present time. On the whole, those who believe that the parts of the cell outside the nucleus contain plasmagenes, which play an important part in controlling the developmental processes and can indefinitely preserve their own character independently of the nucleus, are fighting something of a rear-guard action. Even so, it must be recognized that the investigations on plasmagene-like behaviour in protozoa and other organisms have brought home to us the degree of complexity which we must be prepared to meet in the behaviour of the non-nuclear parts of the cell.

Even if we do not feel justified in invoking plasmagenes to explain how it is that the nerve cells, for example, come to be and to remain different from the muscle cells, this difference is a fundamental fact of biology for which some explanation has to be found. The alternative to the plasmagene theory would be to suppose that in different types of cells different groups of genes become activated, or at any rate operate with greater or lesser intensity. It is well known from experimental studies on embryos that within a newly fertilized egg the regions of the cell outside the nucleus are not all alike. After fertilization, the egg-cell divides many times, forming many nuclei which become scattered throughout the whole extent of the original egg-cell. The evidence indicates that all the nuclei remain alike in their content of genes, but the non-nuclear material associated with any particular nucleus will be different according to the region of the egg-cell from which it came. We may then suppose that these differences in the associated materials sometimes stimulate the activity of one set of genes and sometimes that of another.

There are many indications in experimental embryology of the occurrence of such processes. One of the most striking is the phenomenon of embryonic induction. In this, a substance diffuses out of one part of the embryo into the neighbouring cells and causes them to begin developing in a particular way, forming certain particular substances which must be controlled by genes. Thus under the influence of the inducing substance certain genes become more active than they would otherwise have been. Brachet, who has been one of the most active students of this problem, believes that the inducing substance is closely related to the nucleic acid, which, as we have seen, plays a part both in the cytoplasmic processes by which new proteins are formed and in the genes which ultimately control the nature of the substances.

Although we still know very little about these processes of

differential activation of genes, it is encouraging that in a few cases it has already been possible to see evidence for it in the chromosomes. Some insects have very large "salivary chromosomes", not only in their salivary glands but in other parts of the body. If one compares the chromosomes from, say, the walls of the gut with those in the salivary glands, one finds that they possess the same general pattern of banding (which seems to indicate that the chromosomes in both nuclei contain the same genes); but in one type of nucleus some particular bands may be very swollen and fuzzy, although appearing normal in the nuclei of the other tissue (Fig. 4). This fuzziness seems

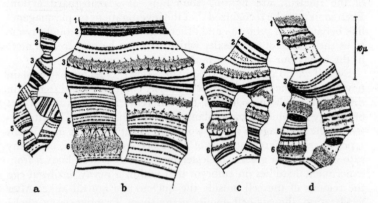

Fig. 4. Salivary-type chromosomes in four different tissues of a fly (*a* mid-gut, *b* salivary gland, *c* excretory tubule, *d* rectum). In the short section in which the chromosomes lie separate, the order of the loci has been reversed in one chromosome, as mentioned on p. 236. Notice that all the bands are always present, but they are differently developed, being sharper and darker in some cases, more fuzzy in others; this is presumably an indication of the different activities of the genes.[1]

to be evidence that the genes located at these particular places on the chromosomes are intensely active in that tissue.

At present genetics is waiting for, or perhaps one should rather say is working towards, a new synthesis, which, when it comes, will open the way towards an understanding of the whole group of problems we have just been discussing. The chemical constitution of the gene, the way it is altered when it mutates, how genes interact with one another, with the environment and with the non-nuclear material of the cell in controlling development, all belong together as facets of the central problem of understanding genes as dynamic entities playing a part in cellular activity. It is this problem rather than further details about how genes are transmitted from parent to offspring which is now in the centre of the stage of genetical interest.

[1] Fig. 4 is a copy of Abbildung 39 from W. Beermann, "Chromomerenkonstanz und spezifische Modifikationen u.s.w." from *Chromosoma* Bd. v, pp. 139-98 (Springer Verlag, Berlin, Gottingen, Heidelberg, 1952).

BOOKS SUGGESTED FOR FURTHER READING

A. M. Srb and R. D. Owen, *General Genetics* (Freeman, San Francisco, 1952).

C. H. Waddington, *Introduction to Modern Genetics* (Allen and Unwin, 1939).

C. Stern, *Principles of Human Genetics* (Freeman, San Francisco, 1949).

T. Dobshansky, *Genetics and the Origin of Species* (Columbia University Press, 1941).

J. S. Huxley, *Evolution, The Modern Synthesis* (Allen and Unwin, 1942).

C. H. Waddington, *The Principles of Embryology* (Allen and Unwin, 1956).

SOCIAL ANTHROPOLOGY

by J. H. M. Beattie

I. Introduction and Historical Background

ANTHROPOLOGY IS etymologically the study of man. Social anthropology is one kind of anthropology; it studies man primarily in his social aspect, that is, in his relations with other men in more or less organized communities. This provisionally defines the subject-matter of our inquiry.

But in fact social anthropologists have tended to study mainly so-called primitive societies, leaving the more advanced ones to sociologists and historians. They have also tended to concentrate attention on the different types of social relationships found in the societies they study, rather than on the individuals who are the foci of these relationships. And in studying these relationships they have generally found it necessary and desirable to take account of their cultural content: that is, of the ideas, values and beliefs associated with them. These points will be developed in later sections of this essay.

Social anthropology is a young study, and though at the present time it is taught in the major universities of Great Britain, the Dominions, the United States, and elsewhere, the first professorial chair in the subject in England was not founded until 1908. Of course scholars were writing about primitive institutions long before this. Modern social anthropology owes much to such eighteenth-century writers as Hume, Adam Smith, Ferguson and the Scottish moral philosophers; and to Montesquieu, Condorcet, Saint-Simon and others on the Continent. For these writers human society was a proper subject of scientific inquiry, the aim of which was to discover universal and necessary laws. Since it was plain that societies developed, some of them at least, and that some were more advanced than others, it appeared probable that all societies everywhere had to develop (if they developed at all) through the same series of stages. These scholars, therefore, set out to determine and relate these different stages. In the nineteenth century the idea of evolutionary progress, already familiar, gained fresh impetus. Writers such as Maine and McLennan in this country, and Morgan in America, reconstructed with great precision and abundant detail the earlier stages of human society. Thus attempts were made to show that the institution of marriage must have been preceded by a stage of primitive promiscuity, monogamy by polygamy, patriarchy by matriarchy, and so on.

Anthropologists no longer attempt pseudo-historical reconstructions of this kind. The principal objection to them is that there is no evidence for the existence of these presumed earlier stages of society. Many of the customs and beliefs which, because they were not properly understood, were supposed to be merely "survivals" of some earlier stage were on further inquiry shown to be something quite different. No particular theory of origins could ever be either proved or refuted by empirical evidence, for such theories were derived not from experience or observation but from *a priori* reasoning. Ethnographic data about primitive peoples, which were becoming increasingly available during these two centuries in the form of reports by missionaries and travellers, were regarded not as raw data calling for scientific analysis, but rather as illustrative material for historical hypotheses already established on other grounds. Social anthropology, none the less, owes much to the keen insight and often brilliant formulations of these scholars.

French writers of this period, such as Comte and de Coulanges, less avowedly empirical and more intellectualist by tradition, were interested rather in the essential nature of human society than in the processes of its development. They considered societies to be systems, the parts of which are organically related to one another and to the whole of which they are parts, in accordance with laws of social organization which the student of society may legitimately seek. This trend reached a peak in Durkheim, still one of the most important influences in social anthropology.

Other strains, too, have gone to make up the fabric of present-day social anthropology; German scholarship as represented by Max Weber and others, the pioneering research of the American Boas, the monumental ethnographic collections of the great fact-collectors, Tylor, Frazer, Westermarck and others, and the researches in Germany and elsewhere of the several diffusionist schools.

II. Relationship to Other Studies

Societies do not exist in a vacuum, and social relations are interconnected with and conditioned by a variety of non-social factors. These form the subject-matter of a number of other studies, and it will be useful to refer to the relationship of social anthropology to certain of these studies, and also to its companion discipline sociology. We shall consider only those with which social anthropology's relations are close, sometimes confused, and occasionally disputed.

Ethnography, which it is useful to distinguish from ethnology,[1] provides social anthropology with its raw material, descriptions of the social life of less advanced peoples. In recent years it has come to be regarded as essential that the social anthropologist should be his own ethnographer. If he wishes to write about a particular people he is expected to visit and live with these people, and to collect his own information about them. We shall return to this topic when we discuss field-work methods.

Cultural anthropology is now often distinguished from social anthropology. It deals with cultural systems rather than with social ones; with the relations, that is, between items of culture, sometimes called "culture traits", rather than with the relations between persons. Culture has been variously defined since the time of Tylor, but in general it is regarded as comprising the total body of customs and beliefs shared by the members of a society; and it is clear that different items in this cultural complex may be systematized in abstraction from the social system in which they are interwoven. Thus for example language (a most important component of all human cultures) may be considered as a separate system, the proper subject of the cultural study of linguistics.

But society and culture can be only analytically distinguished, for both are aspects of the same subject-matter, human beings in society. And social anthropology cannot exclude consideration of culture, for it is impossible to describe any system of human inter-relations without reference to their cultural content. But there is another reason why social anthropologists have generally much to say about culture. This is simply that as a rule they are the only trained observers with first-hand knowledge of the peoples they study; and if they do not describe these cultures, which in many cases are changing rapidly, nobody else will. Thus social anthropologists have described religious systems, agricultural methods, the manufacture of tools and ornaments, and so on, not only in relation to the social organization, but also as systems in their own right. These cultural topics would in our own society be dealt with by specialists.

Psychology is usually distinguished from social anthropology by the fact that it deals with psychical systems, whereas social anthropology deals with social systems. Though human societies are made up of acting and thinking human individuals, and can of course have no existence apart from these individuals, social phenomena cannot be understood solely in terms of individual psychology; for social facts and psychological facts are two quite different kinds of things. It follows that the kind of explanation appropriate on the psycho-

[1] Ethnography is the descriptive account of the life of primitive peoples: ethnology is the attempt to classify peoples in terms of their racial and cultural characteristics, and to explain these in terms of their history.

logical level may be inappropriate on the social level. As Durkheim pointed out, such a social phenomenon as a suicide-rate is not fully understood until it is shown to be connected with the social facts such as group membership and the degree of social integration present therein. It cannot be sociologically explained solely in terms of individual life histories—that is, in terms of individual psychology. Man and society, psychology and social anthropology, are, however, closely interdependent. Thus there has grown up in recent years, mainly in America, a border-line area of study—that of such topics as learning processes and basic personality structure. These studies differ from social anthropology in their primary focus on the individual personality, and from classical psychology in their stress on learning and other social processes as contributing to personality development. The writings of Mead, Kluckhohn and others fall into this category.

Social anthropology is not the same kind of study as *history* (which is interested in particular past events rather than in the general laws or patterns they exemplify); but where genuine historical material is available the social anthropologist, in so far as he aims to achieve the fullest possible understanding of the societies he studies, cannot afford to neglect it. The primitive societies first studied by social anthropologists were for the most part without recorded or verifiable histories to study. So the reaction against the pseudo-historical hypotheses of the early ethnologists was sustained as a protest against any use of historical methods of inquiry in social anthropology. But as social anthropologists began to study more advanced societies, and as, furthermore, European contact and the the passage of years provided with histories even those societies which had none, it became less and less possible for conscientious students to neglect the history of the societies they studied. Thus most contemporary social anthropologists regard it as important to record the histories of the societies they describe, where such histories are ascertainable.

Sociology, like social anthropology, studies systems of institutionalized social relationships. But sociologists study mainly systems of relationships typical of more advanced societies, such as western industrial civilization. Social anthropologists, on the other hand, have chiefly studied societies both less advanced and less familiar, where often the community is numerically smaller and the social organization less complex, and where, in consequence, the society is more readily comprehensible as a totality.

The unfamiliarity of the social anthropologist's field imposes on him, also, a problem of translation: first he must understand the society he studies, then he must render this understanding into the sociological and other categories of his own culture. For the sociologist, who usually works in a culture with which he is more or less familiar, this problem is very much less acute.

III. Modern Field-work Methods

The social anthropologist working in a primitive community regards it as his duty to familiarize himself, as far as possible, with the whole social life of the people in all its aspects. This has certain practical implications. It means that the anthropologist must spend a long time, generally at least two years, in the study of a single society, for in no shorter period can the full social significance of the activities he observes be understood. It means, again, that he must learn the language of the people he studies. Unless he does this, he will never be able either to communicate freely with them or thoroughly to enter into their ways of thought. A field study made through interpreters is no longer regarded as adequate. And it means, finally, that he must, as far as possible, live in and as a member of the community, and not outside it, and participate as far as he can in its ordinary daily social life. Only thus can he come gradually to understand what it is like really to be a member of that community. It is never possible for him to do this wholly, but even this disability has advantages; "stranger value" may be important, and too complete assimilation might mean restriction to one particular status or local group, with consequent loss of social mobility.

To obtain the kind of information he requires the social anthropologist in the field makes use of techniques of participation, observation and informal conversation. He may also employ formal interviews and set informants, and he will certainly make use of written information, such as the records of native court proceedings, where this exists. Where his data are readily quantifiable he will treat them statistically. Literate members of the community may be invited to write texts on social topics of which they have special knowledge; and questionnaires, literary competitions and school essays may be used. Photography and sound recording provide useful adjuncts to the written record. A modern social anthropologist may use any or all of these means, but by themselves they do not provide a substitute for the close personal relations which the anthropologist must achieve if he is to acquire the "feel" of the community, and which are only possible through sympathetic contact over a long period of time.

IV. Theory in Modern Social Anthropology

The ultimate theoretical implication of social anthropology, as of any other reasoned inquiry, is that the data examined "make sense", that they can be shown to fall into some kind of order. We shall consider in this section some of the basic principles in terms of which social anthropologists attempt to organize their material.

We said that the social anthropologist, like the sociologist, studies man in his relationships with other men in more or less organized communities. In fact his interest is in the relationships rather than in the individuals related, in so far as the two are analytically separable. For "persons" may be considered as complexes of institutionalized roles and statuses, and what is important about these is that they may continue to exist, even though the individual human beings who are involved in them may change with the passage of time. It is thus possible to abstract these relationships from the individuals in whom they are temporarily located, and to study them as systems in their own right.

These institutionalized relationships are to be found in every society; there are always special patterns of behaviour and special attitudes and ways of thinking which are held to be appropriate in dealings between persons belonging to particular social groups or categories. This fact enables the people who live in the society to anticipate with reasonable accuracy what their fellows will do in all the ordinary circumstances of their social life. There may of course be deviations from these accepted social patterns or norms, but unless these become sufficiently general to assume social significance (as may happen, for instance, in conditions of rapid social change) social anthropologists will tend to disregard them as pertaining to individual psychology rather than to sociology.

The basic theoretical problem, then, is: how are these systems of institutionalized relationships to be understood? Several conceptual approaches to this problem of understanding, some complementary, some conflicting, are current in modern social anthropology.

(a) The Total Social System

The adoption as a methodological principle in social anthropology of the notion that a society may usefully be studied as a whole is historically associated with the undertaking by Radcliffe-Brown and Malinowski of the first comprehensive first-hand field studies of non-literate communities.[1] For a small island community in the Pacific or the Indian Ocean, or an isolated Australian horde, could (unlike any modern western nation) readily be comprehended as a single self-sufficient whole. Adequately to describe such a community it was seen to be necessary, and not unduly difficult, to show the part played by each element in the whole society and in its relationship to the other elements with which it co-existed. This approach found ready theoretical backing in the writings of the French sociologists, in particular Durkheim, from whom Radcliffe-Brown derived many of his sociological ideas. Though the dangers

---

[1] A. R. Radcliffe-Brown, *The Andaman Islanders* (Cambridge, 1922). B. Malinowski, *Argonauts of the Western Pacific* (Studies in Economic and Political Science, Routledge, 1922).

of too readily assuming a real social unity are nowadays recognized (the precise definition of a social unit even for purposes of a particular study is a matter of some theoretical difficulty), the approach to social phenomena which sees them not as a collection of discrete elements but rather as integral parts of a total social field has now been widely adopted. It is this fact in particular that differentiates modern social anthropology from the older kind of anthropology, which is mainly concerned with such matters as the collection and classification of culture traits, and the plotting of these in "culture areas".

(b) Social Structure

Radcliffe-Brown first elaborated the notion of structure in social anthropology,[1] defining it as the complex network of actually existing social relations in any society. Other anthropologists, while accepting the concept of structure, have found this formulation too wide; thus Evans-Pritchard[2] has preferred to restrict the term to those relatively enduring relationships which unite persisting social groups into a total social system.

These definitions have sometimes tended to suggest that there is in every society something which may be called "the structure", and so rather to obscure the fact that a society may reveal many different social structures, depending on the interest of the observer. The view that structure is something that is "there" in the society, something that the social anthropologist may, if he uses the right techniques, hope to discover and put on record, has been criticized by a recent French writer, Lévi-Strauss.[3] He emphasizes that any kind of structure, in the sense in which anthropologists use the term, is a construct or model, based on but not composed of the empirical data. The validity of a scientific model, unlike that of an empirical fact, is to be judged not by its truth but by its usefulness or "strategic value" in facilitating comparison and leading to new knowledge. There are, this writer points out, two kinds of models in social anthropology; those in terms of which the members of the society being studied represent their own society to themselves, and those constructed by the student from outside the society, as a means of increasing his understanding of the social system, and of communicating his findings to others. The distinction is an important one, sometimes overlooked: the structure, for instance, of a system of kinship relations as it is expounded by a social anthropologist in a learned journal is something very different from the "same" structure as it is understood by a participant in the system.

---

[1] See especially the collection of essays entitled *Structure and Function in Primitive Society* (Cohen and West, 1952).

[2] In *The Nuer* (Oxford, 1940).

[3] In an article in *Anthropology Today* (Chicago, 1953).

(c) *Function*

Associated with the idea of structure is the somewhat ambiguous notion of function, central in modern social anthropology. The concept evidently has reference to an end, the achieving of which is the functioning of whatever it is that is said to have a function. It is not, however, implied that this end must be consciously pursued by anybody; it may be achieved unknown to the agents who bring it about. But basic to all forms of functionalism is the view that the facts of social life may not usefully be thought of as a collection of separate elements. They are, rather, to be conceived as intimately interrelated, so that changes in one part are likely to produce changes in other parts. Most modern social anthropologists would agree with this, and this agreement is reflected in the thoroughness of most modern field-work. But anthropologists still differ as to the ends which the social institutions they study may most usefully be regarded as serving. The most influential views have been those with which the names of Malinowski and Radcliffe-Brown in particular have been associated in this country.

Malinowski considered that all human institutions could best be understood if they were seen as tending, directly or indirectly, towards the satisfaction of certain basic biological needs, and he listed a number of such primary needs. But in addition to these he found it necessary to postulate a number of derived needs, instrumentally related also to the wants of the organism, but arising from the conditions imposed by living together with other organisms in a society. This theory has been criticized on the ground that it can never provide full understanding of social and cultural differences, since basic biological needs are presumably much the same everywhere. To understand the different forms which social institutions take in different societies they will have to be considered not in their relationship to biological needs, but rather as conditioned by their social and cultural environment.

Thus Radcliffe-Brown, following Durkheim, develops the notion of social needs (or necessary conditions for the existence of a society). He sees the function of any social activity as the part it plays in the social life of a community as a whole, and thus the contribution it makes to the maintenance of the structural continuity. This view, implicit in the notion, already discussed, that societies are in some sense integrated totalities, has been profoundly influential in modern social anthropology. It should be noted that the assumption is that any social phenomenon *may* have a functional relation to other aspects of the social life, not that it must have. It is necessary, also, to recognize that certain social phenomena may in fact make no contribution, or a negative one only, to the structural continuity (especially in situations of rapid social change), so that the notion of function as here used implies as its correlative the notion of dysfunction.

Recent American writers who have adopted this approach have sought to define what one of them calls the functional requisites of any society;[1] certain conditions which the social organization must satisfy if it is to continue to exist. Though the kind of requisites listed will depend largely on the terms in which the concept of society is defined, such formulations are of value as guides to further field research. so long as they are subject to constant revision and review.

Mention should also be made of recent American studies directed towards the analysis of the different kinds of inter-personal relationships which go to make up a functioning social system. A major contribution to this problem has been made by Parsons,[2] who starts from the position, first adumbrated by Max Weber, that a system of social action is only possible when the individual actors are consciously "oriented" towards one another. These orientations tend, as we have seen, to assume consistent patterns, and the resulting "complementarity of expectations" is what holds the social structure together. Parsons provides a systematic account of a number of possible types of orientation, conceived both in psychological and in sociological terms. He thus provides an important range of concepts for the description of societies from the point of view of the persons who compose them. It should be said, however, that here, as in certain other American anthropological contexts, the basic unit of study is taken to be man *in* society, rather than society itself, conceived as a system of interrelated value-patterns and norms.

Some contemporary social anthropologists hold that the notion of human societies as functionally integrated systems is misleading or at least inadequate when adopted as an exclusive theoretical framework. While they agree that social phenomena present patterned regularities, and that these may form structures and be compared from one society to another, these writers contend that an approach to the study of human societies which bases itself on the generalizing methods of the natural sciences is bound to be inadequate, and that in consequence this study falls more naturally on the side of the humanities, such as history and morals. This view may be expected to lead, not to the repudiation of the notion that societies for certain purposes may usefully be thought of as totalities and their parts as interrelated (for these ideas have come to stay) but to the broader recognition that other frames of reference also are available for the understanding of social phenomena. Thus anthropologists may legitimately seek understanding in terms of historical, moral, religious and other categories, as well as in terms

[1] Marion J. Levy, Jr., in *The Structure of Society* (Princeton, 1952).

[2] Talcott Parsons, *The Social System* (Tavistock Publications, 1952), and other works.

of functional interconnectedness. This broader approach may prove fruitful especially in the sphere of religion and values.[1]

V. Some Topics of Social Anthropology

A consideration of the present state of knowledge in regard to certain anthropological topics will show how social anthropologists divide up their field of study, and will indicate the kind of topics nowadays considered important. It will also afford a summary of the type and extent of information currently available. Of course not all the work done in the fields selected can be referred to, and advances have been made in many other fields; but in the topics chosen there have been marked advances both in the extent of the data collected and in its theoretical interpretation, during the past twenty years. We consider, then, kinship and marriage, social control in its political and legal aspects, economics, magic and religion, and social change.

(a) Kinship and Marriage

It was early noted that kinship appeared to be much more important in less advanced societies than it is in our own, but it was not understood why this should be so, such widespread phenomena as classificatory systems of kinship terminology[2] being regarded as survivals of a time when owing to the prevalence of original promiscuity it was impossible to tell the difference between certain kinds of relatives. Modern studies are functional rather than aetiological. Thus the classificatory system is seen to provide a method of bringing a large number of relatives under a few simple categories, each having a proper pattern of behaviour appropriate to it. The principle exemplified in this procedure has been called "the unity of the sibling group"; in certain situations siblings (children of the same parents) are regarded as socially equivalent and in certain contexts interchangeable. Thus a man may call both his father and his father's brother by the same term, and roughly the same kinds of attitudes towards and expectations from both may be prescribed. Even his father's sister may be called by the same term, qualified by the adjective "female".

Biological kinship defines a limited number of possible relationships, which can be socially utilized in various ways. These form the patterns, and the idiom, of various kinds of institutionalized social relationships, and thus provide a framework for the organization of social rights and responsibilities. Often these kinship patterns and the prescribed behaviour associated with them form a complete

[1] For a brief statement of this approach see Evans-Pritchard, *Social Anthropology* (Cohen and West, 1951), especially Ch. iii.
[2] i.e. systems in which terms which apply to lineal relatives are also applied to certain collateral ones.

guide to practically all social relationships. For practically all social relationships may be with kin, or conceived as being so. But even where the kinship pattern is less pervasive, relationships based on it may still be of paramount social importance.

Relations of kinship are usefully considered under two heads; those based on the principle of descent in one line, whether male or female, and those more widely based on all cognatic connexions, that is, connexions through both males and females. Taking the former type first, it is evidently possible for people to live together in groups, as the Scottish clans did long ago, because they are, or believe themselves to be, descended from a common ancestor. Descent may be in the male line, in which case a man will inherit from his father or brother by the same father, or in the female line, in which case he will inherit from his mother's brother or his own brother by the same mother. The descent groups thus formed may be called clans or, if the members are aware of their genealogical interrelationships, lineages. The members of such groups may live together on the same piece of land and co-operate in social and economic activities. In many societies in different parts of the world the territorial grouping of the people is based on this principle of unilineal descent, which thus forms the most important structural principle in such societies. For it determines the social group in which each individual must spend his life or a large part of it, and it binds him in a complex network of rights and duties to the other members of this group. In many societies intense solidarity within the group is correlated with a considerable degree of hostility between groups, and an important contribution of recent social anthropology has been to demonstrate the widespread structural importance of relationships of inter-group conflict.

An important feature of this segmentary type of social organization is the relativity of its component sections. It is the nature of a descent group to be at the same time inclusive of and included in other descent groups. Thus the particular group in which an individual's membership is relevant in a given social context depends on the genealogical distance which separates him from the person or group with whom he sees himself as related in this situation. This may be made clear by a diagram:

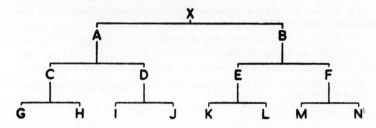

In this patrilineal lineage—the common ancestor of which is X—G, in his relation to J, is a member of the descent group which is headed by his father, C, and which includes his brother, H, and any other brothers (sons of his father) he may have. But in his relations, with, say, M (his second cousin), he is a member of the group which includes D, I and J, and his grandfather A, as well as his own father and brothers. In very much the same way, an Oxford undergraduate is a member of his college *vis-à-vis* another member of his university, but a member of Oxford University in his relations with an undergraduate of Cambridge. His situation, however, differs from that of a member of a localized lineage group in that the latter's lineage membership, unlike the former's college and university membership, is relevant in practically all of his extra-familial relationships.

In a system of this kind new lineages constantly form, as old ones segment. At the same time, in certain situations different but related descent groups unite and act as one. This process of fissure and fusion is typical of and indeed part of what is meant by a lineage system, the essence of which is the maintenance of some kind of political equilibrium between these opposed elements.[1] Typical, also, of such a system is the assimilation of all social links to a kinship pattern, even where there is no genealogical connexion. The creation of fictitious kinship links is thus a feature of lineage-based societies of this kind.

Even where territorial grouping is not based on the lineage principle, unilineal kinship may be of primary importance, in particular in determining the transmission of property and status. It is clear that the inheritance of group membership, or of any particular kind of status or property, must be in either the male line or the female line; it cannot be in both. But both lines may be employed for different purposes. Thus double systems of descent have been described, in which local group membership is transmitted in one line, moveable goods such as livestock and money in the other. Many variations on this theme have been recorded.

In many primitive societies religious practices are closely articulated with the kinship system; shrines to the deceased lineage heads may form the foci of ancestor cults, which unite the members of the descent group in the common discharge of ritual obligations.

Even in societies, like our own, where social groups are organized in terms of principles other than unilineal descent, cognatic relationship may be important. The matrix of nearly every kinship system is the elementary family of father, mother and their children, and

---

[1] For a description of a system of this kind see *The Nuer*, by E. E. Evans-Pritchard (Oxford, 1940).

even where the links through one parent are of major formal importance, those through the other almost always have counterbalancing significance. Often, for example, they provide a range of social ties outside the unilineal group (marriage in such societies being usually exogamous; wives, that is, being taken from outside the group), and so create a breach in the social isolation and exclusiveness of the lineage. For this reason the mother's brother is often a relative of strategic importance in patrilineal societies; he is the representative of the most important body of kin outside the paternal lineage, the mother's agnatic group.

In these and other ways recent studies have exhibited the kinship framework as determining the individual's place in the complex system of inter-personal relations which constitute the social life. These relations may be political, jural, economic or ritual; in those societies where kinship is important there is scarcely any department of the social life which it does not pervade.

Marriage is almost always a great deal more than simply a legalized sexual union between a man and a woman; it has been shown that in many societies it involves a considerable rearrangement of the social structure. In most societies based on exogamous local groups marriage brings into what is expected to be an amicable relationship two separate and potentially hostile groups, the bride's kin-group and the bridegroom's kin-group. The bride's group sustains the loss of a working member and potential childbearer, and the widespread custom of rendering goods or services (sometimes even another woman) to her group on the occasion of marriage may sometimes be understood as a method of indemnifying the bride's people for this loss. Such a payment may also serve as a guarantee of good behaviour on the part of both spouses; for if the wife misbehaves her husband may divorce her and demand the return of the marriage payment, a contingency which her parents will wish to avoid; and if the husband is at fault the woman may leave him and, in certain societies, he may lose both her and the payment he has made. The payment of bride-wealth may, further, constitute legal evidence of the marriage, for in societies where marriage is the concern of neither Church nor State but solely of the two groups of kin involved, the legality of the union, and so the status of the children of the marriage, is often validated by reference to a payment, usually in cattle, of this kind. In the verification of these statements and in other ways recent studies have added to our understanding of marriage in so-called primitive societies, and it is no longer possible for informed missionaries or administrators to assert that unions involving the transfer of goods are not marriages but purchases, and so offensive to morality and good taste. Marriage is now seen to be important not solely as the basis of the family and the spring from which all kinship relations continually flow, but also as a means to social integration in a wider range of social contexts.

In all societies there are certain relatives whom it is not permissible to marry, and in many these include all the members of a person's localized kin-group so that a spouse must be found outside the local community. In such cases marriage regulations, with the kinship system associated with them, may be regarded, as a recent writer[1] has put it, as "the blueprint of a mechanism which 'pumps' women out of their consanguineous families to redistribute them in affinal groups, the result of this process being to create new consanguineous groups"[1] and so, by a continuing process, to perpetuate the social structure. In some societies, also, marriage with certain specified relatives, e.g. cross-cousins,[2] is either prescribed or preferred. This is structurally significant in that it provides that a relationship between two social groups established in one generation may be repeated in subsequent generations.

The foregoing gives a necessarily summary indication of the range and scope of recent studies by social anthropologists of the relationships of kinship and marriage. Instead of trying to discover the origins of the institutions connoted by these terms, the attempt has been made to interpret them as elements in working social systems. In this way the fallacy of too-facile identification with institutions in our own western society, which though similarly named are vastly different, has been at least in part avoided.

(b) Social Control

The maintenance of a more or less ordered system of social relations involves the exercise of some kind of constraint on individuals, whose self-interest may incite behaviour incompatible with the common good. This constraint takes many different forms, and may be exercised through many different channels; and the study of these has been an important concern of modern social anthropology. Where these studies have dealt with the maintenance of social order throughout entire communities and in regard particularly to intergroup relationships, they have usually been considered as dealing with the political organization of the societies concerned; where the emphasis has rather been on inter-personal relationships, and where reference to the possibility of the use of physical force is not usually implicit, the wider generic notion of sanction has been used.

Field research by social anthropologists has shown that the classical definition of the term "political" is adequate only within the societies in which it originated. It is far too narrow to include all the relevant phenomena from many non-European societies.

---

[1] Claude Lèvi-Strauss, op. cit.

[2] Cross-cousins are the children of siblings of opposite sex.

Thus in a modern study of African political systems[1] the proper sphere of the political is defined as "the maintenance or establishment of the social order, within a territorial framework, by the organized exercise of coercive authority through the use, or the possibility of use, of physical force". But several of the studies contained in the book show that political order may sometimes be maintained despite the absence of any organized coercive authority, and with only the most exiguous of references, explicit or implied, to the use of force.

Though there is a great variety of possible types, it has been found useful to distinguish the political systems of the societies dealt with by social anthropologists according to whether they possess a centralized government and judiciary as we do in our own society, or whether they possess no such institutions, yet manage to maintain some sort of political order. Thus distinguished, societies may be described as centralized on the one hand, or "acephalous" or segmentary on the other. But these two types represent poles rather than antitheses; there are many intermediate types.

Descriptions of centralized political systems by trained anthropologists and others are available from many parts of the world, notably from Africa. The investigation of such states as functioning systems, with regard to the different kinds of political equilibrium achieved in them, has marked a considerable advance from the older studies, which often overstressed the autocratic powers of native kings and chiefs, neglecting the less conspicuous counterbalancing forces in the political structure. Interesting analogies with European feudal systems can sometimes be drawn.[2] The evidence has also revealed two distinct structural types of centralized political systems; those in which a ruling class or group has conquered another group and established a central government over them (the typical "conquest state"), and those in which one indigenous individual or group has through personal character or historical circumstance emerged as *primus inter pares* and assumed political authority over the other segments of the society. In the former case, the dominated group may itself have been formerly organized on a centralized pattern, or it may have been originally a segmentary society, the structure of which still persists as a sort of political substratum. All these different possibilities are realized in existing societies.

Perhaps of greater interest (because less familiar) are descriptions by social anthropologists of "acephalous" political systems. These are organized in a number of separate local groups or segments, generally conceived in terms of a system of lineages with which the

---

[1] *African Political Systems*, ed. M. Fortes and E. E. Evans-Pritchard (Oxford, 1940).

[2] As in *A Black Byzantium*, by S. F. Nadel (Oxford, 1942).

local groups may be more or less coterminous. These segments, like the lineage subdivisions which tend to correspond to them, constitute an expanding series, the section in which one's membership is relevant in any situation being correlated, at least ideally, with the spatial remoteness of the group to which one is opposed in that particular context. Relationships between these different groups tend to be maintained in what may best be described as a state of balanced opposition. From one point of view, the groups are united by the necessity for friendly relations, brought about by inter-marriage and common economic and other interests and activities, from another aspect they are in constant conflict and rivalry, sometimes expressed through the institution of the blood feud. It is the equilibrium which results from the balance between these two kinds of relations that maintains the *status quo*, and enables the members of the society to live more or less ordered lives.

Conformity to norms of behaviour may be achieved by a variety of means, and not all of these may usefully be called legal. Social anthropologists have differed as to the terminology appropriate to processes of this kind, some holding that most if not all of the processes of social control may be called legal, others preferring to restrict this term to those modes of restraint which involve organized courts and judges. It does not greatly matter which term is used so long as it is made clear exactly what is being referred to, but there are advantages in adhering to the second usage, referring to those processes of control which do not possess the formal character noted above as sanctions rather than laws.

In this latter sense, many societies have no law. But they do not therefore lack social order. Law is only one sort of sanction, and the same society may utilize sanctions of many different types. Strictly legal sanctions may vary from those imposed by duly constituted courts with professional judges, as in western and some Moslem societies, to those applied by *ad hoc* assemblies of villagers and kinsmen; but always there is a recognized authority to assert the law and to penalize breaches of it.

A useful classification of sanctions[1] is into positive, which approve certain behaviour, and negative, which disapprove certain behaviour (the most usual case), and organized (where some specific and recognized procedure is involved—legal sanctions falling into this category)—and diffuse, where the expression of approval or disapproval is spontaneous and unorganized. As well as the sanctions of the criminal law, the large body of negative sanctions may include diffuse reactions of moral disapproval, ridicule, adverse public opinion and so on. It may also include a wide range of religious or ritual sanctions, depending for their effectiveness on a body of supra-empirical beliefs, as well as the sanction of the

[1] The one given is Radcliffe-Brown's (op. cit. Ch. xi).

possible withdrawal of reciprocity in a wide range of social relationships, a sanction much stressed by Malinowski. Sanctions may also
be distinguished according to whether the action taken or threatened is by the society as a whole or its representatives, or by the
individual or group which has been wronged by the breach, cases
of the latter kind falling, in our society, within the sphere of civil law.
It should be noted, however, that even in cases where the injured
individual or group takes action, the offence reacted against may
still be subject to the general approval or disapproval of the society
as a whole. This type of sanction is, as we might expect, typical of
societies in which there is no centralized government and so no
centralized judiciary. In such societies disputes between groups (e.g.
those arising from homicide) may be settled, if they are settled at
all, by means of retaliation, including the blood-feud and the duel,
or by indemnification, the payment of compensation in some form.
Thus, in a segmentary society, a homicide involving the members
of two separate groups may entail a retaliatory homicide, the group
which has suffered the loss of a member having the right to kill a
member, not necessarily the actual offender, of the other group. In
accordance with the relativity of group membership in such segmentary societies, it will usually be found that the closer are the opposing
groups territorially and genealogically, the more likely it is that
compensation will be accepted in lieu of retaliation. In the case of a
homicide between the closest of kin (for instance, full brothers)
there can be neither retaliation nor compensation, for those who
would avenge and be avenged upon, or who would demand and
receive compensation, are the same people. But often a homicide
within a small group of this kind is regarded as a sin, and calls for
expiation.

This type of sanction is typical of societies composed of small,
lineage-based groups without central authority, like the Bedouin
Arabs. If there is a central government, it tends to arrogate to itself
the right to settle intergroup disputes. This is of course the case in
western societies, where "self-help" in matters of this kind would
itself invite the imposition of a negative sanction. Field-research has
borne out the contention that the less effectively a society is centrally organized (if it is centrally organized at all), the more will
breaches of norms be dealt with as intergroup matters in terms of
the principle of self-help. But we have seen that this does not imply
the negation of law and order, for self-help and the institution of the
feud are ordinarily subject to strict regulation and imply a live
public opinion.

It is noteworthy that the application of sanctions in primitive
communities is not primarily, and in some cases not at all, directed
to the *punishment* of offenders against accepted codes of behaviour.
Thus in the case of blood revenge it is not necessarily the murderer,

but may be any member of his group, who is killed in retaliation. Sometimes it must be a person of equivalent age and status to the original victim. The primary aim is clearly the maintenance or restoration of the *status quo ante*, the maintenance, that is, of the society as a working system; for this is the greatest common interest of its members, and the condition of their effective interaction. Thus what is sought in procedures of this kind is primarily to restore the breached or threatened solidarity, and what is expressed is very commonly the public opinion of the community.

(c) Magic and Religion

In every society there is a body of empirical knowledge; the notion of primitive man as entirely dominated by the mystical and irrational has been shown to be illusory. There is an irrational element in all thought, both "civilized" and "primitive", and the difference between primitive and civilized modes of thought lies not at all in the mental processes, the types of logical inference involved, but in the premisses, the beliefs about the world, from which the inferences are made.

Life always contains an element of unpredictability, and hence anxiety, and this is especially so among peoples less developed technologically than ourselves, and among whom illness and death from starvation, disease and natural calamity are at once more familiar and less understood than they are in our society. Such communities may hold complex systems of belief in what we should call non-natural causal agents and principles, which may be propitiated by prayer or sacrifice, or utilized by the appropriate techniques. It may be said, then, that a function of such beliefs is to relieve ignorance and anxiety, and this is no doubt an important reason for their persistence, even in culturally advanced societies. In many communities illness or other personal misfortune is regarded as due to the anger of a malevolent ghost, an act of witch-craft or sorcery, or failure to observe some ritual avoidance. Any of these alternatives provides an intelligible and acceptable explanation and, what is most important, prescribes the action to be taken. Thus the victim may sacrifice a goat to his father's ghost, seek out and avenge himself against a witch, or do penance for his failure to observe a ritual avoidance. Though these activities do not produce the end desired, they enable the performer to feel that he is coping with the situation, and allow him to express his pent-up anxiety in overt behaviour.

Though individual practitioners may be known or suspected to be charlatans, scepticism in regard to the accepted body of beliefs is rare in primitive societies. For these beliefs are supported by the whole weight of the traditional culture, and are seen constantly to be justified by experience. Thus the activities of rain-makers are óften followed by rain, and sacrifice on behalf of a sick relative by the recovery of the patient. There are many possible explanations of apparent failures; the opposition of more powerful magic, incorrect performance of the rite, interference by spirits, and other causes may be involved, but never the breakdown of the magical principle itself.

Beliefs of this kind are generally closely integrated with other elements in the social system, which support and corroborate them. Thus the Azande people of the southern Sudan[1] attribute many misfortunes to witchcraft. The victim realizes that the witch is likely to be someone he knows and who has a grudge against him, for people bewitch those they hate. The culprit is revealed by consulting an oracle or a diviner and, if his activities have not yet resulted in death, he is approached and politely asked to withdraw his witchcraft. If the victim were to die, formerly vengeance could be exacted, provided that the oracle's decision as to the witch's identity was confirmed by the king's or chief's oracle. Nowadays magic is made against the witch, though nobody knows who he is; and when after a lapse of time somebody in the community dies, this person is believed, after *post hoc* oracular confirmation, to be the witch, and the incident is closed. A similar cycle of events then begins in connexion with the last death.

Thus Azande beliefs about witchcraft form a closed system. They tie up some of the loose ends in experience, and provide a socially acceptable way of thinking about death (a most disruptive experience in any community). They canalize emotions of envy and hatred, and provide a formal way of dealing with them. And since the system of oracles constitutes a hierarchy, like the political system with which it is associated, the body of Azande belief supports and is consistent with the political organization. In these and other ways these beliefs are shown to form a coherent system of thought, closely integrated with social life. Often, also, witchcraft beliefs form an important sanction for good behaviour; for unneighbourly conduct may not only incite the enmity of others and perhaps provoke them to bewitch a man or his family, but it may also bring down on him accusations of witchcraft, with consequent reprisals.

Magic is performed by men to achieve specific ends, and analysis of magical practices from many different societies shows that a causal principle *sui generis* is believed to be involved. It has been said that a magical act normally involves three elements: the spell, or the words used; the rite, or that which is done; and the instruments or medicines used. Often, too, the state of mind and body, the ritual status, of the performer is important. The relative importance of

[1] Described in *Witchcraft, Oracles and Magic among the Azande* by E. E. Evans-Pritchard (Oxford, 1937).

these factors may vary from one society to another, and it is impossible to define magic in terms of any one of them. Thus in Oceania the spell is vital, and a mistake in the words may invalidate the magic; in Africa the power is usually believed to reside in the medicines, and the form of words used is unimportant.

The complex of magico-religious beliefs often provides a means of understanding and coping with the unknown and unpredictable, and so of allaying anxiety and increasing confidence. But sometimes it may have the opposite effect, for magical dangers may be even more terrifying than real ones. Psychological considerations of this kind cannot provide an adequate sociological explanation of magical phenomena; explanations which relate them systematically to other co-existent social phenomena, like those given for the Azande, are more satisfying. Thus it has been pointed out in reference to Melanesia that many ordinary activities are more efficiently carried out because the order of their performance is ritually prescribed.[1] Again, important social obligations may be more readily discharged if the importance of their performance is magically stressed. Finally, magical and ritual beliefs tend to cluster round places, people and periods of special social importance, and so to enhance and emphasize this importance.

Of particular interest are the symbolic elements in magico-religious beliefs and practices. Much ritual behaviour may be regarded as the "acting out" of a situation in symbolic terms; it has an expressive as well as an instrumental aspect. What is essential about such behaviour is that something is made to stand for something else, and Frazer long ago described two of the most important principles, resemblance and contiguity, in terms of which this symbolic reference is made. The use of symbolic representation is widespread in all societies, and calls for much further study. In some contexts what is represented is a value shared by a whole society or by a majority of its members. Thus in many kingdoms the well-being of the whole country is believed to be closely bound up with the well-being of the king's person, and accordingly he is hedged about with many ritual prohibitions and observances, like Frazer's "divine king". Again, in many segmentary societies the unity and solidarity of the component groups is symbolized in some common object, the *totem*, which is specially regarded, and sometimes, as in Australia, forms the centre of a cult.

It is impossible, in considering primitive societies, to keep quite distinct the two fields of magic and religion, however these be defined. But it is often useful to distinguish as religious those supernatural beliefs which involve reference to spiritual beings, however conceived, from those which do not. In fact, beliefs of

[1] e.g. by B. Malinowski in *Argonauts of the Western Pacific* (Studies in Economic and Political Science, Routledge, 1922).

both kinds will constantly be found to be inextricably bound up together.

In terms of this distinction no society known to us is without some form of religious belief. This may assume the form of belief in a high God, the first mover or creator of the universe, sometimes conceived as being now otiose. Or it may assume the form of a belief in the power of the ghosts of deceased ancestors, who may punish and (less often) reward their living descendants. This belief is sometimes found in societies in which localized descent groups form the main structural principle. Or religious belief may assume the form of beliefs in impersonal spirits associated with certain natural phenomena, such as trees, rivers, mountains and especially the earth itself.

It is a mistake, however, to think of religion solely in terms of belief. In societies where there is no priestly class, religion is usually acted out rather than thought out, and often primitive theologies must be in large part inferred from the kinds of rites performed.

Religious activity in its social aspect usually involves group participation, and so tends to unite the adherents of a cult (though it may at the same time put them into opposition with other cult groups). Religious observance may also require in its participants a good state of mind and the absence of anti-social feelings, and so may conduce to social harmony. And it may express powerful supernatural sanctions for good behaviour (though this is unusual in primitive societies), and so play an important part in social control. And, finally, the symbolic framework of religious thought may express, and so assert and reinforce, some of the more important categories in which people conceive themselves and their social system.

It may be remarked, in conclusion, that the way in which social anthropologists have most advanced the comparative study of religions is by the development of techniques of detailed field research, directed to ascertaining the meaning to their performers of religious ceremonies, and their relations to other social activities. But a great deal more remains to be done in this field.

(d) Economics and Property Relations

Economics differs from most other aspects of social life in that it has for years constituted a distinct study possessing its own accepted principles and rules. But it may be doubted if these rules possess the universal validity sometimes claimed for them, for they are based largely on the implications of the economic systems of western society, with their reliance on a price system and wide-range systems of economic relationship. Field studies by social anthropologists have shown some of the ways in which economic ends may be achieved without recourse to economic mechanisms of the kind familiar in western society, and also how apparently economic institutions may serve a great many other social purposes.

A good deal of information is now available in regard to the techniques by means of which goods are actually produced in primitive societies. If information on the organization of labour, incentive patterns, and matters of this kind is less copious, this may be partly because in communities where there is little economic specialization and where face-to-face relationships are the rule, there is simply less to be said about these matters. But much further work on the economics of production in primitive societies is needed.

More can be said about the exchange and transfer of goods. Though a few primitive societies have had price systems with fixed currencies (some single value factor covering a greater or lesser proportion of possible exchanges), most have utilized systems of direct exchange or barter. But it would be a mistake—though one commonly made—to conceive these relationships as determined solely, or in many cases even mainly, by the desire for material advantage. Malinowski's analysis of the *kula* cycle in the western Pacific showed that what was aimed at in the ceremonial exchange of valuables which he described was prestige rather than any kind of economic advantage. There was no bargaining, and the articles concerned possessed no utilitarian exchange value. Similarly, the wholesale destruction of items of economic value on certain ceremonial occasions, reported about peoples as remote from one another as the North American Indians and the Polynesian Tikopians, though "economically" senseless, is perfectly intelligible when it is seen as a means of asserting and validating status. In all these cases the profit motive is replaced by what Firth has called the status increment motive.[1] It is essential in considering property relations in primitive societies to distinguish utilitarian values (based on usage) from ritual values. Items of either of these types may be interchangeable, not only with items of the same type, but also with those of the other kind. Thus, as in the example quoted above, it is possible for a ritual value (enhanced status) to be acquired by the destruction of a utilitarian value. So regarded, practices of this kind, at first sight anomalous, are seen to fit into the general economic pattern of exchange.

The making of gifts, often highly institutionalized in primitive societies, also has its reciprocating economic aspect. Many years ago the French sociologist Mauss pointed out that the giver rarely gives unconditionally; in a sense what he gives is part of himself, and the receiver is in debt until a return is made. Field studies in many parts of the world have amply verified this hypothesis.

[1] In an article in *The Institutions of Primitive Society* (a series of broadcast talks; Oxford, 1954).

All these considerations seem to point to the need to broaden orthodox economic concepts, and in particular to the desirability of recognizing that economic value in the accepted sense of the term does not exhaust the kinds of value significant in exchange relationships.

The thesis that the transfer of property usually has far more than merely utilitarian significance is supported by much ethnographic evidence. We discussed the transfer of cattle or other goods by which marriage is validated in many societies, and we noted that such transactions have many non-economic social implications. It has been shown also that institutionalized gift exchange is usual between individuals or groups between whom there is a possibility of conflict, especially when the social organization requires that good relations should be maintained between them. Thus in many societies the frequent exchange of presents between in-laws (who may, as we have seen, belong to different and opposed social groups) is socially prescribed. Evidently the function of such transactions is rather to increase social solidarity and interdependence by the creation and affirmation of social ties than to further any specifically economic end.

Ideas about property, the nature of rights in things, differ widely in different societies. In most, the notion of private ownership, in the sense of unconditional and exclusive individual rights as against all others, plays a very minor part compared with its place in western society. The difference is not of course simply that between individual and communal ownership; there are no societies in which equal rights in all goods are held by everybody; but often rights are held not by individuals but by specific groups, such as families or lineages, and usually they are held conditionally and not absolutely.

This is particularly clear in the many studies which have been made of primitive systems of land tenure. Where there are no perennial crops, and permanent improvements to the land are lacking (as, for example, in conditions of shifting cultivation), the rights held by individual cultivators are rarely absolute, but depend on residence and cultivation. Ultimate rights are usually held by the social group of which the individual is a member, perhaps an extended family or lineage; and he may be unable to dispose of the land or of any part of it without the agreement of this group or its representatives. In some centralized kingdoms in Africa and elsewhere a feudal type of land-holding has developed, and large areas of populated land have been held by an upper class on condition of homage, service and the payment of tribute to their next superior in the hierarchy. Misunderstanding of the types of land tenure to be found in the less advanced agricultural communities has led, with the coming of European contact, to such anomalies as the "purchase" of land from persons who did not own it, and to the gratuitous establishment as permanent freeholders of people whose rights to the land so vested in them were in reality only temporary and *ex officio*.

(e) Social Change

Change is, of course, a quality of all societies; no society is static, and no comprehensive social study can afford to neglect this element. But the analysis of the actual processes of change may be said to constitute a special study, involving not only the notion of the social structure as a functioning system of relationships, but employing also historical categories, and entailing the observation of particular social processes through time. Social anthropologists have distinguished between synchronic studies, those which apprehend the society being studied as a working system at one moment of time, and diachronic studies, those which take for consideration two successive states of the same society. These approaches, though they are of course concerned with abstractions, do represent opposite poles of interest. It might be said, however, that the approach of the student of social change must be polychronic rather than merely diachronic.

The fact that our understanding of social change has not been more advanced by social anthropologists may be partly due to the inadequacy, in a temporal context, of the "holistic" functional approach used by itself, with its stress on equilibrium, order and stability. For what is noteworthy about many societies undergoing rapid social change is that they have ceased to function properly as working systems. The notion of function has had to be supplemented by the notion of "dysfunction", and the implications of this latter term subjected to analysis.

The kind of social change which primarily interests social anthropologists (and others) is that which results from what has been loosely called culture contact: the impact of two very different social systems on one another, one usually being "advanced", the other "primitive". This has been represented chiefly in the relations between the various European colonial powers and the native populations over which they have assumed political control. Of course the changes brought about by this impact are not confined to the political sphere; the whole range of social relations is affected, and radical alterations thus brought about in economic, ritual, legal, domestic, kinship and other relations have been described from many societies.

It has now become clear that social change is not to be understood in terms of any kind of naïve diffusionism. It is not explained simply by the accretion to an existing culture of new elements, though no doubt there is such an accretion. What results is something new, not resoluble to the mere sum of its parts. The functional emphasis on the essential interdependence of the parts of a given social field, on the fact that they are in some sense a unity (even though not necessarily a harmonious one), has obviated the error of a naïvely diffusionist interpretation.

Even anthropologists have not always clearly understood that for a society to be one it is not necessary that its parts should be in complete harmony with one another. In fact, as we noted when discussing political organization, institutionalized conflict may be an essential structural principle, and in some form or another it seems always to be present. But it is clear that some types of conflict are especially disruptive: those which arise from a conflict of loyalties, for example, or from the breakdown of a conventional morality. It has accordingly been found useful to distinguish two different kinds of conflict. One is that which is provided for in the structure of the society; it operates within the existing normative framework and is subject to the existing social sanctions; it offers no challenge to the institutionalized values of the community. The other type is not provided for in the existing social structure, but rather affects that structure itself, setting one part of it into opposition against another, so that the society must either change or disintegrate. For the co-existence in the same society of mutually incompatible patterns of behaviour with their associated norms must lead to confusion and disequilibrium. Sooner or later some will have to be either modified or abandoned, and radical change will have occurred. Though this distinction between two sorts of change is in the last resort relative and not absolute, it is useful in indicating the kind of social situation with which the student of social change will be mostly concerned. For the type of change with which recent history has made us most familiar is that which results from the contact of cultures, and which is often accompanied by conflicts of this relatively insoluble kind.

An attempt has been made to characterize this type of conflict in terms of unevenness of scale.[1] It has been pointed out that different but related spheres of social interaction may vary widely in range and scope, and that conflict arises when wide-range and narrow-range systems of relationships are required to co-exist in the same social *milieu*. Thus it might be said that in Africa and elsewhere the increase in scale in some sets of relations, such as economic relations, has not been balanced by corresponding increases in the intensity and extent of social relationships in other spheres, such as those of religious practice or of inter-personal relations.

Though in fact insoluble conflict arises because the different institutions which social contact brings into uneasy juxtaposition involve fundamentally different ways of thinking and acting, rather than because there is a difference of scale involved, this account

[1] e.g. by G. and M. Wilson, in *The Analysis of Social Change* (Cambridge, 1942).

does provide an accurate description of what is actually happening in contemporary Africa and elsewhere. For conflict often does arise when wide-range systems impinge on narrow-range ones.

Part of the difficulty which is felt in social anthropology in finding an adequate model for the understanding of social change derives from the unmanageable breadth of the concept thus barely stated. For social change is not a specific social field, it is the whole social field, regarded in its dynamic, processual aspect. We can, therefore, no more study "social change" in general than we can study the whole social field in general; it is necessary here as in other contexts to isolate specific institutions, and to study their modifications through time and against their social background. Here, in particular, social anthropology must supplement the functional approach by the application of historical techniques.

VI. Conclusion

Not quite fifty years ago Sir James Frazer said that social anthropology, like sociology, looked for general laws, but (unlike sociology) only for those exemplified in "the rudimentary phases, the infancy and childhood, of human society". Social anthropologists, accordingly, studied the customs and beliefs of savages, and superstitions and survivals in civilized societies. Today our view has broadened. Social anthropology is no longer confined to savages and survivals: it is interested in all human societies everywhere, and is distinguished from allied studies rather in method than in subject-matter. Of its distinctive methods and achievements something has been said in this essay. There can be no doubt that our understanding of cultures other than our own has been enormously advanced by the intensive studies which characterize modern social anthropology: much that was formerly strange is now intelligible; much that was formerly condemned is now tolerated.

This is the short answer to the question, sometimes put, "What is the use of social anthropology?" But we can be more specific. A knowledge of a people's social organization and, no less important, of what it means to the people who have it, is important for those who have to live among, work among, and perhaps still in some regions administer them. If we must act, it is better to do so in knowledge than in ignorance. But this does not mean that the anthropologist should confine himself to practical problems of administration and such like. Though he may study such problems, and some anthropologists will prefer to do so, experience has shown that to allow anthropologists to pursue the problems which their interests and research suggest may lead to equal and perhaps greater practical good. Nor may the anthropologist prescribe what shall be done or what ought to be done; his task is to ascertain the facts and, sometimes, to suggest the possible consequences of alternative courses of action. *Qua* scientist, his responsibility ends there.

But it is not only about other peoples that social anthropology informs us; through it we may also learn about ourselves. Not long ago we, like the Azande, had a system of witchcraft beliefs; even now our attitude to property, like that of the Indians of the American North-West, is not wholly utilitarian; internal stress and strain are no less present in our own society than they are in those undergoing the strain of culture contact. To understand these phenomena in other societies is to a significant extent to understand them in our own.

BOOKS SUGGESTED FOR FURTHER READING

E. E. Evans-Pritchard, *Social Anthropology* (Cohen and West, 1951).

A. R. Radcliffe-Brown, *Structure and Function* (Cohen and West, 1952).

African Systems of Kinship and Marriage ed. by Radcliffe-Brown and Forde (International African Institute, 1950).

African Political Systems ed. by Fortes and Evans-Pritchard (International African Institute, 1940).

B. Malinowski, *Magic, Science and Religion*, etc. (The Free Press, Glencoe, Illinois, 1948).

B. Malinowski, *Argonauts of the Western Pacific* (Studies in Economic and Political Science, Routledge, 1922).

SECTION THREE

Art

PAINTING

by ROBIN IRONSIDE

IN ONE CRUCIAL respect, modern painting is an absolutely unprecedented phenomenon. Contemporary artists, if they have any merit, are not less sensitive than their forebears to the stimulus of tradition; but the ideals to which they aspire and the forms with which they invest their aspirations have been universally affected by the fateful invention of photography, the results of which, already sufficiently radical, have not yet, in their ultimate scope, become apparent. Though the first appearance, in 1839, of the daguerrotype had no profound effect upon contemporary style, the characteristics of Impressionist painting and of every subsequent movement must be considered as in some measure a response to the disturbing influences of the camera; and future historians, whatever other chronological divisions they may adopt, will be bound to recognize the discovery of photography as, in the most literal sense of the word, an epoch-making event compared with which the effects of the fall of Constantinople, the genius of Titian or the Council of Trent will appear neglible.

Before the invention of photography, it was generally admitted that the art of painting, whatever its potentialities, was in the first place an art of imitation. The conviction that it was not merely an art of imitation was widespread, but just what a painting became, or ought to become, when it transcended that unpretentious level of achievement was a centuries-old subject of philosophical inquiry. But that it was the painter's indispensable, if not his most glorious function to depict nature in some recognizable form was never questioned. It would have occurred to nobody to become an artist who was not prepared to go as far as that. The cultivation of the beautiful, the sublime or the harmonious might be the painter's all-absorbing preoccupation, but the pursuit of these elusive objects was necessarily carried on by means of a technique of imitation. That painting should have been credited with this fundamental, inherent and inalienable function, the performance of which in whatever feeble degree was prerequisite to the assumption of any others, arose from the fact that no other mode of visual representation or recording was available. Whatever might be required in this line, from the holiday souvenir to the image of a god, could only be supplied by the artist. A painter might be called upon or choose to regard himself as the producer exclusively of works of fine art, but this was only one, though it was the most illustrious, of the innumerable purposes to which he might devote his abilities.

With the advent of photography, these long-established conditions ceased to exist. Though the supremacy, as an instrument of self-expression, of the very personal process of painting remained unchallenged, it soon became apparent that the camera's powers must exceed the competence of any imitative technique which might be devised by painters. The researches and explorations of science might now dispense with the hitherto essential services of the artist; the cheap portraitist was no longer required; the illustration of news was no longer entrusted to the free and easy interpretations of "our artist on the spot"; the demand for topographers vanished; and engravers, whose function was to disseminate the productions of this host of professional painters and draughtsmen, were driven from the field. Visual documentation, with negligible and diminishing exceptions, was henceforward undertaken by the superior agency of the camera.

The art of painting, if it was to survive, had, clearly, to abandon its ancient foundation of truth to nature, on which so many imperishable works had been raised. There was no reason why painters should not continue to exploit the elaborate craft of representation bequeathed by the past, but mastery of it ceased to be either sufficient or essential to the single, obscure but noble purpose which was now left them to fulfil. Today a painter who offers his work for sale must believe, unless he is a lunatic or a charlatan, that he is potentially capable of producing a work of art, a work that is to be justified by its aesthetic quality alone.[1] The peculiar difficulty of his situation is not so much due to the indefinable nature of aesthetic quality as to the relatively abrupt disappearance of the old conviction that for a painter this quality was only to be attained through some mode of representing natural appearances. Painters are now released from the obligation to represent anything at all, but the emancipation has been followed by an unparalleled confusion of aims; and, though it cannot be positively asserted that art itself no

[1] To this necessity may be ascribed, in some small part, that specially modern phenomenon of the artist as an exceptional, a privileged being, exempt from many of the conventional rules of conduct, worthy, if not in receipt, of government support and a purveyor of that culture which has become such a conspicuous article in the international commerce of prestige.

longer prospers as before, a generation of false-prophets has arisen
who have sought to replace the obsolete criterion of imitation by
meaningless aesthetic standards which cannot but darken counsel
in those quarters where they are adopted. We may easily conceive
that a good deal of bad painting today is the fruit of some
quixotic endeavour to express "the mathematics of nature" or
the sign of some desperate phase in the quest for "organic form".
In the sphere of contemporary criticism, "universal darkness covers
all".

In the midst of this obscurity and licence, schools of painting are
a conspicuous but not a solitary anachronism. The education of a
painter, before the invention of photography, might be elaborately
prolonged. While proficiency in the techniques of representation
was the essential element of the painter's equipment, the aspirant
might profitably devote himself to the study of anatomy, proportion,
perspective, and to the exercise of drawing from the life. There is
no doubt that, where there is a will, the ability to draw and paint
"correctly" can be taught; and apprenticeship in a school or studio
served, in those days, a need that was not only widespread but
intelligent. The labour thus expended is now uselessly undertaken.
The display of representational skill is not only irrelevant to aesthetic
achievement but is often disparaged as bad in itself; and though, in
truth, such disparagement is unfounded and the techniques of
imitation may still be fruitfully exploited for aesthetic purposes,
natural appearances are much more rapidly and easily expressed by
working from photographs than by learning to draw from nature
with all the expense of time and toil which that process involves.
The most difficult anatomical foreshortenings may now be correctly
reproduced by the painter in a matter almost of minutes by tracing
from a photograph of a body taken in the required position from the
required viewpoint. There is, for the contemporary painter, no
absolutely prescriptive technical capacity which cannot be acquired
at an infant school. The painting of a picture today is no more subject to rules and regulations than the composition of a lyric poem.
No government or local authority would be prepared to incur the
volume of just protest which the endowment of a school for lyric
poets would certainly provoke; yet a meaningless tradition still
sanctions the maintenance of our schools of painting, and it might
be said that the number of the students vindicates the utility of the
training. But there will always be a sufficiency of maladjusted young
people who will turn to painting, without grasping their motives,
for its therapeutic value rather than from an authentic sense of
vocation. The most popular schools no longer pretend that a picture
should necessarily represent anything, and the absence of any standard professional qualifications, the fact that there is really nothing
to learn, are alone sufficient to attract the energy or indolence

of many who feel themselves unequal—and their plight deserves
our sympathy—to the strain of more stereotyped occupations.[1]

Since there are no minimum standards of competence, the painting of pictures has become, in the best and the worst senses of the
term, an amateur activity. The mere application of paint to canvas
stands a reasonable chance of being accepted as aesthetically valuable, whether it is undertaken as an occupational therapy, as a
means of killing time, or with the pretention, genuine or hypo-
critical, of producing a work of art. This drastic extension of the
conceivable limits of critical interest is less deplorable than it may
seem to be. It has brought to light a remarkable capacity for
aesthetic visualization in the pre-adolescent child and has revealed
the occasional survival of the same capacity, in all its pristine *naïveté*,
in the adult productions of the uneducated amateur working in such
moments of leisure as the obligations of wage-earning may afford.
Unfortunately, *naïveté* in art is a trait easily counterfeited; or, at
least, the multitude of indifferent "Sunday" painters (busy at their
easels on every day of the week except, perhaps, the Sabbath) would
seem to prove this point. The potential quality of "Sunday" painting has, however, been established beyond dispute by the genius of
Henri Rousseau. His child-like vision assumed occasionally an epic
character; and if, encouraged by this phenomenon, there has been
an undue tolerance of infantilism in painting it is a tolerance which
has simplified recognition of such peculiar gifts as those of Seraphine,
Hirsfield or Vivin. In the days before photography, the mere ability
to copy nature was liable to be mistaken for artistic talent, and
something has been gained by the recognition that mechanical
excellence of whatever kind is, and always has been, a neutral factor
in the production of a work of fine art. The great masterpieces of the
past, though they are the work of professionals and display professional virtues in abundance, were conceived in an amateur
moment. Nothing could be less professional than inspiration.

The history of art since the invention of the camera has reflected
at every stage the advantages and pitfalls of the liberating effects
of photography. The story may be treated, though it has not often
been considered in this light, as the narrative of an immense and
still incomplete readjustment. Painters sought the assistance of the
camera from the start. Detailed evidence of the extent to which they
did and still do so is slight, for the reason, comprehensible in the

[1] These remarks refer, of course, exclusively to the teaching of fine art. By
providing instruction in the increasingly various technical processes with which,
in the vexed sphere of applied art, the designer has to contend, the art school
performs—or may perform—a most valuable service. It may be symptomatic of the
state of the visual arts that the work of students in the commercial departments of
art schools in this country is aesthetically more effective than that of the students
of fine art.

middle of the nineteenth century but absurd today, that such assistance might be stigmatized as incompatible with the mysterious requirements of artistic probity. It is known, however, that Frith's *Derby Day* and *Paddington Station* were painted from photographs and that Etty, Rossetti, Ruskin and Lehnbach are to be counted among those artists who accepted the aid of photography in its earlier stages.[1] The Impressionists were the first painters to produce a style that competed with the rivalry of the camera and exploited its peculiar effects. The photographer in the seventies of the last century was powerless to reproduce the scintillations of a sunlit landscape with the prismatic fidelity, however charged with art, of which Monet and Renoir were masters. At the same time that mode of composition cultivated primarily by Degas, and with less vigour by Lautrec, would never have developed, notwithstanding the influence of Japanese prints, if the fortuitous "designs" produced by instantaneous photography had not shown the way. Nor is it likely that such works as *L'Absinthe* or *Miss Lola at the Cirque Fernando* would have been conceived without some knowledge of the effects obtainable by variations of the camera angle. Of Degas it might even be said that the interest of his art is greater in proportion to its photographic quality. Certainly, the charms of such pre-eminent examples of his talent as the *Les Courses* of 1870 or the *Répétition d'un Ballet sur la Scène* of 1873-4 depend, intimately, on the painter's transmutation of the peculiar characteristics of the daguerrotype.

The notion of exploiting photography, though its possibilities had been revealed by Degas, though Alma Tadema had hailed the camera as a great boon to the art of painting, was only gradually accepted and is perhaps still frowned upon by those who are reluctant to admit that painting, though it may still be an art, is no longer of much use as a craft. Photography indeed was flouted rather than utilized by the successors of Impressionism. Representational art was abandoned: natural appearances were stylized, and then distorted; in the end, an attempt was made to dispense with representation altogether, and abstract art, the fruit of this attempt, acquired, and retains, a substantial prestige—of that kind, let it be added, which is invariably accorded to any activity that sets out with sufficient clamour to renounce the world and the flesh.

Of those painters who escaped into stylization from the competition of the camera, Gauguin is the obvious and most illustrious example. The tendency to stylize, however, was manifest throughout Europe, and, however gross the aesthetic differences may seem to be, the art of Gauguin shares this trait conspicuously with that of Klimt, Hodler, Burne-Jones and (in his allegorical moods) Segantini. The expedient of distortion is inevitably associated with the Fauve movement whose dislike of tone, in the rendering of which the

[1] H. Gernsheim, *Masterpieces of Victorian Photography* (Phaidon Press, 1950).

camera had, from the first, revealed an inimitable mastery, was almost defiant. The various Expressionist explosions in northern Europe at the turn of the century, though their emotional motive was different, reveal a retreat, similar both in character and precipitancy, from natural or, as it was increasingly coming to be called, photographic vision. Cubism, which pushed this retreat still further, was mainly a Parisian phenomenon; at any rate, the principal monuments of this lofty but forbidding phase of the history of modern art are of Parisian if not French authorship. Their distortions were more organized than those of their predecessors; and it has been claimed for them that in presenting the spectator with a view of an object as if it were perceived simultaneously from various points of vision, they had mysteriously established a relationship of special intimacy with reality. The interest of Cubist painting is not, of course, confined to the problematical degree of success with which it may have pursued this enigmatic aim. It is true, however, that an analytic mode of presenting solid shapes is a characteristic feature of the style; and, cultivated assiduously, it resulted in the production of paintings whose original subject-matter was no longer identifiable by eye. The transition to abstract or, as it might more accurately be called, non-figurative art was easily effected. Painting, it was made to appear, had nothing whatever to do with the imitation of natural appearances; the camera had merely relieved the artist of an obstructive compulsion, and realism might now be comfortably remembered as an adulteration, however formerly imperative, of the purity of the Castalian spring. Reasoning of this specious kind may explain in some measure the now widespread acceptance of the principle of non-representation. But it is difficult to suppose that any protagonist of abstract art should, on reflection, seriously maintain that his independence of nature had disposed finally of any possible competition from photography. The technique of photography is sufficiently advanced to enable the photographer so to photograph natural objects that the result, aesthetically considered, is purely non-figurative.

Surrealism has so far been the only artistic movement during the last hundred years which, manifestly, was unembarrassed by the expanding powers of the camera; it fearlessly exploited the unprecedented accuracy of the camera's vision, and it did so in pursuance of an aim which is outside the scope of the camera's achievement and is likely to remain so. Conceptions which, in the literal sense of the words, are both monstrous and fantastic cannot be photographed. The photographer, to take one concrete instance from the infinity of other possibilities, might produce a satisfactory abstract composition by taking a judicious close-up of the grain of a piece of wood, but he could not photograph a man with a chest of drawers instead of an abdomen; he could only photograph a picture, statue or lay-figure of such a man.[1] Surrealism is now a somewhat discredited faith. The excesses of its original adherents, who were concerned to revolutionize not only painting, but the other arts and every branch of philosophy as well, sufficiently explain the ridicule of liberal minds today. We must smile, however indulgently, at an association of which a condition of membership, it is said, was that clergymen should be kicked on sight. Nevertheless, the primal extravagance of Salvador Dali and his companions had global repercussions, and the lessons of the Surrealist "revolution", in diluted form, remain a source of vigour for contemporary art and have been learnt by many who might, perhaps, deny the identity of their teachers.

Meanwhile, naturalistic paintings, with no other apparent merit beyond the vain one of resemblance to the objects depicted, have been produced in a slackening stream. They are often described, with contemptuous intent, as mere coloured photographs. The contempt would be unfounded, if there were any certainty that that is what they are. The consistence and texture of paint, for cultural and possibly also for intrinsic reasons, is still generally preferred to the surface of a photographic print, though it is doubtful whether it is a preference which can indefinitely withstand the technical progress of photography. While it persists, paintings copied from photographs will command, and deserve to command, a reasonable market. But, at the exhibitions of the Royal Academy and of similar institutions abroad where naturalism of the despised "photographic" kind is said to be feebly entrenched, there is little in the work of its exponent to suggest that the advantages of the camera's help have been recognized. The Royal Academy, though principally a haven of retirement for British Impressionists of all ages, harbours a nucleus of painters (mostly portraitists) who are apparently concerned to achieve a photographic verisimilitude of effect. The inaccuracies they commit, however, lead one to suppose that their powers of hand and eye are on the whole unequal to the task and that they have not seen fit to correct these deficiencies by working from photographs. The real objection to their productions is not that they are like coloured photographs, but that they are not enough like coloured photographs.

Though the invention and development of photographic processes has, beyond question, conditioned the character of modern painting, artists have not ceased to depend upon the past, and the modern school is still bound by innumerable slender but irrefragable strands to everything that has gone before. The ancestry of Impressionism has been interminably discussed; the trail, via Constable,

[1] Imagery of this kind can, of course, be produced by piecing photographs together; but the technique of 'collage' would be improperly described as a photographic process.

Turner and Delacroix to Velasquez, has been trodden flat in
hundreds of seminars, and might, with less monotonous ease, be
pursued still further, as far, perhaps, as the walls of a Graeco-Roman
villa. The early works of the Post-Impressionists closely resemble
those of the Impressionists; the youthful vision of Cézanne in particular was no more than an echo of Pisarro's. Impressionism, however, was the ultimate achievement of naturalistic painting; Monet
was able to imprison the glances of the sun and to avoid miraculously
any effect of petrefaction in the process; the next steps were taken,
and could only be taken, by the colour photograph and the
motion camera. Gauguin and Cézanne realized, with however
unconscious prescience, that the preoccupation of their predecessors
with the rendering of impermanent effects could hardly be carried
farther; and the mature products of Post-Impressionism display a
return to what Cézanne called "the art of the Museum", to static
composition and monumental form. Gustave Moreau, from whose
studio some of the principal figures of the Ecole de Paris curiously
emerged, announced the principle of "inertia"; and though there is
no direct connexion, the principle is fully illustrated in Cézanne's
card players, Gauguin's Tahitian maidens and Seurat's Sunday
excursionists who, with their other qualities, are certainly inert, with
the inertia of idols. The sanction for this reaction was indeed to be
found in the Museum, but since the imitation of nature had been
carried by the Impressionists to a point at which painters, in their
eagerness to depict the fleeting gesture, the evanescence of weather,
were contending in vain with the technical advances of instantaneous
photography, it was from those masters whose art was decorative as
well as descriptive that the Post-Impressionists and their successors
received impetus and authority. Cézanne's reverence for Poussin is
well known; and a reproduction after Puvis de Chavannes accompanied Gauguin to the South Seas, a proof of respect which at once
relates his art to the school of Ingres and more remotely to the
wall-painters of the quattrocento.

It might have seemed at the beginning of the present century as if
the unprecedented challenge of the camera had driven painters to
regard nature with distrust and, in revenge, to concentrate their
energies upon an increasingly widespread exploitation of the art of
the past. Paradoxically, it was by the grace of the camera that this
exploitation flourished. It was now possible, through the medium
of photography, for painters to acquire, without travel or expense,
a knowledge of the art of any period or culture. Photographic
reproductions are, however, notoriously apt to impair or adorn the
qualities of the original; differences, however faint, of scale, tone or
colour may affect profoundly our evaluation of a work of art known
only in reproduction; the inevitable difference of *mise-en-scène*
may exert a still more potent influence on our reactions; and the

rapidly increasing supply of reproductions covering every phase in every country of the history of visual art shortly created what André Malraux has called an "imaginary museum", a ubiquitous Gallery of limitless extent and variety. Its authority, as a source of instruction and inspiration, was bound to dominate that of actual museums with their inevitable gaps and relative inaccessibility. The "imaginary museum" was the argus-eyed Muse of the now defunct School of Paris in which Fauvistes, Cubists, Surrealists and Abstractionists were liberally cradled and which has remained hitherto the most conspicuous manifestation of twentieth-century painting. It was the art of primitive cultures, whether ancient or contemporary, which provided incitement to extreme modes of stylization or distortion. The primitivism of Gauguin's genius, the strong, flat colour and decorative forms in which it was expressed, gave Fauvisme a more immediate stimulus; and if we gaze with sufficient imagination at the facetted escarpments of the Montagne Ste. Victoire we may discern, if not the actual lineaments of *La Femme à la Mandoline*, at least an interaction of rectangular projections and recessions which, given the correct Cézannesque treatment, might easily pass for one of the stock figures of Cubist iconography. But Fauvistes and Cubists alike paid also the indirect debt to the folk-art forms of uncivilized communities, art forms whose interest, as a result of the bankruptcy of naturalistic painting, appeared to transcend the concerns of ethnography.

Abstraction in art is as old as history, and it is possible that man's earliest attempts to draw or paint, could examples ever be unearthed or identified, would be found to have taken the form of abstract design. Certainly, what is beyond doubt the most primitive form of painting practised today, the wall paintings (for lack of a better word) of the male bower birds of Australia, is abstract in character. Though it appears to have been established that the productions of these birds form part of the ritual of courtship, the chosen colour scheme being generally the same as that of the plumage of the female, there is no attempt at representation of the female and the work cannot be said to be less abstract simply because it is functional. In the art of man, abstract design, though its development has never so far as is known been arrested in the service of a rigid sexual ritual, has from the earliest times been employed for the general purposes of ornament and display; and it was not until the present century that combinations of shapes and colours having no intentional resemblance to any natural object might be considered the sufficient material of a picture. This was a novel step; but abstract design in the past, though it had served exclusively the applied arts, exerted nevertheless a fruitful influence on the development of the abstract picture. As was to be expected, archaic types of ornamentation, those which tended to be geometric, which were least manifestly derived from any shape in nature, provided the stimulus. The importance of Abstraction in Romanesque, Carolingian, Mexican and Negro art was revealed, and exaggerated.

It may be said here that the flight from nature and the accompanying enthusiastic interest in historical precedents led to a change in educated taste for which posterity may be grateful but which, in certain of its aspects, appears eccentric in retrospect. The emergence of the neglected grandeurs of Christian painting from the decay of Hellenistic art to the time of Giotto has permanently enlarged the sphere of possible aesthetic appreciations; and the approach, now a commonplace, to the earliest Greek Sculpture, to Etruscan and Cretan antiquities, as subjects primarily of aesthetic rather than archaeological interest is unlikely to be revised by future generations. But it may now seem surprising that educated judgement, during the early years of the century, might—so vigorous was the recoil from naturalism—consider the paintings of Giotto to be superior to those of Raphael and prefer Greek sculpture of the sixth century to the Elgin marbles.

The immediate incentive to abstract painting was provided by the Germanic school of Expressionists, though a somewhat hermetic group of abstractionists inspired by more formal considerations was active in Russia at the beginning of the present century. Van Gogh's metamorphosis of Impressionist technique into a language of the emotions was followed in Northern Europe by an attempt, in which violent distortion played a principal part, to intensify the vigour of emotional communication by means of painting. Inherent in this development, which was exemplified in the art of Munch, lay the possibility that emotion might be expressed with even greater force through the free interplay of lines and colours unrestrained by allusion or illustration of any kind. The art of Kandinsky was exploring this possibility before the outbreak of the First World War, but abstraction as a mode of emotional expression has since received somewhat desultory support. The rise of abstract art to the position of eminence which it at present occupies was promoted by less intelligible considerations. These derived in the main from Fauvist distortions, which were ultimately decorative in character, and from the analytic presentation of natural objects by the Cubists. The latter was not only analytic, but also in a sense constructive, involving a rearrangement of selected aspects of the object so as to build an image of it that should, in some way, have greater significance than a normal retinal impression. It would seem, broadly speaking, that it is the general aim of contemporary abstract painting to construct on the canvas a plastic entity with a reality of its own not referable to nature, and an aesthetic significance depending entirely, as in pure decoration, on formal arrangement. Such a statement cannot be made without infinite, imponderable reserves.

Abstract art has been expounded by those most qualified to do so in terms which resist logical interpretation, and no summary definition of its purpose can hope to embrace the manifold personal aspirations which lurk behind the obscure slogans of its champions.

The exaggerated prestige of archaic art forms of all kinds was considerably modified by the brief prosperity of Surrealist painting in the late twenties and early thirties. The Surrealists practised a wide eclecticism, borrowing freely from the endless departments of the "imaginary museum". They did so with the object not of developing or maturing suggestive aspects of the art of the past, but of perverting or, if that is too strong a word, of transmuting the quality of the model. In the process, various beauties temporarily clouded were again uncovered, even if they were revealed at first in a grotesque illumination. In this way much that was tainted by the imputation of photographic realism, the art—to quote particular and perhaps celebrated examples—of Vermeer, Millet, the Pre-Raphaelites, gradually regained the patronage of advanced opinion; and the respect we are now delighted to pay to schools of painting which we learnt in our youth to shun as decadent is in some measure a result of the eclectic fancies of Surrealism. The ancestors of the movement, however, are not to be found among such artists as might be the victims of its ostentatious acts of reverence, but among exponents of fantastic art from Bosch to Odilon Redon. The specific quality of Surrealist fantasy arose from the fact that it had no rational motive and was at the same time deliberately cultivated. Iconographical research tends to support the assumption that many of the most fantastic productions of the past are allegorical or symbolic and can be interpreted in terms of the painter's cultural environment, however apparent it may also be that unconscious fantasy dictated the choice of subject or its treatment. For the Surrealists, the pursuit of fantasy as such was a policy and they sought especially to conjure it from the unconscious regions of the mind, where notoriously, it flourishes in extreme forms. This, as a programme, was ill-judged; it led to absurdity or affectation and consequently to the breakdown of that rigid cohesion of the movement which the original members—unwisely in so far as they were concerned with the arts—had set out to maintain.

The collapse of Surrealism as an organization fortified the authority of abstract art. Abstract painters have now secured the patronage of Museum Directors who, in their natural eagerness to compensate for their predecessors' exclusive support of an obsolete representational manner, are perhaps unaware that to purchase a picture because it bears no resemblance to nature or because its resemblance to nature is perfect may be two courses equally mistaken. Whether or not official patronage be deluded to this extent, abstract painting, as illustrating the extremity to which the reaction from imitative standards might be carried, enjoys an intellectual prestige greater than that of any other contemporary movement; Impressionism, which survives, has been virtually absorbed by Academies without any improvement of their reputation; and what has been called Neo-Romanticism—which is perhaps a convenient generic term for the art of that large group of painters variously indebted to Surrealism—is not founded on any grand common principle with the recruiting powers of the banner of Abstraction.

In any attempt to convey an impression of the aesthetic achievement of a period of art as opposed to the less exacting task of describing its characteristics and relating their development, attention is at once diverted from movements and programmes to individuals; and there is perhaps no ideal so trivial, no mode of expression so ineffective that an artist of sufficient talent, should he mistakenly adopt them, might not exploit to aesthetic advantage. The Fauvist exhibition of 1906 revealed a close similarity of style among the members of the group, a similarity so briefly preserved that a singular historical interest attaches to examples of their art painted in this manner. It was a manner distinguished by violent colour oppositions, almost prescriptively of reds and blues, and tending to produce an effect less of savagery than of crudity. But Fauvist paintings by Matisse or Derain arouse more than historical interest, and it may be that their remarkable gifts—which time has shown to be of any but a tempestuous character—conferred even at this early stage of their development a faint classic grace upon an essentially ephemeral style. Picasso, who is an omnipresent force in the history of twentieth-century painting, has illustrated with unnatural brilliance the indifference of art to aesthetic platforms. Though Cubism was in theory obscure and likely in practice to prove repetitive, he produced, in the more complex of his monochromatic compositions in this manner, a series of intricate, formal mutations of natural objects which have shed an impassive, compelling lustre on a movement which might otherwise have remained an eccentricity and been remembered or forgotten for that reason. Surrealist pretensions yielded quite as gratefully to his invigorating acknowledgements, and if his adoption of the Surrealist approach had been less transient, the appeal of Abstraction might perhaps have been everywhere less difficult to resist.

Picasso himself did not resist it, but though his submission has proved intermittent, his abstract compositions afford no evidence of any superiority to its restraints. Abstract painters have painted beautiful pictures, but it is doubtful whether any artist can do justice to his potential capacities by the cultivation of pure Abstraction. The art for example of Gris lives in those early works which are in fact near-abstractions, in which the element of abstraction is, so to speak, visibly deduced from identifiable natural forms. Though it is probably true that the fallacies of no exclusively aesthetic dogma, however obstinately believed, could altogether extinguish the expression of an innate talent, they may constrict its development and, in so far as they are accepted by informed taste, damage the interests of art in general.

The fallacies inherent in the practice of abstract painting are fallacies of this objectionable kind. To the criticism most frequently put forward, that a picture which represents nothing can be no more than a framed decoration, the apologist of abstract painting might reply that there is a quality of pure and absolute beauty inherent in forms and colours which is necessarily obscured or alloyed not only when their arrangement is conditioned by the requirements of representation, but equally so if the artist, having rejected representation, assumes that his main concern is to orna-ment the surface of the picture space. But supposing we admit that such a quality exists, we may ask what grounds there are for the claim that it is a quality which is diminished or impaired unless the artist cultivates it to the exclusion of any others. The contrary seems to be true. Whereas the repertoire of shapes available to the repre-sentational artist is as infinite as the visible universe, the painter of abstract pictures must, one supposes, be constantly on his guard against the inadvertent inclusion in his compositions of recognizable shapes. This is a severe restriction, and abstract painters, labouring under its operation, are commonly reduced to the ringing of mono-tonous changes on combinations of geometric form, and in the last analysis—such is the force of association—even the square and the circle will tend to represent some less abstract notions such as a box or a wheel. The abstract virtues of *The School of Athens* are richer, more numerous and more varied than those of any production of the contemporary abstract movement for the simple reason that Raphael was unhampered by any dread of natural appearances and found, effortlessly, in the fall of a cloak, in the moving tissues of the human body, a mine of material for the aesthetic manipulation of form. The view, inevitably adopted as a result of the successes of the camera, that naturalistic standards of representation have no aesthetic validity whatever, was certainly a liberating force in the development of painting; but the absolute abandonment of repre-sentation, which is no less than the abandonment of imagery, was not the logical next step in a process of enfranchisement. Abstract painting is an impoverishment of the art; those who practise or uphold it are a kind of iconoclast; they have, as it were, gone about to decapitate the statues in the cathedral, to dry up its incense-breathing air and extinguish the candles on the altar.

The paintings of Ozenfant, Mondrian and Hélion provide the most conspicuous and perhaps also—though the art of Ozenfant was complicated by an esoteric symbolism—the most uncompromising illustrations of twentieth-century Abstraction. Their work clearly illustrates the narrow confines of their adopted style, and though we may concede to it a tasteful decorative quality which the earliest non-figurative pictures (those of the Russian School of the first decade of the century) seem in retrospect to have lacked, it is not, ultimately, of greater significance than such a work as Mahlevich's *Two Squares* (1913) which constitutes a kind of *reductio ad absurdum*, in advance, of the pretensions of later abstract painting. Comparatively few painters actually maintain the rigours of "total" Abstraction with the consistency of Mondrian or Hélion; and the crowd of abstractionists, while claiming consideration only on the grounds of formal excellence, allow the intrusion in their work of representational elements functioning exclusively as a pretext for abstract composition. It may be hoped that to distinguish these painters by name would be excessive, for it is difficult to believe that the empty character of Abstraction will in the long run be thought sufficient by anyone for more than decorative purposes. Meanwhile, in Paris, London and New York, they sustain and may yet increase their repute. As a faith or a discipline, for those in need of such supports, the simple negativism of Abstraction makes a strong appeal. It provides the critic with a handy if spurious criterion and the painter with an unequivocal but niggardly directive which tends to paralyse the maturation of innate talent. To quote an example from contemporary painting in this country, it is clear that the abstract art of Ben Nicholson and, still more emphatically, that of Victor Pasmore, involves a contraction of the natural range of these artists' capacities; and whatever virtue prejudiced admiration may discover in their abstract compositions, it cannot be denied that the charms of their representational pictures are more various and abundant.

For a time, during the period preceding the last war, an *entente* was maintained between Abstraction and Surrealism, a relationship which might easily amount to something closer as, for instance, in the paintings of Yves Tanguy in which the forms, though nearly always unidentifiable, are at times highly suggestive. Furthermore, in so far as the Surrealists believed in the aesthetic possibilities of automatism, recognition, in some measure, of the artistic interest of meaningless shapes could hardly be avoided. But the relationship was more apparent than real; it was fostered artificially by the need, still pressing at the time, for united action by the different schools of independent art against the persisting opposition of official patronage. In reality there was an irreconcilable conflict of values between Surrealism and Abstraction, the nature of which was clearly revealed by the more extreme productions of either school. The important difference between the painting, say, of Magritte and that of Mondrian is the difference between idolatry and iconoclasm.

The Surrealist revival of iconographical issues, their faith in the power of imagery, may well prove to have been the paramount development in the history of painting during the first half of the present century. The considerations which promoted the movement towards Abstraction had encouraged the idea that in the evaluation of any kind of painting the subject-matter is an irrelevant factor. This, probably, was a view less acceptable to artists than to critics, but a degree of studied indifference to the significance of the subject was a perceptible characteristic of painting under the successive dispensations of Fauvism and Cubism; whatever the original import of the harlequin, the guitar or the *compotier*, their function was commonly reduced to that of a mere starting-point for extraneous formal arrangements; and even in the work of painters who practised what, comparatively speaking, was a strictly representational art, we are aware of a similar detachment. The landscapes, or the nudes, of Derain, Friesz, Dufresne or Duncan Grant seem to be not so much the product of a direct response to the special characteristics of a selected theme as the expression of a general quality of harmonious or rhythmical structure in the ordinary appearances of things. It was a virtue of the Surrealists that they recognized that the specific character of the subject, whether it was a battle or a flower or a Paralytic Father driven from the Home by his Unnatural Offspring, might also constitute the chief merit of the picture. Their assertion of this universal truth might have been of little avail against the hostility of critical thought had they not discovered, at the same time, in the activity of the unconscious mind, a source of imagery which had always, it may be supposed, supplied the imagination of painters, but whose contributions had hitherto been fortuitous. The immediately striking feature of unconscious mental processes, in so far as they can be brought to light, is the establishment of close connexions between ideas or images which any regulated mode of thought would reject as incompatible. Such incongruous associations, which are explained by the assumption that they have a meaning in the unconscious, may exert a fascinating effect on conscious attention; and it is at least arguable that this effect may be communicated with peculiar clarity and force in a picture or, for that matter, in a poem. The possibilities of free association, the most convenient mode of contact with the unconscious, were first exploited by Freud as a mode of investigating for clinical purposes the processes of unconscious thought; but he also drew attention, in a paper on Leonardo da Vinci much publicized by the Surrealists, to the fact that strange or incongruous images in painting might be the involuntary, enigmatic expression of an unconscious impulse. By the application of psychoanalytic theory, historical examples of this kind of imagery might be found in profusion; but the extreme elasticity as an instrument of exegesis of the otherwise rigid body of Freudian doctrine may inspire mistrust, and, where other explanations are sufficient, its findings on this subject should be accepted with caution. Nevertheless, familiarity with the probably complex iconography of a Bellini allegory is not the condition of a charmed response to the quality of its imagery. The same is true of Titian's so-called *Sacred and Profane Love* or Giorgione's *Tempest*. There can be little doubt that the response in such instances is in part evoked by an element of mysterious irrelation in the image, and the unconscious mind might well be taken to indicate the source of the mystery. Unconscious concerns, indeed, would be expected to affect the course of any imaginative visualization, however consciously it was focused on some intelligible theme.

Surrealist painters failed to live up to the promise of their adverttisements. In attempting to excavate, deliberately, the unconscious "areas" of the mind, they were courting self-deception. The authenticity of finds from these elusive depths is difficult to test; nor was it to be assumed that images automatically produced by free association, hypnotic states or dreams were necessarily of aesthetic interest. These difficulties led to the acceptance, as valuable material, of incongruous fancies whose interest fades with the moment of surprise they may provoke at first sight, and even to the purposive contrivance of absurd juxtapositions having the same ephemeral value. Though the singular imaginative vigour of the early art of Miró is surely an irrepressible if not untended quality, and the work of Max Ernst reveals a capacity for dramatic visual association of an almost hallucinatory power, the paintings of Dali (notwithstanding the faint lyrical note appearing fitfully in his earlier work), of Magritte and of Masson are apt to be absurd or horrific and at the same time frigid—an unhappy combination of qualities which was characteristic of the average achievement of Surrealist painting. Conceptions which devotees of the movement might, in their ardour, be impelled to realize in palpable form, such as the fur tea-set, the malleable watch, the stone piano or the hairy apartment, illustrate the extremes of incongruity which, however briefly entertaining, hastened the decline of Surrealism as a force directly affecting the aims of contemporary painting. It may be that images from the unconscious have aesthetic potentiality only when they are strong enough to penetrate consciousness during the conceptual process and magnetize the artist's attention to the exclusion of any "cultured" image of more distinct purport. At any rate, it seems certain that Surrealism failed largely because its adherents were unable, and unwilling, to make critical distinctions between the heterogeneous results of automatism, and seem to have spent their power of volitional conception in a kind of mimicry of the illogical vision of the unconscious.

The permanent value of the Surrealist Revolution, as it was hopefully called by the propagandists of the movement, lay neither in the performance of the revolutionaries nor in the details of their programme, but in a widespread renewal of the function and importance of imagery. That a picture should be primarily an image rather than a pattern was to be inferred from Surrealist doctrine, and it was the Surrealists who recognized that the fascination of an image had no necessary connexion with the degree to which it might be either rational or credible. These ideas were acceptable to artists who could never have assented to the grotesque prescriptions of "official" Surrealism, and may be said to have been the stimulus, stated in the simplest and most general terms, of an imaginative mode of art in whose diffuse potent currents what is best in contemporary painting has since been sustained.

Art criticism during the present century has tended, until comparatively recently, to depreciate or deny the essential value of imagery. Judgements have been based upon fanciful criteria of composition and design. Paintings have been praised for their organic unity, linear rhythms, intersecting planes, balanced masses or even, with extreme ineptitude, because the shapes they comprise have the appearance of solidity. Books have been published intended to stimulate the appreciation of design, with diagrammatic illustrations in which the elements of what is usually called the "underlying" composition of a particular work are given and any features serving primarily to identify the subject-matter are omitted. Presumably, however, nobody would go so far as to say that any of the great paintings of the past, Titian's last *Annunciation*, for example, or even, with all its symmetry, Raphael's *Sposalizio*, would be improved if their plastic content could be purged of its representational character. In the last resort, it is a truism, however neglected in the past, in whatever revived guise it may appear today, that a picture, unlike a frieze, an altar cloth or a brooch, must, if it is to please, depict something. History seems to show that anything whatever may be depicted, provided that it is something of intense concern to the painter and that its image in the picture communicates that concern to the spectator. It is perhaps too soon to consider the achievement of the School of Paris as an historical achievement while any of its leaders are still active in their vocation. But it can be said that since 1939 there has been no sign that its vigour was likely to be renewed; contemporary French painting has been suffering under the influence of lifeless types of neo-Cubism or neo-Fauvism; and the comparative reputations of the principal representatives of the School of Paris, as they stand at present, may be taken as some indication of the verdict upon it of future generations. With the exception of Matisse and Braque, it is those painters whose art has relied on the elaboration of some image, either from external phenomena or in the mind's eye, who have an increasing power to attract, rather than those who, whatever the demands of their subject, devoted their energies as nearly as possible to the arrangement and expression of anonymous forms. The personages of Rouault, looking as though they had stepped from the pages of Huysmans and then been stripped of their most intimate pretences, seem more dangerously exposed than before; the architecture of the early Chirico, dating from some unknown period of pre-Augustan decadence, has grown steadily more self-conscious; Modigliani's sitters, in the crooked prison of their flesh and bone, entreat their spiritual woes with rising pathos; and the vivid levity of Dufy's landscape seems ready to assume a lyrical brilliance to which the taste of twenty years ago was mainly blind. On the other hand, the cubistic art of Gleizes or Metzinger, the ultimately decorative vision of such artists as Lhote or Delaunay, however they may still deserve or receive respect, have become, with the passage of time, more closely connected with the period at which they were produced. This crystallization of values, if that is what it is, may be ascribed in part to Surrealist influence.

If the acknowledged fruits of Surrealist doctrine had been less grossly frivolous, it is conceivable that faith in the virtues of Abstraction would not at present hold so many earnest or uncertain persons in its rigorous grip. It is clear, however, that contemporary Neo-Romantic art could not have brought forth its homonymous flowers unaided by the liberal incentives of Surrealist thought. The kind of fantasy elaborated or released in the paintings of Bérard, Tchelitschef, Berman; the expanding vigour of Graham Sutherland's talismanic vision of natural objects; even the idiosyncrasy of such artists as Morris Graves or David Jones: these things are found to be acceptable, let alone admirable or impressive, because Surrealism has enlarged the sphere of possible appreciations to make room—too much room—for the irrational beauties of the imagery of the unconscious. In doing so, it performed the additional service of establishing, experimentally, the restrictive limitations of abstract painting. Abstract shapes can be produced by the techniques of automatism; that such shapes are in fact "meaningful" no school of contemporary psychologists would deny; and when the agent of any automatic method of drawing has, like most people, some faint natural capacity for draughtsmanship, the results are unlikely to be so abstract as to reveal no perceptible analogy with recognizable phenomena. The devoted abstract artist is thus called upon to protect himself not only against the possibility of his composition suggesting some image to the spectator but also against the disguised intrusion of imagery from his own unconscious. In particular cases, deep-seated motives must remain a matter of speculation, but a conspicuous feature of the recent history of painting has been the rejection by artists of maturity and repute of the intellectual pressures of Abstraction in favour of the imaginative expression of a personal view of reality in terms licensed, as it were, by Surrealist precedent. A study of the drawings of Henry Moore reveals a transition of this kind, and it is not necessarily an idle fancy to suppose the involuntary presence, in his earlier drawings, of the hieratic figures with which he was subsequently concerned. The protean vicissitudes of Picasso's inconsonant genius have, latterly, indicated that the tendency to imagine, rather than to construct, will in the end prevail with him. Klee, whose art has influenced the vision of his contemporaries less violently but to a scarcely lesser extent than that of Picasso, has, like him, been described both as a Surrealist and as a painter of abstractions. With Picasso he was at one moment prepared to acknowledge the Surrealist affiliation; and the unique eloquence of his images, the seriousness and accuracy of their lightest innuendo, must deter criticism from any unique concentration of praise on the delicately sprung rhythm of lines and colours in whose motion the artist's imaginative fancy is visibly sustained. That he should sometimes have found the subjects of his pictures only after they had been painted is evidence, of a most felicitous kind, of the irrepressible function of imagery in art.

Though it appears that Abstraction is in no immediate peril (except, perhaps, in this country) of declining for want of youthful support, the countless ranks of "younger" artists are increasingly susceptible to the challenge, as it might be called, of representation. Realism, either of the "magic-symbolic" or of the "social" kind, is a declared object of the most up-to-date aesthetic modes. The terms "Magic Realist", and "Symbolic Realist", which originated in America, have been applied to the younger exponents of that contemporary Neo-Romantic trend whose Surrealist heredity has already been discussed. Social Realism is a narrower and more tendentious phenomenon, specializing in the illustration of modern life as endured, rather than enjoyed, by the common man. Communists, as might be expected, are among its adherents and its bias may, in some measure, be the fruit of official or semi-official directives. If it is a purpose of the Social Realists to provide an art that should appeal to the masses they are likely to be as disappointed as Fernand Léger, who mistakenly supposed that the *style mécanique* would appeal to mechanics. The sink-basket or the used packet of cornflakes may be objects of poetic significance to distressed gentle-folk, but the aesthetic taste of the common man would more probably be gratified by the opening of a casement on the fairyland of Snow White and her prince. Though it is, of course, true that the value of art is independent of the artist's success or failure as a political instrument, Social Realism has hitherto produced little that can be said either to transcend its prescribed iconographical sphere or to endow its subject-matter with unexpected poignancy. The realism it practises seems insufficiently based on the study of reality and, in certain instances, is a mere echo of the sounding brass of the mammoth film hoarding. The view, however, that reality is the raw material of art—fantastic in an infinity of ways as the finished product may prove to be—is one that can never be considered as anything but sound; to condemn Social Realism on the basis of what it has already achieved might be premature; and a movement capable of diverting the talent of a rising generation from the stupefying pursuit of plastic absolutes should not be regarded as unpropitious. The present vigorous revival, in Paris, of interest in the realistic vision of the age of Louis XIII may excuse a hope that the example of such artists as the brothers Le Nain will inspire contemporary realists to study social realities, however vile, with a less contrived sympathy than has so far, apparently, been possible.

BOOKS SUGGESTED FOR FURTHER READING

(*a*) GENERAL

Maurice Denis, *Théories* (Paris, Roualt, 1912).
Kenneth Clark, *Landscape into Art* (Murray, 1949).
Andre Malraux, *The Psychology of Art* (Zwemmer, 1949).

(*b*) FACTUAL

R. H. Wilenski, *Modern French Painters* (Faber, 1940). (Contains a comprehensive Bibliography of painters of the School of Paris.)
The Catalogues of the Museum of Modern Art, New York. (Available at the Library of the Victoria and Albert Museum. They contain extensive information on almost every aspect of contemporary painting.)

SCULPTURE

by SIR LEIGH ASHTON

IT IS, OF COURSE, a platitude (but truth may often be a platitude) that sculpture, since classical times, has been less popular, in the widest sense of that word, than painting. This is not difficult to appreciate, because sculpture is a far more varied process than painting. Painting, portraiture apart, projects an image from the painter's brain on to canvas or paper by a method which, except in a few difficult inspirations, is immediately intelligible to the eye; and if the painter does not like what he has done, he may at his leisure repaint his image, without any further loss of material. The sculptor's task is far more difficult; he has to cope with any number of different materials. If he is working at direct sculpture, he may need the knowledge of a number of different tools and abrasives. It is not so long ago that the art of carving in porphyry has been virtually lost; and it would be perfectly true to say that the man who carved alabaster at Nottingham in the Middle Ages would, possibly, or probably, have been quite incapable of making a statue of the Virgin and Child in Carrara. Direct carving in the sculptural sense involves such different media as wood, ivory, jade, stone in varying qualities, soft and hard; in marble or something harder, all have to be understood in respect of their consistency and fractural element, and all need a far more difficult approach than painting for their reception, when carved, by the person whom—for want of another word—we may refer to as the man in the street.

The other side of sculpture, the modelling side, provides an even more complicated problem. The sketch, whether in clay or wax, has to be executed in bronze or terra cotta; and while this is normally done, particularly in modern times, at least as far as bronze is concerned, by an outside firm of casters, it almost always used to be executed in the good old days by the sculptor himself or under his direct supervision. It follows that normally there may be in this mechanical transference some loss between the sculptor's original image and the ultimate result. But this may also have occurred at any time in the passage between the original concept and the final achievement. It is not to be supposed that every sculptor was so technically accomplished in the methods of transference from sketch to finished achievement in, let us say, the bronze process that he did not sometimes have a failure; and what is equally important to understand is that if his concept became popular, the resultant difference between the model as first cast and the subsequent "reproductions" (if we may refer to them as such, without using the word in its normal sense) is very considerable. Two bronzes in the Victoria and Albert Museum by the celebrated fifteenth-century Paduan sculptor Andrea Briosco, called "Il Riccio", illustrate this lesson exceptionally well. One, the pristine model, dates from the close of the fifteenth century; the second, of the same subject, was cast perhaps thirty years later. Nothing could be more instructive in the history of taste than the adaptation of the original model to suit later developments of ideas; nothing more interesting technically than the softening of the original power.

The technical side of sculpture must always take first place in the eyes of the viewer and it is fortunate that the history of modern sculpture starts from a great technician, Auguste Rodin (1840-1917). Rodin was a revolutionary as were Michaelangelo, whom he so much admired, and Raphael. Both of those great Renaissance artists were really capable of expressing themselves in all media, though Raphael never in fact executed any sculpture. Raphael's cartoons for his tapestries are superb paintings; the resultant tapestries, as transported into the medium of thread, adorn the medium they were intended for. Michaelangelo's paintings for the Sistine Chapel remain in my view an inspired presentation of over-muscular individuals, conceived under direct sculptural vision and controlled by an architectural scheme of which most sculptors would through their knowledge of architecture be aware, and which he, as the designer of the incomparable Piazza del Campidoglio in Rome, could be well relied on to put into execution. But this simply underlines the fact that even the giants of art may at times be in danger of entering into a medium they do not understand, and that it is on the supreme knowledge of technique that all great sculpture must depend. Sculpture at a great many stages of its life is bound to be allied to architecture. Given the materials, architecture must equally at certain stages of its planning be married with sculpture. This planning must at times modify certain conceptions of sculpture and in those conceptions as well as in the more direct and separate presentations of sculpture Rodin must still emerge as the progenitor of the modern age of sculpture.

Invention is seldom completely new; it is in the absorption of the past and its readaptation to the present that aesthetic conception takes its major life. Modern invention is often only a re-alignment, but for the great artists it is a re-alignment "beamed", to use a modern word, on the future. It is perhaps, a platitude, though a philosophical one, to say "πάντα ῥεῖ" ("everything flows"); but nothing is truer of art than that in its widest sense it must always flow, unless it is to become static or dead. Who could think that there is hardly half a century between Rodin and Henry Moore? One admires the great qualities of Academic Sculpture, and yet is aware, from observing the development of the aesthetic impulse of sculpture throughout the ages, that a lively repulsion has always been present against those who are lost in the sense of their own present academic importance. Without such repulsion no art can flow.

Rodin had none of this self-centred academism. His exquisite pornographic water-colours of women contrast strongly with his almost violent sculptural control of the human form; but his perception that a wholly new kind of life must take place in the concept of sculpture put him in a sense (odd though this may seem) in the same idealistic pigeon-hole as his English contemporaries the Pre-Raphaelites. We are fortunate in possessing many of the writings of Rodin, as of many other sculptors, and there is no doubt as to what his intentions were. What he did was to try to put himself into the state of mind of such men as Pheidias and Praxiteles; and he was passionately involved in a study of ancient methods. Rodin is the complete antithesis of such sculptors as Canova and Thorwaldsen, with their smooth, exquisite technical achievement in the highly-polished neo-classical style. He disliked this photographic perfection and based his art on the technical structure of his forms. For him what to leave out was as important as what to put in. Contrast of mountain and valley gives light and shade, and contrast of projection and recession give a similar effect in sculpture. If your planes were properly conceived you could exaggerate or underplay according to the vision of the subject that was affecting you. The handling of these problems was for him the thing that made a great artist; this handling denoted the individual and was something which would no doubt be imitated but could not bring real fame to the imitator. The artist transmitted his ideas, but, unless those ideas were adapted to another's individual conception, the other remained a mere imitator and could or should never be inscribed in the hall of Fame.

In a celebrated passage on his own art Rodin gave his views to the future:

"I invent nothing; I rediscover. And the thing seems new because people have generally lost sight of the aim and the means of art; they take that for an innovation which is nothing but a return to the laws of the great sculpture of long ago. Obviously, I think; I like certain symbols, I see things in a synthetic way, but it is nature that gives me all that. I do not imitate the Greeks; I try to put myself in the spiritual state of the men who have left us the antique statues. The 'Ecole' copies their works; the thing that signifies is to *recover their method.* I began by showing close studies from nature like

The Age of Brass. Afterwards I came to understand that art required a little more largeness, a little exaggeration, and my whole aim, from the time of the *Burghers*, was to find a method of exaggerating logically: that method consists in the deliberate amplification of the modelling. It consists also in the constant reduction of the figure to a geometrical figure, and in the determination to sacrifice any part of a figure to the synthesis of its aspect. See what the Gothic sculptors did. Look at the cathedral of Chartres; one of the towers is massive and without ornament: they sacrificed it to give value to the exquisite delicacy of the other tower.

"In sculpture the projection of the muscular *fasciculi* must be accentuated, the proportions altered, the hollows deepened; sculpture is the art of the hole and the lump, not of clear, well-smoothed, unmodelled figures. Ignorant people, when they see close-knitted fine surfaces, say that "it is not finished". No notion is falser than that of *finish* unless it be that of elegance; by means of these two ideas people would kill our art. The way to obtain solidity and life is by work carried out to the fullest, not in the direction of achievement and of copying details, but in that of truth in the successive schemes. The public, perverted by academic prejudices, confounds art with neatness. Art intervenes to exaggerate certain surfaces, and also to fine down others. In sculpture everything depends upon the way in which the modelling is carried out with a constant thought of the main line of the scheme, upon the rendering of hollows, of the projections and of their connections; thus it is that one may get fine lights, and especially fine shadows that are not opaque. Everything should be emphasized according to the accent that it is desired to render, and the degree of amplification is personal, according to the fact and the temperament of each sculptor, and for this reason there is no transmissible process, no studio recipe, but only a true law. I see it in the antique and in Michael Angelo.[1] The human body is like a *walking temple*, and like a temple it has a central point around which the volumes place and spread themselves. When one understands that, one has everything.[2] I am not a dreamer, but a mathematician; and if my sculpture is good it is because it is geometrical.[3] . . . When you follow nature, you get everything. When I have a beautiful woman's body for a model, the drawings that I make from it give me images of insects, birds, and fishes. That seems improbable, and I had no suspicion of it myself. . . . The point is not to create. Creation and improvisation are useless words. Genius only comes to the man who understands with his eye and his brain.[4] . . . A woman, a mountain, a horse, in conception they are all the same thing, they are made on the same

[1] Camille Mauclair, Rodin, *The Man—His Ideas—His Works*, tr. C. Black (Duckworth, 1905), pp. 60-2.

[2] Ibid., p. 68.   [3] Ibid., p. 69.   [4] Ibid., p. 70.

principles.¹ . . . Beauty is not the starting-point, but the point of
arrival; a thing can only be beautiful if it is true. Truth itself is only
a complete harmony, and harmony is finally only a bundle of
utilities. The miracle of life could not be perpetuated but for the
constant renewal of universal balance.''²

In words such as these we understand then (though how infinitely
more eloquent they are in French) what Rodin was aiming at.
He wished to bring a new vitality to sculpture; he wanted to abandon the dryness of the industrial Victorians for what amounted to a
revolution in sculptural ideas. In this it can be safely stated that he
succeeded in no uncertain degree; long before his death Rodin was
regarded as the supreme sculptor of his time and he was inspiring
in a supreme way the younger generation. It follows therefore from
the words quoted that Rodin's great preoccupation was to control
the play of light and shade and that he was at heart concerned
with the same problem as the Impressionist painters. His technical
ability in transferring his clay models in their rough, nervous
modelling into bronze quickly demonstrated this intense interest in
the play of light. The statue of Balzac is a good instance of this.
The almost violent modelling of the face, the tension of the folded
arms, the immense strength of the planted legs show quite clearly
his preoccupation with a technique which would give him the result
he wanted in terms of light and shade. The figure is vividly alive
and by a method which was a revolution in sculpture at his date.

His studio assistants Antoine Bourdelle (1861-1929) and Charles
Despiau (1874-1946) had nothing of Rodin's intense inventive
powers. Bourdelle, himself a masterly technician, is now very out of
fashion. He gives something of the impression of having a municipal
outlook, and one may suspect that his work was so much occupied
in carrying out his master's instructions that his real achievement
lay in the teaching line, for which he had considerable gifts. Despiau,
on the other hand, who would consent to become Rodin's assistant
only if he was allowed a proportion of time off for his own work,
developed an extremely delicate talent for portrait sculpture; and
many of his busts belong to the most sensitive group of works of this
nature. Beside Rodin he has, of course, a silver talent, but there is a
place for silver talents everywhere—the giants are not always with
us; and if Rodin is a Beethoven, Despiau may certainly qualify as a
Corelli.

The nearest of all to Rodin among those who followed after may
be reckoned Jacob Epstein (b. 1880), now a British subject. This
ebullient and attractive personality, whose activities have made
news for a quarter of a century, has remained, despite his interest in
ethnographical by-ways, a Rodinist at heart. His best work is almost

¹ Camille Mauclair, Rodin, *The Man—His Ideas—His Works*, p. 71.
² Ibid., p. 78.

certainly in the realm of his portrait busts; but some of his monumental work, such as his much-maligned *Rima*, made for the bird
sanctuary in Hyde Park, displays him as an authentic poet. Modern
sculpture would have been much the poorer without him.

Contemporary with Rodin, two of the most celebrated painters
of the nineteenth century must be considered in the light of their
sculptural works. Edgar Degas (1834-1917) made waxes all his life.
Whether they were ever intended to be cast is doubtful, and my own
belief is that he used these wonderful little studies of ballet-dancers,
race-horses, etc., as models for his painting. His problems of form
in painting were, of course, interrelated with those of sculpture, and
many critics have thought that he tried his hand at sculpture to
solve more directly the problem of volume and movement in his
painting. The waxes were cast mainly as a means of preservation
or as a skilful piece of salesmanship after his death in 1917, and the
most famous, *The Dancer*, with or without her ballet skirt, may be
seen in many galleries. The other celebrated painter, Auguste
Renoir (1840-1919), only began to try his hand at sculpture at the
suggestion of Ambrose Vollard, the dealer, when he could no
longer, owing to his rheumatic state, continue to paint. His *œuvre*
is not large, but the superb control of modelling and of the interplay
of light of which he had so long been a master enabled him without
much difficulty to transfer his talent from one medium to another.
He also made some interesting experiments in coloured terracotta,
which might well have been profitable if he had continued.

A new giant was, however, appearing on the horizon—Aristide
Maillol (1861-1944). Maillol, who did not begin to work on sculpture before he was forty, is the very antithesis of Rodin. Instead of
the restless, impressionistic concept with emphasis on light and shade
Maillol concentrated on smooth surfaces, on rhythmic curves; and
many of his finest conceptions such as the early *Mediterranean* have,
even making allowance in this case for the fact that it is virtually an
adaptation of Michaelangelo's *Night*, a grace that belongs to
Classical antiquity. Much of this can be accounted for by the fact
that Maillol was steeped in the pagan atmosphere of the country-
side in which he lived. *Les Banyuls* is in the heart of that primitive
south where tradition and folklore die hard, and where the treading
of the grapes may still produce a Bacchic revel and Pan and Silenus
still live. In this atmosphere it is hardly surprising that Maillol
became preoccupied with the female form; Cybele, Astarte, Artemis,
the Golden Bough are weighed down in Maillol's story by the fruits
of his romantic imagination, and certainly it is due to his conception
of the eternal female form that so many sculptors at a later date
were inspired by him. Frank Dobson, Lehmbruck, Kolbe, Karen
Janzen all owe much to him, and his reclining figures of women
in the nude offer some of the most remarkable of all modern

presentations in their complete resolution of the concept with the realization. If we may regard Maillol as an idealist (and he frequently expressed this view in his writings), we must equally regard him as a master in the art of transferring his ideals to a concrete and expressive shape, which left no doubt as to his intention, but at the same time gave it a somewhat remote and hieratic form, combining both sensual and intellectual reactions into a common, if at times intangible, realization. His nudes, exquisite and complete, are nudes for "Everyman". In some curious way, entirely opposite to Rodin's highly sexual drawings, they create no prurient ideas, and when they first appeared, became immediately popular in the best sense of the word. These majestic but human creations, slumbering on a pagan bed of hot earth, exhale an afflatus of everything that the mysteries of the ancients must have created. They excite, but they satisfy; and such a concept as the wonderful plaster relief of *Desire* in the Museum of Modern Art, New York, with its extraordinarily successful rhythmic circular movement, conveys both the implication of the title and the touching quality of its application to youth. It is a sculpture which expresses in its own medium what Shakespeare set out to do in *Romeo and Juliet*. This is high praise for any artist, but there is no doubt that Maillol deserves it.

Of the names mentioned above as connected with Maillol, by far the most important is the German sculptor, Wilhelm Lehmbruck (1881-1919). Lehmbruck, who committed suicide at the end of the First World War, was a particularly gifted artist. He was concerned primarily with the relative values of proportional adjustments and considered that on the determination of this principle good sculpture depended. In this he was of course setting himself a standard which at base was an architectural one, but the personal element that must always enter into an artist's conception led him to prefer that his basic units tend towards elongation. This probably was due to the fact that elongation contributed for him more of the melancholy emotion which characterizes most of his work. The *Kneeling Woman*, one of the most beautiful of all twentieth-century sculptures, is an elegiac of glyptic composition. Its elegant proportions, its tender expression and the complete control of the relationship between the kneeling leg and the torso, are so perfectly combined and carried out that it will always rank as an outstanding piece of modern sculpture. Equally the harrowing statue of a seated youth, his head buried in despair in his hand, symbolizes for all time the defeat of a young generation overtaken by the hazards of war and deprived of its ideals. The exquisitely tender modelling of the thin, ravaged, hopeless youth are so eloquently expressed, without a trace of false emotion, that, contrary to the case of so many prophets *manqués*, the town of his birth saw fit to use it as a war memorial.

Lehmbruck must be associated in some measure, by his influence on him, with the present-day Swiss sculptor Alberto Giacometti (b. 1901). Giacometti, one of the most gifted sculptors of the present epoch, has not the same romantic melancholy as Lehmbruck, but his preoccupation with elongated forms, which constitute for him an almost Pantheist observation on the relationship of man to space, invests his work with a poetic remoteness which comes pretty close to producing an impact similar to that of Lehmbruck's work.

Other sculptors of importance of the pre-World War I period are Ernst Barlach (1870-1938), a traditional artist much influenced by folk wood-carving, whose powerful studies of peasants have a particular and private significance; and Julio Gonzalez (1876-1942), an erratic Cubist genius, who worked mainly in forged iron, but whose impressive results combine intense observation with an ideal which is a commentary on contemporary life rather than an aesthetic essay.

About the beginning of the century there burst on a somewhat astonished world Constantin Brancusi (b. 1876), a Roumanian whose work was destined to stand out as a landmark in the history of modern sculpture. It is not clear how he came to turn away almost immediately from the academic virtuosity of most of his contemporaries to an absolutely new type of sculpture, the abstract form. It may be that Negro sculpture, then beginning to be looked at in Paris, where he lived, had some influence on him or that he concerned himself with other forms of primitive art. The fact remains that he plunged straight into a world of sculpture as yet entirely unimagined. These pure geometric shapes, intensely thought out and directly carved for the most part in marbles of subtle hue and polish, cannot have been understood by his contemporary public. Indeed his celebrated *Bird in Space*, when imported into America, was refused exemption from Customs duty on the grounds that it was only a piece of metal! He has exercised an enormous influence, though he cannot be said in any strict sense to have founded a school. No sculptor so individual and so experimental could ever found a school, because the pupils would never know what his next work was liable to look like. Brancusi has told us of his intense interest in direct carving, and it is certain that he had an equally intense interest in the material itself. He seems to have a complete relationship with his material, an understanding of its organism, which enable him to complete his often complicated combination of forms in a manner which always leaves them vividly alive. His use of polish, sometimes high, sometimes low, is controlled by extreme sensitivity for both his ovoid forms and the material he is carving them from; and in the resulting simplicity the utmost combination of sophistication and intelligence is realized.

Many people have been heard to comment on the ease with

which such sculpture must be produced. Few can have achieved such production without realizing the enormous effort of thought and technique which have gone into the making. Brancusi was also one of the first to use revolving stands. As one of his egg-like shapes revolves before the spectator's eye the light caught on the moving surface of the polished marble gives an illusion of a living entity, which is not always present when the object is static. Whether this is a legitimate use of the artist's conception or a trick is a matter on which there has always been and always will be controversy.

Associated in some measure with Brancusi's work is that of another individualist, Amedeo Modigliani (1884-1920). This exceptionally gifted artist died much too young. It is always difficult to assess the exact niche occupied by someone who has died prematurely; Modigliani settled in Paris in 1906 and quitted it and the world fourteen years later. His main output was a series of intense and unusual portraits, whose elongated, pear-shaped faces mark a completely individual conception in their approach to the structure of the human form; their essential quality is a sculptural one. They may well have been inspired by Negro sculpture, but a closer comparison may be found in the human-headed ivory handles of Malayan *kris*. Modigliani is a typical genius; he was much in advance of his time and little understood by his contemporaries. His genuine talent, however, could not be ignored. What Brancusi achieved in his portrait of Mlle. Pogany, Modigliani achieved in his caryatides. These elongated, sphinx-like creatures were probably intended as door-jambs or mantelpiece pillars. The finest and most complete one, aesthetically speaking, is in the Victoria and Albert Museum, which houses the British national collection of sculpture. It was brought in one day to me by Modigliani's friend Miss Jones. She explained how she and Modigliani used often to have supper by the light of a guttering candle fixed to the top of its head. These caryatides are conceived in a pure and rigid scheme, with which is combined a somewhat romantic vision that has transformed the human element into an austere divinity.

Another individualist whose output was small, and who died at an early age fighting in the 1914-18 war, was Henri Gaudier-Brzeska (1891-1915). Henri, who was desperately poor, is perhaps better known for his exquisite drawings of animals, with a single-line technique which catches the form of the beast perfectly; he left behind a small group of animal-sculptures, mainly in a very simple abstract technique, and a few sculptures of human studies, distinguished by a fidelity of observation and a high quality of execution which have been much underestimated, though not immediately after his death.

The two best known sculptors who, under the influence of Brancusi, have developed abstract sculpture to its fullest are Jean Arp

(b. 1888) and ˇHenry Moore (b. 1898). Arp has been strongly
influenced by Surrealism. His conceptions of form, arduously and
tenderly polished, do not convey easily to the spectator the sculptor's aims, but no one can be unaware that in these queer, odd shapes
there is a vitality which testifies to an original mind. Many of them
have some relationship to natural forms, but natural forms translated by the imagination of the sculptor into highly intellectual
patterns. Moore has been influenced by a number of the more exotic
primitive cultures. Like many other modern artists he has been
profoundly interested in Negro Art; but Sumerian and Mexican art
have attracted him at different times. It is probably to the latter
that we owe the inspiration of Moore's large recumbent figures.
Moore normally carves directly in stone or wood and has all his life
been profoundly interested in inner characteristics of his materials.
He often tries to solve a set problem within a block of stone or wood
of known dimensions and to carve out his forms within the limits so
set. At the same time his problem will have assumed in his mind what
for want of a better word we may call a personality—this is how
Moore himself refers to it—and with the growth of that personality
so the success or failure of the conception will result. A courageous
clergyman in Northampton commissioned Moore to carve a
large group of the Virgin and Child. This monumental work is
certainly a masterpiece of religious expression. The Virgin in her
sublime repose appears to typify the mother-goddess of every age,
while the child equally seems to represent all children. More
recently Moore has turned to modelling bronze and lead, in which
media he has shown himself to be equally at home. His large group of
a seated king and queen with their hieratic poses suggests in an
extremely simple and direct way "majesty" and is one of the most
successful of his recent compositions. The large marble group of
three over-life-size figures, which was exhibited in the open-air
exhibition in Battersea Park, suffered in some people's eyes from
the smallness of the heads set on the massive torsos; but Moore has
always had a leaning towards small heads, as can be seen in many
of his lovely drawings. What this large group possesses in no uncertain degree is its three-dimensional success. As is essential in all
great groups of this type it is equally satisfactory from every angle;
the movement of each of the three torsos is combined into one
complete composition, and the sweeping lines of the drapery emphasize in the most noble way the essence of the conception. If Moore
had completed, on a grand scale, only these two groups it would
have been quite enough to put him in the forefront of modern
sculptors; but one of the greatest of his merits is that no matter on
what scale he decides to work he is equally capable of executing his
ideas without sacrificing in any way the nobility of his conception
or the skill of his technique. Henry Moore is often referred to as the

greatest sculptor of his generation; he is often denigrated by unintelligent persons, who seem unaware of the difference between comprehension and non-comprehension. Moore happens to be one of those sensitive beings who can tell one what he thinks about his own ideas and how he cares to express them; his critics should absorb his writings. Let us look at what he said in *Unit One*, published in 1934. I do not suppose that Moore would rewrite it because it expresses in the highest degree what is really the essence of sculpture. And, once it is expressed, there can be very little change. "Each sculptor," he says, "through his past experience, through observation of natural laws, through criticism of his own work and of other sculpture, through his character and psychological make-up, finds that certain qualities in sculpture become of fundamental importance to him."

How wise, how sensible, are these preliminaries. But even more sensible are the resolving paragraphs which put in a crystalline form everything that a critic or a mere essayist would wish to say about the art.

"For me," says Moore, "the distinctive qualities remain the same; primarily the sculptor must have *truth to material*." How right, how true this is. Each material has its own quality, and unless the sculptor understands his material his conception will not stand up to its medium. "Stone," says Moore, "is hard and concentrated and should not be falsified to look like soft flesh; it should not be forced beyond its constructive build to a point of weakness. It should keep its hard, tense stoniness." Here again speaks the technician controlling the basis of his inspiration.

His second generalization or "principle" is that all great sculpture must have "full three-dimensional realization". Here, I think, he has made a slight *portmanteau* of the problem involved and is really emphasizing the world that opened out to him when he first saw Negro sculpture. What Moore has put perpetually before the modern sculptors is the necessity of seeing the object entirely in the round, as the Negro sculptors did. These were able, without turning any intellectual handspring, to produce out of a block of wood or stone a complete realization of the understanding of block-presentation, which gives no individual specialization from any one angle, but equally gives at any one angle a complete realization of the sculptor's idea of volume. Negro sculpture, as all primitive sculpture, Aztec, Polynesian, etc., is always able to present itself from any angle and in any light as a completely understood image. Where Moore's generalization may fall down is in the question of reliefs. A relief, an important arrow in the quiver of the direct sculptor's repertoire, as it is in the "plaquette form" in the modeller's repertoire, is a sculptural presentation which can under no circumstances be regarded in the round. It is a legitimate glyptic conception which has no bearing whatever on the three-dimensional aspect of sculpture, on which Moore rightly lays such emphasis.

Sculpture is a highly complex and difficult subject, often misinterpreted and often misunderstood. "Between beauty of expression and power of expression there is a difference of function. The first aims at pleasure, the second has a spiritual vitality, which for me is more moving and goes deeper than the senses." Here Moore firmly states his views and he expresses them in a way which leaves no doubt of what his intellectual vision is. He believes as Rodin did that the reproduction or rather the readaptation of natural forms is not necessarily a repulsion from human forms, but is in fact a wider concentration on the eternal aspect of nature; and also that nature itself provides its own significance, its own "poster", to put it vulgarly, on what life may provide. It is infinitely more difficult for the sculptor than for the painter to produce this vision, but it is quite certain that this Yorkshire sculptor has in his own blunt way put this idea on the map; and we may well suppose that Henry Moore, in many people's view the greatest living sculptor, will continue to put this ideal before our eyes for the rest of his life.

The first thirty years of the twentieth century have provided a cauldron in which seethed and bubbled all sorts of ideas. Many of the sculptors were also painters, and we must now examine what were the effects on sculpture of the Cubist movement. While others (notably Juan Gris) had a considerable influence on the painting side, it cannot be denied that the master influence was that tremendously powerful artist, both technically and emotionally, Pablo Picasso (b. 1881). It is hardly possible that any artist should have had more attacks made on him than Picasso. But the attackers seem also to be disinclined to correlate his various activities. The assailants of his violent paintings conceived under the "Resistance" have perhaps forgotten the powerful and exquisite illustrations to Buffon. Those who do not care about the hot colour of his present-day efforts forget the exquisite subtleties of his "blue" and "pink" periods. His work for Diaghilev is beyond praise—that for De Falla's *Tricorne* being possibly the greatest stage design of modern times—and no one should resist the cool outline of his illustrations to the *Eclogues*. It is, therefore, hardly surprising that when this gifted creature turned his attention to other media than painting he should have turned it in a whole-hearted way; he is also one of the few artists who do not commit themselves to print on their art.

It was during his Cubist period that Picasso began to turn his attention to sculpture; his "collages" and his Cubist paintings were highly intellectual experiments in a world of dissection, a world that with the advent of the mechanical and scientific age was bound to occur to an impatient and experimental mind. Picasso and his friend and fellow-countryman Julio Gonzalez (1876-1942), whose highly interesting experiments in metal-work were to create a considerable impression during a brief period, were eager to transfer their ideas of metal structure to sculpture, while continuing the normal dissection and resolution of form in paint. Gonzalez does not seem to have painted, but the fact that Picasso could transfer these ideas to the round made it easier for the more purely sculptural members of the Cubist Group, Henri Laurens (b. 1885) and Jacques Lipchitz (b. 1891), to fulfil the Cubist ideal to its ultimate finality. Laurens, probably the greater of the two, is a more exuberant sculptor than Lipchitz; but there are times, as in his well-known group *Le Poseur*, when his satirical wit seems destined to defeat his sculptural integrity and to turn his powerful representation into something more decorative than sincere. Lipchitz has a far less romantic approach. His complicated Cubist ideas are controlled by an extremely geometrical and even severe approach; he makes no compromises and lets the composition work itself out under the control of a rigidly architectural direction—which while it may leave the final result at times cold and forbidding, at least suggests that its originator is not disposed to allow this instinct for form to be sentimentalized.

The ultimate development of Cubist sculpture was in the direction of movement; the latest of the group, Raymond Duchamp-Villon (1876-1918) and Umberto Boccioni (1882-1916), were mainly concerned with movement in sculpture and evolved a theory of sculpture which they christened "Futurist". In somewhat the same way in which Constable observed the relation of one colour to another by the refraction that occurred in sunlight by the juxtaposition of two colours in nature, so the Futurists considered that any given object, by its relation to its surroundings, created movement. This movement, as a natural concomitant, created drama; and so in representing the object it became necessary to create not merely the object itself but its relation with its glyptic realization, and this could be achieved only by the creation also in the finished sculpture of the emotions engendered by the inner kernel of the subject and its whole essence. The resultant effect of the Futurist sculptors was to make their compositions often difficult of comprehension, frequently restless and very dated.

Two further well-known sculptors, Alexander Archipenko (b. 1887) and Ossip Zadkine (b. 1890), belong by now to the old guard of the Cubists. Both of them were interested in the problem of the use of the convex and the concave in their resolution of modelling problems, but both soon reduced this schematization to a formula which appears now to be not much more than a facile and decorative system that hardly stands up to the test of time. It would be unfair to qualify it as a trick, but it is not very far from that; and even if the integrity of the artist is not to be questioned, it is in the ultimate result that his work must be seen. The Cubists and the Futurists were controlled too much by technique, and this led to a still further emanation of technology usually referred to as the Constructivist school. Here the sculptors entirely abandoned any approach to natural forms, but relied entirely on a complicated system of symbols and abstract ideas, which when transformed into living practicality were seen to be concerning themselves with a control of space. In fact, in the end, it is space which becomes in Constructivist art the main theme. Naum Gabo (b. 1890) and Antoine Peuner (b. 1886), who worked chiefly in conjunction, are the chief exponents of this theory. Both produce exceptionally complicated abstractions often in rather unusual materials, Gabo being particularly fond of transparent plastic. Brilliantly decorative as they are and often attractive in the manner in which they intrigue the observer, it is still open to doubt if they in fact qualify as sculpture. It might be more fair to say that, while there is no doubt that their creators are genuine sculptors, in many of these conceptions they have indulged in *ballons d'essai*, which may have floated off into an empyrean world hardly to be described as sculptural. Perhaps equally difficult to appreciate as sculpture are the "mobiles" of Alexander Calder (b. 1898); they appear to have strayed into a classification which is apt only because we lack any other pigeonhole in which to place them. These quivering, imaginative constructions of wire and solid, which move at the slightest breath or change of atmosphere, are intellectual toys more closely akin to jewellery, of which Calder is also a superb designer. Part of the impact of the mobiles is caused by the play of shadow and light that they always make in any room in which they are placed. In a curious way Calder has solved in some measure the relationship of solid and void and in this sense it may be right to classify his work as sculpture. There can be no question of their imagination; these moving entities are creations in the highest sense of the word. If they do not seem to fall into the accepted definition of sculpture, they are not to be cast out for that reason. His main pupil in this field is a young Englishman, Lynn Chadwick (b. 1914). Chadwick, trained as an architect, has a more solid proportional approach to the subject and lacks the biting wit that sometimes appears in Calder's conceptions. It remains to be seen whether Chadwick will continue on these lines or strike out in new fields of his own.

It is time, perhaps, to reconsider the development of what, for want of a better word, we may refer to as the painter-sculptors. During the last war it was mainly the older generation that were able to carry on their experiments and it is certainly among the old giants that the most interesting work was taking place. Maillol, who died in 1944, was working on his last great composition *The River*. There seems, looking at this traditional conception, hardly any difference between it and any of the static compositions of his early youth. There is a little more movement, a slightly more graceful approach to the human body, but the majestic classicism of his early work has disappeared in favour of a suave, competent control, which *imprimis* is academic. Maillol is fast disappearing into the kind of temporary eclipse that happens to many artists, celebrated in their day, for half a century. He has suffered the fate of a Victor Hugo or a George Meredith. Picasso, on the other hand, that indefatigable inventor, for whom there is never repose from discovery, has, in a sense, reverted to the Rodinesque conception. While the strength and vitality of his new ideals correspond with his wonderful new lithographs or his outburst of pottery, such sculptures as his bronze *Goat* show a preoccupation with direct modelling which is a startling innovation at this stage in his career. As he approaches his seventy-fifth year, it would be easy to say that one supposes that age is mellowing him; it would be highly rash to do so. There is only one thing that anyone should say about Picasso. In the course of a long and varied life there is no branch of art which his insatiable curiosity has not tempted him to explore; and in every branch that he has explored, his consummate, innate technique has enabled him to complete a satisfactory working-out of this or that problem of technique, if the results have not always maintained the highest level.

Similarly Lipchitz and Laurens have both emerged into a less violent and distorted phase. Lipchitz, it is true, still employs the Cubist inspiration with which he was so preoccupied in his younger days, but this has become more or less an architectural dictionary from which to invest his more naturalistic conceptions with a structure which will combine the best of both his intellectual worlds. Laurens, on the other hand, appears to have emerged into a serene field of presentation, in which his former stylizations have been overtaken by a breadth of composition and a control of form that mark the coming of age of a great sculptor, who is unlikely to depart from his present highly-developed control into any fresh world of experiment. He has found what he wants and is unlikely to abandon it.

Since the last war, sculpture has shown signs of a great increase in vitality. It would not be fair to say that any new school has emerged; but certainly in Italy, in England and the U.S.A., where many of the older masters are now living, there has been a renewed and extremely creditable resuscitation of interest in sculpture. In Italy there are now at least two sculptors who deserve consideration: Marino Marini (b. 1901) and Giacomo Manzù (b. 1908). Both Milanese, their primary concern is with modelling. Marini, who has concentrated on secular ideas and has a comparatively small repertoire of subjects, horses, women, portraits, is perhaps more directly dependent on derived motives than is Manzù. Certainly his

Horse in the Nelson Rockefeller Collection can be related very
clearly to a well-known early Chinese model, while the Quadriga at
Basle can equally be connected with a well-known Roman ivory
diptych. They are not exactly pastiches, because Marini has
transformed them by his own strength of modelling into something
completely new. Manzù, whose forte lies in religious reliefs, derives
directly from the great masters of the Renaissance, Donatello or
Desiderio da Settignano, but his mastery of his medium and his
delicate sense of humour have transformed his undoubtedly
classical talent in a manner which make him one of the most
interesting of modern sculptors. He certainly has nothing of the
imitative spirit that the two great *pasticheurs* of the last 100 years,
Bastianini and d'Ossena, had. Manzù is also an exceptionally
accomplished portraitist, with a curious sense of the nineteenth
century in his execution.

For this post-war period we must also return for a brief period
to Alberto Giacometti (b. 1901), who has been mentioned before in
connexion with Lehmbruck. Giacometti's preoccupation with space
has induced him to continue his experiments in elongation to a
point where there may seem a real exaggeration. But it is an
intentional exaggeration which never forgets the emotional content
of the figure. His extraordinary composition, the *City Square*, in
which five nude figures move about a square base, is an exceptionally delicate resolution of the problem between the human figure
and its environment. Groups of this type have hardly been attempted
except in ancient Mexican sculpture, and the idea of a square base
with a few elongated figures simply walking about is one that could
in the wrong hands be reduced to the most intense disruption.
These elongated conceptions probably owe a certain amount to the
thin archaic figures of ancient Greece and Etruria, but in Giacometti's hands they have attained a correctness and an emotional
intensity which are entirely requisite to the successful handling of his
composition. Certainly Giacometti has had a considerable impact on
some of the much younger sculptors of the international world,
particularly on Reg Butler (b. 1913). Butler, a young Englishman
trained as an architect, has within comparatively recent years
turned to sculpture, in which he almost invariably works in wrought
iron. His elegant highly individual compositions approximate very
closely to the drawings which precede them. Indeed in one sense,
unlike many sculptural drawings, Butler's are so close to the
finished composition that he almost transposes the drawings into
metal. But he is a man of great originality and imagination, with
an innate sense of his material, and his conception of the human
form, which differs greatly from that of Giacometti, though influenced by Giacometti's preoccupation with space, may be said to
have a touch of universal nature in it; and like Picasso by whom he

has also been influenced, he perceives the disagreeableness of the present world and escapes from it into a world of images of which he himself is the creator. He is, in addition, a most beautiful craftsman, with all the tradition of English ironwork behind him. Ironwork is a particularly native product of Britain. The Sussex ironworks were working strongly in Roman times, and if, as a smith, Butler is following in an ancient English tradition it is quite certain that his technical ability is something that supplements a fastidious and controlled inspiration.

What seems difficult in modern times is to find a method or rather a means of giving sculptors an opportunity to work hand in hand with architecture. Almost always sculptors must be content with their own compositions or with memorials or portrait busts. The days of the grand patron are long since past; it is only business corporations or august and rich national bodies that can afford to indulge this taste. In England recently Henry Moore was able to carve four large reliefs for the "Time and Life" building; Epstein has recently been commissioned to do a monumental group for the outside of a convent in the West of London; but such commissions are rare. Modern architecture is not necessarily conducive to ornamental groups, whereas in the past the marriage of sculpture and architecture was one of the essentials of a well-ordered civilization.

Before proceeding to some estimate of the most modern trends one ought perhaps to mention two artists who fall rather outside the normal run: Henri Matisse (1869-1955) and Carl Milles (b. 1875). Matisse during a long life of painting has at frequent intervals turned to sculpture. Matisse, a follower of Rodin, by choice elaborated Rodin's system and, consciously, under the influence of his own painting, created a whole series of busts modelled on Cubist lines, which form an exceptionally interesting study of a painter's power to carry out successful work in a totally different medium. Carl Milles is mainly known as the creator of fountains; he came up the hard way, and it was only when Rodin recognized his gifts and took him on as an apprentice in his studio at Meudon that the young sculptor began to spread his wings. At the same time he had the courage to recognize in 1917 that his work up to that year belonged to an academic school and had no real inspiration, technically competent though it was. His instinct, perhaps due to an unhappy childhood, drove him instinctively to become horrified when he found imitators. He shared the idea of the Euston Road school of painting in London, that the duty of an instructor was primarily to give technical achievement, and when he was appointed in 1920 to be the Professor in Modelling at the Stockholm Royal Academy he devoted the majority of his time to ensure that technical teaching was his primary contribution. Milles is first and foremost a Nordic; all his compositions—the "Orpheus" fountain at

Stockholm, composed in 1936; the "Meeting of the Waters" Fountain (1940) in St. Louis, where a few miles from the city the two great rivers of America, the Mississipi and the Missouri, flow into each other; the new figures for the pool of the restaurant of the Metropolitan Museum—are characteristic of this innate national flavour, based on an extreme preoccupation with natural instincts characteristic of all Scandinavian countries, where the sagas of ancient times, the climate of eternal sun, tend to create a stark and—to people living in a warmer and more languorous climate—an at times depressing aspect. Milles is primarily an academic sculptor, but since he went to Cranbrook Foundation, the remarkable conception instigated by a Detroit visionary, George Booth, in 1931, his work has undergone a remarkable expansion. It was not that he changed his style, but that under a new freedom from care and an assured patronage he was able to devote himself to a far more extensive interest in his particular speciality, fountains. His series of groups owe a great deal, of course, to such master creators of fountains as Giovanni da Bologna or Pietro Tacca; but his Nordic nymphs and tritons have a rich humour, in addition to their essential avoidance of the ordinary commonplace of academic sweetness: they fulfil in every way the Nordic theme, while remaining a product of the saga tradition and of a characteristic Nordic inhumanness in face of the difficulties of technique. The charge that can be levelled against Milles is his eclecticism. There is almost no process or idea that he has not tried out, but this was probably due to the fact that his early repression prevented him from acquiring the knowledge that he needed, and consequently that when he had the chance to see works from the past the immediate impact was more disturbing than it otherwise would have been. And it is necessary here to state that while he is primarily an academic sculptor, he has clearly broken out of the pure academic tradition to absorb the traditional folk-art of his country and adapt and fuse it into his own particular modern conception. In discussing the more revolutionary aspects of the development of sculpture in the last 100 years it cannot be forgotten that Milles is a considerable sculptor, who is unconcerned with the dictates of fashion, and whose academic basis has developed into a personal style, coloured by his distinctly national reactions. Since he went to America his close associations at Cranbrook with the great Finnish architect Saarinen have, quite naturally, served to extend this national flavour. But there is nothing against that. It is true that art should be entirely unrelated to politics. It is not for art, except perhaps in moments of great disruption within countries or in moments of deep distaste for placidity in politics, to enter the realm of politics, and it is at these moments only that the artist may legitimately express his disgust or his anger in symbolic form. And yet no one could possibly think of Rodin,

Degas or Maillol as belonging to any other nationality than the French, Lehmbruck or Kolbe as other than German, Henry Moore as other than characteristically English. All have strong intellectual connexions with international thought; but all are influenced strongly by environment, and Milles, while cosmopolitan to a strong degree, remains at heart a Scandinavian.

The sculptors of the most modern generation are at a moment when little has yet resolved itself; but it is significant and hopeful that there is at present an outburst of new talent, particularly in England and America. It is an equally hopeful sign that much of this new sculptural output is regarded as extremely controversial. Nothing is *more* hopeful for the continued expansion of sculpture in a vital and experimental way than that it should be received with violent criticism and equally violent approbation. All the groups and ideas that the older generation were interested in, the abstract, the constructivist, the impressionistic, still flourish. That there is a tendency to experiment in material is equally healthy. The popular technique of working directly in wrought metal is as difficult as to work in marble; but it is a medium that was not used in any great volume before this war.

But many of the sculptors, by putting before us compositions often of an ugly and difficult nature, do not allow their public an easy approach to appreciation. Consider for instance the work of Eduardo Paolozzi (b. 1924), a young Englishman born of an Italian father. His curious intellectual constructions of an expressly abstract nature really require some explanation. But even on observing his works without, let us say, a catalogue, which will merely give a title, sometimes non-explanatory, it is impossible not to recognize that here is a young mind which creates for itself and for reasons known only to itself a certain composition, and that these reasons are valid and that his creations live. Paolozzi has been much influenced by plant and animal forms, as has another young Englishman, William Turnbull (b. 1922); and both have learnt much from Picasso; but Turnbull in his more simple and direct way produces a less complex impact on the audience and appears to have a much more open mind towards his experiments.

We always find ourselves coming back to Picasso. He is, in my view, a bad influence, as is T. S. Eliot and a number of other figures in the past. The complete inventors, who as I have said are exceptionally rare, must create an impact which, as in the case of a violent storm at sea or the bore in a river, has to run its way until exhausted. This may be a tiresome generalization, but it is particularly true in sculpture. Rodin, Brancusi, Moore, Michaelangelo, Bernini, Houdon, Praxiteles, Pheidias, Meiron, the sculptor of Chartres, of Wells, of Naumburg; the equally unknown sculptors of Borobodhur, of Chichenitza, of Yüng-Kang: what do they ultimately add up to: what in fact does sculpture give which differentiates it from the results of painting? We must feel that this, in modern times, is a problem in dissolution, which must ultimately find a resolution. In the present state of dissolving scientific values, the aesthetic and intellectual values become of more importance to a world which must or should concern itself with the less gross or less concrete terms of life in order to retain its happiness. If these scientific values are to overwhelm the more spiritual values of the world—and by this I do not mean to enter into the religious field—then music, painting, literature and sculpture become of supreme importance in the opposition camp and must fight for the ultimate survival of the humanities.

In the world of sculpture the present-day tendencies are towards any sort of new idea which will express the artist's feelings. The priorities accorded to technical schools have become an obsession with the controllers of our destinies. The arts have no political or technical priority and they must be entirely free from such control. But in sculpture, technical facilities have become a dire necessity owing to the enormously rapid increase in the price of material. Let us look at the Land of Promise, the U.S.A. Here because patronage is available and because a number of young sculptors have patronage the art is comparatively flourishing; but in most countries sculpture is in a particularly bad way because of the lack of desire for ornament, to put it on its lowest level, and the lack of the possibility of commissions. In the United States a number of youngish sculptors are able to make their way for the time being. David Smith (b. 1906) and Mary Callery (b. 1903) are both established artists, the former with somewhat mechanical realization of an imaginative mood which recalls the paintings of Léger, the latter with a more exotic control of her open-work conceptions, which recall the bronzes made by the nomadic tribes all over Central Asia, from the Kuban to the territories of the Ords tribes.

What is exceptionally refreshing is that despite the difficulties of patronage, a market, a major interest in a world where "art" normally seems to mean painting, there is no lack of sculptors. They are all prepared to try, and for that let us be thankful. It is a horrid sign that almost everywhere in this century it is State patronage that has increasingly become essential. State patronage is something which, if intelligently administered, is a force for extreme good; but if it is unintelligently administered and if bureaucratic control becomes a passion for some official who thinks he has "the right ideas" and can deal with the financial end, then goodbye to any sensitive interpretation of the word. This does not mean that the idea is not right. As regards sculpture, the Arts Council in Great Britain has been particularly alive to the possibilities of patronage to sculpture, and in a number of competitions, and by prizes and purchase, has endeavoured to further what is, after all, the main ideal, that the development of ideas will continue. We do not know whether everyone's new idea in sculpture as in the other arts may necessarily be a good one; we do not know if what has been done in the past can necessarily survive; but, as all Directors of Museums know, it is our bounden duty to recognize that no one must condemn rashly what is being done in the present and no one must destroy rashly the work of the past. "Taste" and "fashion" are two of the most difficult words in the repertoire of the art critic or the art historian. Who would like to be the arbiter in sculpture? "Taste" is a word which has been more misapplied than almost any other; it is a word like a red rag to a bull in some quarters. And yet there is at base an instinctive quality in all works of art, which is normally recognizable in a varying degree; this degree is often qualified by the dictates of fashion, and it becomes evident that one or other artist may have a sudden success not commensurate with his quality. Over the centuries there are ups and downs in all schools of artists. Edith Wharton's enchanting story of the unsatisfactory son who was sent out to buy paintings for his father's new gallery, and came back with a small collection of Italian primitives when he was expected to produce a Raphael, is a classic; and is equally applicable to sculpture. No one looks a great deal at Rodin's works now, great master though he was; Dalou, a sensitive and highly skilled sculptor, is almost forgotten; Mestrovic, an exceptionally powerful though mannered sculptor, whom I have not discussed in this essay, is hardly known any longer except in his own country, Yugoslavia; works of the nineteenth-century French sculptors Rude and Barye, celebrated in their day, fetch nothing in the market. It is the swing of the pendulum. Our ancestors paid enormous prices for sickly madonnas by Carlo Dolci, and it is only within the last years that they have begun to fetch a modest price. We must not worry, particularly in the realm of sculpture, about "taste" or "fashion". In this particularly difficult realm of art, nothing matters except three things. First, integrity of purpose on the part of the artist; it does not matter if you do not understand his purpose at first. Secondly, technical understanding by the artist of his material; and here, according to his age and experience, certain allowances must be made, though not too much. Thirdly, his integrity of purpose must add up to the problem he has set himself; if not, then his problem and its solution have become a failure. And above all experiment and trial must go on. Fortunately for the future of sculpture, there appears to be no doubt that in all countries there is a large body of young people who have decided to devote their lives to this difficult and valuable profession, and who will shape the future of it on whatever lines they may find most desirable for its future experimentation and development.

BOOKS SUGGESTED FOR FURTHER READING

E. Hartley Ramsden, *Twentieth-Century Sculpture* (Pleiades Books, 1949).

Sir Herbert Read, *Art Now* (Faber, 1948).

Sir Herbert Read, *Henry Moore* (Zwemmer, 1934).

William R. Valentiner, *Origins of Modern Sculpture* (Wittenborn, New York, 1946).

WRITING

by G. S. FRASER

I. Relativistic

LITERATURE has at once an intimate and an indefinitely various relationship to the other subjects discussed in this book. The man of letters, as such, rarely originates new ideas, but he is always in some degree affected by them. And he is aware, more vividly than the originators themselves often are, of the moods and atmospheres which ideas engender. Thus, one thing we look for in literature— quite apart from intrinsic formal qualities and the kind of universal moral significance that seems to transcend time—is a clue to the hopes, pleasures and anxieties of any period, to the directions of human striving. The man of letters tells us what it felt like to be there. Thus, literature is in one sense the most "interesting" and in another the most "impure" of the arts. The student of literature must have a more widely ranging general curiosity than the student of any other art. He must have read, for instance, for their purely literary value, a work of history like Gibbon's *Decline and Fall of the Roman Empire*, a work of philosophy like Berkeley's *Three Dialogues Between Hylas and Philonous, In Opposition to Sceptics and Atheists*, a work of polemical popular theology, like Pascal's *Provincial Letters*; but he cannot judge even the purely literary value of such master-pieces without becoming deeply involved in their subjects. Even when he is dealing with fiction or poetry, his relationship to the work he is considering remains one of involvement rather than detachment. The great literary critics ask questions about the works they are considering which have not merely to do with formal organization but are broadly moral and philosophical. They ask not only how well a book is written but how sincere it is, what wide human relevance it has, to what degree the moral attitudes it seems to express are right or wrong.

More profoundly still, behind at least every major work of literature there does lie something that can be variously described as a faith, a policy, a coherent set of moral attitudes, a "vision of life". No great writer intends to leave his readers just as he found them. Thus whether or not the enjoyment of literature does raise what Dr. I. A. Richards and Miss Kathleen Nott call a problem of belief, or what M. Sartre calls a problem of commitment, that enjoyment certainly does call for a certain openness of response and flexibility of attitude, a willingness to be changed. The good reader must be ready to shift his perspective. Pliability is not a virtue in a reader, any more than in other capacities, but neither is obstinacy; and the good reader should certainly have something of Keats's "negative capability" or plasticity of response. The most obvious benefit that we can get in the long run from discriminating reading is, in fact, a deeper understanding of our human condition and a readier sympathy with, and more patient regard for, our fellows.

Literature is thus, perhaps more than any of the other subjects discussed in this book, typically *the* humane discipline. It is true enough that the mere man of letters may often appear to the man following some narrower discipline a rhetorician or a trifler. There are even periods, like the Ciceronian period of the early Renaissance, when an excessive literary cult of style for its own sake is a positive danger not only to original thought and to emotional sincerity but even to the production of strictly literary works that have real original force; it is not "literary" periods, in the fussiest sense, that produce the greatest literature. More broadly, a literary convention, like that of the Petrarchan love-poem, that outlives its day, can have a positively stultifying effect on actual human relationships; and a decadent literary diction, breeding thinly from past poems, instead of enriching men's natural sensibility can positively impoverish it— this happened, for instance, in the late eighteenth century in England just before Wordsworth and Coleridge. Writing, moreover, like other trades, has its smell of the shop. Perhaps at all periods in metropolitan literary circles there is a certain preciosity, and there are pretenders who are accepted. The career of letters, moreover, has been at all times a morally dangerous one, exposing those who follow it to the temptations especially of idleness, vanity, envy, flattery, dissipation and more or less deliberate comic or pathetic self-deception. For all that, literature remains, apart from the great religions and the great philosophical moral codes like Stoicism and Confucianism, the most obvious single massive humanizing influence in history. And the man of action, like Hitler, or the man of thought, like Luther or Herbert Spencer, who has no deep respect for literature is at all times a much more dangerous portent to civilization than the most inane, pedantic or pretentious mere literary man.

II. *Contextualistic*

These remarks on the social function and human significance of literature need elaboration and qualification, if they are to be related to our own age. I take that age, I think not arbitrarily, as having begun around 1880, and as being one of four main creative periods in English literary history, of which the others began around 1580, 1660 and 1790; the others are generally known, from the period of their commencement or from the period of their greatest flourishing, as the Elizabethan, Augustan and Romantic Ages. Our own we can call in a nondescript way the Modern Age.

There are important parallels between the historical conditions which give rise to each large movement. Roughly the topics which most interest men at any period are, in this order, religion, politics and science—I use science in the widest sense, to cover any movement towards new discoveries or towards the extension and reorganization of familiar knowledge. Economic factors have only comparatively recently begun to excite a similar conscious attention, but economic changes have obviously a profound effect on men's attitudes towards religion, politics and science. Using these four factors, we can construct the following tables.

(1) *The Elizabethan, Jacobean and Caroline Period*

(R) The Anglican state settlement in religion was accepted because of fear of Papal domination. When it became clear that this fear was exaggerated, there was a strong Puritan reaction against the settlement.

(P) A strong centralized Monarchy was accepted because of memories of feudal disorder. When it became clear that feudal days had passed, there was a strong Parliamentary reaction against the Monarchy.

(S) The Voyages of Discovery; the New Cosmology of Copernicus, tending to destroy the medieval world-picture; experimental attitude to politics, as in Macchiavelli; Bacon's propaganda for experiment in Natural Science; continued reaction against Schoolmen and prestige of Renaissance Humanism.

(E) Growing wealth of city merchants and bankers; impoverishment of minor country gentry through litigation, cost of court life, bad management, and finally the Civil Wars.

(2) *The Restoration and Early and Late Augustan Period*

(R) Growth of Religious Toleration. Progress of Deism, Scepticism and religious moderatism among upper classes, and of movements like Methodism among the lower classes. Reaction against Scepticism at the period of the French Revolution.

(P) The establishment of a principle of mainly Parliamentary rule, under the early Hanoverians, with Parliament mainly consisting of, and representing, landed country gentry. Attempts to secure greater share in Government for the Crown under George III, with popular agitation against this of Wilkes and

Junius, and aristocratic agitation against it, with Burke as spokesman.

(S) The establishment of the Royal Society. Newton's new cosmology. Foundation of British Empirical Philosophy by Locke, Berkeley and Hume. Beginnings of the Industrial Revolution.

(E) Beginnings of growth of a new class of wealthy manufacturers without a due share of political power. Improvements in Agriculture and rise in population. New wealth from the East and West Indies.

(3) *The Romantic and Early and Late Victorian Period*

(R) Reaction against Religious Scepticism and moderatism, growth of Evangelicalism, rise of Anglo-Catholicism. Later, after Darwin and the Higher Criticism, growth of Agnosticism. Utilitarianism to some extent a left-wing secular religion. Attempts by writers like Carlyle and Arnold to combine free-thinking with traditional religious sentiment.

(P) Intellectual sympathy with and reaction against French Revolution. Steady extensions of franchise. Combination, as in ancient Athens, of Liberalism at home and Imperialism abroad. Early Socialist ideas. Tendency towards isolation from Europe.

(S) Massive advances in all branches of science. Notable moral effect of Darwinianism, and complex practical effect of improved communications (railways, cables, etc.).

(E) Massive industrialization and huge growth of population. Uneasiness about working and living conditions of lower classes. Free trade helps to make London financial centre of world. Rejection by many fastidious spirits (Carlyle, Ruskin, Arnold, Tennyson) of prevailing commercial ethos.

(4) *The Modern Period, to Date*

(R) Tendency among intellectuals to substitute various types of Hegelian idealism (Bradley, Bosanquet) or ideal utilitarianism (Sidgwick, Moore) for traditional Christianity. Modernism or accommodation to modern thought among some Churchmen (Dean Inge), contrasts with a movement in some creative writers back to traditional Christianity (Lionel Johnson, Chesterton, Mr. T. S. Eliot). Left-wing tendency to make Socialism a substitute for religion (Shaw, H. G. Wells). Growing religious indifference of masses.

(P) A general progress throughout the present century among all parties away from nineteenth-century individualism towards idea of government intervention for purposes of welfare, security, etc. Disturbing effect of two wars. Sympathy with and reaction against Russian Revolution among intellectuals comparable with reaction of Wordsworth, Coleridge and others to French Revolution. Disappearance for practical purposes of Liberal Party and growing strength and prestige of Labour Party. Important measures of nationalization, etc., under Labour Government of 1945.

(S) Massive advances again in all branches of science. Practical importance of physics (atom bomb and atomic power, hydrogen bomb). Moral importance of psychology (particularly Freud), semantics and analytic philosophy, in discouraging too simple dogmatic attitudes in ethics, politics, etc.

(E) Slowing down in rate of both population growth and capital expansion, partly due to competition from advanced countries, partly due to movements of nationalism and industrialization in backward or semi-backward market areas. Tariff barriers and growing complexity of international regulation of flow of trade and investment. Heavy capital cost of bringing plant up to date, in line with new scientific discoveries. Attempts to control unemployment, booms and slumps by Government intervention on Keynesian lines in the West; State Socialism in Russia and elsewhere. Growing strength and bargaining power of Trade Unions in Western countries, combined with growing control by the state, especially in wartime, of choice of job, home, etc., by ordinary employee.

These notes are very scrappy, and they are not intended to be evaluative. They are, however, the kind of points that would occur to anyone, not an expert, as having salient significance during these four periods. If we can generalize at all from four sample periods about the kinds of broad social condition that give rise to literary creativity, we might say that a creative period, at least in England and since the Renaissance, has been:

(a) Never fundamentally a period of religious indifference, but usually one of defined disagreement in religious matters (of disagreement not so fundamental as to forbid discussion), with as time goes on a growing number of rival centres, at different social and intellectual levels, of "orthodoxy", and with a tendency, in the latter two periods, for religious emotions to be projected into secular philosophies.

(b) Usually a period for most of its length (the exception is the Civil Wars and the Commonwealth) of at least superficial political stability, but always with some social forces working for radical change;

(c) Always a period of considerable extension of knowledge, of a kind that affects traditional world-pictures, practical life, and

moral attitudes, and that more broadly may affect fundamental
philosophical or religious beliefs;

(d) Always a period of economic growth, though at varying rates;
this growth involves increasing technical complexity and new
power and significance for rising social classes, and often a loss
in power and significance for established social classes.

In any literary period, of course, the creative writer's awareness
of his situation will not be of this somewhat dry and repulsive
schematic sort. It will be an awareness of the "form and pressure of
the time", of vaguely defined forces making for change, vaguely
defined forces resisting it. And the writer, like the rest of us, according to his perspective on the world, will tend to project his own
personal evaluation of life either into the forces, as he sees them,
making for "progress" or into those making for "stability". (He
may be wrong, like the rest of us, in judging which are which.)
But the writer is more sensitive than the rest of us; he feels often the
attractive tug of what he disagrees with; he sees the case for "the
other side". He is never, by the very nature of his profession, that of
a critical observer of life, quite fully integrated into "his own
side". Thus at times he may, like Addison perhaps, or like Pope as
he claimed ("For Tories called him Whig, and Whigs a Tory"),
function as a trimmer, a relaxer of tensions between extremes, a
moderating influence. At other times, his feeling of tension may be so
extreme as to make him turn away from society in disgust, despair
or indifference (like the Symbolists and Decadents). Or he may
suddenly perceive that something he looks to as the conserver of
order will not in fact conserve it; thus, Shakespeare "believes in"
a stable and hierarchical political order, but in *Troilus and Cressida*
he has begun to doubt whether such an order exists except as a
rhetorician's ideal. The writer, again, can hold together in his
mind sometimes, with a feeling of emotional discomfort but not of
logical impossibility, two apparently quite contradictory world-
views. Gide combines quite genuinely the scrupulous conscience of a
Calvinist with a forthright though fastidious hedonism; he might
even be said to combine a genuinely humble attitude towards a
transcendent God with a deep conviction that a transcendent God
cannot exist. John Donne holds together in his head the Copernican
and the Ptolemaic cosmologies; it is not for him so much as if
Copernicus had proved that the medieval picture of the universe,
with the successive spheres, and the world and man at the centre,
was wrong, but rather as if that medieval world had existed comfortably enough, as a real entity, till Copernicus came along,
destroyed it, and substituted another one. Donne similarly, perhaps
rather like Gide, manages to combine or alternate severe Christian
morals with a harsh and cynical Renaissance sensuality, and that

sensuality itself with true and tender human love. This capacity of
the creative writer for "plural belonging" is one reason why he, rather
than any type of more formal thinker, can give us the whole complex image of an age. He not only houses, he even gives hospitality
to, contradictions. The writer, as such, is at once a focus of change
and a centre of resistance.

III. Formalistic

The reader, however, who deeply and sincerely cares for literature may feel that we have so far been dealing with secondary
matters, that we have left out what must be an essential aspect of
literature, as of all the arts—the aspect of form. However impure,
literature may be compared with the other arts—or compared with
mathematics or formal logic: it remains true that the history of literature, like the history of other arts, can be treated, almost entirely
in abstraction from the social context, as a history of changes in form,
brought about mainly not by outward pressure, but by the inherent
logic of form itself. That, for instance, is the approach of George
Sainsbury in his great books on English rhythms in verse and prose. We
can consider literature as an effort at the perpetual renewal of form.

Form needs renewal because it can be exhausted. It is a commonplace of criticism today, for instance, that Milton by his very
genius exhausted the possibilities, or all except the most marginal
possibilities, of Miltonic blank verse. Again, some modern critics of
Italian poetry, like Mr. Ezra Pound, prefer the often technically
rough and clumsy sonnets of Guido Cavalcanti to the later and more
technically perfect sonnets of Petrarch, because they feel that with
Petrarch the sonnet had become something mechanical, a trick
anyone could learn; and we probably do prefer today the subtle,
hesitant, halting love-poems of Sir Thomas Wyatt, written in
Henry VIII's reign as a first innocent response to Italian poetry, to
the monotonous sweetness and trite imagery of the average Elizabethan lyric. When everybody can do a thing, it begins to be a question whether it is worth doing—whether it retains much value,
except as a social accomplishment or an empty exhibition of skill.
And it may not be a matter of everybody being able to do it.
Nobody but Dickens could have written Dickens's novels, but,
quite apart from that, a later nineteenth-century novelist like
Henry James, considering and up to a point admiring the rich,
untidy, various worlds of Balzac and Dickens, was right in noting
one lack in them: an intelligent centre of appreciation (or the
character who makes sense of what is happening); and right in
weighing the possibility of making the novel more tidy, even at the
cost of making it less rich. Again, a genuine formal invention in
literature is a very rare thing, and for any writer a very rash

attempt; but when Mr. T. S. Eliot invented the unique form of
The Waste Land—a form which has no close resemblance to that of
any previous kind of poetry, and which moreover has never been
successfully imitated by any subsequent poet—he was right in seeing
that what he had to express would not fit into even the most subtle
alteration and adaptation of any existing mould. An opposite case is
that of Mr. William Empson, a poet very much aware that his way
of thinking was individual, intricate and difficult to grasp, who
therefore holds the reader's attention with strict traditional forms,
like that of the villanelle, which had formerly been used for the
expression of pleasant commonplaces and were now turned to the
purposes of packed, ironic meditation.

Form reacts upon form. A novelist like Virginia Woolf, considering what seems to her the failure of the second wind of the Thackeray-
Dickens tradition in Galsworthy, Wells, Bennett, tries to bring into
the novel (even at the cost of seeming aloof, precious, teasing) the
hesitations, the incommunicabilities at the centre of human
experience that they seem to her to leave out. But novelists of the
next generation, like Mr. Graham Greene or Mr. Christopher
Isherwood, confronted with the immense elaboration of *Ulysses* or
Remembrance of Things Past or the delicate elaboration of *The Waves*,
begin to wonder whether they can profitably go further in that
direction—would it not be better to turn, even as a starting-point,
to what everybody reads, to see where the novelist can go if he
starts from simple, direct narrative, from the pattern of the light
social comedy or the thriller? Straight, simple narrative will have
its innings for twenty years, and then a still younger novelist, like Mr.
Philip Toynbee, will ask whether we should indeed assume that the
age of experiment is past, will write a novel not about individuals
but about the various archetypal roles and situations that are lived
through over even a short period in one individual life. And the
wheel comes full circle when the very youngest novelists, Mr. John
Wain or Mr. Kingsley Amis, ask whether Mrs. Woolf was after all
right to dismiss Wells and Bennett so entirely out of hand.

Thus, because of this reaction of form upon form, there tends to
be at all times a war between literary generations: the younger
people saying, "Surely, we have had enough of that, the dead horse
has been quite sufficiently flogged"; the older people saying, "Surely
that is not new, it is quite old-fashioned, it was out of date when I
was young". All this tends to make for misunderstanding and bad
feeling, for that perpetual bickering which in all ages has been such
a notorious feature of the literary life. It is an irony of that life that
the very moment when a writer, deservedly and after a long struggle,
begins to be widely known to the public is also often the very
moment when, from the point of view of younger writers, he has
ceased to be interesting, or when the more critical among them are

beginning to wonder whether he was ever interesting at all. There are good writers the relevance of whose writing seems to belong not to their whole adult life but to a particular short, intensely felt period. In imagination, we place Sir Max Beerbohm in the 1890's, Mr. E. M. Forster in Edwardian England, Mr. Aldous Huxley in the 1920's; and we still think of Mr. Auden and the group of his friends, in spite of the good work they have done since, as "poets of the 1930's". There are on the other hand writers of another kind, like Dr. Edwin Muir or Mr. Robert Graves, who write fine poems, and are praised by critics, from their youth onwards, but only in later middle age find a wide audience of young people saying, "This is what we have been waiting for". Only the greatest writers perhaps escape this time-bound condition. Yeats escapes it by suppleness, by being "in the picture" in the 1890's and "in the picture" in a quite different way in 1939; even so, there were long intervening periods when he was rather "out of the picture". Hardy escapes it by being utterly indifferent to fashion. The reader, therefore, who wishes to study the various renewals and decays of form in contemporary literature will have to possess a vivid and exact sense of period. We come back, though in a roundabout way, even in the strictly formal study of literature, to the social scene.

IV. *Linguistic and Stylistic*

If we can think of form (by a convenient and attractive though in many ways deceptive metaphor) as the architect's design for the house of literature, we can think of words as the very bricks out of which the house is built. But that does not quite suggest the full importance of language, unless we remember that a new style of architecture often springs largely from the exploitation of new building materials, such, for instance, in our own age, as reinforced concrete and plate glass. Whatever may be true of building, it is true, I think, that a renewal of language, when it takes place in literature, is nearly always more fundamentally important than a renewal of form. Language is what we all use, and it is where literature most intimately touches life; and throughout all English literary history (again, since the Renaissance) we can trace a fruitful tension between two concepts of what literary language should be: a concept of purity, elegance, artificial loftiness ("sublimity" or "the grand style"), on the one hand; and a concept of natural force and directness—a force and directness verging even on the tones of informal speech—on the other. The tension between these two concepts continues to be felt in our own day.

Examples which literary historians habitually use to illustrate this tension are, for example, the contrast between Sidney and Spenser as followers of a sweet, smooth, artificial Petrarchan tradition and

John Donne as harshly returning to the rhythms and idioms of common speech, to the complexities of real feeling. Similarly, in our own period, Mr. Eliot in his earlier poems, that develop Browning's tradition of the dramatic monologue in conversational tones, like "Prufrock" and "Portrait of a Lady", might be contrasted with Yeats, at least with Yeats up to his volume of 1914, *Responsibilities*. The typically "natural" prose of Swift and Addison in the early Augustan period is similarly often contrasted with the typically "artificial" prose, sonorous and periodic, of Burke and Johnson and Gibbon in the late Augustan period.

Such contrasts have something in them. Yet there is a sense in which this antithesis of the "natural" and the "artificial", like most convenient commonplaces, is much too simple. (We can see where the over-simplicity is likely to come in, if we think, for a moment, not of literature but of ordinary life; we all know people who have a rather *affected* "naturalness" of manner, and other people whose "artificiality" has become second nature.) There are many passages, for instance, in Spenser and Sidney that have, in fact, a plain simplicity of effect that is not often found in Donne; and some of Donne's own finest effects are due to a more consciously rhetorical organization of his material, a more oratorical emphasis, than is to be found anywhere in Spenser or Sidney. Again, the later Yeats combines his traditional metrical forms, and his moments of exalted rhetoric, with a more directly intimate conversational *tone* than is to be found anywhere else in English, and Mr. Eliot, in spite of his early innovations, moves from "Ash Wednesday" onwards towards hieratic rhythms, elliptical *sententiae* and ritual repetitions that get further and further from any tone resembling that of ordinary conversation.

Moreover, "naturalness" in language is neither an intrinsically unambiguous nor, in its application over any considerable period, a highly stable concept. What is "natural" is what we are used to; but when we get excessively used to it, when we have had too much of a good thing, we begin again to find it "artificial". Donne's "naturalness" has become "artificial" in Cowley; Dryden, as against Cowley, initiating a new style, though his tone is less intimate, though his intentions are less sincere, more those of the political rhetorician than those of any metaphysical poet, seems by comparison "natural" again. And against Dryden, Pope, with his more involute polish and complexity, his more interesting and more highly-bred blend of frankness and reserve, moral pretensions and bitter honesty, false flattery, real respect, true affection and genuine hate, seems highly "artificial" again, but by no means disagreeably so; he is at the same time the most brilliant conversational poet in our language, and the poet who, next to Milton, most obviously thinks of poetic language itself as an artificial construction. He makes us pause to reflect that good conversation, the

speech of cultivated people, is not itself "natural", it is an "art".
And, once again, Burke, Johnson and Gibbon, as soon as we have got
used to their artifice, may seem to give themselves to us with a more
spontaneous fulness than Addison in his artful simplicity. Milton,
and Wordsworth in his deliberate early experiments in natural
language, do perhaps, indeed, mark two almost pure poles. But
most of Wordsworth's more doggedly experimental early poems are
not successful, and Milton's success in an almost wholly artificial
language is of a unique and precarious kind. Finally, when we turn
to Shakespeare's greatest uses of language, for instance in *Antony
and Cleopatra* or *The Tempest*, we do not find ourselves making this
distinction, or asking if this is near or not to "the language of real
life". It has the freedom and flexibility of the language of real
life, or an even greater freedom and flexibility. It has the splendour
of the language of poetry. It is the language of Shakespeare, a
heightening and transmutation of all other written or spoken speech.
It is not what we would say, but what with perfect appropriateness
Antony or Prospero do say. And in some ways comparable alembica-
tion of language, which makes the contrast between artifice and
nature meaningless, is to be found perhaps, in our own century,
not only in the best verse of Yeats and Eliot but in the best prose of
James Joyce.

Only very exceptional writers indeed, however, do ever achieve
this transcendent fusion. The problem of a diction has been a very
real and a never quite finally or perfectly solved problem for many
distinguished contemporary writers; and much of what is called the
"difficulty" of contemporary literature is really perhaps the uneasiness of a reader, perhaps with old-fashioned expectations, when
faced with a diction that strikes him as inappropriate, as jarring or
odd. Such a diction, for instance, is to be found in the works of Miss
Gertrude Stein and her pupil, Mr. Ernest Hemingway. It is as if
Miss Stein and Mr. Hemingway had put up a kind of grid-screen
against the light, through which only certain colours could filter.
Thus, the effect of their works, even when they are aiming at the
most extreme naturalism, is oddly didactic—as if they were saying,
"Only this is real, only what gets through real, anybody who uses
an abstract word or a complex sentence is not real, because he cannot
get through". Thus what we find in these writers, instrumented
by their diction, is a highly "artificial" cult of "natural" simple-
mindedness; just as what we find in a writer of an opposite sort,
Ronald Firbank, might be called a slightly simple-minded if not
exactly "natural" cult of "artificiality"—instrumented again by a
diction, by a jadedly effete and cunningly *recherché* choice of inappropriate words.

The problem has struck other writers in other ways. English
literature, indeed, can offer few examples of writers like Rilke and

Valéry, who have retreated from the gross communicative uses of language, who have built for themselves a private though translucent verbal kingdom; Yeats is possibly the greatest of symbolist poets, greater than Rilke or Valéry, but he became such a poet only by accepting once again, in early middle age, the unpurified "language of the tribe", by taking his readers into his confidence about his personal life, his ideas, his political interests, by breaking the symbolist mould. And a common concern of the better English poets of this century, at least till around 1940, has been in one way or another to avoid making their poetry too "literary", to give it one way or another the ring of speech. This was one purpose of the early work of Pound and Eliot; it was the point also of the jokes, the topical allusions, the roughness and off-handedness, even perhaps of the special kind of obscurity—the "knowing" kind—of poets of the 1930's like Mr. Auden and Mr. MacNeice and, in his very different way, of Mr. Empson. This is one point also of the reaction of the youngest English poets today, poets like Mr. Thom Gunn, Mr. Kingsley Amis, Mr. John Wain, against the various types of neo-romantic or of consciously "literary" poetry of the 1940's—against Dylan Thomas, on the one hand, and, say, Mr. John Heath-Stubbs on the other. Yet all such judgements are tricky, and it appears to some critics that many of these youngest poets, especially those who come straight out of Mr. Empson's pocket, have only succeeded in being "literary" in another way.

It does, however, speaking very generally, look as if it is necessary for English poetry to touch the ground, at fairly close recurrent intervals, if it is to regain its strength, and as if literary conventions of language, in English, wear out with disturbing rapidity. There is an obvious contrast here with the state of affairs in France, where the language of poetry is still thought of as something chaste, pure, and elevated, quite distinct from the language of life, and where the important revolutions that have taken place over the modern period have been much less in the poet's diction than in his use of symbols or of imagery, and in his attitude to logic and rhetoric. Even a very good French poem tends to look and sound rather excessively "poetical" for our taste, when rendered literally into English; and on the other hand a poet like Paul Eluard, revolutionary in his elliptical logic and his Surrealist use of images, is considered by competent French critics to belong to the classical tradition by his diction and tone. We have no "classical tradition" in English in this sense, whether that is a good or bad thing. It is also disturbingly true that the conventions of English *spoken* speech change very rapidly, so that for instance the slangy, naturalistic dialogue of Mr. Noel Coward's early comedies, of twenty or thirty years ago, now looks embarrassingly "period" like old snapshots or cloche-hats. Thus young English poets today are faced with the double problem of relating their poetry to common speech and of attempting also, by the force and elegance of their diction, by the example of that force and elegance, to preserve our common speech from its growing slovenliness, invasion by foreign slang and official jargon, and semi-literate decay.

Thus, perhaps this whole problem of diction is rather specially related to the need which any good poet, or indeed writer of prose, feels to arouse and sustain in his readers a certain alertness. Ours is not an alert age: films, television, popular newspapers, the turning on of the wireless in many houses at all hours as a kind of audible wall-paper; political cynicism, fear of war combined with a sense of individual powerlessness to prevent it, overcrowded schools, the decay of faith, the lack among most people of either firm rejection or firm acceptance of traditional moral standards; a creeping, grey dreary prurience fastening with equal zest on lust and murder; a widespread passive but grumbling attitude to life; a lack of a sense of responsibility in the middle-aged and of ambition in the young: all these things make it unlikely that it should be an alert age. But to preserve and encourage what alertness there is, to arouse people when possible from half-awakeness, is one of the socially useful functions of literature. And problems of diction, of tone, and so on are—from a social point of view—problems of getting at and holding the audience.

V. *Thematic: Negative and Positive*

We have discussed modern literature so far from the perspectives of its social background, its formal developments, the linguistic problems it must face. We have not asked what it is mainly *about*. Mr. Donald Carne-Ross, a young critic of great perceptiveness, learning, wit and originality, and a man of what we should have called in the good old days of the 1930's very reactionary views, has an ingenious theory that the main theme of the best modern literature is the decay of our present civilization, and that therefore there is really no such thing as a genuine "modern movement" in literature, in the sense of a movement with a future; both because the decay of a civilization, though a profound theme, is a narrow one, and has already been exhausted; and because literature pre-occupied with this theme will inevitably tend to look not forward but back.

Thus, for Mr. Carne-Ross, writers like Joyce, Pound, Eliot and Proust are perhaps a little like Lot's wife, looking back sadly on the ruined city even though they know it has deserved its destruction; and like her they have been transformed into their own sad, salty, glittering monuments. Nothing, he feels, will ever grow on our present sterile plain. Mr. Carne-Ross, to give him his due, does not apply his melancholy theory to Yeats, for whom he has perhaps a

more whole-hearted admiration than for the other writers I have
mentioned. Yeats he sees as an anachronistic survival of the heroic
spirit of the Renaissance, a spirit which for him, with its revival of
classic values, with its proud humanistic splendour, is the true spirit
of the noblest European art and literature. Mr. Carne-Ross sees
the modern period as resembling in many ways the Alexandrian
age of the ancient world, an age learned, derivative, in small ways
extremely experimental, capable of producing charmingly erudite
minor work, but not of creating major form; though he admits,
certainly, that Joyce and Mr. Pound and Mr. Eliot are in the scale
and ambition of their work much more impressive than any
Alexandrian writers known to us. Mr. Carne-Ross also thinks that
the various attempts, in the 1930's, to produce a literature devoted
to some other theme than the decay of a civilization, devoted to the
theme of political hope, quite obviously failed—though in a respectable and worthy way. He thinks that since 1940 (when the hopes of
the 1930's exploded) the best we have been able to produce—in
Great Britain, and in the field of poetry, in which he is most interested—is good minor occasional poems of exile or war, like those of
Bernard Spencer or Keith Douglas or F. T. Prince, and good poems
on the traditional commonplaces of love and death, like those of
Dylan Thomas. We no longer love and admire man enough, he
thinks, to be able to conceive him heroically. Roughly, one might
sum up Mr. Carne-Ross's point of view thus: in a period like ours,
you can produce *The Waste Land*, and it is a fine poem, but once is
enough. If you attempt to write a succession of variations on *The
Waste Land* you reduce its impact. (I suppose he might describe
Mr. Connolly's *The Unquiet Grave* as a slacker though more genial
and various prose *Waste Land*.)

There is something bracing about such a view, however much
one disagrees with it, and I am grateful to Mr. Carne-Ross for at
least enabling me, by his frankly dismissive attitude towards most
modern literature, to get a grip on my untidy theme: it is not a
question with him of whom dare we leave out but one, really, of
whom need we keep in. How far can we go with him, and where do
we part company? It is, of course, true that signs of the apparent
decay of civilization are one of the main preoccupations of some of
the best modern literature. It is also true that this theme naturally
exhausts itself; we could not digest a new novel of the type of
Ulysses (even if it was almost as good) or a new poem of the type of
The Waste Land (even, again, if it was almost as good) every successive year. Nobody among us will ever cry "wolf" again so soundingly
as Joyce and Eliot, our early masters. But in dealing with the poetry
of the 1930's, Mr. Carne-Ross does not seem to me to make allowances for how much of the best of it, the best of Mr. Auden, Mr.
MacNeice and Mr. Empson, for instance, has a permanent value

as social satire, moral commentary or statement of a complex personal attitude, and not merely value of a topical political sort. And in dealing with poetry since 1940, and with literature in general since 1940, he seems to me not to make sufficient allowances for the literature of a certain limited hopefulness (Sartre, Camus) or for the poetry, like that of Dr. Edwin Muir and Miss Kathleen Raine, that expresses a genuine religious attitude, a faith not so much in human contrivances as in the sources of life. I think that M. Sartre has an unpleasant literary personality, that he writes very often, so far as I can judge style in a foreign language, in a turgid, confused and pretentious prose; I think that whenever he deals, for instance, with poetry he shows himself an arrogant philistine. Yet out of an embittered atheism, a pessimistic view of the world and of conscious existence, he *has* built himself a kind of humanism. He does not, in Mr. Carne-Ross's sense, love and admire man; one fancies him, indeed, as turning scowlingly away from human grace or beauty; but he does admire such human virtues as staunchness and courage. In M. Camus, there is much more sensitivity towards what is gracious and touching in life, as well as to what is merely sourly staunch, and he seems to me to write beautiful prose. I would hazard the judgement that *La Peste* is an allegory that will rank in future as a classic of its kind, with *The Pilgrim's Progress* and *Gulliver's Travels*. M. Camus does seem to me, in spite or indeed partly because of his modest admission that he cannot make final sense of the universe or justify by a long train of abstruse reasoning his moral compulsions, a modern humanist in Mr. Carne-Ross's desired sense.

Apart from the poetry of Dr. Edwin Muir, which I have mentioned, and that of Miss Kathleen Raine, Mr. Carne-Ross also leaves out of account that of Mr. Robert Graves. Mr. Graves himself, conscious of his preoccupation with a single "prehistoric and posthistoric theme", would perhaps not wish to be considered a figure in the "modern movement" in the sense that Pound, Eliot and Joyce obviously are. He dealt, ironically and toughly perhaps rather than tragically, with Mr. Carne-Ross's theme of the decay of civilization in two early prose works, the autobiography *Good-Bye to All That*, and the play, which has autobiographical elements, *But It Still Goes On*. In an excellent short poem, "The Fallen Tower of Siloam", he has explicitly stated that he does not consider it a sufficiently *serious* theme for poetry:

> It behoved us, indeed, as poets
> To be silent in Siloam, to foretell
> No visible calamity. Though kings
> Were crowned and gold coin minted still and horses
> Still munched at nose-bags in the public streets,
> All such sad emblems were to be condoned:
> An old wives' tale, not ours.

The "sad emblems", with Mr. Graves's typical irony, are not of
disaster but of continuance, of "it still going on." Civilization may
preserve the illusion of its body after it has lost the illusion of its
soul, but for Mr. Graves the true poet is concerned with something
else, with a reality that is not that of history but of ritual and myth.
The myth itself may be a tragic one, a myth of disaster, but of
disaster worth achieving. Mr. Graves's attitude to love and the
death-love may in a very profound sense indeed be traditional,
but it is not in Mr. Carne-Ross's sense commonplace. It is,
in Mr. Carne-Ross's sense, humanist, in that Mr. Graves's
supernatural is the embodied and the finite, the local, the humanly
re-enacted supernatural of the early Mediterranean world—the
supernatural of a time before Socrates had rationalized morals and
Plato had invented idealist philosophy, had seen the world of actual
existence and tragic change as not wholly real and reality as conceptual, impersonal, inhuman and unchanging, "a ghostly paradigm
of things". The spirit of Dr. Edwin Muir's poetry and Miss Raine's,
though very different in its ultimate mood, is broadly comparable.
They are both students of Jung and for both of them the idea of
archetypal patterns as shapers of the individual life, of great myths
as the experiences that the individual lives through, of ritual
responses as tests to be passed and tributes exacted from us by a life's
high moments, is fundamentally important. This again is not
exactly—though like all new insights, in weaker disciples it can
become rote—a mere rhetorical variation on a commonplace.

Again, though no doubt after his tragic and untimely death the
achievement of Dylan Thomas was very much exaggerated, though
it is perhaps wrong to claim him as a major poet (I think he is a
major minor poet), it does seem to me wrong to dismiss him, either,
as a mere good writer on the traditional commonplaces of love and
death. He was more than that. He has been described as a religious
poet, celebrating the idea of process, seeking always to praise,
refusing to reject or condemn: a poet of "life" rather than of the
particular problems, always involving discrimination and choice, of
living. This is what our Cambridge friends call a "limiting judgement", but it seems to me by no means an ultimately dismissive one.
He wrote and lived for the glory of God, as he understood God,
and the love of man, and in his humility he was perhaps nearer to
God than the moralistic critics who, perhaps having in mind the
innocent excesses of his life, sought to condemn his work for a
dangerous confusion. That confusion, anyway, was vanishing from
his later poetry, and when we read such lines as these, with their
grateful celebration of the act of love, we cannot take them as a
rhetorical variation on a commonplace, or agree with Mr. Carne-
Ross that no significant contemporary writer, except Yeats, has
really loved and admired the human image:

Bird he was brought low,
Burning in the bride bed of love, in the whirl-
Pool at the wanting centre, in the folds
Of Paradise, in the spun bud of the world.
And she rose with him flowering in her melting snow.

As my wife has remarked in an article in a Japanese magazine, in these lines Dylan Thomas "celebrates the glories of physical love almost as a mystic".

How then do we stand in regard to Mr. Carne-Ross's thesis? It does seem to me broadly true, here I agree with him, that writers who began in the first or second decade of this century, like Joyce, Pound, Eliot or Lawrence, or whose style went through important changes in these early years of the century, as was the case with Yeats, do on the whole have a more imposing stature, were much more significant as initiators, than even their most distinguished successors. However much we may admire, for instance, Mr. Auden or Mr. Isherwood, we do not feel that the one is built on quite the same scale as Yeats or Mr. Eliot, the other on quite the same scale as Joyce or Lawrence. The successors of the great experimental writers, of what Mr. Spender calls the "visionary individualists" of the early part of the century, are men of about our own moral stature, grappling with the kind of problems we face ourselves. In that sense it may be true, as Mr. Spender like Mr. Carne-Ross has claimed, that "the modern movement is dead". But it does not follow that the theme which the great experimentalists may indeed have exhausted, the theme of the decay of civilization, is the only theme for our time, or that there is nothing more, on topics that are not commonplace, for their successors to say.

It even seems to me possible that this "decay of civilization" itself exists more positively and movingly for us in *The Waste Land* or *Ulysses* than in the actual world in which we move. Mr. Eliot himself made this point when he said that *The Waste Land* expressed really not a generation's disillusionment but its illusion of being disillusioned. We can, at least, fairly easily see that in works which are distinguished but not of the stature of *The Waste Land*, works like Kafka's *The Castle*, George Orwell's *1984* and Arthur Koestler's *Darkness at Noon*, there is something like an arbitrary and imposed hopelessness, a luxury of self-torture. Mr. Alan Pryce-Jones has a penetrating remark about one of the functions of the novel, which comes in aptly here. "Don't think you read novels in order to be moved by imaginary circumstances. You read them, as others have said their prayers, in order to find yourself. The final discovery is never made; the novel never dies." In Kafka, Koestler and Orwell we do not "find ourselves" but find our maladies; or find ourselves at the most in a state of extreme moral stress, perhaps even of mental illness, from which in time we recover, and see that the account of experience which we took as blackly central is only warningly marginal. In the whole history of the literature of our time, such works—such "tales of terror" screwed up to a level at which they make a claim to universal metaphysical validity—have the importance, no less, but no more, of *Timon* in Shakespeare's total production. Both in the individual mind, and in the moods of society, there is, providentially, a kind of self-balancing mechanism. After wars, plagues, famines, revolutions, tyrannies, human interest always, with its blessed short-sightedness, its permanent appetite for the ordinary, reverts to what President Harding called "normalcy". "Time, and the hour, runs through the roughest day." "Let the dead bury their dead." These two quotations, from Shakespeare and the Gospels, express a kind of tenacity and an impulse to move onwards that keep man going on this troubled earth. We shall find this spirit, not merely the spirit of fear and disgust and heart-corroding anxiety, expressed, if we look for it properly, in the greatest modern literature.

What modern literature expresses *is*, of course, the predicament of the human spirit in a world so perplexed by anxieties—though so full also of resources—as we know ours to be; but what it also, and even more fundamentally, expresses is that human spirit's own resiliency, its refusal to surrender finally either to outward pressure or inward tension, its power of self-renewal, its power of transcending its circumstances. Yeats—and Mr. Carne-Ross is right to claim that he carries on the heroic tradition, with a more direct dignity than any other modern writer—expresses this idea in two famous stanzas:

> An intellectual hatred is the worst,
> So let her think opinions are accursed.
> Have I not seen the loveliest woman born
> Out of the myth of Plenty's horn,
> Because of her opinionated mind
> Barter that horn and every good
> By quiet natures understood
> For an old bellows full of angry wind?

> Considering that, all hatred driven hence,
> The soul recovers radical innocence
> And learns that it is self-delighting,
> Self-appeasing, self-affrighting,
> And that its own sweet will is Heaven's will;
> She can, though every face should scowl
> And every windy quarter howl
> Or bellows burst, be happy still.

Even in *The Waste Land* and *Ulysses*, which Mr. Carne-Ross takes as fundamental for his argument, and which he sees also as fundamentally negative in their realized values, it seems to me that the great moments, the moments which suddenly allow us to make rewarding sense of a huge distressing complexity, are those in which the human spirit does after all transcend its limitations, realizing that these limitations are, in so far at least as they are self-destructive, self-imposed.

Thus, what the thunder said in *The Waste Land*, "Give, sympathize, control", is in one sense a sudden frightening revelation from heaven; but in another sense it is early man reading into the imagined voices of his unreal gods in the sky the deepest lessons of his own moral experience, hearing in the thunder the voice of his conscience or, if you like, the voice of the real God. One can read the poem as a Christian or as an agnostic, getting this idea, but my point is that one does not really have to read it as an actual superstitious early pagan. A "miracle" of a sort *is*, of course, needed at this moment for the poem's purposes, but a crucial symbolic experience (superficially misinterpreted but at a deeper level interpreted correctly) is also, for the poem's purposes, miracle enough. Thus a mentally sick person, for instance, often interprets accidental occurrences as signs or omens; he sees communicative intention everywhere; but the right kind of sign, occurring at the right moment, and propitiously interpreted, may set him on the road to recovery. And if he has any sense of reverence for life, he probably does look back afterwards on this fortunate misinterpretation as a kind of miracle, and not *fundamentally* a misinterpretation at all. In *Ulysses*, on the other hand, the moment that has a similar effect on me is when Stephen, walking home with Bloom, has his creed expressed for him by his creator: the belief in art as the eternal voice of the spirit of man. The weak, silly and vicious young Stephen regains in a moment—after being a kind of butt throughout so much of the book, the victim of Joyce's humorous contempt, or bitter shame, for his younger self—the dignity which he had in *A Portrait of the Artist as a Young Man*. It is a moment of re-dedication. The thunder also calls for re-dedication in *The Waste Land*, and not vainly, in spite of Eliot's harsh insistence on our weakness or failure in acting ever steadily and consistently on our sudden insights into what we should be. Throughout the whole course of modern literature, however sadly it may be concerned with drift and loss, such moments expressing the re-dedication that comes with sudden insight are the great moments.

VI. Sincerity and the Problematic

One general characteristic of modern literature I have not yet

touched on, and yet it is centrally important; I shall touch on it
now, and then sweep this drifting survey out to sea. It is a characteristic that I can evoke but not describe or define. It comes out in the
famous anecdote about the death of Gertrude Stein. Clutching
the sheets, staring up at the ceiling, she asked suddenly, "But then
what is the answer?" She lay silent for a moment, but there was no
answer. "But then," she asked, "what is the question?" Then she
died. The mood of that story is that of much modern philosophy,
the mood for instance of Ludwig Wittgenstein's posthumously
published *Philosophical Investigations*, the mood of the paragraph in
which he asks himself what could it mean—or fundamentally, could
it mean anything?—to say that a man "believed he was pretending". Whatever psychological or logical problem, whatever nicety
about the possible or impossible verification of statements about
other people (when we cannot be both outside, observing them,
and inside, knowing what it is like to be them) may have been in
Wittgenstein's mind; to say that a man "believes he is pretending"
and may as probably be wrong as right in this belief, has a meaning
in the language—which no philosopher has yet investigated, which
perhaps few philosophers have enough localized sensibility to
language to investigate profitably—of the literary critic.

Gide is, perhaps, the most typical modern example of a great
writer who spent his whole life asking whether in his attitudes towards God, towards conduct, towards politics, towards literary taste,
he did or did not believe he was pretending. He struck experimentally one attitude after another, and then asked himself whether,
after all, they were mere attitudes, or whether he had discovered
his real self. His pursuit of sincerity was so conscious, subtle and
public that, as he slipped in turn through the nets of the Roman
Catholic Church and the Communist Party, there were those who
said that all his life he had been posing in front of a mirror, making
notes; there were others again to whom it seemed that his pursuit
of sincerity was an excuse merely for a discreetly defiant indulgence
in vice; that he would have turned from the truth, even knowing it
in his heart to *be* the truth, if the truth had forbidden him to "be
himself". It must be said for Gide that he would have been ready
at any time to discuss, with lucidity and candour, such arguments.

He is an unfashionable writer in France today, but Sartre, in his
cruder way, makes similar points. I am what I am, but not as a
stone or a tree is; I am what I choose to be, but since I know that I
can revoke or reverse my choice at any time, since I am conscious of
myself always as playing a chosen part, must my choice not always
have about it an air of pose, of the arbitary? For Sartre, in fact, the
notion of total sincerity is finally logically incompatible with the
intrinsic nature of conscious existence. We must all play parts, we
must all observe the parts we are playing, and we are all uneasily

aware that it is possible to play a part—on the lines of Diderot's paradox of the actor—effectively but mechanically, knowing from sharp observation and long practice what we ought to say and do, but not in any sense putting our inner spirit into it. We need not, in a word, identify ourselves with ourselves, and perhaps fundamentally we cannot. Thus a great writer may, even at his finest moments "believe that he is pretending". Is it his readers who decide finally that, in such a belief, he must have been mistaken? Or can nobody at all, in this world, make any such final decision?

This deep fundamental uncertainty, this need for certainty, this lucid conviction that it is impossible quite finally to attain to certainty, this haunting suspicion that at some moment of our lives we may have grasped certainty and let it go, underlies the mood of very much of the best modern writing. It gives the writing of a man like Gide a peculiarly disturbing quality but also a peculiar suppleness and freedom. If we are to look at all in modern literature for philosophical truth, we shall not find that truth under the aspect of any method or system but rather under the aspect of this urgent inner need for sincerity and this instinctive grasp of the problematic, or mysterious, quality of life. It is possible, however, to face the problematic quality of life with gaiety and courage, as Mr. William Empson does in these fine lines of his, in praise of writers and thinkers who accept a plausible, unproved hypothesis, and see how it works out:

> Assume what answers any wits have found
> In evening-dress on rafts upon the main,
> Not therefore uneventful or soon drowned.

That modern literature, in spite of its difficulty and complexity, in spite of its frequent gloom, *is* worth investigating, has value for all of us in helping us to probe and test life, I should like my readers to accept as a plausible, unproved hypothesis.

BOOKS SUGGESTED FOR FURTHER READING

R. P. Blackmur, *Language as Gesture* (Allen and Unwin, 1954).

T. S. Eliot, *Selected Essays* (Faber, 1951).

William Empson, *Seven Types of Ambiguity* (Chatto and Windus, 1947).

Wyndham Lewis, *Time and Western Man* (Chatto and Windus, 1927).

I. A. Richards, *The Principles of Literary Criticism* (Kegan Paul, 1925).

MUSIC

by WILFRID MELLERS

I.

THE WORLD IS growing old, and we live under a burden of accumulated knowledge. Calling ourselves a scientific age, we are proud to pursue knowledge as an end in itself: as though knowledge could ever have a meaning, or indeed an existence, except in the context of human life. Knowledge is to be used; and civilization depends on our ability to use it.

No one, surveying the field of twentieth-century music, could doubt that a large number of composers appear today to have command of many and varied techniques. It is, however, much more difficult to decide to what end or ends this knowledge is being put; to discover any unifying purpose behind apparent chaos. Of course it is possible that we exaggerate the heterogeneous nature of contemporary styles. Already we have learned to recognize a pattern in the superficially erratic development of a Stravinsky; and an observer a hundred years hence may discover points of accord between composers who seem to us as extravagantly dissimilar as Stravinsky and Vaughan Williams. None the less it remains true that there is today no socially sanctioned musical idiom of the kind that was available to the composer in the sixteenth or eighteenth century. In Shakespeare's time, in England, the young composer was taught to write like Byrd, who in turn based his style on the European convention which we associate with Palestrina; in Handel's day the young composer was taught to write like Handel. There was no other way: for both Palestrinian and Handelian style were a deduction in musical terms from a coherent view of human life. Conformity to an established idiom meant the acceptance of inherited ideas about man's place in the universe and the relation of man to man. Personal feeling could flower when rooted in such acceptance, but though Bach tells us through his music what he personally thinks and feels about man and God, that is not his primary intention. His music is not a conscious expression of self, but at once a religious and social act. He has said that he composed for the glory of God and the *instruction* of his neighbour.

Some of the more obvious stylizations in musical history—

Handel's noble harmonic perorations spring readily to mind—now seem to imply so sublime a spiritual complacency that they can seem, if only momentarily, comic. Yet the complacency is the music's strength; the unequivocal *belief* in the stylization places it ultimately beyond the reach of parody. Today there is no such clearly defined relation between musical techniques and the values and beliefs in the light of which people live. This does not mean that no such relation exists: only that it is confused rather than clear, for the obvious reason that our values are themselves confused. We doubt whether there can be "the" right musical technique because we doubt whether there can be "the" right conception of moral order. When in the middle years of the eighteenth century Rameau deduced his theory of harmony from the practice of his contemporaries he was convinced that he had given a scientifically unanswerable account of the laws which governed musical composition. He was equally convinced that music composed according to his prescription would culminate in the perfection of his art: for the perfectibility of Music must complement that of Man. As a matter of scientific fact he was wrong on both counts. But what he said was true while it lasted, in so far as it was deduced from man's creative instincts and imaginative needs. His truth was the kind that matters to artists because it was at once a technique and a morality. For artists it is a hindrance, not a help, to know more but believe less.

Since the twentieth-century composer has no socially sanctioned norm to which he may appeal, he has not only to learn a technique; he has also to decide which techniques among many alternatives will be appropriate to his needs. He may even spend many years learning the wrong techniques. Neither Dufay, nor Palestrina, nor Handel had any doubts as to the kind of music he wished to write; he was concerned only to write it as well as he could. Even the composers of the epoch of the classical sonata, who were all revolutionaries in the sense that they reacted against certain elements in the world in which they lived, still worked within a stable tradition. Mozart's reaction was more conscious than Haydn's (he walked out on his patron); and Beethoven's was more conscious than Mozart's. Yet Beethoven no less than his predecessors believed in society. At least until the last years of his life he thought that change was necessary and, through the regenerating power of his music, feasible. He was egoist enough to believe that his music made the future worth living for; but he did not re-create in the interests of a personal spiritual aggrandizement. He laboured for enlightenment, and a civilization reborn. He destroyed in the interest of order.

Perhaps Schubert is the first composer to be aware of a dilemma which we are apt to consider typical of our time. Living in a decaying Viennese civilization he was acutely aware, even to the point of revolutionary fervour, of hostility between himself and the community in which he worked. Yet as a free-lance musician he had, in order to keep himself alive, to produce quantities of entertainment music for a degenerate aristocracy and a comfortable sentimental bourgeoisie whose standards and tastes he could no longer fully share. Beethoven came to despise his public, but apart from an occasional sport like *The Battle of Vittoria* he never wrote down to it; he was able proudly to follow his destiny. Schubert was not. He was forced to write little salon pieces when he would have preferred to write sonatas, and the fact that he learned to make something personal and significant out of these salon pieces is irrelevant to the main issue.

Although both Beethoven and Schubert were conscious of political oppression in Austria, Schubert's attitude differed from Beethoven's in that he did not think it was possible, or perhaps even desirable, to do anything about it. Greatly as he revered Beethoven, he deplored what he called Beethoven's "eccentricity, which drives a man to distraction, instead of resolving him in love". Distraction, or madness, was not the only possible resolution of Beethoven's vehement protest, as he himself proved. Yet it might have seemed such to men cast on a less heroic mould; and so Schubert's own music seems to be created simultaneously out of conflict with the world as it was (the Beethovenian aspect of his work), and a utopian yearning for Viennese civilization as it had once been or as he nostalgically imagined it (the early Mozartian, lyrical and vocal aspect of his work). From one point of view, like Beethoven, he heroically protests; from another he seeks in his music to resolve his frustration in love, to create an Eden in which a perfect simplicity of being is not corrupted by people's wickedness and stupidity. "Often I feel I do not belong to this world at all", he once said. In this aspect of his work he is his own Wanderer and pilgrim; communing with solitude he discovers a world of the imagination which can soothe and satisfy as real life cannot.

This dualism between innocence and experience becomes especially evident in Schubert's last creations, and most of all in the strange, prophetic G major Quartet, opus 161. The slow movement, like so many of Schubert's andantes, is in modified rondo form; a sweetly lyrical melody, with nostalgically yearning rising sixths, is repeatedly interrupted by a feverish agitato section. This both disrupts the flow of melody and figuration with its feverish tremolandos, and splinters the music's tonal stability with its weird enharmonic modulations. An obsessively reiterated figure tries frantically to preserve a tonal centre against these destructive forces; in the coda the terrifying Reality is resolved in a major apotheosis of the Dream. The innocence attained, if attained it is, is retrospective, and therefore melancholy. In music such as this one might almost say that Schubert has become a "modern" composer: not merely because the technique is advanced but because the experience which the technique serves evokes the terrors of moral isolation rather than the solidarities of belief. Bach, we saw, wrote for the glory of God and the instruction of his neighbour. Haydn composed to celebrate a God whose ideal was humanitarian and to entertain a society which believed in those ideals. Beethoven wrote as a means to a better world. But Schubert wrote for himself and for the sake of friendship. The core of his work is the intimate solo song; and his partiality for the piano duet is not fortuitous. One of his last works was a piano duet dedicated to friendship, in which the two players link arms and sing to each other sweetly or sadly, while the world goes by.

It is not surprising that Schubert's last works, and in particular the very unliturgical church music, should be full of anticipations of Wagner; for the substitution of the dream for reality becomes epitomized in the career of Wagner, who called himself "an outlaw for life". His early interest in revolutionary movements differs even more significantly than Schubert's from that of Beethoven. Revolution, both political and musical, was for Beethoven a means to a new world. Wagner was interested in it in a purely negative sense, in so far as the corruptions of society hampered the free expression of his desires and the fulfilment of his artistic ambitions. Beethoven wrote music for revolution; Wagner wanted revolution for the sake of music. He arraigned contemporary society, using the Jews as a scapegoat; but he extolled the German Folk not for themselves but as a kind of allegorical presentation of Richard Wagner the Aryan Hero. "A nation of high-souled dreamers and deep-brained thinkers", he called them. That is exactly how he would have described himself.

Early in Wagner's career we can find in *Lohengrin* the theme of the solitary hero in an alien world. His treatment of the Siegfried story is a vastly expanded version of the same theme. When Wagner said, "We two, the world and I, are stubborn fellows at loggerheads, and naturally whichever has the thinner skull will get it broken", he was the heir to Beethoven. But his later egoism passes far beyond Beethoven's assertiveness. "I'm not made like other people", he said, "I have finer nerves. I must have beauty, and brilliance, and light. The world owes me what I need. . . . Mine is a highly susceptible, intense and voracious sensuality which must somehow or other be flattered if my mind is to accomplish the agonizing labour of calling a non-existent world into being." To do this—to realize his dream—became for him the main purpose of living; and he sincerely believed that the function of society was to make that realization possible. He was to create a new art; and art was to be the future's religion. The one-time revolutionary ended by stating that he believed art to be a dream-image, lifting us above sordid actualities; and that his dream was more real than the waking life. It is Wagner's stupendous achievement that he brought it off. The myth became fact, even if through the agency of a young, mad king.

We can see this clearly enough in the development of Wagner's technique. In his early days he regarded himself as Beethoven's successor. Not only in his first abortive symphonic experiments but also in his early operas Wagner remains a revolutionary composer exploiting the conflict theme; in *The Flying Dutchman* Senta's arpeggio motive is treated in a manner comparable with Beethoven's treatment of similar themes in the development section of a symphony. But by the time of *Tristan* Wagner's style has undergone a radical transformation. The clear sharp rhythms of Haydn and the explosive metres of Beethoven have disappeared; instead we have a continuous surge of sound. Moreover, whereas the orchestration of the classical age had aimed at the clearest definition of the main melody, in Wagner's orchestration melodic definition is submerged in the rich flood of harmony; Wagner exploits, still more than Beethoven, the *physical* impact of sound on the listener's nerves. Moreover, this continuous surge of sound negates the structural principles—the exposition, development and recapitulation—which had characterized the classical sonata up to Beethoven's last works, and begins to negate also the key system on which that form depended. Expressive thematic fragments take the place of developed melodies, and the logic of the music tends to become equated with the succession of different harmonic tensions, corresponding to different degrees of nervous sensation. The effect of this on the eighteenth-century key system is the same as that of the violent chromatic madrigal of the early seventeenth century on vocal modality. In Gesualdo's "Moro Lasso" or Weelkes's "Cease Sorrows Now" the emotive effect of dissonance splinters both the extended vocal line and the fugal structure of the Palestrinian motet. The effect becomes operatic; indeed it is frequently called Tristanesque. Chromaticism corresponds to the end of a world. After the disintegration of Gesualdo's madrigal comes the new tonal order of the classical age. That in its turn disintegrates in Wagner's chromaticism, and we still do not know what is to take its place.

From this point of view the leitmotive technique—Wagner's association of particular places or characters or ideas with specific musical figures—is especially interesting. The leitmotives are not themes that are developed either in fugue style or in sonata style. They are brief fragments of melody which may be used to give a psychological coherence to the ebb and flow of emotion, represented by the ebb and flow of the harmony. This coherence may of course be musical as well as psychological, and in Wagner's case usually is. But Wagner has established a dangerous precedent in that composers who have not his genius and his imaginative range can easily use the leitmotive as a substitute for a coherence that is lacking in the music. The music may consist of isolated moments of sensation, while the mechanical recurrence of the motives gives a spurious illusion that the moments are interrelated.

Now, the opening pages of *Tristan* have been analysed in innumerable ways according to orthodox harmonic principles, and the variety is itself evidence of the music's disintegration of traditional techniques. But what anyone can agree on is that the music's overwhelming emotional intensity derives from the fact that Wagner concentrates on the tense or dissonant harmony at the expense of its resolution; it is always the dissonant chord which falls on the strong beat. Moreover, the effect of the passage as a whole depends on the way in which the brief yearning phrase, underlined by its dissonance, is repeated several times at progressively rising intervals. This mounting excitement leads one to expect a big climax when the discord will finally be resolved on to the tonic; instead we get an unexpected chord (the submediant). This building up of tension, followed by only a partial resolution, is used repeatedly by Wagner, and just such a combination of passionate yearning with frustration is the essential theme of Wagner's adaptation of the Tristan story. Between this and Wagner's own psychological make-up there is a more than usually direct connexion. Indeed Wagner's Tristan story is a direct dramatization of the relationship existing between himself and Otto and Mathilde Wesendonck. He is at once Mark and Tristan, enjoying his renunciation as much as his erotic passion. Such is the intensity of his feelings that only death can complement this violent love. His yearning passion dissolves in the desire for oblivion.

In effect Wagner is saying: "My feelings *are* life; there is nothing except them and death." This is the ultimate apotheosis of humanism: and also a profound revelation of its inherent fallacy. Wagner has created a myth and a world out of his own passions. Music and the opera are now not so much an expression of the values and beliefs of a civilization as a projection of the individual's ego. The deification of the ego could hardly go further than the Wagner cult at Bayreuth, where a temple is built for the performances of the Master's creations—instead of the music being composed to fulfil the needs of the temple. Wagner thus effects a curious inversion of the ritualistic or religious attitude to music. In sixteenth-century motet style the personal element, the expressive harmony, grows out of the flowering of religious polyphony. Wagner, in *Tristan* and in parts of *Parsifal*, starts from the passionate tensions of harmony and then "spreads out" the chords into a series of linear motives which he called a new polyphony. The "religion" which he celebrates is a fanatical belief not in God, nor in civilization, but in Richard

Wagner. He himself said that Bayreuth was the fulfilment of the destiny he had planned for himself—and Humanity!

Self-deification on so heroic a scale is certainly one of the supreme achievements of the human mind; but Wagner forgot that his religion of art, which was a religion of self, implied the existence of a race of heroes. The logical development of Wagnerian chromaticism is in the mature work of Delius, who was obsessed by Wagner's last work as Wagner had been obsessed by Beethoven. Loathing industrial England, and eventually disliking all music except his own, Delius was one of the supreme egoists of European history. He was a completely a-social personality, for whom music meant the flow of sensation through the creator. In a piece such as "In a Summer Garden", the fluctuating tensions and relaxations of the harmony, reinforced by the lustrous orchestral colours, correspond to the flow of sensation through the composer as he sits in his garden at Grez. While it is not true to say that no norm of consonance and dissonance exists in Delius's music, one can say that the norm is no longer the arbitrary one of classical convention. It is personal to the composer rather than the property of a tradition.

Thus the problem of Delius's harmony is inseparable from his personal interpretation of form. For him, music was "simply emotion", and the process of writing it was instinctive and intuitive. Of course he could have held this only because he worked with the long and rich tradition of German Romanticism behind him, so that he did not need to think about first principles. He could say that "Learning kills instinct", and strive, even more than Wagner in his last works, towards a conception in which the graded tensions of the harmony are themselves the form, the texture being continuous, the logic of the music provided by the sincerity and power of the surge of emotion behind it. In one particular, however, Delius goes beyond Wagner. In *Tristan* Wagner reduces God, civilization and society to projections of his ego; other people and things exist only as the object of his loves and hatreds. But loving and hating at least imply the existence of people to be loved and hated; whereas in Delius's most typical music there is no human population at all, only himself and solitude. There is a significant technical development from this. Although the woof of chromatic harmony—the flux of sensation—is the essence of the music, all the component lines in the mature works *sing* and are, individually, vocal in contour: consider the wordless chorus in *Song of the High Hills*. Still more in the works involving a solo voice or instrument along with orchestra and chorus, the rhapsodic solo melody tends to be pentatonic, like folk-song or medieval monody, as though it were seeking a oneness beyond the sensory flux. Again the dominance of the personality leads to the desire to lose the self in the contemplation of nature or the supposedly simpler satisfactions of a lost youth; for the passion is too strong to be borne. Hatred of orthodox religiosity leads to a metaphysical or pantheistic view of human experience. The theme of *A Village Romeo and Juliet* is that life renders impossible the only things that give life meaning.

Although the logic of Delius's harmonic progressions is becoming increasingly a matter of personal feeling rather than of traditional sanction, the idea of progression is still relevant to his music. From this point of view he is the end of the nineteenth-century Germanic tradition and intelligible in relation to that tradition. It is in some of the music of Debussy that we find a still more radical exploration of the moment of sensation, in that he tends, especially in his middle-period works, to isolate chords from the sense of time.

For Debussy a chord almost became an emotional experience in itself. As Wagner and Delius translated their feelings as directly as possible into sound, so Debussy tried to transform into music the reactions of his nervous system to the noises, smells and colours of nature. We observe a similar paradox to that which we noticed in Delius: the absolute reliance on personal sensation leads, not to domination over things, but to subservience to them. A chord became for Debussy a complex of aural vibrations which are also nervous sensation, ranging from the absolute calm of the unison and the octave and the relative tranquillity of the fifth and fourth, to the acute tensions of the higher chromatic relations of the harmonic series. One can say, if one likes, that in such a passage as the opening of *Nuages* Debussy is reviving the technique of medieval organum. But his attitude to his material is completely different from that of the medieval composer. To Debussy the passage is not a linear structure but a complex of sounds, an aural phenomenon: "the effect of fifths and fourths", he seems to be saying, "is very calm". The medieval composer also wanted his organum to sound calm, in so far as it was an act of praise which was free from personal accident or distress. But he did not think of it in terms of his own nervous system. He used this technique because it was an accepted convention, and it was an accepted convention because it was a natural way to write for voices. The nerves remain calm and relaxed during this passage in which Debussy employs parallel fifths and fourths, whereas they are subtly disturbed in the frequent passages in which he employs parallel ninths and elevenths. But the method is identical in both cases; the chords reflect isolated moments of experience, sensation in and for itself.

By far the most extreme instances of Debussy's tendency of isolating chords from the development of line and structure occur in those places which are sometimes described as being in the whole-tone scale, though it would be more accurate to refer to them as experiments in the use of augmented fifths suggested by the whole-tone scale. No chord is more completely devoid of tonal implications. *Voiles* presents the chord in varied "registrations" and sometimes in the form of melodic figurations, but the piece depends entirely on the composer's exploitation of the impression made by the chord on the listener's aural and nervous system. The music is static, has no growth and, in the conventional sense of the term, no structure. As nearly as is possible, the time sense is annihilated.

Of course pieces such as this are not what gives Debussy his position as one of the great figures in musical history; and in later years he explicitly repudiated the aesthetic of personal sensation. None the less, the concentration on the isolated moment which we find in these pieces is of enormous historical significance. For each Debussy who is able to create a new world out of moments of sensation there are twenty who are content to become a kind of aural seismograph. One could not wish for a more complete example of the triumph of a personal aesthetic and the collapse of traditional ideas of order. One remembers Debussy's reply to the outraged professor who asked him what "rules" he followed: "*Mon plaisir.*"

Logically the seismographic conception of music would imply the complete rejection of metre and tonality; indeed logically it would imply the rejection of all convention and therefore the denial of art—music would return to the condition of noise. It is not therefore surprising that not only Debussy's own development, but the subsequent history of modern music, can be construed as a series of attempts to escape or evade subjugation to the isolated moment. The career of Schoenberg illustrates this more clearly than that of any other composer, if only because he starts from the most complete acceptance of chromatic disintegration.

II.

Schoenberg was born into a specific cultural tradition. Among his early works the *Gurrelieder* were an opulent, gargantuan inflation of the world of the Viennese symphony; *Verklärte Nacht* was *Tristan* in a still riper stage of deliquescence. Quite early in his career he came to the conclusion that Wagner's last works, let alone his own first works, already implied the demise of eighteenth-century tonality and the classical conception of order. During the nineteenth century, he argued, the boundaries of tonality had been so much expanded by the addition of passing-notes and non-essential notes that it was possible to introduce into any given key any note foreign to that key. If a key can be expressed by other notes as well as by those proper to its scale, can it be said to exist? To talk of any note as being "foreign" to the harmony is nonsensical; because harmony is simply a sounding together of tones. In Wagner's last works and still more in Debussy's mature music orthodox notions of passing-notes and subsidiary harmonies have become obsolete. The time has come to accept equal-tempered chromaticism unequivocally; to admit that each of the twelve chromatic semitones is of equal significance, and therefore to admit the absolute liberty of chords.

In his first "free" atonal works Schoenberg attempted to carry through the implications of this case, and to create a completely chromatic music which had no reference to tonal concepts based on the triad and the cycle of fifths. He was doing consciously what Debussy intuitively arrived at in some of his middle-period piano pieces; and he too came to see that if all notes are equally organic and no one chord has greater tonal significance than another, there will be a natural tendency for the music to be apprehensible only as fragments of sensation. Schoenberg's "seismographic" music, notably the little piano pieces, opus 19, achieves a remarkable nervous concentration, but is by its very nature incapable of development. Debussy had evaded this dilemma by a compromise with tradition and tonality. For Schoenberg compromise was inadmissable. For him there were two possible ways out. One was to make music the handmaid of drama, in which coherence and development were provided by the literary and scenic elements; this was only a stop-gap since it left unsolved the problem of musical form. The other was what has come to be known as the twelve-note technique.

The twelve-note method is perhaps the only occasion in musical history on which a technique of composition has been deliberately worked out in theory, rather than deduced from the practice of composers. Yet in a sense it was the result of practical exigencies in so far as it, or something like it, was necessary if Schoenberg was to continue composing without relinquishing the premises on which his work had been based. By the end of the First World War three points must have seemed to Schoenberg reasonably obvious: (1) that "free" atonalism is an impractical abstraction, since some principle of coherence is essential if music is to advance beyond the seismographic stage; (2) that since the last years of the nineteenth century had seen the breakdown of the classical, harmonic methods achieving order through tonality and metre, any new form of organization, to begin with, at least, would have to be linear rather than harmonic; (3) that this linear organization would have to be chromatic rather than diatonic or modal, since Wagner and the piano had committed us to equal-tempered chromaticism, and the diatonic and modal systems were played out.

Now the technique of the "row" is in itself no new thing. Several examples can be found in late medieval polyphony in which whole movements are completely thematic, all the parts being derived from a single sequence of notes, usually a plain-song melody; and Schoenberg himself quotes examples from the late work of Beethoven. The essence of the twelve-note technique is that the composer uses this method of organizing and unifying a composition by deriving every element from a given sequence of notes; only in his case the rows are based not on a pentatonic, modal or diatonic formula but on a chromatic one. In twelve-note music each movement is derived from a specific arrangement of the twelve semitones of the chromatic scale. This arrangement is not itself a scale, though it fulfils some of the functions of a scale in so far as it dominates every aspect of the composition. The initial arrangement of the semi-tones is the prime row. The composer may also use this row with the intervals inverted; he may use it backwards; or backwards and inverted. These are the secondary rows; and they and the prime row may be used in any rhythm, and transposed to any chromatic semitone, at any pitch. Successive members of the row, in any ver-sion, may be combined together to form chords. Segments of the rows can be adapted to form accompanying figures. As a general principle octave doublings and repetitions of notes out of their established order in the series are prohibited. This is designed to prevent concentration on one note at the expense of the others, since such concentration might suggest tonal implications. Notes may be repeated in the established serial order, and the ear will be conscious of repetitions outside it, since each part of the composition will not normally be simultaneously at the same point in the series.

The row is not a theme. Indeed, since it occurs either forwards or backwards or upside down, or in any rhythmic combination and subdivided between many parts, it is seldom intelligible to the ear as a melody. It is simply a linear means of achieving integration between every note of a composition, and is thus of interest to the composer, not the listener. Two crucial questions suggest themselves. (1) According to what principles does the composer select his original row? Why does he choose this arrangement of notes rather than another? (2) Can one properly speak of "horizontal" order without reference to "vertical" order? In other words, must not the row establish some tonal function different from, but comparable with, that of the diatonic and modal scales?

Schoenberg's answers to these questions would seem to be interlinked. The composer chooses his row for its potentialities, just as Bach devised the subject of *The Art of the Fugue* more for what he could do with it than for its intrinsic beauty. At present the row the composer selects will tend to be divorced from harmonic implications because in attempting to write a purely chromatic music it is necessary to purge the mind of all trace of diatonicism. A purely chromatic linear music will, however, eventually begin to evolve its own principles of tonal order. It will then be possible to reintroduce consonances, though they will bear a different sig-nificance from that which they had in diatonic music. This process seems to have started in late works of Schoenberg such as the *Ode to Napoleon* and the opera *Moses and Aaron*. It certainly seems legitimate to suggest that the history of twelve-note music since its inception has centred in a search for a common denominator between horizontal and vertical organization—the establishment of relative, if unorthodox, norms of consonance and dissonance.

Precisely where one puts the stress in considering this partial rapprochement with tonality is of some importance. For the more the twelve-note composer comes to terms with traditional tonality the less need would there seem to be for any purely linear method of ordering the semitone. Schoenberg would no doubt say that any apparently traditional harmonies which may be introduced must be crystallized out of the linear structure itself, just as diatonic harmony gradually evolved out of fourteenth-century polyphony, in which vertical considerations were of minor importance. The parallel is perhaps fallacious. For although the vertical aspect was not paramount in fourteenth-century polyphony, the contour of each individual line was founded on a theory of consonance. It is true that all musical techniques are artificial, artifacts that are man-made. It is true that if a twelve-note composer works within preconceived patterns so does a pentatonic or modal or diatonic composer. But it is indisputable that the pentatonic is related to simpler, more fundamental acoustical facts than the chromatic; and that there is a difference between Mozart's equal-tempered scale and Schoenberg's. The logic of classical tonality depends on the admission that some intervals are more important than others; and the intervals which are accorded this centrality are those which, owing to their primacy in the harmonic series, can most easily be sung "by ear". Mental vocalization is still the means whereby melodies become memorable; and not all our familiarity with equal-tempered scales can alter the fact that a purely chromatic music is difficult to memorize because it is difficult to sing.

This is why Berg, the twelve-note adherent who has made the most radical compromise with traditional tonality, is the only one who has achieved a sizeable audience, and why he has been accepted, rightly or wrongly, as the most potent creative spirit of the group. It may well be wrongly. Certainly Schoenberg's answer to the problem involved in mental vocalization is not that the evolution of music must wait on the human ear, but that the human ear must catch up with the evolution of music; and he has some evidence on his side if it is true that, as he claims, singers find his music less difficult to sing when they have acquired a deep consciousness of the basic row. It is certainly true that the impact of Schoenberg's music has not decreased with the passage of time; and that a work such as *Moses and Aaron* can make a tremendous impression on an audience with no technical initiation and probably with a barrier of prejudice.

The fascination of the twelve-note method for composers is easy to understand. It is the only technique of composition which is today as internationally valid as was Palestrinian polyphony or Handelian homophony. Its theory is logical, if its first premises are accepted; and it is a European stylization which allows latitude for local and personal expression. It can be reconciled with such apparently remote styles as Lisztian virtuosity, as in some of the music of Humphrey Searle; or Italian vocal lyricism, as in the music of Dallapiccola, who significantly allows the row to acquire an easily apprehensible thematic significance. Partly for this reason, Dallapiccola's music is much easier to listen to than most of Schoenberg's, while it is in fact much more rigorously restricted by its method. The conventional objection to twelve-note technique—that it deprives the composer of his liberty of choice—is clearly irrelevant.

In so far as it is essentially monistic—since every note of a composition is to be derived from a single sequence—the twelve-note method is at the furthest extreme from the dualistic sonata principle of the eighteenth and nineteenth century, and has more in common with the religious techniques of the Middle Ages. Indeed it seems almost to have become an act of faith in itself; even the "truth" of the theory is perhaps unimportant, as was the truth of Rameau's. What matters is that the technique provides an answer to first questions, and liberates the spirit through the imposition of a Law. Perhaps "I believe in twelve equal-tempered semitones" seems a barren creed when compared with belief in the medieval God or the King-State of eighteenth-century autocracy. But we do not yet know what lies behind this faith in a technique. In a hundred years' time we may see it as the birth-pangs of some vast international belief such as might emerge from the mingling of western cultures with those of the east. It is interesting that, as a purely linear method of organizing musical sound, the twelve-note method has something in common with the techniques of eastern music.

III.

Schoenberg started from the aesthetic of momentary sensation, accepted the disintegration of the past, and created a new criterion of order from that acceptance. His logic is inescapable if one admits his postulates. Many contemporary composers, however, did not. For them, chromaticism may have been a disintegrative process, but it did not seem to them that the only course was to accept chromaticism uncompromisingly and to start afresh. On the contrary, they regarded chromaticism as an aberration from the main line of development in European music. The composer's task was thus to re-establish the modal and diatonic materials of tradition and to reinterpret them, profiting from the awareness of new resources which chromaticism had given. From this point of view the work of a minor composer, Erik Satie, is worthy of comment for its profoundly "documentary" significance.

What Satie seems to be saying in principle is: "Chromaticism has splintered tonality and form, and the fragments are lying around me. These fragments are musical synonyms for the disintegrated world in which I live. But life is impossible without order. If Society does not offer a criterion, there is no alternative but to create one oneself. One cannot build afresh, however, if one has not a clear notion of the materials in which one is to work. It was part of the disintegration which chromaticism represents that the traditional materials of European music grew flabby and amorphous. Thus what one has to do first of all is to see the traditional bricks—the pentatonic and diatonic formulae and triadic chord formations out of which European music has been built—as they essentially were, before the chromatic corruption. Then one must try to build these bricks into a fresh and significant order. The logic that connects the parts to the whole is bound to be a personal logic, since there is now nothing but one's own honesty to appeal to. For this reason the logic will be difficult to achieve and when it is achieved perhaps not easily intelligible." The difficulty of the task instinctively led Satie to restrict himself to works of tiny dimensions. If challenged he might have said that the difficulties of the twentieth-century composer were so considerable that it was best not to be pretentious. If one could honestly achieve this little bit of reintegration, one would have done well enough.

Satie's technique is in many ways comparable with that of the Cubist painters. Just as they wished to reintegrate with a personal logic the visual facets of a disrupted world, so Satie wished to reintegrate the basic materials of European music in a fresh vision. The brief melodic phrases and the harmonies which he employs are in themselves all simple and traditional; but they are reintegrated in the most disturbing and untraditional combinations. Satie, having the innocent eye and ear of childhood, is almost completely unsentimental. His music is never the egoistic expression of personality, but rather the losing of the self in the creation of form. In order to insist on cohesion and pattern, while using materials that are fragmentary, Satie preserves a uniformly regular metre; and metrical symmetry and pattern lead him to the objectivity of the ballet. *Parade*, which he created in 1916 in collaboration with Cocteau, Picasso and Picabia, was described as "the Cubist manifesto". It is the furthest swing of the pendulum from Wagnerian egomania. Cocteau said that in it he wished to create an art not out of things that move (people), but from the things around which one moves.

Satie is of interest to us mainly because the techniques which he explores in, as it were, a skeletonic form are also the core of the work of a composer no less great and influential than Schoenberg—namely, Igor Stravinsky. In his early work there is a good deal of chromatic disintegration of the established tonal order—for instance, in the tritones of King Kastchei's tune in *Firebird*, or in the elaborate linear chromaticism of *Le Rossignol*. But there is also an attempt, similar to Satie's, to reintegrate traditional materials in untraditional ways. The "horizontalization" of chords, producing two or more harmonic streams which proceed independently, is a typical method; so is the notorious bitonal passage on the triads of C and F sharp in *Petrouchka*. The effect of this passage is percussive, rather than a matter of tonal conflict. The bitonal clash is the substance of the ensuing cadenza, much as Satie will construct a piece out of the unexpected relationship of two simple chords or a melodic pattern.

In the next phase of Stravinsky's work—that represented by the primitive-nationalist works such as *Le Sacre du Printemps* and *Les Noces*—the patterns the composer imposes on his material are almost entirely metrical. He feels it necessary, in opposition to the chromatic flux, to insist at all costs on the validity of metre; for even the wildest metrical eccentricities are conceivable only in relation to a basic norm. Thus all the elements of music are adapted to reinforce rhythm. Line is reduced to a series of insistently repeated patterns whose effect is dynamic, harmony becomes a means of marking tensions percussively, instrumentation is exploited for its physical and nervous impact. The long passages of parallel thirds, fourths, fifths, sixths, sevenths, tritones and so on, often moving simultaneously a semitone apart, are not harmonic devices. They are thickened line, and since the line is deliberately without lyrical interest, the effect is purely rhythmic and incantatory. Intentionally, they are comparable more with the orgiastic effect of primitive music than with the music of civilized Europe. Thus although in one sense these works are a reaction against chromaticism—a regression to the collective Unconscious, as against the egocentric cult of personal sensibility—in another sense they are a part of the same disruptive process. As Debussy in some of his middle-period piano pieces, and Schoenberg in some "free" atonal pieces, reduced music to the vertical effect of simultaneously sounding notes, so Stravinsky reduces melody and harmony to rhythm. Without melody, rhythm is indistinguishable from metre. Harmony without melody and rhythm, rhythm without melody and harmony, are static. In *Le Sacre*, as in Debussy's *Voiles*, we have music deprived of the sense of motion from one point to another. At least development in *Le Sacre* is simply the incremental rise of excitement through repetition.

It is not therefore surprising—remarkably impressive a work though *Le Sacre* may be—that Stravinsky should have felt that the metrical organization of pattern could go no further. In his next works, such as the Wind Symphony and the Octet for wind, he turns to the organization of linear patterns. It is often said that in this period Stravinsky returns to the principles of Bachian counterpoint, but this would seem to be no more than partially true. For Bach, counterpoint was a compromise between the horizontal and the vertical discipline. The lines had to move within certain specified tonal progressions while retaining the maximum of individual freedom. In Stravinsky's counterpoint, on the other hand, the lines are usually diatonic and the tonal basis is periodically affirmed by the appearance of triadic harmonies. What happens in between the points of consonance has, however, little or no harmonic significance. Thus the principle Stravinsky follows is comparable with that of a late medieval composer such as Machaut, except that whereas Machaut's lines are vocally designed, Stravinsky's are usually instrumental in shape. Stravinsky's attempt to combine some of the principles of classical structure—especially seventeenth- and early eighteenth-century toccata, aria and variation—with the freedom of medieval polyphony would seem to be one of the most potentially fruitful lines of development for twentieth-century music. The recent *Mass* and *Cantata*, which are explicitly founded on fourteenth-century techniques, are thus an extension of processes which Stravinsky first explored in the early nineteen-twenties.

In that he favours the monistic principles of medieval and baroque music rather than the dualistic sonata Stravinsky is perhaps closer to Schoenberg than might superficially appear; it is interesting that in his most recent works, notably the Cantata and Septet, he has intermittently employed a serial method, though the rows are not chromatic. Stravinsky's preoccupation with texture is, however, more normally a part of his attempt to recover clarity of structure. The chromaticism of the late nineteenth century had led to a blurring, not merely of tonality and of melodic outline, but of the tone-colour of each instrument; the ideal aimed at was a blurring of the aural palate similar to the visual blurring of Impressionist painting. Just as Stravinsky wants to re-create the sense of melodic and rhythmic pattern, so he wishes to experience afresh the sound-stuff which is his basic material. In a work such as *L'Histoire du Soldat* he seems to be inviting us to listen to the noises instruments make. The composer's task, as he conceives it, is to integrate certain specified noises. Every aspect of the composer's art—tone-colour as much as melody and rhythm—is fundamentally a question of form, of the creation of a convention that can stand as an adequate "objective correlative". What the music expresses is what the form creates.

It is no accident that Stravinsky, like Satie, has always been associated with the ballet. The problem of formal integration and pattern-making which is expressed explicitly in the ballet music is implicit in his absolute instrumental music also. All through his career he is, in attempting to renew the materials of tradition, trying also to solve a problem of style: How is the composer, living in a chaotic society which offers him no criterion of order, to evolve a stylization which shall be at once appropriate to twentieth-century experience and at the same time integrated rather than chaotic? There are those who feel that his many borrowings from different periods of Europe's past are no answer, for a convention that meant this or the other to a society that knew precisely what it believed in cannot possibly mean the same to us. The objection is perhaps frivolous; for in the relatively self-conscious society in which we live, culture is bound to be largely a reinterpretation of our European heritage. Stravinsky borrows almost exclusively from composers whose attitude to their experience accords with his own—from medieval and baroque composers and, when he ventures into the nineteenth century, from music which, like the ballet dances of Tchaikowsky, is turned outward to the world, expressing itself in physical movement. His borrowings are consistent with his reinterpretation of traditional melodic and harmonic material, and were even implicit in his "nationalist" origins, since sophisticated as opposed to popular Russian culture has always been cosmopolitan. Certainly today, whether we like it or not, our culture is cosmopolitan when it is not parochial. Again, the twelve-note exponent would retort that he has found the only stylization which is adequate to our time in that it is not parochial, nor cosmopolitan, but international.

IV.

In Stravinsky's development folk-music was a liberating force. It widened the musical perspective, suggesting means whereby the conventions of European music could be broadened; in particular, primitive contortions of rhythm seemed to suggest some analogy with the violence of the contemporary world. But such primitivism could be no more than a transitional phase. The "civilized" composer must liberate himself from conventions that are moribund, only in order to establish wider, richer relationships with the whole of Europe's past. If he cannot avoid self-consciousness, then let him be conscious of himself as something greater than any individual. Twice deracinated, and now settled in a country of the future, which for a musician has virtually no past, Stravinsky has become almost the type of the modern artist who must shore such fragments as he can against our ruins.

For some composers, born into a society that remained predominantly agricultural, folk-music could have a more positive significance than it had for the exiled Stravinsky. When Bartók started composing he soon became aware, as had Stravinsky, that the effectiveness of "vertical" harmony seemed to be exhausted; the senses no longer thrilled to the successive superimposed thirds of the seventh, ninth, eleventh and thirteenth. Bartók's first works were dominated by Liszt, Strauss and Debussy. Some trace of Debussian sensuousness lasted until the final years; but by the time of the piano *Bagatelles* of 1908 the Germanic element had been completely routed. The force which effected the rout was Hungarian folk-song: not because Bartók collected songs and dances in an antiquarian spirit, but because the varied modes, the complex rhythms and in particular the eastern affiliations of Magyar songs suggested to him freer, more flexible types of melody than those of the classical European tradition. Unlike Stravinsky, Bartók is basically a lyrical composer; the length and strength of the melodies which Magyar song inspired in him preserved our sense of the importance of melody at a time when lyrical stamina seemed to be at a low ebb.

But the writing of free-rhythmed modal melodies cannot be separated from questions of harmony and of form. Pentatonic and seven-note modal scales, even the "irregular" modes of Asiatic origin, are for scientific reasons the most natural formulas for melodic speech and therefore for monodic and polyphonic music. Their melodic variety was sacrificed during the eighteenth century in favour of a tonal system which offered the maximum possibilities for harmonic tension and conflict. Between harmonic thought and, in the widest sense, modal thought, there is thus a natural antipathy; and it would seem an almost insoluble task to create a work which should on the one hand derive from a vocal, modal conception of melody and on the other have some analogy with the tonal principles of the classical traditions. Bartók's historical importance consists largely in the profound manner in which he has achieved this fusion.

In his first "nationalistic" works he employed dissonance in a purely percussive way, as did Stravinsky in his neo-primitive pieces. But in his middle period Bartók begins to use dissonance in a fashion that is comparable with the "melodic" dissonance of Bach, and even of Haydn and Mozart. In eighteenth-century classical music dissonance seldom has a specifically harmonic function as it does in Wagner or Strauss. The discordant passing-note rather serves to keep the melodic parts moving, to differentiate the melodic part from the accompanying chord, and to add emotional and rhythmic intensity. In the Second Violin Sonata—a key work in Bartók's career—the composer returns to this conception of dissonance, with the difference that the resolution of the dissonance is usually implicit rather than explicit. Every harmonic device is subservient to melodic line, and the purpose of dissonance, whether appearing vertically in chord structures or in passing-notes in the melody itself, is to give increased vitality to the line. The basic relation to classical tonality remains, even though Bartók experiments in melody which is not diatonic but polymodal.

This technique has interesting potentialities. For instance an unresolved passing dissonance on D sharp may accompany a C major triad; the result is a bitonal ambiguity between major and minor. Further, the unresolved passing-note suggests the unresolved passing-chord, and that in turn suggests the unresolved neighbouring tonality. Two different keys may be suggested by the presence of two fundamental fifths, yet though the effect is polytonal the relationship to a root is maintained: the two lower notes are unresolved appogiaturas which are taken as identical with the note to which they should resolve. Thus Bartók can introduce long passages in, say, G, during which the key of G flat is never relinquished. In the later quartets there are passages in which the four instruments enter in the space of successive half-beats a semitone apart. The effect is sharply dissonant; but the passage is not anarchic like true polytonality, because it remains rooted in a single tonality and triad. Bartók's later works broaden, without destroying, the boundaries of tonality.

Bartók's reconciliation of linear techniques with a tonal concept was developed in his practice over a number of years. The same is true of Hindemith; for although he has written a theoretical work which gives an account of tonality that can be applied to the music of any period, this theory has been deduced from his creative practice. Hindemith offers a theory of tonality, not a method of composition like the twelve-note technique. Since, however, this theory implies a criterion of order it must be numbered among the resources of the twentieth-century composer; some account of its nature, if not a summary of its closely reasoned argument, must be attempted.

Hindemith accepts the tempered chromatic scale as the basis on which any composer today must work; but he does not admit that equal-tempered chromaticism has broken down all criteria of consonance and dissonance. The acceptance of chromaticism merely means that chromatic elements will broaden the tonal horizon in ways analysable with reference to the facts of acoustics. Each chromatic semitone may become a tonal centre. Round it the other semitones may be grouped in certain functional relationships which are derived from the Harmonic Series in a manner too complicated to be described here. This sequence of the chromatic semitones Hindemith calls Series I. It is not a series in the same sense as Schoenberg's row, to be used as the basis of a composition. It is a functional mode, a means of grading the relation of any chromatic semitone to its position in the overtone series. The graph of the intervals ranges from the "strong" fifth to the ambiguous tritone.

But the semitones have relationships not only to a given tonic but also to one another. Whereas Hindemith's Series I gives the melodic value of intervals, his Series II shows their harmonic value. This series is derived in an elaborate way from the theory of combination tones, which may be used to find the root of any interval; since "if one of the tones of the directly produced interval is doubled, either in the unison or in the lower octave, by a combination tone, this accretion of strength gives it the upper hand over its partner". Hindemith's table of harmonic relationships is bounded at one side by the absolute consonance of the octave and at the other by the harmonically neutral tritone.

In all intervals of two notes one is predominant over the other. The dominating interval can be deduced from the theory of combination tones referred to above. In some intervals (thirds and fifths) it is the lower note, in others (fourths and sixths) it is the higher. The sequence of the root-notes of a series of intervals constitutes the Degree Progression. If the Degree Progression makes an interesting and tonally stable line when judged in accordance with the principles of Series I, the chances are that the progression of the intervals will sound convincing. The Degree Progression is not a substitute for invention; it offers a means of checking up on a harmonic progression that sounds dubious.

All intervals have a dual value, as parts of a melodic series related to a tonic, and as part of a scale of interval relationships. The two functions overlap. The "simple" intervals of Series II will tend to imply harmonic significance even when they occur not simultaneously but in succession in a melody. Such linear progressions—for instance a major followed by a minor third—create what Hindemith calls Harmonic Cells in a melodic line. When they are strongly marked through a passage of some length he calls them Harmonic Fields. The existence of Harmonic Fields in the melody complements the existence of Degree Progressions in the harmony. A convincing musical idiom depends on a satisfactory equilibrium between the two. The harmony must have a Degree Progression which shows a firm relation to a centre; the Harmonic Fields of the melody must not be so obtrusive as to overbalance the Degree Progression. Step Progression is the chief means of avoiding an excess of harmonic implications in the melody, since intervals of major and minor seconds—of which step progression is constituted—come at the "weak" end of the table of harmonic relationships. The conventional notions of passing-notes and auxiliary notes are absorbed into the conception of Step Progression. Two-part writing is the basis of composition, because an effective melody must achieve a balance between Step Progression and the Degree Progression of the whole structure.

So far we have considered only melody formations and interval relationships. But to chords composed of any number of notes the Degree Progression is still relevant. Whereas in an interval of two notes the dominant note is the root, in dealing with a complex chord formation one must first extract the "strongest" interval, according to Series II; the root of that becomes the root of the whole chord. The Degree Progression can then be applied to the series of chords, and a criterion established whereby the musical logic of the passage may be evaluated.

Several complex chords may, on this principle, have the same root. Hindemith has therefore evolved a subsidiary method of classifying them in two groups, according to whether or no the chord contains a tritone (the most harmonically ambiguous interval); these tables provide a comprehensive gradient of harmonic tensions. In accordance with his theory, Hindemith can take any sequence of chords, which are not analysable by the methods of any orthodox system, and can tell us both how they are effective or ineffective and why. He has thrown over the orthodox conception of key, while creating a theory of tonality that can be applied to the music of any period, as is shown by his analyses of Machaut, and even Schoenberg.

There are of course points in Hindemith's theory which are puzzling and obscure—notably his insistence that the value of chords is independent of their context; and as yet his treatment of the nature of melody is much more superficial than his treatment of tonal relationships. None the less his book is a landmark in the history of musical theory; it may well become a testament of our time in the same way as Rameau's book is a testament of his. Hindemith's theory is almost certainly "truer" than Rameau's; but again it is not its truth that makes it significant so much as the fact that it offers a criterion of order which is imaginatively as well as scientifically valid.

If tonality is a scientific fact—as Hindemith maintains—and not an artificial abstraction, then the postulates from which Schoenberg started are fallacious. No twelve-note theorist has attempted to answer Hindemith on his own ground; and in so far as Hindemith offers a theory of tonality and Schoenberg a method of composition perhaps no answer is called for. Hindemith tells us that we can extend and expand our diatonic processes of composition, and shows how we can judge whether what we have done is logical. Schoenberg offers a method which makes it unnecessary for us to consider first principles. "Composing with twelve notes" is no easier than any other way of composing, and may be more difficult. But it relieves us of the oppressive consciousness of dilemma. It is in this sense that it is a faith as much as a technique.

V.

During the course of his book[1] Hindemith remarks that scales arise in two ways: through the filling in of the octave with intervals

[1] *The Craft of Musical Composition* (Associated Music Publishers, 1937).

measured by the proportions of the overtone series; and through the arithmetical division of the octave. The first method is that through which the pentatonic, modal and diatonic formulae have grown up; and in his own theoretical work Hindemith has demonstrated that the chromatic scale may be derived and "evaluated" in the same way. The twelve-note technique accepts the tempered semitones which are now the traditional material of European music, but treats them as an arithemetical division of the octave. On this principle there is no reason why the octave should not be divided into any microtonal proportions. Many such private scale systems have been devised, of which the simplest is the quarter-note system associated with Alois Haba. None of these techniques has, however, as yet shown much staying-power. If ever one of them has a vital influence on musical history, it will not be simply as an intellectual construction. It will grow out of creative necessity. We have seen that the twelve-note technique is as much an evolutionary as a revolutionary process.

A more fruitful line of development is probably the influence on European composers of non-European techniques. We have suggested that twelve-note style might be a possible meeting-ground for eastern and western styles; so perhaps the experiments of a composer such as Messiaen may in the long run have more than an esoteric, hermetic and personal significance. Messiaen has created some fascinating noises out of the complex scales and polyrhythms of Indian music, the percussive sonorities of Balinese and Chinese music, and from stylizations of bird-song. The expansion of the resources of music through the "translation" of the sounds of nature into art is found not merely in such a controversial and marginal figure as Messiaen, but also in some of the work of the great European masters, Bartók and Janáček.

Experimental techniques are especially evident in the work of the Americans, partly because they have no very vital native tradition behind them. Primitive heterophony—the simultaneous performance of several (originally improvised) variations on a single line—was investigated by Charles Ives some fifty years ago; while in the aftermath of the First World War the Parisian-American Edgar Varèse explored the possibilities of a more flexible relation between noise and musical sound. In the decade after the Second World War there has been a significant revival of interest in the work of Ives and Varèse, and a new crop of comparably experimental composers, notably John Cage. The development of mechanical reproduction has suggested more complicated means of exploiting noise; both in the States and in Paris composers have experimented in *musique concrète*—sound strips recording various combinations of noises at different dynamic levels and at different speeds (and therefore pitch). One would not claim that *musique concrète* has as yet

created a work of art; but it has given intimation of technical
resources which composers dealing in more traditional materials
and in more recognizably human experience might make use of,
especially in music for radio.

This suggests that of all the new techniques available to composers today the most significant are those associated with a functional discipline closely related to modern life. Thus even the most
"serious" and difficult absolute music of the American composer
Copland has been powerfully affected in texture, rhythm, orchestration and even form by his admirably authentic work for cinema and
radio. In his case, more than in that of a European composer with
a more traditional background, there is no need for a sharp division
between the music he writes for himself and that which he writes
for a functional purpose. It is a remarkable achievement that Hans
Eisler should have seen in so apparently esoteric a medium as the
twelve-note technique a method of composition which could
appositely be adapted to film music. Such an achievement does
something to break down the disastrous barriers which separate
twentieth-century "art" techniques from "function", and at the
same time suggests ways of using sound (electronic instruments,
etc.) which may be of value to the "straight" composer. Copland's
and Eisler's film music is of more significance from this point of
view than any self-conscious attempt to establish a liaison between
art music and popular music. Such a liaison is hardly a practical
possibility under present conditions, since the idiom of popular
music is more a commercialized industry than an act of creative
expression.

In this survey we have for the most part confined our attention
to various creative and theoretical aspects of the four great central
figures in twentieth-century music—Schoenberg, Stravinsky, Bartók
and Hindemith; for they prompt all the essential questions. It has
not been our intention to provide all, or indeed any, of the answers;
and looking back, perhaps the only guiding principle we can
observe in the multifarious complexities of twentieth-century
music is a growing insistence on order and discipline, involving a
reassertion of the primacy of line. Harmonic systems are susceptible
to the vagaries of fashion; rhythm does not become fully significant
until it is a part of melody; but a melodic line that convinces will go
on convincing. In different ways we have observed the reassertion of
line in the work of the twelve-note composers, and we may note in
this connexion that a serial technique has been used by other
composers, such as Stravinsky and Alan Bush, who do not accept
pure chromaticism. We have seen it in the late work of Stravinsky
and in that of Bartók; while the result of Hindemith's theoretical
deductions from his practice has been to make harmonic progressions

dependent on the progression of line. Such an attitude safeguards the composer's craftsmanship, for a linear music cannot call on relatively fortuitous and extra-musical devices.

But this does not mean that the composer is indifferent to the quality and kind of his experience. The extreme cult of objectivity characteristic of the 1920's, leading either to the deliberate suppression of personal feeling as in Satie and the middle-period music of Stravinsky or to deliberate emotional irresponsibility as in *Les Six*, has passed away. In so far as such generalizations are valid, we may say that the composer nowadays is interested in his own personality ("the new Romanticism"), though interested in it not as the be-all and end-all of existence, but as part of something greater than himself. He is aware, or tries to be aware, of his obligations to himself, to society and to God, as were composers in what are considered to be creatively more fortunate epochs. If he does not yet know clearly what he believes in, at least he is becoming convinced of the necessity for belief.

BOOKS SUGGESTED FOR FURTHER READING

Stravinsky, *The Poetics of Music* (Oxford, 1947).
Schoenberg, *Style and Idea* (Williams and Norgate, 1951).
Hindemith, *The Craft of Musical Composition* (Associated Music Publishers, 1937).
Hindemith, *A Composer's World* (Harvard, 1952).
Gerald Abraham, *A Hundred Years of Music* (Duckworth, 1949).

ARCHITECTURE
by J. M. RICHARDS
I.

THE DIFFERENCE between architecture and mere building is that architecture involves the pursuit of beauty or, if that is too high-sounding a word to use in connexion with some of the structures architects are concerned with, the pursuit of the aesthetic satisfaction that results from a necessary job being done appropriately, economically and tastefully. But the aesthetic qualities possessed by good architecture emerge as part of the process of solving the practical problems presented. If the architect tries to add artistic effects by dressing up his building in some way that has no connexion with its structure or purpose, like hanging stone columns reminiscent of a Renaissance palace on to the steel frame of a block of offices, to look as though they support the building when in fact it supports them, he is guilty not only of creating a sham but of shirking the challenge offered by the technical resources special to his own time, a challenge that each generation in turn has to meet and to answer by showing its ability to produce something of real interest and aesthetic significance out of them.

The architect must thus combine the exercise of the scientific mind and that of the imagination. He has to be at one and the same time a technician continually inquiring, in collaboration with the engineer, into the best use of materials and manufacturing methods; a planner and administrator, analysing his clients' needs, translating them into a building programme and overseeing the financial complexities involved; and an artist. In so far as he is an artist he differs from the sculptor not only because his creations serve a practical purpose, but because a sculptor is concerned with external form and an architect with both external form and internal space. The forms the architect creates are to be appreciated from within as well as from without; and indeed to him an exterior is simply the visible outer surface of a structure primarily devised in order to enclose a given space or sequence of spaces. The history of architecture is very largely the history of the ways that have been found of providing the covered spaces that changing human needs have demanded. The art of architecture has developed in response to these changes, and especially as man's ingenuity has been stimulated by his search for the means of covering larger and larger spaces.

The earliest architecture that was at all highly developed, that of the ancient Egyptians, was limited to simple post and beam construction: vertical supports with the roof resting on beams running across them; and the architecture of ancient Greece was structurally much the same. Its special quality, which has been so consistently admired ever since, was given it not by any structural complexities but by the refinement of its proportions, every part being mathematically related to every other, and by its sculptural enrichment. The spaces enclosed were relatively small. There was no demand for bigger spaces since life was lived for the most part out of doors. The Greek temple was a shrine, entered only by a privileged few, and religious ceremonies were held in the open air in front of it. It was left to the ingenuity of the Romans, who expended much of their wealth on secular buildings like law courts and public baths, and who by temperament preferred magnificence of effect to sculptural refinement, to enclose really large areas. They were far bolder as engineers and, inspired by the demand for great spaces where crowds could assemble, they evolved the arch and the vault. Thus do social needs and technical means progress hand in hand.

The process continued under the Byzantine engineer-architects, who invented the dome, and the master-masons of the Middle Ages who, starting with what the barbarians had left of the Roman tradition of building with piers and arches, evolved their own system of roofing over the large spaces required by the forms of Christian worship, adapted to the smaller stones to which they were restricted by their quarrying methods and by the absence of the slave labour with the aid of which the great blocks of stone used by the Egyptians, Greeks and Romans had been hewn and transported.

A large part of the energies of the medieval civilization were concentrated on erecting great churches to the glory of God, and the arts of stone-carving and glass-painting were perfected with the sole aim of enriching them. Having discovered the potentialities of the pointed arch, the medieval engineers far surpassed the Romans in their understanding of the mechanics of construction, learning how to buttress their walls against the outward thrust of their towering vaults and to stabilize the buttresses by the weight of the pinnacles that crowned them; so that the whole building became one precisely calculated system of thrust and counter-thrust, in which each element had its part to play while contributing at the same time to the rhythmic patterns of vertical lines and arches that give its inspiring effect to Gothic church architecture.

Occasional catastrophes, the result of their daring overreaching itself, did not discourage the Gothic builders from persisting with their experiments in stone construction right up to the time when the Gothic civilization became submerged in the new ideas that had been let loose in Renaissance Italy; so much so that in the very last Gothic churches the whole conception was simplified down to one basic idea: that of a high, vaulted rectangular hall (as at King's College Chapel, Cambridge) with walls largely of glass, interrupted by the slenderest possible supporting piers—a miracle of lightness and transparency. But the renaissance of classical learning that took place when the power of the Church disintegrated, brought these single-minded notions to an end; and although it replaced the age of faith by an age of reason, and stimulated a new curiosity about man's place in the natural world, opening up a new era of scientific study, architecture regarded as the imaginative exploitation of structure came to a halt which lasted for several hundred years.

The new architecture which established itself all over Europe—and eventually in America—was based on Roman forms and was content to employ the simple, static constructional principles of the Romans, without even pursuing the Roman engineers' interest in the feats of construction represented by their baths and aqueducts. Apart from isolated improvisations like those required in the construction of large domes, architectural energies were concentrated not on ways of enclosing space economically and dramatically, but on logic expressed geometrically: on the infinitely subtle arrangements and rearrangements, especially in the matter of façades, to which the elements of classical architecture lent themselves: arrangements regulated—in the same way that the social system was increasingly regulated to conform to a settled hierarchy—by an agreed system of proportions and relationships, taste being governed, as it never was in the Middle Ages, by knowledge and precedent. The well-ordered sumptuousness of palaces and mansions aptly reflected the value increasingly set on material pomps and powers. Even the churches were civic monuments first and religious shrines afterwards.

This conception of the art of architecture was maintained throughout the post-Renaissance era, in spite of successive superficial changes of style: changes from the exuberance of the baroque in southern Europe to the doctrinaire subservience in eighteenth-century England to the precedents set up by the Italian architect Palladio; and from there to the subsequent era of sophisticated tastes and fashions, in which motifs drawn from many sources—Pompeiian, Etruscan, Roman and even Gothic and Chinese—were combined to create exquisite effects of decoration but led, as novelty ousted novelty and fashion succeeded fashion, to the indiscriminate revival of past styles, and to a concern solely with pictorial values, which dominated nineteenth-century architecture. It has only ceased to dominate architecture within our own generation, as the result of a revolution brought about by the invention of new building materials and processes which demanded a reconsideration of accepted technical practices, and the simultaneous arrival of social changes which created a demand for buildings of many new types.

II.

The glance backward into architectural history taken in the foregoing paragraphs has as its purpose to make clear the great significance of the architectural revolution, defined in its final sentences, in the midst of which we still find ourselves. It is not only a revolution in taste and aesthetic ideals, but a return to first principles, especially the principle that the basis of architectural design is the economical enclosure of space; and in this sense modern architecture may be said to have picked up again the threads of tradition that were broken when the coming of the Renaissance put an end to the further development of Gothic architecture. The abundant vitality of modern architecture is derived from exactly this: its preoccupation with structure and space instead of with stylistic niceties.

To contrast the dynamic, structurally experimental character that modern architecture possesses in common with the Byzantine and the Gothic, with the static character of Egyptian, Greek and Renaissance architecture, based on a few simple structural expedients, is not, however, to imply the inferiority of the latter, or to suggest that Roman architecture was finer than Greek because the Romans were engineers as well as artists. Different civilizations demand different qualities in their architecture because they require it to symbolize different ideals and aspirations as well as to provide different kinds of accommodation. Emphasis is laid now on one aspect and now on another, and if modern architecture has taken on a different emphasis from that of the Renaissance, that is the natural result of the forces that have shaped it: first, the need, following the Industrial Revolution, for new types of building like factories and warehouses and railway stations, which revived interest in problems of enclosing large spaces; secondly, the invention, also a consequence of the Industrial Revolution, of iron and steel construction and later of reinforced concrete, enabling the new needs to be met by new and aesthetically stimulating means—another instance of that interaction of cause and effect previously seen when the Roman demand for covered public spaces coincided with the Roman engineers' development of the vault; and finally a psychological need to return to first principles and the disciplines imposed by them as the only way of escape from the confusion of rival stylistic conventions among which architecture had become entangled.

As soon as the Industrial Revolution was well under way the process began of questioning the assumptions on which eighteenth-century tastes and preconceptions had been based, and exploring the constructional possibilities of the new techniques that were themselves the instruments of the new industrial power. This exploratory work, however, was left to the engineers; while the architects pursued their way along the seductive paths of period revivalism, exciting themselves over the battle of the styles, little aware that a more significant battle was already joined, which was eventually to threaten their very status in society: the battle between constructing and decorating. The Victorian architects, men of deep conviction, learning and ingenuity, produced some noble and charming, as well as some absurd, buildings, which we do well not to despise today, but history was passing them by: that divorce of architecture from engineering had already begun which it has been the special task of our generation to remedy; also that segregation of architecture from the most pressing social problems of the day, like housing, traffic planning and land-use, which the architect-aestheticians thought beneath their attention but which the present generation has discovered to be the only proper starting-point for any attempts to impose order on the human environment, a thing that it has been the architect's role throughout history to do.

That there was a widespread consciousness during the nine-teenth century that more important problems were waiting to be solved than those to which most architects were devoting their talents, is shown by the number of independent contributions towards a new and a more rational form of architecture, technically and philosophically, that were made in different parts of the world. Since the Industrial Revolution began in England, it was British engineers—that empirically minded generation of canal, railway, bridge and harbour builders which flourished from the end of the eighteenth century until the middle of the nineteenth, led by Telford, Rennie, Robert Stephenson and the two Brunels—who showed what power and drama could be extracted from iron and steam and the vast structures they engendered; and it was the last genius of this same generation, Joseph Paxton, who showed in his Crystal Palace building of 1851 how the factory-production of standardized building components—in this case lengths of iron framing and sheets of glass—could produce not only unprecedented speed and economy while the building was under construction, but a marvel of spaciousness and airy grace when it was finished.

But after that the English contribution lapsed, and it was French engineers—de Dion, Cottancin, Eiffel—who developed the use of steel for structural purposes and French engineers, too, who invented reinforced concrete. It was a French architect, Auguste Perret, who pioneered the use of concrete in buildings and a Swiss engineer,

Robert Maillart, who perfected it as a structural material of un-suspected verve and elegance. And it was the American architects of the Chicago school—Jenney, Sullivan, Holabrid and Roche—who transformed the steel frame from a mere convenient armature for some monumental disguise into a form of construction with its own aesthetic disciplines and potentialities, creating the rhythmical pattern of frame and panel and window of which nearly all the large buildings of today are basically composed.

At the same time another American, Frank Lloyd Wright, was revolutionizing house design with his broad-eaved prairie houses; and British and European architects—among them Philip Webb, Voysey, Mackintosh, Adolf Loos and Henri van de Velde, inspired by the Arts and Crafts movement that William Morris had founded—were liberating the domestic architecture of their own countries from the artificialities of taste and from the academic strait-jacket by the example of numerous informally planned houses of simple geo-metrical form and of a texture derived from the nature of their materials.

Numerous other trends and experiments pointed in the same direction, and the threads of all of them were gathered together in Europe in the years after the First World War and woven into a fabric with whose qualities we are now becoming familiar. Among the names associated with this time are two which are now the most famous in modern architecture—Le Corbusier in France and Walter Gropius in Germany, the former the visionary who proclaimed a new ideal world, the latter the prophet who proclaimed the need to come to terms with the machine that was beginning to dominate the old world.

The principal characteristics of modern architecture can thus largely be deduced from the ideas and experiments in which it had its origins. I have already emphasized how much it draws from the new forms of structure that science has made available for it. Its favourite materials, steel and reinforced concrete, lend themselves, unlike the blocks of stone used by the Renaissance builders, to exact calculation. Buildings can be designed as live structures, in which each element contributes its share to the stability of the whole and is, moreover, made to do so with the minimum expenditure of material; for it is the fact of every component part being stressed to its utmost, with all superfluous material pared away, that gives a live structure—whether it be a vaulted Gothic hall or a modern pre-stressed concrete factory building—its aesthetic vitality.

The aim, moreover, is to make clear to the eye that the whole building is supported by the framework and that the walls are simply screens to keep out the weather and give privacy within. Even when traditional materials like brick and stone are used for this purpose, for the sake of their lasting surfaces and their insulation and fire-protection properties, they are treated in a manner appropriate to their function as walls that carry nothing but their own weight. They are not jointed as a thick wall is jointed to give it strength; nor do they have deeply set openings to give an effect of mass. Sheer mass, in fact, which used to be so highly valued an architectural attribute because of the suggestion of stability it conveyed, is losing its significance as an aesthetic expedient now that stability can be more economically attained by other means.

Emphasis is placed on economy, instead of on amplitude, of means. Buildings are made to seem lightly poised on the surface of the ground rather than rooted solidly in it (once again, more like their Gothic than their Renaissance predecessors); and this effect is enhanced by the bright surfaces and smooth finishes of many of the materials used, especially glass, which plays so ubiquitous a part in modern architecture and often, by its transparency, reveals the structural form of the building by allowing the inside and the outside to be viewed simultaneously. A good example is the Royal Festival Hall in London, where even in the distant view the basic conception of the building can be apprehended thus. Through the lightly built, transparent walls of the foyers and restaurants can be seen the compact shape of the auditorium—solid-walled to keep out noise—like an egg nestling in a glass-walled box.

The production in factories of ready-made building components, whether these are the stanchions and girders that make up the steel frame of the type of building referred to above, the panels of synthetic walling material or glass that fill the spaces between them, or fittings and equipment of various kinds, has lately changed the whole nature of building, as Paxton unknowingly forecast when he designed the Crystal Palace as a prefabricated structure in 1851. It is this that makes the architectural revolution set in train by the Industrial Revolution of a hundred and fifty years ago so much more than a revolution in style. The factory has increasingly taken over the role originally played by the craftsman working in and upon the building itself.

The measurements of ready-made building components are of course determined before the building itself has been planned, and to make efficient use of them the building must be designed specially to fit them. Ideally, all factory-made building parts—windows, doors, partitioning units, plumbing fixtures and even floor-coverings and such things as cookers, refrigerators and bookcases—ought to be manufactured to conform to the same set of dimensions or to multiples of a given dimension, so that as little as possible in the way of cutting and fitting is required on the site. This principle is called "modular co-ordination", the module being the lowest common denominator, the key dimension of which others are a multiple; and diligent efforts are being made by architects and manufacturers to bring it about. Perfect modular co-ordination would involve complex, and perhaps insuperable, problems of industrial organization; yet on a far simpler scale a precedent for it already exists—in the traditional Japanese house. This type of house has a timber frame, and the walls and partitions consist of light screens of paper, bamboo or similar material (lightness is essential because of earthquakes). Dimensions are co-ordinated in the sense that the sizes of all rooms are based on those of the mat with which all floors are covered. This mat is always of the same size; so each room is a multiple of this size, making it easy to specify how big each room in a house should be (so many mats wide and so many long), as well as giving to the appearance of all houses a consistent rhythm and proportion.

The logical ultimate end to the increasing industrialization of building methods is the factory production of complete buildings or sections of buildings, in the same way that motor-cars are mass produced. In the case of small buildings like houses, this is already possible. Ready-made sections of small timber buildings like garages and chicken-houses have in fact been on the market for a long time, and during the war attempts were made to prefabricate dwelling-houses in the same way and on a large scale as the best means of catching up quickly with the housing shortage. Some thousands of "prefabs" were put up in Britain alone and there has since grown up a flourishing export industry, mass producing small buildings and parts of buildings for shipping chiefly to tropical countries. But the pre-fabricated houses put up in Britain were expensive, and were discontinued because to make their use economical would have required a thorough reorganization of the house-building industry, which has stubbornly continued, as regards the training of workmen, their grouping into trades and the way the contracting firms set about their work, as though the old handicraft methods of building still prevailed. This is one of the difficulties that are preventing the best use being made in architecture of modern scientific developments.

It is unlikely that the practice of prefabricating complete buildings will become widespread, as it is, for example, in the case of motor-cars, because few types of building are required in large quantities to an identical design; and its application even to small houses is limited because—unlike motor-cars—each must be considered in relation to the peculiarities of its site, to which the design may have to be adjusted. But the prefabrication of *parts* of buildings is bound to increase. And it need not lead to monotony. The variations that are possible with the use of relatively small standardized components are almost infinite; and, after all, the familiar brick is nothing but a standard-size prefabricated building unit—admittedly of the smallest size conceivable.

A British example of the intelligent use of prefabrication, in conjunction with a modular system of planning, is provided by the group of schools built in Hertfordshire during the years after the Second World War. It was necessary to build a large number as speedily and as economically as possible. A method of frame construction, using a fixed size of light steel beam and column, was devised by the county architects in collaboration with a manufacturer; and the length of the beam (which determined the distance between columns) became the planning module, of which all room dimensions were designed as a multiple: it was in fact 8 ft. 3 in. A pre-cast concrete external wall-unit was designed in the form of a horizontal slab of which the length was an exact subdivision of the module and the height an exact subdivision of the height of the column. Doors, windows, partitions and so on were designed according to the same system, with the result that any number of schools could be constructed out of a relatively small number of standard parts—rather after the fashion of a Meccano set. The result was economical, because the parts could be made in large numbers, and, being the same for each school, could be delivered to one depot in the middle of the county and supplied from it to the school sites as needed, thereby simplifying organization and speeding up construction.

By this means, over forty new schools were completed in less than five years. Yet no two schools were alike; the slope of the site, its orientation, the position of existing trees, the number of children to be accommodated in the different departments and so on, all demanded a different design in each case, which there was no difficulty in providing within the limitations laid down by the planning module and the use of the standard constructional parts. Aesthetically the buildings have considerable charm. They are light and airy and a rhythmic pattern is spread over their façades and throughout their semi-transparent interiors by the standard proportions of the wall, window and partition units. At the least they are pleasantly unassuming, and where changes of level and variations of plan shape have been imaginatively exploited, some of them achieve genuine architectural distinction.

Architecture's growing dependence on machinery has been responsible for other changes besides those outlined above; notably a changed attitude to ornament. There was for a time a tendency for modern architects to eschew applied ornament altogether simply as a puritan reaction against the over-indulgence in ornament for its own sake which accompanied the nineteenth-century revival of historic styles. But the chief reason why buildings are plainer is that the systems of ornament employed in the past were the result of the efforts of craftsmen, carving and modelling largely on their own initiative, to enrich the buildings they worked on, not only by the elaboration they added to the various forms and surfaces but by the loving care of which their work was evidence. Now that hand-carving and other kinds of ornament can be copied by machinery there is not the same virtue in them. We have to look in other directions for the means of enriching our buildings with the proof that we have devoted time and money and imagination to making them as perfect as we can.

The machine-age equivalents of good hand-craftsmanship lie of course in those qualities produced by the most skilful use of the machine: precision of outline and perfection of finish, reinforcing still further that lightness and elegance that the use of steel and reinforced-concrete construction have already engendered. But although modern architects have made it their task to bring out the beauties latent in the nature of the materials that modern technology has given them—new metal alloys, laminated woods, glass in its many forms, each with its characteristic texture and colour—they are by no means restricted, of course, to new machine-made materials. The time has passed when modern-minded architects felt impelled to underline their allegiance to the new world of science that was flourishing about them by cutting themselves off from all traditional techniques. It is a sign of their growing maturity that they can now, for instance, use rough stone-walling for the sake of its texture and colour, or because it does what needs to be done better than anything else, without feeling that they are associating themselves with the imitators of Cotswold rusticity.

The characteristic products of the material world in which the architect himself operates are no doubt the raw materials that give him his greatest opportunities, but in discussing the developments that have influenced him we must not forget those that have taken place in the other arts in his generation. His interest in pure geometrical form, for example, and in the visual excitements created by the interpenetrating planes in a glass-walled building, are in part derived from the revelations of the Cubist movement in painting. Thus technical innovations did not always appear on the scene before the aesthetic ideals to which they are now said to have given birth.

Notwithstanding such occasional anomalies, architecture, for better or worse, has become in this century a branch of science in all ways subject to the disciplines science imposes. It is one of the activities through which we express our determination to command our own environment, and in this sense we are still children of the Renaissance. Earlier I described modern architecture as representing a return to Gothic principles of construction and as therefore having certain aesthetic attributes in common with it. That is true as far as it goes, but is due only to an accident of technological history. Spiritually we are far removed from our Gothic forebears.

We are as we are because the Renaissance happened, and the lessons of order and discipline taught by it, and the spirit of inquiry it awakened, are part of the permanent fund of ideas on which our Western culture is founded.

III.

The architectural landscape we see around us is infinitely confused because that which is new and truly of our time emerges but slowly from the mass of other architecture contemporaneous with it; comprising among other kinds the frankly reminiscent, still hankering after the pictorial effects gained by historical association; the disguised scientific, employing modern techniques but not accepting their full implications, aesthetic and otherwise, and thereby denying them their proper effectiveness as well as creating a false character; the modernistic, employing superficially the tricks of style that have grown up with modern architecture as a means of seeming up to date; and the merely clumsy, confused and disorganized, on which the disciplines of modern architecture could confer order at least, if not in every case beauty.

It is still not easy to see where architecture is going. The picture just given of the kind of art that it is slowly becoming touches on some of the factors that have made it different from what it used to be. Others, equally important in their way, are concerned less with form than with content and the means by which the two are made to coalesce. In our generation the architect has come forward as a planner. The planning of buildings—meaning the arrangement of the different parts and in particular the allocation of internal space in accordance with the needs of the occupiers—has been part of the architect's task since the profession of architecture became a distinct one at the beginning of the seventeenth century. But in those days planning was simple; the plan of a house, a church or a town hall followed the accepted pattern for buildings of the kind, with only minor variations.

Nowadays, with the far more complex kinds of building required, the architect cannot begin his design until he has analysed in some detail the needs the building has to fulfil. He has to become an expert on, say, hospital routine or the running of a department-store in order to exercise his ingenuity in devising plans of hospitals and stores that will help doctors, nurses and shopkeepers to do their jobs more efficiently and economically than ever before. As a result of never-ending research into the way they function, specialist buildings like these are continually being improved. Similarly the architect has to study manufacturing processes in order to plan factories efficiently, and often the new ideas of layout that he is able to suggest contribute substantially to cheapening and speeding up production; for logical thought and scientific methods of analysis are as effective when applied to the planning of buildings as to their structure. The order that the architect can create out of disorder is of increasing value as life grows more complex. As a planner alone (leaving aside his significance as an artist and constructor) his services to society are invaluable, whether his field of operations be a new type of kitchen or a new town.

Only when the best plan arrangement has begun to clarify itself in his mind is the architect ready to think in terms of what his building will look like, although all the time he has been thinking in three dimensions, because planning is an affair of spaces; his imagination has been moving vertically as well as horizontally. And as the general form of the building takes shape in his mind, he considers what kind of structure will suit it best. So he must understand the basic principles of engineering. I have mentioned that the divorce of architecture from engineering in the nineteenth century was a disaster both for the art and for the profession of architecture. While the engineers enthusiastically explored the possibilities of the new types of structure, the architects became more and more closely concerned with the details of external appearance; until the time came when the architect was regarded simply as the man who added the artistic trimmings to the engineer's constructions. When artistic trimmings were not thought necessary, for example in the case of utilitarian buildings like factories, the architect was not brought in at all; we were spared, no doubt, some absurdities in the way of factory buildings dressed in period costume, but we lost— by what was, in effect, the architect's abdication of his responsibilities—all chance of his trained eye being applied to their proportions, massing and colour, or of his skill as a planner being applied to their proper siting and layout. This situation can to some extent be blamed for the ugliness and squalor of the regions industrialized in the nineteenth century.

The modern architect is a constructor as well as a designer. He cannot, however, expect to combine all the engineer's functions in his own person, as he did as a matter of course before the Industrial Revolution, because the quantity of knowledge and experience required on account of the complexities of contemporary constructional and other techniques are too much for one man to encompass. He must collaborate therefore with specialist engineers: specialists in steelwork, reinforced concrete, heating, ventilation and many other sciences. But he must be sufficiently familiar with them all to be capable of taking the initial decisions from which their part in the enterprise will follow, and to act as leader of the team they constitute. The vital thing is that they should act as a team from the earliest stages.

The practice of architecture is increasingly a matter of teamwork.

The architect has had to come down from the pedestal on which he was planted by the Victorian conception of him as a man of superior taste with a right—indeed a duty to his art—to regard practical affairs as beneath his notice. This popular idealization does not accurately describe the Victorian architect, who was more often than not an astute business man; but at the same time he was an authoritarian. To him the building contractor was there to carry out his commands. Today it is becoming evident that the contractor too should be admitted to the architect's team of collaborators, and consulted at an early stage. The efficient use of new building techniques depends on the building being designed with full knowledge of their potentialities and limitations, which means in close consultation with the men who will have to operate them. We saw in the case of the Hertfordshire schools how a successful system of prefabrication was brought into being by the architect collaborating with the manufacturer from the very beginning. Only thus can that common fund of experience be built up within the building industry on which permanent improvements in technique are founded.

Modern buildings call for the services of many other specialists besides those already mentioned: specialists on acoustics, lighting, sanitation, fire-fighting, subsoil-mechanics and numerous other sciences, as well as painters, sculptors, garden-designers and the like. Architecture is the efficient and imaginative co-ordination of all their efforts; and to obtain a picture of contemporary architecture in its full complexity and variety, it is necessary to take a rather closer view of some of the widely different problems, in the shape of buildings for different purposes, with which these teams of experts are confronted today. I have already said that one of the occurrences that gave its impetus to the series of far-reaching architectural changes that had its beginnings in the Industrial Revolution was the sudden need for new types of building, hitherto unimagined. Previously the types required were relatively few, and whatever subtleties and refinements were developed in detail, in their basic conception they were all variations on a few simple themes. There was the formal, symmetrically planned dwelling-house, and the mansion and palace, which were only dwelling-houses writ large. There was a limited range of secular buildings—colleges, assembly-halls, court-houses and the like—each consisting of a central hall of some kind with ancillary rooms grouped round it and designed by a process of rearranging the same architectural elements into a different pattern, so that in outward appearance they were all but indistinguishable. Even churches, which in the eighteenth century were predominantly preaching halls, conformed to this general pattern. Shops were still simply the ground floors of the shop-keepers' residences. The design of a building required taste and

ingenuity, but not the capacity to create forms and structures derived from, and expressive of, a wide range of complex human
activities.

Contrast that situation with the one that prevails today. Hospitals,
cinemas, factories and railway-stations respond to needs so different
in each case that they cannot be expected to conform to the same
sort of over-all pattern. When modern architects have progressed
rather further towards crystallizing out of, as it were, their
aesthetic experiments, a widely accepted idiom—in fact have
achieved a contemporary *style*—there will be more appearance of
unity between buildings, but not of the kind that existed before the
Industrial Revolution, which was a unity of scale. The disparate
scales of contemporary buildings, ranging from the small dwelling-
house to the vast office building, power station or air terminal, is
one of the causes of the present confused architectural scene; for
their size bears no relation to their social importance, as did the
size of the great churches and castles that once dominated the
towns. But this is a problem for the sociologist and the town-planner
as much as for the architect.

Instead of conforming to a predetermined type, the modern
building, in its planning, construction and the effect it has on the
eye, becomes increasingly a law to itself, and is continually subject
to change, as developments in architectural technique suggest ways
of enabling it to fulfil its function more effectively. But let us begin
by considering the oldest type of building of all, which has, in fact,
changed the least: the house. Houses have changed relatively little
as a result of the scientific age we live in, because family life, round
which they are planned, has remained the same. Minor social
changes have affected them a little, like the virtual disappearance
of the domestic servant—which has made tall houses less popular
because of the labour of carrying things up and down stairs; and in
America different social habits, especially the Americans' informal
way of living, are producing differently planned houses; large all-
purpose rooms are replacing the numerous separate rooms for
reading, eating, studying, sleeping, dressing, smoking, each secluded
from the other, that go to make up the conventional house-plan.
But basically the architectural type remains the same, as we can
judge from the comfort with which we still inhabit old houses of,
say, the Georgian period, only requiring the installation of up-to-
date services like plumbing and electricity. We should be nothing
like so comfortable being ill in an eighteenth-century hospital or
trying to manufacture something in an eighteenth-century factory.

In Britain especially, houses have undergone fewer changes in
their appearance because it is more economical, for the reasons
already described, to build them in traditional fashion with brick
walls, timber floors and tiled roofs than to employ more modern

materials and techniques. The modern house is by nature simple in its geometrical form, and is often only distinguishable from the equally simple Georgian or Regency house by small differences of proportion and modelling, reflecting the modern architect's aesthetic preferences; by the absence of the ornamented cornices and doorheads that the Georgian rule of taste dictated; and by its large-paned windows (the small-paned Georgian window, originally due to glass being obtainable only in small sizes, was later simply a stylistic convention). In modern houses the windows themselves are often larger, too, because improved methods of heating allow more light to be admitted to the interior without the rooms becoming chilly—also because we are a generation that *prefers* more light.

A more difficult problem presented to the modern architect is the layout and grouping of houses in quantity. The rapid spread of population in the last hundred and fifty years, together with the development of rail and motor transport, has created vast suburban housing estates, often ill-sited and utterly formless compared with the compact residential areas previously designed as parts of towns. They were the result of *laissez-faire* economics and failure to foresee the need to plan land-use in advance. They were the work of speculative builders or municipal housing officials, architects having taken hardly any part in multiple housing since first they failed to meet the challenge offered by industrial expansion and withdrew into the position of mere purveyors of artistic fashions.

Now that they have rediscovered their social responsibilities, and are armed with planning laws designed to regulate the siting of new buildings, architects are making it their task to reintroduce some order and shapeliness into public housing. The improvement effected by replacing the familiar monotonous lines of detached and semi-detached villas by houses grouped into squares and terraces, themselves conceived in three dimensions as sequences of enclosed spaces, can be seen in the best British local-authority housing, which is inspired in part by the example of pre-industrial England and in part by the more recent example of Scandinavia, where well-designed housing is the rule rather than the exception. More especially is the beneficial effect of the British architect's return to the field of mass-produced housing to be seen in the new towns, designed after the Second World War to relieve the over-crowding of London; although here—as in Britain generally—the houses are too widely scattered over too large an area for a truly urban character to be attained. This weakness is largely attributable to a misunderstanding, on the part of those who make the planning by-laws and those who operate them, of the purpose of the Garden City movement, founded by Ebenezer Howard in 1892 as a remedy for overcrowding in big cities but not meant by him to justify covering square miles of country-side with widely dispersed housing lacking form or focus.

Apart from the social defects of such a policy, land in Britain—as indeed in most European countries—is too valuable to be wasted in this way. As populations grow it becomes scarcer, especially in cities; and increasingly housing takes the form of flats. I am not concerned here with the social aspect of high-density housing so much as with the architectural problems it presents and the opportunities it offers. On the continent of Europe to live in flats has long been the normal experience for all kinds of people, but in England there has been a prejudice against them partly because of their associations with the grim tenement blocks erected during the last seventy years by municipal authorities or charitable organizations as an alternative to slum housing, and partly because of the English tradition (linked to the English devotion to gardening) of living in separate houses, of which English country towns—as contrasted with Continental towns—are largely composed. But flat-life has many advantages for people without children; and some of the flats recently put up by public authorities have succeeded in avoiding both the dreariness and congestion of the earlier working-class tenement and the uneconomical use of space of the late Victorian luxury flats (which, rather than a separate architectural type, were, in effect, country houses piled one upon another). Recent designs for flats have gone far to create a welcome for them for their own sake instead of as an expedient for saving space.

Lessons have been learnt from Continental experience and especially from Scandinavia, where architects and public-housing authorities have done much to make flat-life less restricted than it is elsewhere and to bring it into closer relationship with natural surroundings. Instead of having long cliff-like façades facing the streets, Swedish flats are often star-shaped or Y-shaped to admit all possible light and air. The several arms of the building, radiating from a central stair and lift hall, contain only one flat on each floor, and the nuisance of noise transmitted from one flat to another is thus avoided. They stand among gardens that belong jointly to all their occupants.

For reasons connected with their local building resources and traditions these Swedish flats are usually of conventional construction, but high blocks of flats elsewhere have been the subject of intensive technical experiment. Involving as they do the repetition of identical units they lend themselves structurally to the use of the steel or concrete frame, and visually to the rhythmic façade patterns that frame-construction naturally promotes. Outstanding English examples occur in the London County Council housing estates begun in 1950 in the Wimbledon-Roehampton area. Here high flats in the form of towers, or of long narrow blocks in parallel formation, are set among lower blocks and terraces of houses, creating a varied landscape, enabling the widely spaced tall blocks to command distant views over the roofs of the lower ones and allowing the estate as a whole to cater for the needs of all kinds of people, which has obvious advantages socially.

The conception of groups of tall flats rising at intervals from a green landscape, as a logical response to the changes in our lives brought about by motor transport, has been put forward in its most whole-hearted, as well as its most seductive, form by the French-Swiss architect Le Corbusier, whose published designs for what he called a *ville radieuse* have had a far-reaching influence on town-planning. A project of the kind he envisaged has not yet been fully realized; but between 1947 and 1952 Le Corbusier built, on the outskirts of Marseilles, a single eighteen-story apartment block housing 1,600 people, which he called a *Unité d'Habitation*, conceived as the first instalment of such a project. It is at the same time an impressive work of architecture in its own right, and has powerfully influenced the design of large blocks of flats everywhere. Its planning is ingenious: interlocking two-story maisonettes with spacious balconies, stacked one above the other and reached from either side of a central corridor on every third floor. This building also convincingly demonstrates that concrete as a plastic material has unimagined aesthetic potentialities, although lately the tendency has been to think of it as more suited to a structural framework, requiring some other, more attractive, finishing material. This lesson from Marseilles, however, is not one to be too eagerly applied in northern climates, where the defects of raw concrete wall-surfaces were made apparent by a number of unwise experiments in the 1930's. In sunny countries like Brazil, on the other hand, where in the last few years modern architecture, which took root there less than twenty years ago largely at the instance of Le Corbusier, has flowered more rapidly and confidently than anywhere else, much of the virile character of the buildings is derived from the uninhibited use of concrete as a plastic building material.

Presenting many of the same problems as large blocks of flats are large office buildings, equally the product of that urbanization of everyday life which has offered modern architects their greatest opportunities. These, too, are an aggregation of many identical units, and various architectural devices have been tried, apart from the device of resorting to period-style embellishment, to overcome the monotony inherent in them and to prevent their massive bulk from overpowering their surroundings; such as giving an artificial emphasis to groups of windows and balconies or patterning the façades with materials of different colours and textures. Yet some of the most successful buildings of this kind have been those which have accepted unreservedly the impersonal, cellular nature of offices and flats, and have relied on the dramatic effect of repetition when it occurs on so grand a scale, and on proportion and precision of finish, creating an architecture which is simply a pattern of windows in the sky.

It is in America that this conception of city architecture has been most readily accepted. Prominent examples are the United Nations Secretariat and the Lever Building in New York City, and the Lake Shore Drive apartments in Chicago, the latter designed by Mies van der Rohe. This architect of German origin, who was at one time associated with Walter Gropius at the Bauhaus in Germany—that pioneering university of design which flourished in the 1920's, where the first efforts were made to bring architecture into its proper relationship with the new industrial civilization—is the chief prophet of this schematic style of architecture, a style as precise and unemotional as a mathematical equation and productive of the same kind of aesthetic satisfaction.

Appropriate though it may be for large commercial and residential structures, this impersonal, highly intellectual approach to architecture has its obvious limitations, which are particularly evident when we come to consider buildings that depend for their success on evoking a more active response in the onlooker, such as churches. We can correctly describe most modern buildings as functional if we include among their functions those of conveying a sense of order and purpose and giving aesthetic pleasure. A church has, in addition, to create a devotional atmosphere, but for most people devotion is associated exclusively with traditional—especially with Gothic—styles and decorations. The several admirable and thoughtfully designed churches that have been put up in, for example, France and Switzerland can only partly fulfil their purpose while their emotional appeal is to the architect and the connoisseur of architecture rather than to the mass of the public. The modern architectural idiom is still in many ways tentative and immature, and has far to go before it is capable of establishing itself as the universal language in which ordinary people think architecturally as a matter of course. In the case of church architecture, moreover, we cannot expect to create buildings that compare with those of the past, as regards architectural richness and the depth of feeling they are able to engender, since religion is no longer, as it was for example in the Middle Ages, the central fact of everybody's life.

The central facts of our own lives are, rather, social and administrative organizations of various kinds. Every age has its characteristic buildings. In ancient Egypt it was the tomb, symbolizing the belief of survival after death: in ancient Greece the temple, dedicated to

the Gods who controlled human destinies; in Rome the public halls
and arenas; in the Middle Ages the castles and cathedrals; in the
Renaissance the palaces and the planned city streets and squares,
reflecting the bigger, more authoritarian scale on which men were
beginning to mould their own environment; in the nineteenth century
the civic buildings and the monuments of the new technocratic age,
such as the great railway termini. The buildings most characteristic
of our day, reflecting our high degree of social organization, are
perhaps our vast housing schemes, our planned neighbourhoods,
equipped with their own shopping, educational and medical services. It is on these that we lavish the most painstaking care.
The architectural form appropriate to them is of a fairly restrained
and workaday type, but they require focal points; civic buildings in
central squares, concert halls, exhibition buildings and the like,
where the purpose of architecture goes beyond that of housing
necessary functions agreeably and imaginatively; where it is
required to represent, in the eye of the public, civic dignity and pride
of achievement. One of the next tasks of architecture is so to equip
itself as to be capable of fulfilling this purpose after its own style as
fruitfully and unselfconsciously as the architecture of other days
fulfilled it after their style.

IV.

The boundaries of architecture have never been exactly defined,
but have varied from century to century. In the Middle Ages the
architect was called by the relatively humble title of master-mason
or master-carpenter, but was responsible for the planning and
decoration, as well as the construction, of the building. The minds of
the engineer, the architect and the artist were one. Even in the
changed circumstances of the eighteenth century, the architect
managed to keep control over the total picture; as often as not the
design of furniture and decorations was within his province. The
far greater specialization that prevails today means that the architect, instead of being the sole arbiter of what is proper and what is
not proper, is simply the leader and chief co-ordinator of a team of
specialists. But to compensate for his loss of personal control over
the smaller details (which in any case are now selected from a
catalogue quite as often as they are specially designed for the
occasion), he has acquired some degree of control over a far larger
picture. The spread of building due to modern transport and the
competition that has sprung up for the use of every acre of land has
made territorial planning—on a scale never attempted before—
the only alternative to chaos; and as the man with a mind trained
for tasks of this kind, the architect, accustomed at first to plan only
the single building, and then the building and its surroundings, has

taken to himself the planning of the street or sequences of streets (like Wood of Bath or Nash of the Prince Regent's London) and, in modern times, the neighbourhood, the town, the city and even the region.

There has lately grown up, it is true, with the increase of town and country planning, of planning-legislation and of the need for officials to operate it, a separate profession of town-planner. But the members of it are frequently drawn from the architectural profession and so interdependent are their responsibilities and so similar are the processes by which they both correlate human needs with the physical resources available to satisfy them, that their roles may be regarded as two aspects of the same one.

Especially is this true if we endeavour to look into the future. The architect remains first and foremost an artist in the construction of buildings; but he casts his eye over a larger scene as well, as he discovers the importance of exercising visual control—which he alone is equipped to do—over the urban landscape of which the single building constitutes but a part. Being the co-ordinating member of the varied team of artists and technicians who come together to create the modern architectural picture, he may not see every detail of it but he sees it whole.

BOOKS SUGGESTED FOR FURTHER READING

Sigfried Giedion, *Space, Time and Architecture* (Oxford University Press, 1954).

Le Corbusier, *Towards a New Architecture* (Architectural Press, 1946).

W. R. Lethaby, *Architecture* (Oxford University Press, 1939).

Lewis Mumford, *The Culture of Cities* (Secker and Warburg, 1938).

Nikolaus Pevsner, *Outline of European Architecture* (Penguin, 1951).

J. M. Richards, *Introduction to Modern Architecture* (Penguin, 1940).

ARCHAEOLOGY

by SIR MORTIMER WHEELER

THE MAIN FUNCTION of this essay will be to indicate something
of the preoccupations and skills of twentieth-century archaeology,
and stress will be laid upon the advancing application of scientific
method to the study of man during the past decade or two. In an
age dominated by science and technology, humanism has not
escaped the prevailing mode. But for that reason a dual warning may
be permitted at the outset: first, the application of scientific techniques and concepts to archaeology is no recent innovation; and
secondly, archaeology is not, by reason of that application, itself a
science in the normal usage of the term.

Let us glance at the second point first. When our senior learned
society, the Royal Society, was founded in the time of Charles II,
its purpose was to comprehend all "philosophy" or learning, in so
far as it might be susceptible to objective proof. At a time when
almost the sum total of knowledge was still within the compass of a
single ingenious mind—when a Christopher Wren might turn
lightly from astronomy, anatomy and medicine to the re-building of
St. Paul's cathedral—archaeology fitted aptly into an assemblage
of the sciences. And even the foundation of the Society of Antiquaries
of London in 1707 at first did little to dissolve the unity. Until the
present century (and indeed after) the link was sustained, but it
was sustained with an increasing tenuity. Long before the end of
the nineteenth century the vastly widening scope of the natural
sciences and their accompanying departmentalism had begun to
exclude the more subjective study of human achievement. In 1902
the humanities were formally relegated to a new foundation, the
British Academy, and the severance seemed to be complete.

Now, more than half a century later, the gap between archaeology
and the sciences might be thought to have narrowed significantly.
Today, archaeology draws freely upon geology, botany, climatology,
zoology, palaeontology, astronomy and even atomic research, and
has in turn lent occasionally to these disciplines something of a new
personality. Nevertheless, the cleavage remains a just one. The
primary concern of archaeology is the material expression of human
devices and ideas, direct products of the human brain; and it stands

ARCHAEOLOGY 387

to reason that the human brain can never comprehend itself with the objectivity wherewith it can seek to comprehend external nature. In the last resort, man's study of himself is a subjective study. Archaeology, if it be a science, is necessarily an uncertain and inaccurate science; and the Royal Society did right to relinquish it, however reluctantly.

The other point is this. The recent and lively rapprochement between archaeology and science should not be allowed to obscure the successful efforts of previous generations to apply reason and logic of a scientific kind to the study of human records, whether material or literary. Our forebears were no fools in these matters; the emphasis on scientific innovation in the following pages carries with it no implication that science has hitherto been absent from humanistic investigation. As long ago as 1786 and as far away as Calcutta, Sir William Jones was already enunciating the evolutionary relationship of languages—Sanskrit, Greek, Latin, Persian, Celtic, "Gothick". Three quarters of a century later, General Pitt Rivers (as Col. Lane Fox) was applying the evolutionary principle to the study of fire-arms and other artifacts. Before the end of the nineteenth century the same soldier-scholar had laid down the basic methods of scientific excavation and archaeological field-record. At the same time, in Sweden, Baron de Geer was perfecting his analysis of the annual ice-field deposits, which were for the first time to give us a scientific time-table for the early prehistory of a considerable part of northern Europe. And the turn of the century saw the later prehistory of western America enlightened by study of the growth-rings of timber. Of these and other methods, more will be said. Meanwhile, in the recollection of them, it will suffice to observe that the scientific tests which have more recently added dramatically to the proficiency of archaeology are not generically alien to that study.

Both the points which have just been discussed may perhaps be included in the rough definition of Archaeology as a study which is, and has long been, an art that employs a scientific technique.

I. Modern Techniques

From these generalities we may turn to specific skills. Many of these relate to the recovery and analysis of archaeological material from the soil, but it should be emphasized that archaeology and excavation are not synonymous terms. Whilst it is sufficiently certain that major archaeological discoveries will, in the future as in the past, be the result of excavation, no cleavage is here implied between the preoccupations of the digger and those of the antiquary whose chosen field may be Georgian architecture or church vestments. From neolithic pottery to Victorian gas-lamps, the study of the past is essentially integral; and the actual overlapping of techniques is surprisingly recurrent throughout the range of that study. If emphasis is here laid upon those procedures which are especially applicable to prehistory, that is only because prehistory is manifestly dependent to a special degree upon such precision as scientific aids can lend to it.

With that proviso, it may be averred that the basis of systematic archaeological excavation is the observation and record of the *stratigraphy* of an ancient site. The term, like much else in archaeological technique, is borrowed from geology, into which it was introduced early in the nineteenth century by William ("Strata") Smith, author of *Strata Identified by Organized Fossils*. The principle of stratification is simple enough: it is the layering or lamination of a deposit resulting from the successive operations either of nature or of mankind. In the latter case, the human occupation of a patch of ground for any appreciable time will normally produce a succession of layers due to construction or occupation; floor succeeding floor, interleaved by débris of one kind or another, and forming in section an aggregation of strata which, with their contents, may be compared with the pages of a book. The implication follows that in the process of dismemberment the strata (or pages), with the contained relics (or words), must be kept in proper sequence if the section (or book) is to be read and understood. It is therefore the constant endeavour of the archaeologist, digging down through a stratified site, to isolate scrupulously the successive layers and their contents and to record their interrelationship. How this principle is carried into practice lies beyond the scope of the present essay; it must suffice here to affirm the primary and overriding importance of stratigraphy as a means to the recovery of the relative sequence of structures and cultures, from the lower or earlier to the higher or later, as they lie buried beneath the modern surface of an ancient site.

This process of stratigraphical excavation was carried to a fine art by General Pitt Rivers in Dorset at the end of the nineteenth century, but a precocious instance of it is recorded as long ago as 1784. The practitioner was none other than Thomas Jefferson, then Governor of Virginia and later third President of the United States; and the circumstance is worth recalling. Jefferson, as Governor, concerned himself in the course of his sociological investigations with certain mounds or barrows which he observed in his State. One of these mounds, situated "on the low grounds of the Rivanna, about two miles above its principal fork, and opposite to some hills, on which had been an Indian town", he opened in order to satisfy himself of the correctness of opinions and traditions relating to them. His report, a model of careful conciseness, records that the mound had "derived both origin and growth from the accustomary collection of bones"; that "the first collection had been deposited on the common surface of the earth, a few stones put over it, and then a covering of earth; that the second had been laid on this . . . and was then covered with earth, and so on". The nature of the accumulations, the presence of infants' bones with those of adults, and the absence of weapon-wounds disposed of the theory that the burials were the sequel to a battle and, with other evidences, led the excavator to sound conclusions which need not be further elaborated. Unfortunately, it was many years before his successors in the archaeological field caught up with this remarkable pioneer.

The scrupulous observance of stratification, then, has two primary aims: first, to group relics, layer by layer, in their time-relationship with one another—relics from the same layer being normally of approximate date; and secondly, to indicate the relative time-sequence of one group of relics with another, lower groups being manifestly earlier than superimposed groups. But a *relative* chronology such as that implies, useful though it be, is not enough. Only an *absolute* chronology—calendar dates—can in the long run enable us to equate one culture or civilization with another and so to produce a comprehensive and intelligent picture of human achievement in its significant interrelationships. Unless that ultimate aim can be achieved, our archaeology will be a mere scrapbook, without plot and purpose. Written record, where it exists, is of course a vital aid in this process of rationalization; but written record carries us back no more than 5,000 years, and very inadequately at that. Prehistory is a hundred times as long as history, and other aids must be sought. Let it be said again that in recent years science has come dramatically to the rescue.

In the present century an early example of the impact of science upon archaeological chronology has been cited already. The Swedish geologist, Baron Gerard de Geer, recognized in the clearly varved or laminated clays of his country the annual deposits of the retreating ice-field; the principle being that during the summer seasons the fringe of the ice-field had melted and deposited the geological material which it contained, and that the process had been interrupted or punctuated by the intervening winter seasons. The gradual amelioration of the climate had led to a slow over-all recession of the ice, so that (to simplify the process) from south to north the annual deposits overlapped one another like the slates on a roof. The deposits differed sufficiently in content and thickness to enable the geologists to identify them with fair certainty from pit to pit from south to north-central Sweden, where the process has continued approximately to the present day, and so to count the actual number of summers which have elapsed since the south of Sweden was first released from the ice-field. De Geer calculated the initial date as 6839 B.C.; others have preferred a slightly earlier date, but the difference is not very material. It is now generally agreed that something like 9,000 years have elapsed since Sweden first became habitable by animals and therefore by man, and the estimate has set a term to wild guessing in this fundamental matter. In consequence it has been possible to give approximate dates to a series of changes in the Scandinavian coast-line, climate and vegetation, and to produce an absolute time-frame for the cultures of post-glacial man in northern Europe.

This attainment is an outstanding instance of the application of a purely geological stratification to archaeology. We turn now from vertical stratification to what is in effect horizontal stratification: from geology to botany, and from Sweden to Arizona. Here a younger contemporary of de Geer's, Dr. A. E. Douglass, has worked upon the tree-ring sequence of long-lived trees in the western states of America, where, for example, some of the Sequoia trees of California have lived for over 3,000 years. Again, the principle is not difficult, albeit its application is a highly technical process. It is a familiar fact that a section across a tree grown in a climate with seasonal variations reveals concentric growth-rings, usually representing annual accretions, which will differ with the age of the tree and the climate of the particular year. In years of drought the growth will naturally be less than in wet years, but a tendency for the rings to group in 11-year cycles, in conformity with the 11-year sun-spot cycle, has suggested that solar radiation is a further and independent factor. The variant features of individual rings or their groups are indeed sufficiently distinctive to enable them to be plotted chronologically from long-lived trees of recent terminal date, and to use the plot for comparison with timbers derived from ancient structures. When it be recalled that in America almost everything prior to the sixteenth century is prehistoric, the potentiality of this method as a means of extending a time-scale backwards into the equivalent of our Middle Ages is obvious. And some of the results have in fact been astonishing. In the south-western states, particularly Arizona, are prehistoric Indian villages or *pueblos* which incorporate logs or beams in their structures; and comparison of the growth-rings of these timbers with the Sequoia and other time-charts has not infrequently made it possible to date them with a remarkable precision back to several centuries before the European conquest. Thus, individual *pueblo* timbers have been dated as early as the eighth century A.D., though most of them are after rather than before A.D. 1000. There remains, of course, the imponderable factor of the date of construction relative to the date at which the component timbers were actually cut. Timbers were liable to be reused from building to successive building, and a particular structure may thus be appreciably later than the tree-ring dating that one or more of its timbers would alone suggest. But the method itself has won acceptance, and is of great use within range of modern trees sufficiently aged to provide the necessary comparisons and controls.

Very recently, another kind of time-test has been applied to these *pueblo* timbers, as to many other organic relics related to the study of man in many parts of the world. The test is one that can, without exaggeration, be described as the most important addition to archaeological technique in the present century. It is a byproduct of atomic research, and was first announced by Dr. W. F. Libby and his colleagues from Chicago as recently as 1949. Its mechanism is still short of perfect, but its results are already revolutionary. It is known as the Radio-Carbon or the Carbon 14 (C14) test, and its principle is as follows.

Coming from the outer space, cosmic rays produce in the atmosphere radioactive carbon atoms of atomic weight 14. The Carbon 14 or C14 thus formed is an isotope of ordinary carbon of atomic weight 12 (C12); and both are contained in the carbon dioxide of the atmosphere in a *constant proportion* to each other. Now this carbon dioxide is taken in by plants, and, since all animals—even carnivores—derive their body-material ultimately from plants, it is universally incorporated in living organic matter. Therefore, the proportion of C14 to C12 in all living organic matter is the same as in the atmosphere.

But, once an organism is dead (for example, when a tree is cut down), it ceases to take up carbon from the atmosphere. On the contrary, the C14 content slowly diminishes, reverting to nitrogen at such a rate that after about 5,600 years (termed the "half-life") only half the original amount of C14 is left. After twice that period, only half the residue—i.e. a quarter of the original quantity—is left, and so forth until all the C14 has disappeared.

In dead organic matter, therefore, the ratio of C14 to C12 decreases with time *at a known rate*. The surviving proportion of C14 to C12 in a given organic specimen can be determined in the laboratory, and from it the time elapsed since the "death" of this organic matter can be calculated.

That is the principle. In practice the difficulty is that even the initial ratio of C14 to C12 is exceedingly small and therefore difficult to compute with precision. At first it seemed likely that about 20,000 years would be the maximum range of computation; but now the maximum has been doubled and, with the increasing perfection of the computing machinery, something approaching 100,000 is prophesied. Even with the inevitable margins of error and other complications as yet incompletely understood, that represents a very formidable advance of precision into prehistory, and will lead during the next generation to an extensive reassessment and enlargement of our understanding of human "progress".

Meanwhile a few examples of the application of the C14 test may serve to illustrate its present scope. Thus in North America the last (Mankato) advance of the Wisconsin glaciation passed over tree-trunks the average age of which by the C14 method is about 11,400 years from the present day, less than half the age expected by geologists. It is shortly after that time that man is thought to have first appeared in North America. The oldest artifacts determined by this method in America are several pairs of rope sandals covered by volcanic deposits in Oregon; the age indicated was about 9,050 years, i.e. about 7000 B.C. In the eastern United States, the earliest cultures are proving so far to be later than in the west. Carbon 14 dates suggest that man spread there under 5,000 years ago, but much verification is needed. Other C14 determinations are reported to confirm the beginning of the First Dynasty of Egypt at about 3000 B.C. Charcoal and shells of land-mollusca from a village site, Jarmo, in the foothills of northern Iraq, where agriculture was seemingly practised but pottery-making was unknown, have yielded average dates of about 4700 B.C., making Jarmo at present the earliest known agricultural settlement in the world. Nearer home, C14 has ascribed a date of about 7000 B.C. to a settlement of primitive mesolithic food-gatherers at Star Carr in east Yorkshire. These and other evidences of the kind are beginning to shine like small beacons in the long dark vistas of human achievement, dimly lighting new paths for the bemused prehistorian and gradually softening the transition from history to prehistory.

Parallel with the Carbon 14 analysis, other tests have recently been applied to buried bones, in some instances with dramatic results. One of these tests is based upon the fact that fluorine, an element which is widely distributed in ground waters, is absorbed by bones and teeth buried in them. The rate of absorption varies from place to place, but bones which have lain for the same period of time in the same deposit will contain approximately the same amount of fluorine. Thus, whilst the quantity of fluorine taken in by a particular bone is no index of absolute date, it is a clear indication of relative antiquity in a comparison with the fluorine content of other bones from the *same* area.

Three notable examples will show how this method works. In 1888 a human skeleton was found by gravel-diggers at Galley Hill, near Swanscombe in Kent, at a depth, it was said, of eight feet. The same gravels produced Early Palaeolithic hand-axes of flint and remains of extinct elephant, rhinoceros and lion. The human skeleton was substantially of modern type, and if it also was of Early Palaeolithic date it was a very remarkable testimony to the antiquity of modern man. Expert opinion was divided, however, as to whether the human bones were or were not intrusive into this ancient deposit, and the matter remained in doubt until 1948. In that year both the Galley Hill skeleton and a selection of the animal bones were submitted to the fluorine test. The animal bones were found to contain approximately 1·5 per cent. of fluorine, the human skeleton only 0·5 per cent.; thus the relative modernity of the latter was proved beyond doubt, and Galley Hill man has ceased to trouble the scene.

But in the same Swanscombe gravels were found in 1935-6 fragments of another human skull, also of relatively recent type. This time the discovery was made at a depth of twenty-four feet, so that the risks of intrusion were *prima facie* very much less. Application of the fluorine test in 1948 in fact removed any possibility of doubt; the reaction was 1·7 per cent., if anything therefore slightly more than that of the bones of fossil mammals (1·5 per cent.) from the same deposit. Swanscombe man is a genuine antique; he can boast the oldest human brain-case known in Europe, and may be claimed as a veritable ancestor of modern man although he lived perhaps a quarter of a million years ago.

It was however in 1953 that the fluorine test achieved its greatest triumph, albeit a melancholy one. In this year tests were renewed upon the famous bones and implements found at Piltdown in Sussex before and after 1911. The bones included parts of a cranium comparable with that of *Homo sapiens*, a mandible and canine tooth of ape-like character, and a number of fossil mammalian specimens. Attempts to assemble the cranium and the jaw had produced an incongruous "dawn man" which had been accepted by some palaeontologists and rejected by others; but none had suspected the simple truth, namely, that the whole discovery was a fraud. Initial proof of this solution of the problem was provided by successive fluorine analyses. These showed that the jawbone, with a fluorine content of only 0·03 per cent., was utterly modern, whilst the skull bones contained just enough to show that they were ancient, though probably less than one-tenth as old as had been claimed. Further examination demonstrated that the jaw and canine were actually those of a modern chimpanzee or orang, rubbed down and coloured to simulate antiquity.

It is unnecessary here to follow the process of detection in its details, but reference may be made to a confirmatory test of another kind. It has been shown that bones preserved under the same conditions lose the nitrogen of their protein at a relatively slow and uniform rate. Thus new bones retain a proportionately large quantity of nitrogen, old bones a proportionately small quantity—a reverse process to that of the gradually *increasing* fluorine content. As applied to the groups of bones which have been described above, this test indicated that the Galley Hill skeleton retained 1·6 per cent. of nitrogen, whereas the fossil mammals ostensibly from the same deposit showed only a scarcely-measurable trace; the Swanscombe skull appropriately retained a similar faint trace; whilst the Piltdown jawbone retained as much as 3·9 per cent., which may be compared with the 4·0 per cent. in a fresh bone. In one way and another the Piltdown "discovery" has been shown up as one of the oustanding hoaxes in the history of science, and today the only remaining interest of *Eoanthropus dawsonii* rests in the personality and motive of his modern creator!

Enough has now been said, perhaps, to indicate something of the extent to which modern science is variously contributing to the study of man. Examples only have been chosen; thus nothing has been said of important estimates of time based upon the rate of sedimentation in certain Swiss lakes since the withdrawal of the ice, or of the more accurate and marvellous calculations based upon measurable variations in the amount of radiation received by the earth from the sun. Suffice it that these and other calculations, beyond the easy comprehension of the layman, are combining to provide a graded vista of the slowly accelerating efforts of man or near-man to "make" himself during the last half-million years or more. In one way and another, science has brought a new orderliness into our study of our remoter selves.

From these various efforts to create something approaching a calendar for human prehistory, we may turn to modern methods of collecting and assembling archaeological evidence in the field. Amongst the more familiar of these is air-photography, which during the past thirty-five years has won a leading place amongst archaeological techniques and has added more substantially to knowledge than has any other form of field-survey. As long ago as 1880 attempts were made to photograph ancient sites from the air by the attachment of cameras to small balloons, and photographs of Stonehenge were taken from a war-balloon in 1906. But it was not until the First World War that serious attempts were made to procure archaeological photographs from an aeroplane, and the main credit for this pioneer-work goes to the Germans. When the German forces were operating in Sinai and southern Palestine, a special Commission under Theodor Wiegand was attached to them for the specific purpose of photographing ancient sites, and some of the admirable results of this enterprise were published in 1920. About the same time, Lieut.-Col. G. A. Beazeley observed and photographed ancient town-sites and irrigation-channels near Baghdad; he published a brief account of them in 1919, actually a year before the appearance of the German volume. But it was not until 1923 that the possibilities of archaeological air-photography penetrated beyond a limited circle of interest.

In that year Dr. O. G. S. Crawford, examining air-photographs of the Stonehenge area taken two years previously, observed upon them indications of the complete course of the "Avenue" between the monument and the river Avon. The Avenue is a processional way flanked by banks and ditches which are now visible on the

surface only for a short distance from the stones. The remainder,
long flattened, appeared upon the photographs as dark lines which
represent the course of the former ditches and are now seen season-
ally from the air owing to the ranker growth of the vegetation over
the relatively loose and moist ditch-filling. The completion of the
plan of the Avenue suggests its function: to provide a ceremonial
approach from a water-way up which pilgrims and indeed some of
the stones themselves may have been transported. For geology has
established the fact that the smaller ("blue") stones of Stonehenge
were brought anciently from as far afield as the Prescelly Mountains
of Pembrokeshire.

Under the leadership of Dr. Crawford, this discovery was followed by many others through the same medium. In particular,
whole field-systems dating roughly from 500 B.C. to A.D. 500 have
been identified on the Wiltshire, Dorset and Sussex downs and
elsewhere, and our knowledge of ancient agriculture has thereby
been revolutionized. New types of prehistoric structure—notably,
timber circles or temples of the late Stone and early Bronze ages—
have been recognized, and buried buildings and fortifications of
prehistoric and Roman dates have been added almost without cease
to our archaeological maps. Abroad, above all in deserts such as
those of North Africa and the Near and Middle East, Roman and
pre-Roman forts, town-plans and adjacent agricultural systems have
been surveyed from the air. In Algeria and Syria, Roman frontier-
works and the social economy of the Roman frontier-zone have for
the first time been made intelligible by systematic air-photography.
It is fair to say that not a year passes without some significant
addition to our knowledge in this fashion.

How does air-photography "work"? In fact, there is no great
mystery about this. In the first place, the camera sees nothing that
the eye cannot see; indeed, it sees less since it cannot see colour.
But on the one hand it provides a conveniently static instead of a
moving picture; and, on the other, it integrates the *disjecta* of an
ancient site—its banks, ditches, pot-holes, pits and buried walls—
in a manner rarely feasible in haste or at close range. Less immediately obvious, perhaps, is the answer to the question, How does the
air-camera see *at all* vestiges which may be wholly or nearly invisible
on the ground? Yet here again the principle is sufficiently simple.

It is this way. Soil, once disturbed by man, scarcely ever again
consolidates into the semblance of unmoved earth. An ancient ditch
may be filled flush with the adjacent surfaces, but its filling remains
looser and more sponge-like than the latter. Roots penetrate more
easily into it and find more moisture. Vegetation along the line of
the filling is ranker and greener. From a height the ditch is liable
to appear as a dark line along the surface of the ground. Alternatively, the favourable bedding may attract a luxuriant growth of

nettles or poppies. The poppies still sold for charity on "Poppy Day" in our streets commemorate the lines of poppies which marked the filled or partially filled trenches of the First World War in France and Flanders.

Conversely, an underlying band of hard material, such as buried road-metalling or wall-foundations, is *less* permeable than the adjacent soils. Over it the vegetation, receiving less moisture, will tend to grow shorter and, in the case of corn, will ripen sooner than uninhibited vegetation in the neighbourhood. Thus the streets of a Roman town may show clearly through a ripening crop as light lines across a greener field. Here colour is the main factor, though differential relief helps. On landscape, or in seasons, marked by more uniform growing-conditions, relief will be the main factor, so that observation and photography should then be undertaken in the early morning or the evening, when the sun is low and shadows emphatic. Choice of light and choice of season are thus the two main controls in archaeological air-photography.

Since the Second World War, Dr. J. K. S. St. Joseph, of Cambridge University, has co-operated skilfully with the Royal Air Force in systematic photography of this kind; and his results, stored at Cambridge, have added very remarkably to our knowledge of old sites and new in England and southern Scotland. In particular, our knowledge or potential knowledge of the Roman conquest and military occupation of northern Britain has been enormously enlarged by his work, and it will be many years before mere earthbound archaeologists are able adequately to exploit and define his discoveries.

Since 1946, by way of supplementing uncertain indications from air-photography or other records, an ingenious electrical device has been used effectively under suitable conditions for the planning of buried ditches, walls or roads. It has long been known that the subsoil, or rather the moisture contained by the subsoil, is a conductor of electricity, and that the degree of conductivity varies with the nature of the soil. The method is briefly as follows. A measuring-tape is laid out across the presumed line of the buried feature, and alongside the tape at regular intervals four (or five) steel rods are driven to a depth of about eight inches into the ground. These rods are electrodes and are linked with an apparatus which comprises (*a*) a generator worked by a handle and (*b*) an instrument for recording the resistance encountered by the current thus generated as it passes through the soil from electrode to electrode. The varying resistances are registered in ohms, and, when plotted, may be expected to indicate a higher resistance than normal when the current is obstructed by buried stone-work or a lower resistance than normal when the looser and moister filling of a pit or buried ditch is encountered. The sensitivity of the instrument is limited to a depth of about four feet, and a pre-condition is a relatively uniform subsoil free from rocks or stone-debris. The best subsoils are gravel, sand, clay, peat and chalk; and in these materials surprisingly accurate results have been obtained by Mr. R. J. C. Atkinson in England and by other investigators in France, Germany and America. A classic example is the plotting of neolithic and Early Bronze Age earth-circles at Dorchester near Oxford, where subsequent excavation revealed less than a two per cent. error. The outer walls of a Roman house near Oxford were also traced exactly, and the Saxon town-walls of Cricklade in Wiltshire were first detected by this method. Roman roads in the Oxford region have similarly been mapped and their width ascertained; and the extent of an Anglo-Saxon cemetery near Croydon in Surrey has been tested, the results being confirmed by excavation. Whilst no universal utility is claimed for this apparatus, its occasional utility is indubitable.

Any sketch of modern archaeological preoccupations would be incomplete without a word or two upon the advances in geographical analysis which have marked the last half-century. Here, again, a pioneer was Dr. O. G. S. Crawford who, shortly before the First World War, was already mapping Bronze Age and other distributions, and so beginning to relate ancient man specifically to his environment. But it was Sir Cyril Fox who, first in his study of the Cambridge region and later in that of Britain as a whole, set the new standard for environmental geography as the background of pre- and proto-history—or indeed of history in its fullest amplitude. The reconstruction of a landscape on the basis of its surface-geology and the careful relation of human vestiges to its controlling features gave archaeology a three-dimensional quality which it had largely lacked, and lent an authority to sociological generalizations that was substantially new in spite of Pitt Rivers's pronouncement long ago that "distribution is a necessary prelude to generalization". With all allowance for highly important work in Scandinavia, in this matter of environment British archaeologists have tended in recent years to outpace their foreign colleagues.

Alongside the mapping of the ancient population-pattern goes the somewhat simpler problem of ancient travel and trade. It is now over thirty years since geology proved that the "blue-stones" of Stonehenge came from Pembrokeshire, although the full significance of this remarkable fact remains hidden. More recently much work has been done by geologists on the distribution of neolithic stone axes in Britain with notable but more readily intelligible results. These results, based as they are upon the microscopic examination of rock-sections, are as objective and reliable as geological science can make them, after allowance for the unlikely accident of un-identified outcrops. They prove the unsuspected extent to which artifacts in ancient times were liable to move from their place of origin. Thus stone axes quarried on Penmaenmawr in North Wales reached Hampshire on the one hand and the lowlands of Scotland on the other, and other Neolithic or Early Bronze Age industries covered a comparably wide field. This petrological survey, which has now been carried on systematically for some years, is opening a new chapter in British prehistory, and its methodical extension to the Continent is an obvious need of the near future.

II. Recent Archaeological Fieldwork and Excavation (1955)

So much for modern technical methods. To turn to their application is to confront a vast field of research which does not lend itself easily to summary. A few examples may however be cited to indicate the range of work carried out since the Second World War, and the general trends of investigation at the present day.

Since the accidental finding of the famous painted cave of Lascaux at Montignac (Dordogne) in 1940, the most original contributions to the study of late palaeolithic man (perhaps 20,000 to 50,000 years ago) are probably those made by two women-archaeologists, Dr. Dorothy Garrod and Mlle. Suzanne de St. Mathurin, near the town of Angles, in the Department of Vienne, France.[1] Here, at the foot of a cliff above the river Anglin, lies a great block of limestone known locally as *le roc aux sorciers*, behind which excavation has revealed a rock-shelter obscured by earth, vegetation and ancient falls of rock. Amongst the fallen fragments were many carved representations of horses, bison, ibexes, chamois, and at least one human figure; and it was evident that the wall and roof of the shelter had formerly carried a sculptured frieze of surpassing interest dating from the apogee of Magdalenian Cave Art. Clearance of the surviving and undisturbed face of the cliff has subsequently revealed intact figures—human and animal—in high relief; and, when fully published, this amazing sculpture-gallery will add materially to our knowledge of Cave Man, his environment, art and religion. Meanwhile the preliminary reports sufficiently indicate the assurance and vividness of the carving, and, furthermore, suggest that here, as rarely in Magdalenian art, there is a sense of composition and grouping, as though the artist had in mind something more ambitious than the mere representation of individual unrelated figures. Thus a group of ibex is provisionally interpreted as representing a herd on the first impact of alarm, as the palaeolithic hunter must often enough have seen it; the young males of the herd turn and stand to confront the danger whilst the others make their way to safety. Another group is that of three human females, with the head and shoulders missing and the sex-organs emphasized, presumably in relation to a fertility-cult. On

[1] *Illustrated London News* (July 16, 1949; July 7, 1951; March 15, 1952).

the other hand one of the rock fragments shows a human head which is our most precious document for the living appearance of the Cave-hunter himself. In one way and another, the local association of the spot with witches and sorcerers is sufficiently intelligible.

For the age following that of the Palaeolithic hunters the most striking recent illustration is provided by Dr. Garrod's successor in the Disney Chair of Archaeology at Cambridge—Professor Grahame Clark. In the Vale of Pickering some five miles south of Scarborough in Yorkshire, a site located by Mr. John Moore was fully explored by Professor Clark in and after 1949 with results which have amplified manifold our previous knowledge of the Mesolithic food-gatherers of Britain, and indeed of northern Europe as a whole.[1] The ancient settlement, 220-240 square yards in area, lay on the flank of a low hillock rising a few feet above the peat which represents a former lake. On the marshy shore of this lake a crude platform of birchwood and moss had been laid down, doubtless to carry tents or lightly built huts which have long disappeared without trace. The little community—probably not more than fifteen or twenty people—had lived mainly by hunting, and bones of elk and ox, red and roe deer and of water-birds are the most numerous. To what extent fish and plants contributed to the diet is less certain, but remains of leisters or fish-spears made of serrated splinters of antler were very numerous and compensate for the complete absence of fish-bones. The use of the bow is indicated by the microlithic armatures of about a hundred arrows, though no actual bow was preserved. Some sort of raft or boat, possibly a skin canoe or coracle, is implied by a birchwood paddle which is the oldest implement of its kind known. There is no hint of the domestication of animals, even of the dog.

A radio-carbon dating gives 7538 B.C. (with a possible error ± of 350 years) for the settlement, and this is consistent with geological stratigraphy and pollen-evidence. The culture is equated with an early phase of the Maglemose of Scandinavia in the transition from the latest Palaeolithic to the more evolved Mesolithic, when Britain from Yorkshire to Sussex was still joined by a continuous land-surface with the Continent.

When we pass from the basic food-gathering communities of the Mesolithic period to the early phases of food-production in the forms of animal-domestication and agriculture, we reach a period upon which new light has been thrown by recent work in the Near and Middle East. Where the first stages of the "agricultural revolution" were first achieved on any significant scale is a problem which is unlikely to be solved in the foreseeable future, but exploration carried out since 1948 in northern Iraq by Dr. R. J. Braidwood for

[1] J. G. D. Clark, *Excavations at Star Carr* (Cambridge, 1954).

the Oriental Institute of the University of Chicago has given us a new and useful fixed point. It is now known that villagers in the grassy uplands north of Kirkuk kept herds of cattle and flocks of sheep or goats and, above all, grew two varieties of wheat, which they reaped with composite flint sickles (blades of flint set in a curved wooden backing by means of a bitumen adhesive). Radio-carbon analyses of carbon and shells of land-mollusca from one of the sites give dates between 5000 and 4500 B.C.; so that these obscure villagers are at present the earliest known farmers in the world.

The sites in question are Jarmo, Karim Shahir, Palegawra and Barda Balka, all appropriately within the so-called "Fertile Crescent" which extends from Palestine and the Syrian coastlands across the upper waters of the Euphrates and the Tigris and into the western margins of the Iranian plateau. Within that Crescent lie many of the most ancient attempts at village-life, here and there already approaching market-town status, and pointing to the great civic developments of third millennium Sumer in the plains to the south. The new discoveries fit happily therefore into the existing frame of knowledge, but they lend a new precision to the picture.

Jarmo, the most amply explored site of the group, was originally a village of three acres or more on a hilltop above a stream. It lasted long enough to rise to a height of over twenty feet above its first building-level; but although cultural modifications occurred during its long life, no revolutionary change is indicated by them. The houses were of rectangular plan and were constructed of pressed mud walling, sometimes with rough stone foundations. The cultural equipment included flint and obsidian tools, many in the form of microliths; ground stone objects such as bracelets, beads, pestles and mortars; and bone hafts, awls, needles, beads and spoons. A striking feature was the complete absence of pottery until a late period, when a few potsherds of painted and burnished ware came in from some unidentified source and started a rather woebegone local pottery industry. Prior to that occurrence the baking of clay did not suggest itself to the villagers; even the clay figurines of pregnant mother-goddesses, which were found at all levels of occupa-tion, were not baked.[1]

This absence of pottery from early settlements otherwise familiar with the normal economy of the Neolithic phase has recently been observed on other sites in the Near and Middle East. Thus in 1951-2 a mound known as Kile Gul Mohammad near Quetta in Baluchistan revealed in its lowest levels a village-culture with mud-brick houses and chert tools but no pottery. Bones of sheep or goat were present, and some sort of crop-production is a likely postulate. Unfortunately, no date is at present available for this

[1] See R. J. Braidwood in *Illustrated London News* (December 15, 1951).

settlement.[1] Nor has a date yet been found for the equivalent phases of the famous site of Jericho, in Jordan, where excavations have been renewed since 1952 by Dr. Kathleen Kenyon as Director of the British School at Jerusalem.[2] But here the pre-pottery stage of the Neolithic was certainly long-lived in itself and was succeeded by a lengthy succession of Neolithic phases associated with abundant and complicated pottery-series; so that it is likely to date back to the fifth or even sixth millennium. It seems to represent here a somewhat more evolved society or societies than that of the Jarmo site but is not on that account necessarily later. On at least two successive occasions the platform which carried pre-pottery Jericho was revetted with a heavy stone facing which may have been carried up as a defensive wall or parapet. Further information is required (and is being sought) as to the extent and character of these early essays in urban fortification at Jericho, but there can be no doubt as to their importance in the development of static settlement based upon an economy in which agriculture may be supposed to have played an important part. Incidentally, the earlier Neolithic houses have walls which are curved or convex on plan; but already before the introduction of pottery relatively sophisticated buildings were being erected, with straight walls and smooth plastered floors.

This is not the place to review the present Jericho excavations in any detail. They are being actively pursued and are adding appreciably and sometimes vividly to our knowledge of the urban cultures of the Jordan valley in the Neolithic and Bronze Ages. It seems now less likely than at one time it did that much will be found of the time of Joshua; man and nature have combined to remove the upper strata of the mound, and the overturned town-walls which were thought to represent the Joshua episode are now known to be of considerably earlier date. But in the period when, before 1600 B.C., the Hyksos with their war-chariots were streaming southwards into Egypt, Jericho was on three occasions fortified with the formidable smooth escarpment which is characteristic of the period and was designed to keep the charioteers at a suitable distance from the town-walls; and earlier systems of defence extend the vista backwards through a richer succession of cultural phases than any Palestinian site has hitherto produced. One detail may be mentioned. From a pre-pottery Neolithic layer were extracted seven human skulls, which had anciently been packed with earth and then covered with plaster on which the features had been modelled in lifelike fashion. One has cowrie-shell eyes, the others have eyes inset with flat plaques of shell leaving a central gap for the pupil. In one case the top of the skull had been decorated with bands of black

[1] W. A. Fairservis, *American Museum Novitates*, No. 1587 (September, 1952), p. 18.

[2] Interim reports in *Palestine Exploration Quarterly* for 1952-4.

paint. The function of these skulls can only be conjectured, though modern analogies from the New Guinea area suggest that they may have been either heads of ancestors preserved in honour, or of foes preserved as trophies. In a restricted sense they may be claimed as the earliest attempts at something approaching human portraiture.

In Egypt the principal focus of recent research has been Saqqara, the necropolis of Memphis, capital of Lower Egypt. There the Egyptian authorities, led by M. Zakaria Goneim, have uncovered an unfinished step-pyramid and its enclosure, though unhappily the burial-chamber was empty and had apparently never been used. Near by, Professor W. B. Emery has continued the excavations which he began before the War, in a series of royal and other tombs of a remarkable kind, dating from about 3000 B.C. The body was in several instances buried in a shaft-grave beneath a large *mastaba* or monumental superstructure, the exterior of which was an alternation of grooved or fluted projections and recesses, evidently in imitation of a palace-façade, though devoid of structural entrance. Strangely enough, the façade had been completely masked by surrounding brick walls and was intended solely as the private housing of the dead. Round about were serried lines of graves containing concubines and attendants slaughtered to accompany their master.

Certain of these *mastabas* have been identified as those of Early Dynastic pharaohs, but the identification is complicated by the fact that other tombs of these same kings have been discovered at Abydos which, as the ancient This, was the capital of Upper Egypt. That the two capitals should have contained duplicate royal tombs is readily intelligible, but which of the two in any particular case actually possessed the royal body is disputed now as it may have been disputed anciently.

Overlapping the last phase of ancient Jericho and representing a different range of problems is the late Bronze and Early Iron Age capital identified and partially excavated by Dr. Claude Schaeffer at Enkomi on Cyprus since 1946.[1] The former name of the place was Alasia, and it is referred to in the Tell el-Amarna Letters and other cuneiform records found in Syria and Anatolia. The excavations suggest that the city was laid out in the fifteenth century B.C., possibly under the direction of Achaean rulers, on a grid plan, with buildings sometimes constructed of superb masonry and with tombs hollowed in the chalk subsoil beneath them. At the beginning of the twelfth century B.C. the place was burnt by Early Iron Age invaders, identified with the mysterious Sea People who, whatever their general history and antecedents may have been, included Philistines and were later defeated in Egypt by Rameses III (about 1163 B.C.). These invaders were in a lower stage of civilization than

[1] *Illustrated London News* (August 20 and 27, 1949; May 24 and 31, 1952).

their Bronze Age predecessors, and their arrival is marked by the building of small, roughly constructed houses and workshops and by rough pottery which has been described as sub-Mycenaean. They in turn were confronted by fresh Aegean influence not yet clearly analysed; and sometime during the eleventh century the site was, for reasons unknown, deserted and ultimately lost to view.

The varied and important material recovered by Dr. Schaeffer includes one object of outstanding quality. One of the chalk-cut graves, dating from the early part of the fourteenth century B.C. and therefore antedating the coming of the Sea People, contained the burials possibly of priests, one of whom had a gold pectoral embossed with a tree-symbol flanked by griffins. On his right hand he wore a gold ring similarly engraved, and near his elbow had been placed two large silver cups. One of the cups, of exquisite workmanship, is decorated with six bulls' heads and a series of linked rosettes, all inlaid in gold and niello (a black metallic compound)—incidentally a far earlier example of the niello technique than any previously known. The sureness and beauty of the design and its execution give the cup an almost unique place in the history of craftsmanship; matched, if at all, by a gold-lined cup found between the wars at Dendra in the Peloponnese. A fuller publication is awaited.

From Cyprus we may return to northern Iraq, and in particular to the historic site of Nimrud, near Mosul, where Professor M. E. L. Mallowan has been digging since 1949.[1] Nimrud is the site of the rich and powerful Assyrian capital of Kalhu or Calah which flourished between 880 and 612 B.C. and, since the time of Layard in the middle of the nineteenth century, has been known to contain buildings and sculptures of an impressive kind. Most though not all of the digging has been concentrated upon the acropolis and, in particular, upon two palaces, of which the North-west Palace has produced specially remarkable "finds". Outside its northern entrance was discovered a sandstone *stele* which is in the literal sense a document of unique value; for it bears an inscription, 154 lines in length, which records in the first place the building of the palace by King Assur-nasirpal II (883-859 B.C.), the names of the principal gods, the countries that the king had conquered, the buildings which he had erected in the city, and the canals that he had dug. It includes also a record of his lion and elephant hunts, and a catalogue of the different kinds of flora and fauna within the city's boundaries. But, above all, it concludes with an account of a great feast given to no fewer than 69,574 persons after the completion of his palace, and it is in effect therefore a census of the (free?) citizens in and around the metropolis in the year 879 B.C. As such, it

[1] *Illustrated London News* (July 22 and 29, 1950; July 28, and August 4, 1951; August 16 and 23, 1952; August 8 and 15, 1953).

is an historical record of unsurpassed importance, and will in future be basic to the study of the sociological problems of the region and period.

To the same reign belongs a brick-lined well, eighty-three feet deep, which was completely excavated and produced from its silt a series of ivory carvings of the eighth century B.C. without parallel in the Near East. Amongst these is a female head, about half life-size, which is cut from a large tusk and is a masterpiece of the ivory-cutter's art. The eyebrows, pupils and hair are coloured black, and the lips are reddened; the modelling is smooth and finished, and the mouth suggests the archaic smile of the "aunts" from the Athenian acropolis. At least as remarkable are two identical plaques from the same sludge, carved in relief with the representation of a lioness killing a Nubian in a field of lotuses. The small head of the negro in particular is exquisitely rendered. The work is picked out in colour by gold overlay and by inlaid carnelians and lapis lazuli. One of these plaques is now in the Iraq Museum at Baghdad, the other is in the British Museum.

Of a nearer and more familiar age is the work which has been done since the War on the Punic, Greek and Roman cities inherited along the Libyan coast from the old Italian régime. In this matter the British School at Rome has taken the lead, and the field-operations have been directed mainly by Mr. J. B. Ward Perkins, Director of the School, Mr. R. G. Goodchild and Dr. Kathleen Kenyon.[1] The principal tasks so far have been: the ground-survey and mapping of Roman Tripolitania and Cyrenaica, the collection of Tripolitanian inscriptions, the analytical planning of Lepcis Magna, the further excavation of Sabratha, and the planning and publication of the Roman and Byzantine churches of Tripolitania. Before the War, the Italians had cleared extensive areas at Lepcis, Sabratha and Cyrene, but the work had been indifferently published and there had been little scientific exploration in depth. This last omission has now been remedied to some extent at Sabratha, where remains of the Phoenician city have been examined beneath its Roman successors and much new information obtained from them. The earliest occupation, dating perhaps from the sixth century B.C., seems to indicate intermittent (seasonal?) visitation by Phoenician traders, who set up tents and shacks near the shore for their chaffering with the natives. Towards 400 B.C. a more permanent occupation, amounting to colonization, took place, and a massive defensive wall was added on the landward side. Subsequently, the town spread beyond its fortified nucleus, and was seemingly a flourishing market when, at the end of the first century B.C., the Romans took it over and largely replanned it. By the end of the second century A.D. it was one of the great emporia of

[1] *Illustrated London News* (March 29, 1952).

North Africa with all the amenities of a first-class Roman city. The Vandal invasions of the fifth century brought it to an end, save for a small-scale Byzantine revival, which succumbed a century later to the Arabs. When fully published, the work will add materially to our present very indifferent knowledge of the Phoenician and Roman cultures of the southern Mediterranean coast.

Partially contemporary with Sabratha but of another world is the romantic city of Hatra, set in the heart of the desert between the Tigris and the Euphrates, in central Iraq. Here since 1951 the Iraq Department of Antiquities has been carrying out fruitful excavations, revealing buildings, sculptures and inscriptions of great interest.[1] The date and circumstances of the city's foundation are still uncertain; but it probably came into existence in the first century B.C. as an independent Arab capital dominating the trade-routes between the Parthian capital of Ctesiphon and such northern cities as Singara and Nisibis. It was besieged in vain by Trajan and Septimius Severus and did not fall until it was attacked by the Sasanian king Shapur I in the middle of the third century A.D. The city was circular on plan, with a diameter of more than a mile, and was defended by two lines of wall. In the centre stands the sanctuary of Shamash the Sun-god, consisting of a range of great vaulted recesses or *iwans* of superb ashlar. Elsewhere, nine other temples were dedicated each to a single deity, who was sometimes equated with a classical god such as Hercules or Hermes. The sculpture from these shrines is remarkable; though it occasionally apes classical prototypes, at its best it has the stiff, formal dignity of Parthian sculpture with a markedly orientalizing aspect. The material is commonly marble, and the eyes are sometimes given a penetrating stare by means of shell and black-stone inlays. Portrait statuary has also been found; it combines rigidity and schematic rendering with an expressive individuality in the rendering of the face. The collection as a whole has thrown a new and vivid light on the art and religion of this remote city which, in spite of its isolation, was larger than Roman London and long served as a pivot for desert-traffic.

Finally, even a summary and selective survey of recent work must include a reference to the submarine exploration which has in recent years been carried out with the aid of breathing-apparatus borne by the diver, who is thus enabled to work independently of surface-machinery. Up to date, this exploration, largely in French hands, has been marked by enthusiasm rather than scientific control, but its potentialities are not negligible. To a depth of 100 feet or more it is possible for trained divers to remain submerged for a quarter of an hour at a time, to take notes and photographs,

[1] *Illustrated London News* (November 10 and 17, 1951; December 18 and 25, 1954).

and even to "televise"; and the astonishing number of ancient wrecks already identified along the French and Spanish coasts and further afield in the Aegean holds abundant promise. An example which has been much publicized is that of a Graeco-Italian trading-vessel of about 200 B.C. which has been examined by Commandant J. Y. Cousteau at the base of a rocky islet called *Le Grand Congloué* near Marseille. The vessel was evidently of considerable size and possibly had more than one deck, but the reports available are deficient in exact information. The main cargo was of wine, and it would seem that the ship had first taken on a load of wine-jars at one of the Greek islands and had subsequently added a deck-cargo in or near the Bay of Naples. There is also a quantity of Campanian table-ware, some of it bearing Greek inscriptions. Many of the wine-jars are themselves stamped or bear stamped sealings, and their evidence is likely to be helpful in the investigation of similar jars from native sites in the Gaulish hinterland. It is to be hoped, however, that in cases of this kind future exploration may be more informative, particularly in relation to the character and construction of the ship itself which, in some instances, is thought to be reasonably intact.

BOOKS SUGGESTED FOR FURTHER READING

V. Gordon Childe, *Man Makes Himself* (Watts, 1939); *New Light on the Most Ancient East* (Routledge and Kegan Paul, 1952).

Grahame Clark, *Prehistoric Europe* (Cambridge University Press, 1954).

O. G. S. Crawford, *Archaeology in the Field* (Phoenix House, 1953).

Glyn E. Daniel, *A Hundred Years of Archaeology* (Gerald Duckworth, 1950).

C. and J. Hawkes, *Prehistoric Britain* (Chatto and Windus, 1951).

Sir Mortimer Wheeler, *Archaeology from the Earth* (Clarendon Press, 1954).

THE NEW ARTS OF THE TWENTIETH CENTURY

by HARMAN GRISEWOOD

THE ARTS IN OUR time have usually made a difficult and even dangerous subject for discussion. Thirty years ago this was so on account of the fierce disagreements evoked. Nowadays embarrassment is more usual because of the ensuing boredom or bewilderment. Discussion is left to those with administrative zeal who feel that protection for the arts is bound up with a social conscience. The illustrious figures of today are more peaceful than polemical. In the twenties there was more belief and fervour among those who cherished the arts. The endeavours now are of expediency. The heaviest demands were formerly upon faith; they are now upon prudence.

This development has borne more hardly upon the newer arts than upon the old. State patronage has concentrated upon providing the amenities of the concert hall and the picture gallery, which are kept supplied by artists working in the old individualistic tradition. The new collaborative arts, the cinema and broadcasting, have been more and more left to themselves. They both possess self-generating sources of wealth and power. This altered mood and concentration of the attention upon the ailing tradition of the older arts has withdrawn an aesthetic succour from the new, with the result that their status as arts is now less secure. If Robert Bridges had written his "Testament of Beauty" in the fifties it is doubtful if he would feel prompted to include the confident salutation to Broadcasting:

> . . . yet hath modern culture enriched a wasting soul;
> Science comforting man's animal poverty. . . .

The new arts of the twentieth century are diffusionary arts, as were those of Byzantium. Some would rather call them techniques or technical inventions; but most would agree upon the description "mass media of communication". It is agreed too that by these media much larger numbers than before are enabled to enjoy the results of artistic endeavour.

Two important visual inventions were perfected under Byzantine

influence: the art of the great aulic mosaics, an art of public display;
and the art of the small portable mosaic or painted ikon, an art for
private individual appreciation. The diffusionary arts of this century offer some similarities. The cinema and broadcasting are great
distributive inventions. The one offers scope for the art of public
display; the other, heard or seen in the home, is meant for private
or family enjoyment. In so far as both of these are visual arts, each
takes to itself some of the energy, creative and appreciative, which
was formerly used in words. The first great period of Byzantine
visual art in the sixth century succeeded what had been an ascendency of the written or the spoken word—the Alexandrian Hellenic
tradition of philosophic or theological literature. In this previous
literary epoch the artist or philosopher had made his impression as
an individual. The writer—Plotinus or Augustine—founded or
influenced a "school" or a style, and by his own personal effort
created a wave of philosophical thought which affected the art of
the time in all its modes. This was a great period of discussion, the
age of the Fathers and the age of the great heresiarchs. Like our
own eighteenth and nineteenth centuries, it was predominantly
a literary age and an age of precise, quickly moving ideas and ideals.
What succeeded—in the sixth century, as in our own—was largely
visual in character; it was also largely anonymous and impersonal;
thirdly, in each case the new arts were responsive technically to a
diffusionary impulse.

The cinema and broadcasting are not new in the sense that they
differ altogether from the old arts, as painting is a different art from
music, but they are something more than new departures within an
artistic tradition. They are not merely a new style as the Renaissance
style was new following the medieval centuries. The *materia technica*
of broadcasting and of the cinema considered in themselves are
sufficiently different to afford the opportunity of altogether new
sound and visual art works. Yet there is still room for doubt as to
whether these inventions do in fact truly represent new arts. In so
far as they serve to convey art works that already exist, they are
scarcely new arts; they are rather techniques of reproduction.
Where these techniques are used neither to reproduce art works
which exist nor to make new ones, the cinema and broadcasting are
merely the technical means of conveying information or instruction
or the data for various types of amusement. These thoughts should
prevent the description "new arts" being applied generally to the
cinema and broadcasting until certain clarifications and definitions
are established. But whatever the results of these definitions, there is
a secure though limited entitlement to the description by the fact
that these new *materia technica* have been used for genuine art works—
works which have been made for the new medium and which could
not exist without it. It must be remembered that an art medium is

not wholly coextensive with the art. Paint and words and musical sounds may be used for effects which are not, and which are not meant to be, artistic effects and there is no misuse involved in these non-artistic activities. The film, the microphone and the electronic camera are not essentially reserved for deliberate art works. These media are not abused when the results are a newsreel, a geography lesson, an ice-hockey match or "What's My Line?"

But however these distinctions may comfort the mind, there are grounds—other grounds—for doubts and fears about the art situation to which these two new arts contribute. The fears I believe justified are lest the technical nature of the new arts absorb all the other arts, and lest the appetite for the new arts together with the exploiters of the appetite degrade art itself and bring it to a point of near extinction. Those who care for what some may continue to call "the real arts" and those who discern that civilizational enfeeblement is bound up with a cultural and artistic ill health— these vigilantes of contemporary history—may well be anxious lest a degradation of the new arts is accompanied by a débâcle not only in the world of art but far beyond it. To illuminate this predicament, art discussion carried on in the old style of aesthetic controversy is not enough.

French academic thought of the 1830's spoke of the classical imitators of David as "real artists" and the results as "real art". Thus they contended for a generation against the Romantic impulse. By 1880 the Romantic artists defended themselves and were defended as "real artists" against the Impressionists. But this lively and logical sequence has failed in our century, like an old family dying out for lack of heirs; the defenders of "real art" now are confused and scattered. The new arts are like a new religion among the sects, threatening the old foundations and compelling a regrouping of forces. Vitality is dying away in the old disputes. The Orontes is flowing into the Tiber.

An attempt must be made, however uncertain the results, at a close-up inspection of these ideas which have been thrust upon our consciousness pell-mell and hastily by the rapid and still primitive development of the new arts themselves. The situation has not been favourable to careful analysis and discussion. Both are popular arts and suffer a neglect by serious critics through an unspoken assumption that the cinema and broadcasting are mere vulgarizations of "real art". They are, too, in most parts of the world heavily commercialized and are in this aspect industries rather than arts. Indeed the cinema and broadcasting are more easily comprehended in commercial or sociological terms. But if the attention of society is concentrated upon them in such terms, their development will respond more and more to sociological and mercantile considerations. The artist will have no place. Yet the media themselves are to a large extent artistic media, and the expulsion of the artist is dangerous. It is dangerous because falsity is always dangerous, and falsity on the grand scale is very dangerous indeed.

The typical artist in regard to his material is a man of pure motive. What he desires is the good of the work. This good and this purity of motive is what a successful art work communicates. The artist characteristically is not at his best in proceeding from a mixture of diverse inducements, though he often has to work within such a setting. If the work is subject to contradictory strains of mixed motive it is liable to collapse artistically, and though the result may be a popular triumph, in fact a deceit will have been contrived. And if such deceit is organized on a vast scale and popularized by the pressure of advertisement, the results for art must surely be disastrous and the results for society cannot be wholesome.

Three descriptive ideas may be disengaged from the preceding introductory glance at the two new arts of broadcasting and the cinema. These are: their anonymity, their visual appeal and a diffusionary impulse. A fourth should be added which was not a limitation for the Byzantine mosaicists nor upon other arts of the past: the ephemeral limitation.

It is necessary to examine these four factors if the predicament of the two twentieth-century arts is to be grasped. First the characteristic of anonymity. This might best be called an impersonal rather than an anonymous quality, since there are usually more signatures upon these new art works than their interest requires. The long lists of artists, directors, producers and assistants which precede a film and follow a broadcast production more often give rise to a restless lassitude than to lively interest. They make a different impression from that caused by the little gilt label at the bottom of a picture, or by the jacket of a book, or by the more complex handbill of a play. The reason for our recoil is partly because no one expects to recognize or remember the names except for the few already well known. The experience is not unlike that of meeting too many people at a party whose names you are sure to forget afterwards. But in the case of the cinema work or the broadcast work, those whose names are announced seem to claim their recognition as artists: and this the spectator cannot always concede, however well disposed he may be. The work of the devisers, arrangers, animators, assembly cutters, caption writers and lighting experts cannot be identified in the result. And yet some identity is sought. Here is a genuine problem for the artist. In our century this problem is exaggerated by the fact that we have been so long conditioned by a tradition of Romantic individualism and by various sorts of Expressionism that we mostly assume that the main endeavour of the artist is to express himself in his art. This assumption was not overthrown by our revolt earlier in the century against Romanticism nor by the various sorts of ideological art, responding to the social and political disturbance of our time, nor by the new psychological influences which invite the artist to explore his own mysterious processes. None of these twentieth-century situations relieves the artist from the burden of that individualism, fastened upon him during the Renaissance, which produced the isolation of the artist from the impersonal world of craftsman and designer, carpenter and colour-maker. At that time the artisans of art were split away from the artist. So nowadays, while these piteous lists are being announced upon the screen or from the loudspeaker, we might use the time to reflect upon that splendour and burden of the artists' isolation as it painfully dissolves in the technical complexity of the twentieth-century arts. Such effacement distresses the mind which cannot reach back to a pre-Renaissance condition. And yet this exercise would bring a sense of relief through the realization that an artist's dignity and satisfaction need not depend upon the assertion of himself as solely dominant upon the material of his art. An artist need not be a revolutionary dictator elbowing others out of his way so that a single signature appears upon his work as upon a decree of state. Some art works—certainly the types of art that have been in modern times most cherished—must be individual creations, but not all art forms are at their best when held by a single artist in a monopolistic grasp.

We of the audience are more aware of this strain and disorder in the art work as we see it on the screen and hear it than are the artists who contribute to the result. Certainly those who have witnessed at the studios the production of a film or broadcast do not observe except now and then the element of individualism in the artist affecting adversely the processes of production. There is of course at times a clash of personality and an assertiveness, but this is not the artist seeking an ascendency as an artist; it is the ordinary display of human assertiveness which shows often enough elsewhere in private or public life. The performers and directors and the artist-artisans who propel the machines or arrange the lighting—these work in amiable harmony for the sake of "the show". But when it comes to the finished product they do not seem to us to take their bow as a trained troupe but as a sequence of individuals each of whom has an individual's reputation, however small, that seeks nourishment from the work itself. An attempt by the audience to consider all these subjective efforts as a unity is bewildering. A sense of order rarely emerges. And yet an art work is a unity and the human intelligence naturally looks for a unity in it and in its makers. This failure is not merely on the part of the public to appreciate the various roles which each individual plays. However well acquainted with the techniques the spectator or listener may be, this sense of disorder and inconsistency remains. It is derived I believe from a doubt as to the status of the individual participants. There is no doubt about what the artist or artisan is to do. The doubt is not of that kind. It is ultimately a doubt as to his aesthetic relation to the art work and even a doubt as to whether the work itself is an art work or not. The work is conveniently designated "a show", which is an ambiguous term aesthetically.

It is significant that the current system of identification follows what has been customary in the theatre. Those who act or speak or sing are known as "artists", and the announcement of their names makes some impression of coherence. The director's or producer's status as an artist is in fact more doubtful, though he is acknowledged as the master of the work in the sense of the conductor of an orchestra. Then there are the various sorts of writers or composers whose importance often depends upon a reputation gained outside the studio. Their connexion with the result is sometimes an uncertain one and is lost to the consciousness in many cases because the nature of "the show" overpowers the purely literary and musical element considered aesthetically in itself. There are, too, the various sorts of technical assistants. The chief men are sometimes named, but their function is hardly known to the audience, and in fact they each have numerous sub-assistants under them who are not named but who often contribute vitally to the aesthetic effect.

There are in fact two art works involved in cinema or broadcast production. One is preparatory for the other. The first is the composition—as it were the writing of a score by a composer or the text of a play by the dramatist. That is one complete art process. In the case of a cinema film and often in the case of a broadcast for television or for sound a large number of people take part in this. And then there is "the show"—the production, the performance—and in this a yet larger number participate. The audience is invited to see and hear both together. Thus the difficulty of acquainting the public with the exact responsibility in each case of each artist-contributor is insuperable and the attempt is often absurd. A confusion results which is inevitable if the basis of acknowledgement is to be the Romantic conception of individualism in art.

The confusion concerns the role of the artist and the integrity of the show considered as an art work. Confusion as mere perplexity among the spectators would matter little, but confusion about the reality of the art work and of the artist is obviously crucial. And I believe there is a hesitancy of this sort.

If we admit there is a genuine difficulty here from the standpoint of art, we should naturally turn to wonder about a remedy. This is not likely to be found in attempts to make the cinema and broadcasting flourish in the soil that is favourable to the individualistic arts. The humanistic post-Renaissance hankering for Man as Hero produced a concept of the artist-hero which can be disastrously misapplied to a collaborative art such as a film or a broadcasting production. There is no artist-hero of Chartres or of the Torcello *Madonna*. And in our own day, there is no single artist-hero of the ballet or opera. These have living artistic traditions of collaboration by which the participants know their roles, and we too do not question them. We do not find it unnatural that Bakst and Bonnard, Stravinski and Poulenc collaborated with the great Russian dancers. True, the daemonic personality of Diaghilev was necessary to bring this about. And some might point to him as the artist-hero of the result. But however Diaghilev's role should be described, he did nothing to arouse hesitancy among those who contributed to the art work in regard to their role as artists. There was no atmosphere of aesthetic confusion and no bewilderment among us in regard to the work itself or in regard to those who made it. But this happy situation does not apply in the cinema or in broadcasting.

There are at least two influences which work against an aesthetic coherence in the works of the new arts. These two arts are enthralled by two anti-artistic tyrannies—the Box Office and the Machine. Neither of these need be disastrous, yet in practice they often are. To placate such baleful influences, sacrifices must be offered at their shrines not only by those who work in the cinema and in broadcasting but by the whole community. Our society has a bad conscience in regard to both tyrants. It has deified them both and now goes in fear of them. In spite of such figures as Ruskin, the nineteenth century elaborated a cult of Trade and of the Machine; it made of them twin redemptive divinities who were expected to produce a millennium of human happiness. The cult is no longer as popular as it was, and in our own time there has grown up a literature of revolt which has upset our nerves and has produced some dramatic extravagances of reaction. It would be beyond the scope of this essay to discuss the purpose of such books as Mumford's *Technics and Civilization* or Bernanos' *La France contre les Robots*. Their theme is well known. But its particular application to our artistic predicament is less often considered than the general panorama of civilizational crisis which they display. If we are to enjoy a recovery, our art may share in that recovery; if we are to be doomed by our man-made divinities our art is doomed along with the rest of our culture. Efforts to realize our predicament must be made along the whole front of human activity. Such writers as Malraux and Mounier afford grounds for some cheerfulness. In the clarity of *Les Voix du Silence* and *La Petite Peur du XXième Siècle* we can perhaps begin to see how twentieth-century man might overcome his fear of commercial systems and of the machine by a realization of his essential human condition. The disciplines of a collaborative art cannot easily be established in a society which has been trained to think of art in the individualistic terms of the Romantic hero.

The question turns on whether art as an activity is an essential part of our human condition. That is what is being tested in the cinema and by broadcasting. Is *homo poeta* contained within *homo faber*? Is man the maker of art works merely a special sort of man, and those who enjoy art works a special sort of caste which society can tolerate or not? Is popular entertainment altogether set apart from this art activity? There were for many centuries well established answers, though at the time there was no need to ask the questions. Can the condition which made it certain that art was a genuinely popular activity be reproduced in our society? If it can, the tyrannies of the box office and of the machine are overthrown. If it cannot, we remain enslaved. Before discussing this question further we should consider the other three characteristics of the new arts—their diffusionary character, the predominance of the visual, and their ephemeral nature.

It will be convenient here to discuss the last-named as it is allied to the first-mentioned quality of impersonality in being a drawback to the artistic development of the cinema and broadcasting. It is in the nature of art that the artist takes as his medium the hard, enduring substance. There could be no great sculpture in lard and no great art of words without writing. The musical composer, too, whose work exists in sound, needs writing to complete and stabilize his medium. This stability is required to fulfil what is intended by the act of making. For the artist nothing is made in material unless the result stays "made"; if the material itself unmakes the making, the maker's purpose is frustrated.

The two mass media have developed an unequal stability. The cinema is the more fortunate of the two. The film in its coils of celluloid is as fixed as a poem upon its bound paper sheets. But the artist is suspicious, and with some reason. For the cinema does not revive its successful achievements. The classics of the screen exist only in the memory of the cinema-goer and in the essays of the *cinéaste*. They do not recur as does the repertory of fine achievements in the concert hall or theatre. But the medium itself can scarcely be blamed. Considered physically, the medium of the film should prove an attraction to the artist since the work itself in its performance is caught and fixed by a recording on film. The same attraction is seemingly offered by broadcasting, where the techniques of recording are fast becoming as perfect and as secure as in the case of the cinema film. And yet the suspicion of the artist is often as great. Broadcasting has waited nearly thirty years for the day when the radio artist will take his place as of right beside the painter and poet. But there is no sign that this long-expected day has dawned. Distinguished artists in most fields have worked for the cinema and the radio, yet few artists would say that the fruits of these occasional visitations are among their most vigorous and respected offspring. A stability is lacking that would legitimatize them. Working in the new media, the artist would like to feel that the chances of survival are at least as good as in the older and established arts. If it is not a physical disability which deprives these new arts of the indispensable quality of stability, where else should the cause be sought? It is surely in the use of the media and not in their nature. The cinema everywhere and broadcasting in many places are industries as well as arts. As industrial activities they share the character of industrial organizations. The studio is also the factory workshop. They submit not only to the disciplines of the Muses but to the rigours of the profit motive. And, as in the marketing of any manufactured product, the currents of fashion and change are used to the utmost. All the commercial techniques developed to sell goods competitively are applied to attract the largest number of customers. And this is often best done by seeming to offer something new. And so it is largely by the compulsion of the industrial promoter that the classics of film are relegated to the memory. A similar compulsion—the journalistic compulsion of newness—brings about much the same effect in the sequence of broadcast programmes. But that it is so is surely better than if the cause were found in the media themselves; if it were an inherent defect the cinema film would be for ever as lard to the sculptor and would offer opportunities for the artist only in a freakish sense. But in fact the artist does turn to these media and has done fine work in them. The reason why they have not securely established themselves as artistic media is more their organization and use by the promoters than for any intrinsic reason. The world of printed books could suffer in the same way but for certain moderating accidents. The book is a private, portable possession. The art of letters is older than publishing and older than printing. The demand for old works to be printed again can be satisfied within the commercial organization that has been established. But were this to cease to be the case, if the production of a book were as expensive and elaborate as, say, the production of one issue of a newspaper, then the art of letters would go underground and grope vainly in a new Dark Age for some stable means of giving currency to the poet's word.

The arts themselves are not coextensive with their means of publication or performance. Each art must find a place within a medium that will be of far larger scope. Neither the cinema nor broadcasting has yet found a place where the artist can confidently expect to make his art work evident. Broadcasting freed from the salesman is able to offer more to the artist. But under present conditions not much more. Broadcasting is a mass medium, though its communication is mostly received in the privacy of the home. Broadcasting fails essentially if it does not succeed in holding the attention of what is by any other standards a vast audience. Fifty thousand is a small audience even for the experiments of the B.B.C.'s Third Programme. If the characteristic audience became no more than a few hundreds—however enthusiastic these supporters might be—the communication would fall outside the scope of what is at present meant by broadcasting. Some of the most important new departures in writing and poetry have had to make their way with the support of far fewer. Consider the patience and tenacity of Vollard. If a response from an audience on the scale of a sports stadium were a necessity at the outset, not only the painting of Cézanne, let us say, but most of what we now value in art would never have come to maturity or won recognition. Art needs conditions that allow experimentation. It is hard to gain those conditions in broadcasting, and all but impossible in the cinema. Something can be achieved in a highly developed broadcasting system where the conception of a public service ensures that some contribution is made to develop the resources of the medium, even though the initial response to these experiments cannot be great. Under such a system some obligations are admitted towards the arts of the medium. But even in these relatively favourable conditions the nature of the medium itself and the sheer awareness of a vast public causes a recoil by the artists who customarily work outside broadcasting. It would apply less to a broadcasting art that grew up wholly within the technical sphere of broadcasting itself. This efflorescence is possible. What would assist it should be carefully studied. The easily associated stimuli of journalistic success and the profit motive are not enough by themselves to explain the ephemeral condition in the two new arts. If both stimuli vanished or were greatly lessened, an ephemeral drawback would still remain. What seems to be the case is that these new arts have created for themselves an environment of flux which is now congenial and even essential to them. One of the reasons of their pervasiveness and popularity is surely that they are easily made part of the flux of experience as we feel it in our daily lives; whereas most of art experience seems to be outside the experience of daily living. A particularly intense perception of a picture or a poem will seem to abstract us from the flux of living and we return to it enriched by having stepped out of the Heraclitean stream into a world of more dense and abiding reality. But the arts of the loud-speaker and of the moving image remain part of the world of flux.

Few know perhaps that films exist or existed until very recently that presented Réjane in *Madame Sans-Gêne*, Bernhardt in *Adrienne Lecouvreur*, and Tree in *Macbeth*. The knowledge of these may stir the blood of the theatre-goer but hardly of the film fan. It is not only the commercial coarseness of the distributor that prevents these from becoming as well known as the *Winged Victory* in the Louvre. The fact is they are not classics of the cinema but curiosities of primitive film history. It is hard to imagine how artists are to accept this quality of flux as a congenial characteristic of the new arts. It is as though the armies of slave-artisans building the Gizeh pyramids were told that their colossal achievement could not expect to endure after the first contemporary astonishment had worn off.

And yet the material for genuine art work does in fact exist. Maybe a new beginning will be made in quarters that are now thought of little account artistically. The theatre in our Western tradition has disreputable origins; the *jongleurs* and *trouvères* were not always artist-heroes. The technician may be the man who will find the new departures for the camera arts: he may be the innovator first of a modest companionable art easily amenable to the flux of daily life; then perhaps a more developed and highly wrought art will grow from these discoveries. Even now the artist's touch upon these fluid media gives to the results here and there a greater substantiality and a richer texture than is observable in the average sample. But this touch is fitful and seems to have no power to develop a marked artistic style. It too often comes from without. In the hand and eye of the technician it would be from within.

The two other characteristics that remain to be considered, the diffusionary and the visual element, are more encouraging. The word "diffusionary" is used of the two new arts because they are both successful techniques of communication upon a vast scale. They would have an immense and important effect upon our century even if they were never used as forms of original art. They would perhaps still attract the name of art as being supreme arts of communication. Both are means of diffusing ideas, jokes, instruction, news, political persuasion, drama and music to a single person at his television or radio-receiver or to an audience that has come together in a cinema theatre. The experiences of the audience are different and the two arts have developed differently; of the two, the cinema is more limited. The world of broadcasting is far richer and more variegated than the world of the cinema. You would not go to a cinema to see a weather chart or for a religious service, nor for "In Town Tonight" or "Family Favourites". The cinema technically could convey most of these things, but so used it would be misused; it would be attempting what can be more suitably and conveniently done by the art of broadcasting. Broadcasting has other advantages. It is provided as a service like the water in the tap. You pay either nothing or a very small rate for using it. What you pay does not vary with the amount you use. Most people use very large amounts compared with cinema attendance. Broadcasting is a portable service; you can take it with you in motor-cars or boats or hotel bedrooms.

Moreover, television broadcasting can bring you the product of the film studios as completely as can a projector in a cinema theatre. It is not through technical inadequacy that the cinema films are not shown on the television screen, but because the film companies must recoup themselves by the box-office; and so they impose restrictions by which the films must be shown to large paying audiences. It may be that broadcasting will have a box-office of its own in the future. If that were established the future of the cinema theatre and of broadcasting would become uncertain. Experiments are proceeding in the U.S.A. with devices such as Telemeter or Phonevision—known generally as Pay As You See. By P.A.Y.S. you pay your money into a "box-office" or coin-box attachment fixed to your television set, and this releases to you the film or sporting event or other spectacle, previously advertised, that you intend to see. The attachments are expensive, and there are technical difficulties to overcome. To equip with P.A.Y.S. apparatus all the television sets at present used in Britain might need a capital expenditure of about £50,000,000. Though such an outlay is large, the calculated returns too are very large. The change to P.A.Y.S. would take place of course on account of financial, not artistic considerations. If such a change were made, the television set might well replace the cinema screen for all purposes. One giant would have eaten another and would grow to twice the size. The century might end with one new art, not two. Not only the cinema would have changed. Broadcasting too as we know it would have been transformed.

These arts may be called diffusionary not only because they are powerful vehicles for communication but also because, as they are now used, they diffuse certain fixed patterns of thought and experience which could not otherwise gain so extensive a distribution. It is for this reason that the agents of political power at times of emergency—to establish a revolutionary régime, for example—make great efforts to control the cinema and the radio. In such conditions the area of freedom left to the artist shrinks to almost nothing. But even without extreme and unnatural conditions the attraction of these media for political interests is very great. Where they are dominant, the artist has no place. In effect, a political censorship becomes established. A will to political conformity is not in the artist's nature. Thus it is that the society which provides best for the arts tends to be a liberal and tolerant society; or a society in which toleration and freedom are allowed to be an issue and are worth fighting to establish or preserve. In our own time the areas designated as "the free world" are more favourable to the artist than the areas of political despotism.

But political compulsion is not the only conformity that is disagreeable to the artist's nature. He dislikes the merely repetitious.

One of the values to a society of the artist is his capacity for being bored by the banal. A society is impoverished when this priceless gift is neglected. The artist is the natural ally of the wit, and both contend together, generation after generation, to defeat the bore. The struggle is an unequal one. The bore is never vanquished. He has numbers on his side and powerful allies. But he can be defeated here and there; and in a vigorous society he is held in check. In these societies the arts flourish and the opportunities for art are open and well developed. The artist's aversion from the repetitious and the banal is not widely shared. It can never be popular. The cliché is popular. Even great classical artists, such as Reynolds or Pope, seem innovators—innovators by the sheer fact of winning perfection within a style—by comparison with the contemporary standard of popular taste. There is always a tension between the artist who as a creator in physical form is concerned with discovery and invention, and the public who in varying degrees is resistant or suspicious of the unfamiliar and of course suspicious of perfection because it is rare and rarely sought.

This state of tension is not a constant in society. In times of revolutionary change when a new order may be assisted to gain a general acceptance by a change in fashion—in the Florence of Lorenzo de Medici, for example, or in the Paris of the First Empire —new art forms can gain a popularity along with changes in fashions of all sorts. But the purely aesthetic impetus towards change does not seem to be great, and the cause of welcome domestically for such artistic changes is their association with a popular or powerful régime. At such times the arts play a diffusionary role. There is one style of visual décor associated with Louis XIV and another with Napoleon I. There is nothing surprising in the fact that these stylistic associations are with strongly marked absolutist systems. That there are no glass cases in our museums marked "Early Nazi" or "Fascist: Middle Period" is partly because these régimes were short-lived for the purpose of cultural productivity and partly because the curators and ourselves are not yet detached enough for such efforts of classification. We pride ourselves now upon our opposition to absolute systems. But there are political and aesthetic contrarieties. Does the certainty of our aversion from dictatorship mean that we are free from a "directed" art? Because there is no *imperator* does it follow that there is no *adulatio*? A despot may be repulsive politically but a glorious inspiration in matters of taste. Democratization and the welfare state could create a social millennium in an aesthetic desert. It would be rash to pronounce upon this situation in our own society while the evidence is still in the making. But in a fully organized democracy it is unlikely that we could wholly escape the imposition of patterns in art by the paid organizers of art creation. This tendency is specially marked in the cinema. Thrillers and romances, spy stories and tales of adventure are turned out with a remarkable sameness. Those who contrive these stories must contrive situations and characters suitable to the natural qualities of the stars who are to take part. The result too must aim at the maximum box-office returns. These are adverse factors for the writer of original talent. A good deal of this too applies to broadcasting. Thus the popular requirement of cliché and repetition has come to be a necessary part of the output in these two new arts and the typical artist of free creative talent is kept away.

But the historian should not despond. Though these art media are often used inartistically they remain potentially a great resource that could in the future under some more favourable system be used by true artists for works of the highest quality. The drama for example has often endured periods of worthless output. The *longueurs* have been succeeded by years of brilliant achievement and, after this creative force has spent itself, the theatre has again relapsed. The cinema is a form of dramatic experience. Given the circumstances of today, there is nothing surprising in the fact that the film produced under strong commercial influence must conform to certain types and must fulfil certain traditional expectancies. These types and expectancies may be thought of as the cult patterns and myths of our contemporary world, moulded by their purveyors for their own purposes—convenience and self-enrichment very often —and of course responding to a popular appetite. Cults and myths are friendly to the arts, and there is nothing fatal to that friendship even when the results are rather boring and commonplace. Much of the Hercules cult as expressed visually in the first century B.C. must have seemed tedious and banal to the *neoterici* of the Augustan Age. But there is an important difference between that sort of popular art associated with a living *cultus* and the forms of entertainment-art which are mostly shown in the cinema and by radio. If we consider the pervasive Hercules cult, the proper comparison with our art forms today is debased church art—repository art as it is sometimes called—and the commonplaces of *bondieuserie*. But however debased and inconsiderable as art, none the less these forms are associated with the dynamic of a lived religion which gives dignity and depth to the experience. This associative dynamic is much less in evidence in the entertainment art of today. The myths displayed by the cinema have no mystery or dedication. The cults have no divinity. The resemblance of our popular entertainments is probably more with the *spectaculae* of the Roman world, with the triumphs and shows in the circus and arena. These feed a different appetite from the drama and are harder to redeem. The modern "myths" diffused by the two twentieth-century arts are the comedy patterns of erotic excitement and the happy ending, the melodramatic patterns of retribution, the sentimental patterns of reconciliation and the romantic patterns of bravery and success. These are the fantasies with which the tedium or misery of today is relieved or consoled. There is little that is morbid or perverse in these dreams. They are not revolutionary or cynical. They are the dream world of the people actualized upon the screen and conventionalized repetitively like an acanthus pattern round a wall. Though it is difficult for the artist to break in, it is not impossible. Part of the difficulty is contributed by the public. In his work *The Dehumanization of Art*, Ortega y Gasset writes:

> The majority of people are unable to adjust their attention to the glass and the transparency which is the work of art; instead they penetrate through it to wallow passionately in the human reality which the work of art refers to. If they are invited to let loose their prey and fix their attention upon the work of art itself, they will say they see nothing in it, because, indeed, they see no human realities there, but only artistic transparencies, pure essences.[1]

The public likes the illusion of human realities to which a highly subjective and emotional attachment can easily be made; and the two new arts are readily exploited by the contrivers of these illusions. The aim of the authors and producers is often not an artistic one at all, but incitement towards an illusion of real feeling; an "I-was-there" sense of actuality is sought and induced. This can of course be used by an artist; but it can also exist without the artist. There can be a realism in art; but there can be realism without art.

The visual element is the most obvious and fecund of the four. It is thought of now with some alarm as though it may lead to degradation. This is because we have so refined our system of word-communication that a flight from the written word seems itself a cultural decline. Indeed it has its dangers. The strip cartoon or the cinema "short" is not a cultural advance on the short story. The encroachment upon the newspaper of the photograph is not just another way of presenting news. It is more often a substitution of another kind of interest. It is doubtful if the hours spent in staring at the television receiver are better spent than in former occupations which have thus been superseded. But it is easy to grow needlessly apprehensive and morbid with such thoughts. Our subject is the arts. And for the arts the visual medium itself has equal qualities with that of sound. And in their visual qualities the new arts offer their strongest attraction. The dangers for art lie not in the fact of the visual medium but in its likely neglect. And this neglect would be not on account of some distaste for the visual itself but because

[1] Quoted by Susanne K. Langer in *Feeling and Form* (Routledge and Kegan Paul, 1953), p. 54, from *La Deshumanizacion del Arte* (Madrid, 1925).

the two new arts are enemy-occupied territory from which the
artist is mostly a refugee. There is no combat possible, as there is no
issue, or rarely an issue. The aims are not directly aesthetic aims.
The aims are to attract not the admiration but the attention of large
numbers of people. And this can be done by anything notable or
out-of-the-way from a street accident to a conjuring trick. The
attention-getting device is the "thrill". The thrill indeed is useful
to the artist. To the entertainer it is essential. The thrill is not itself
an art work. It has to be made so. The thrills in *Macbeth* could be
displayed by a Whodunit author with some hope of success; but
the result, however skilful, would not be artistically interesting
unless the author was an artist. Indeed, it has been remarked that
Shakespeare's achievement dramatically is often to take over the
non-artist's work of others—sometimes of the Whodunit writers of
that day—and to use it for ends that are artistically triumphant.
There is no intrinsic reason why this development should not take
place in the cinema and in broadcasting. Indeed it has taken place
here and there. But there are plenty of external reasons why it
does not take place more often.

Broadcasting is a more flexible instrument than the cinema and
has already provided artistic opportunities which have been taken
advantage of more often than in the cinema. It is a less pretentious
medium, less tied to the spectacular; it has room for the small-scale
effect, for modest ambitions, for short-lived experiment, for an
easily exhausted talent and for the *tour de force*. It is more journalistic
in scope, more "decorative", more domestic. Its programme is like
the furnishings of a room. There is a reasonable harmony of the
utile with the aesthetic. The merely comfortable is made to be
companionable with books and pictures and music. All this is within
the capacity of broadcasting, which is essentially a domestic art.
Whereas the cinema film is public, and its typical output is best
suited for showing to a congregation of people assembled for the
purpose.

These two new arts will claim more and more attention, as it is
their nature to be absorbent. They are at present casual and popular. They seem to leave unaltered the older individual arts. But this
may not long continue. The vitality of art will be drawn to the foci
of creative energy. Economically the individualistic arts are becoming harder and harder for the artist. The poet now is a spare-time
poet. The musical composer and the painter are lecturers or writers
or teachers. Their work as artists is less and less well paid. The
cinema and broadcasting are rich patrons. But patronage is not
enough. "Whenever the arts have not been upheld by the good sense
of their professors", said Constable in one of his lectures, "patronage
and honours so far from checking their downward course must
inevitably accelerate it." Our predicament now is surely that the

cinema and broadcasting have no professors, in Constable's meaning, no authorities in the sense that Reynolds and Poussin were authorities. In place of these, there are various sorts of managers, controllers, directors, financiers and exploiters.

The new arts must evolve their own artists from their own environment. And these will grow when both climate and soil are favourable. A difficulty will have to be overcome in broadcasting, where the opportunities for art works must be recognized as distinct from the other sorts of communication of which the medium is capable—the communication of instruction and information, for example. But most important of all and most difficult to achieve is a favourable ecological setting for the artist. This must be an achievement of society itself.

An Edict of Diocletian remains on record fixing the wages of the third-century mosaicists: an *imaginarius*, 175 sesterces a day; a *pictor parietarius*, 75; less for the *lapidarius structor*, for the *calcis coctor* and the *musearius*. We do not know the role of each of these. But we can be sure that they were artists. We can be sure of this not only by what remains of their work but by what we know of the texture of their society. It is important to remember them. These various sorts of *structores* and *imaginarii* were the dolly-pushers, the cameramen, the directors, the animators and caption men of the ancient world. Their work—through their successors—is upon the walls in Byzantium and Ravenna. They are important because they prove the possibility of a collaborative art. They have little connexion with an individualistic tradition; that tradition can, I believe, provide little nourishment to our own new arts. These must help themselves. If the artist is an essential part of *homo faber* they will help themselves. The artist is not ultimately expendable. But it is one of the successful deceptions of our time to act as though he were.

M. Maritain in the course of his recent Mellon Lectures said: "Man is *homo faber* and *homo poeta* together. But in the historical evolution of mankind, *homo faber* carries *homo poeta* on his shoulders." This is a painful image and painfully illustrated in our own epoch. The identity remarked by M. Maritain is one that is not likely to be much discussed. If the implications of this identity are to help the artist, the philosopher who explains it will need the assistance, not only of his fellow-intellectuals, the historian and the scientist, but also of society, in making the necessary adaptations to allow *homo poeta* a flourishing life. The intellectual argument can never hope to carry the day by popular acclamation. But truth is made evident not only by the demonstration of argument. It struggles against perversion and malevolence by its own virtues and strength. There is never any complete eclipse nor any complete victory. At times the cultural setting is more favourable; at times less so. What must be reckoned with in this century are the new factors in our art predicament, which factors the new arts themselves create. It has been suggested in this essay that the leading character-istics of the new arts are an impersonal or anonymous quality, a growing visual predominance, the claims of easily diffused patterns, and the drawback of the ephemeral. These are the *données* for the artist of the new arts. But if man is merely a workman or a tradesman the works produced in these new arts will be as much like other commercial products as the forces of trade and the ingenuity of work techniques can make them. They will never be exactly like other items of manufacture because their essential nature is other. The most banal and vulgar film story imaginable is still a drama. Vulgarity can deform but cannot transform. And those who make these works, however degraded the result, cannot wholly be absorbed into the world of technics. It is worth asking about those who produce these new art works not only what they are but how they are to discover themselves.

A poet before his typewriter, however bewildered by the problems of the art work, knows what he is at. And he is aware of a distinction however imprecise between his aims and processes and those of his brother at the lathe. He is fortunate in his awareness and is favoured by 2,000 years of history. But he can give very little help to the men and women in the control gallery of a television show or in the cubicle at a broadcasting studio. These people are in an ambiguous position. They are not yet aware of *homo poeta* upon their shoulders. They are aware only of the necessities of what they have been trained to do and aware too of their involvement in the work which is being made. They know they are of the world of makers rather than of doers and they know they have a responsibility for the arti-fact. This realization would itself redeem the work if there were not other factors which contend against its artistic nature and which thus keep the artisan-artist in his ambiguous state of subjection. These are managerial forces applied through director and producer and with the ultimate sanction of the board-room and the share-holders' meeting; they are derived too from less measurable and less definable sources of power—sources of conformity which co-ordinate, as efficiently as a machine, one mass product with another and which will see to it that the appetite for the banal is appeased and that surprises are contrived within a convention that is not itself surprising, so that the resulting experience is both exciting and superficial. The illusion of significance is given by the intensity of the excitement or by a vivid evocation of memory. This is the re-placement for profundity. But there is no disturbance in depth. The inner layers are untouched. To achieve these skilful effects the imponderable forces of social conformism are applied through the usual managerial channels.

It is doubtful if the release for *homo faber*, if his identification with man-the-creator upon his shoulder, can come about through a conversion of the superior members of the team who "realize" the production. The stars are set in their courses. They are committed to an artistic individualism; they are captive to an *adulatio* so pervasive and so strong that they cannot work freely as artists upon their material. They are executive artists, responding to requirements that come from without. But some are indeed artists. No one can deny this designation to Charlie Chaplin, Garbo, Jannings and others whose quality as artists shines through their material and who as artists give undeniably that special kind of delight which is the artist's province. But however unreservedly as artists they may be praised, they do little to affect the new arts as arts. They belong to the company of Guitry, Kean, Bernhardt or Irving. Their art is not identical with the art of the drama itself. Henry Irving in *The Bells*, from all accounts, can be admired as an artist whose accomplishment was altogether independent of the authorship of Leopold Lewis.

The star-system does little that is favourable to the artistic value of the work itself. The works are merely means by which the stars are best shown off. They are the filigree for the stars' effulgence. The material is moulded round their iridescent charm. The process is the reverse of the typical art process by which the human artist moulds the material towards the ideal art work of his own spirit.

Nor is there much to be hoped for from the present-day *imaginarius*, the director of the film, the producer of the radio show. His freedom is not the artist's freedom. He is given the managerial data and though he may seem a colossus in publicity he is a hero in chains, a puppet emperor, and a creature of the mob. He is powerless to exceed the conventions which have been set; and as these are not artistic conventions, the results of their observance are not genuine artistic results.

There remain the artist-artisans. It is more likely that these will show the way. Artistically theirs is a modest role. They are not conscious of the artist-hero tradition. And helped by this very fact they may succeed in bringing the work within the scope of art. But they will do so only if the assumption is valid which identifies the poet and the workman. There is no knock-down argument to prove this identification. But some support for it may be gained by recalling the findings of those who have been concerned to research into the origin and nature of art. Some have found these origins in magic, some in religion, and some have contended for the autonomy of art in dissociation from ritual, religious or magical. But it is remarkable that most of this testimony supports the notion that art instincts are part of a human instinct widely shared. It includes the boy carving a piece of soft wood, the nameless draughtsmen on the walls at Lascaux, and Michelangelo at the Sistine. This too will bring in the vision mixer in the control gallery and the man at the knobs in the cubicle.

But it will be not only through the self-recognition of these, through the discovery within themselves of their artists' natures, that the change for the better will be brought about. This recognition must be met by a corresponding recognition in the beholder and a predisposition in him to be affected by an artist's work.

The cinema and broadcasting to a large extent are part of what is called show-business. The term is apt. The results are shows and the activity is a business. But a good deal of it is art and most of it is potentially so; yet if you were to say "show-art" and to try to establish the term, you would give rise to the typical tensions and antipathies that in our own time are associated with the word "art". Art in our current tradition must be kept in its place, as religion and war in theirs. That place varies a little from generation to generation. From century to century the change in the "place" of art is observably significant. And over longer spans of history, when epoch is divided from epoch by great historic chasms such as that of the Renaissance or the break-up of the Roman Empire, the place of the artist, or priest, or warrior, can be seen as very different indeed. The words bear the meanings of what relationships to the community are tolerated by the community at the time. So were you now to argue in favour of including show-business among the arts and were you to point out some of the *desiderata* for this inclusion you should be prepared to encounter the antagonism of those who will resent the change as fanciful or as destructive of something cherished as it is. The artist has his place and it is a small place compared with the warrior's or the magnate's or political leader's. The priest too has a lesser place than these great ones, but a higher place than the artist. Those who resent or who are suspicious of fundamental criticisms of our society will declare that both the priest and the artist are deeply respected and honoured no less or perhaps only a little less than at other periods. It will be pointed out too that ours is a painful period of transition and the practical men of affairs must naturally take the centre of the stage while order itself and survival is in peril. The drift of my argument does not conflict with these observations. I am concerned with what is fundamental in human nature and with questions of whether certain works of that fundamental nature—art works—are to be respected as such. And it is pertinent to observe that art—the activity of making art works—is not currently regarded as part of human nature, and art works are not universally cherished and sought as are successful works of other kinds. Nor is man's relation with material thought of as an artist's relation. The making of a shop-front or a drinking-trough for cattle, or the icing of a birthday cake—these are not now within the scope of the artist. These activities, like those of artisans of the cinema and radio, are outside. A drinking-trough by Brancusi would be counted an art work because Brancusi from his quite other sorts of work was reckoned to be an artist. The question is whether the artist is a special sort of man or whether art is a special sort of activity which all men do or can do. Our civilization has been for long in favour of the first proposition. But if that proposition is true the new arts stand little chance of attracting or holding that special sort of man. There are professionals of these new arts, but they do not resemble the special sorts of men hitherto called artists. But are they in fact artists? Or are they all artists? I believe an examination of what they do shows they are. But they are artists under the constraint of technics. And the technician is the ambiguous figure of our day—partly hero and partly victim.

"There is no progress in the arts", said Renoir. This was a wise admonition to the mercantile and mechanistic world which believed in progress as a dynamic. Yet there is progress of a situational kind by which the conditions in which the artist works become more or less favourable. This is important for the arts under discussion. They may remain the *ludi* and *spectacula* of the twentieth century; or they may develop according to their nature in fulfilment of the great capacities which they have as artistic media. If they fail they will do so in virtue of the systems which govern them—a failure for which society is responsible—rather than because the professionals are not artists. The technician is estranged from the world of art not because he is a technician and therefore functionally distinct but because the world of technics to which he belongs is itself estranged.

The reconciliation will test to the uttermost the cultural coherence of our age. The estrangement is a twentieth-century commonplace; and many, most perhaps, see no need for a change. The necessity for a change involves, as has been suggested, fundamental questions. These are not frequently debated and very rarely in terms of the arts. The discussion involves the place of art in human nature. We are easily tired by such a topic nowadays. We have preoccupations that seem to be more immediate. But the realities exist whether the discussion proceeds or lapses. The twentieth-century arts will struggle to birth and grow; or will be smothered by other forces which will monopolize and consume the media.

The problem is to develop broadcasting and the cinema as genuine collaborative arts that must also be popular arts; and the first requirement is to desire and tolerate conditions which art itself will find congenial. It may be doubted if these conditions will become general through acts of policy applied from without by the usual processes of discussion and formal statement. This could only be carried through by a reformist movement with strong popular support. If the assumptions put forward in this way are correct, it is more likely that the artist will secure his place by pressure from within: that is by the artistic nature of the artifact relieving the unnatural constraint in which he now too often works. The traditional individualistic arts can render valuable though limited assistance. All who know the artist's nature, whether they work as artists or not, have some responsibility here and now for these new arts.

BOOKS SUGGESTED FOR FURTHER READING

M. Bardeche and R. Brasillach, *History of the Film*, tr. and ed. by I. Barry (Allen and Unwin, 1938).

A. Malraux, *The Voices of Silence*, tr. by S. Gilbert (Secker and Warburg, 1954).

J. Maritain, *Creative Intuition in Art and Poetry* (Mellon Lectures in the Fine Arts Series, 1952) (Harvill Press, 1954).

E. Mounier, *Be not Afraid* (Rockliff, 1951).

L. Mumford, *Technics and Civilization* (Routledge, 1934).

D. Jones, Preface to *The Anathemata* (Faber, 1954).

SECTION FOUR

Politics and Economics

DEMOCRACY AND TOTALITARIANISM

by T. E. UTLEY

FOR THE LAST twenty years, the words "democratic" and "totalitarian" have provided, for the purposes of day-to-day discussion of politics, one of the main accepted classifications of political régimes. Only the very naïve would suppose that this classification was exhaustive, but it has supplied a good working basis for popular political thought and a convenient form of journalistic shorthand. Possibly, the best introduction to a survey of the present state of political thinking is a consideration of the change which has come about in the associations surrounding these words during this period.

Political thinking always reflects the arrangements of diplomacy. The most important diplomatic division in the years immediately before the war was between Germany and her satellites on the one hand, and Britain and France on the other; and the words totalitarian and democratic were commonly used to describe these two groups respectively. It was most convenient both for the Right and for the Left to leave Russia unclassified; for the Right, because to lump Russian Communism together with Nazism and Fascism under an insulting label was to proclaim the diplomatic isolation of Britain and France, a fact which it was more comfortable to ignore; for the Left, because Russia still remained the only country in which Socialism had been achieved, and it was pleasanter, at the moment, to avoid calculating the price at which this had been done. The U.S.A. would have been put unequivocally in the category of democracies, but American isolationism and the dominant position which Europe still believed herself to occupy in the world made it possible to ignore or underrate the specifically American contributions to political thought and practice. Furthermore, some of those contributions, when examined closely, presented embarrassing difficulties both to the Left and the Right in the European democracies. The "New Deal" might appeal to European Socialists as a daring and generous way of coping with the crucial economic and social evil of unemployment, a dazzling contrast with the niggardly economies and the cramping restrictions on international trade which were all that European Conservatives and Liberals could offer in this context until the armaments race came, or, as it was fashionable to hint, was brought to the rescue; on the other hand it was equally logical to regard the "New Deal" as a capitalist manoeuvre designed to preserve the economic system from its natural fate. Conservatives in the European democracies simply did not understand the "New Deal", reserving for it the suspicion which they were then accustomed to feel for nearly all forms of economic thought. Thus, when Professor Michael Oakeshott published his influential text book *The Social and Political Doctrines of Contemporary Europe* in 1939, he was quite justified in excluding references to contemporary American sources, since contemporary American thought had virtually no influence on European political thinking at the time.

In this pre-war world of which Europe was the centre, the "Totalitarian Powers" were those which had repudiated the liberal and rationalist tradition in favour of an attitude of mind of which the chief ingredients were contempt for reason, denial of the possibility of universal judgements about morals and politics, denial of the idea that the individual had any rights other than those which he enjoyed at the pleasure of the group to which he belonged, and denial that the national state had any duties towards other national states. This, at least, was the average European liberal's impression of what Fascism and Nazism meant. For academic purposes it was indeed a grossly over-simplified impression, for it ignored some important differences between Fascism and Nazism. It ignored, for example, the essential point that, in strict theory, Fascism was an authoritarian rather than a totalitarian creed, since one of its cardinal principles was the encouragement of forms of independent corporate life within the State, a principle which, of course, was neglected in practice; in Nazism, on the other hand, revolutionary and socialist elements were from the first far more in evidence. Many purely socialist doctrines found their place, alongside romantic State-worship and racialist dogma, in Nazi theory. Nevertheless, the assumption, in nearly all discussion of Fascism and Nazism before the war, was that these doctrines were doctrines of the Right, appealing to extravagant traditionalism and aimed chiefly against the liberal rationalist heritage; since the ambiguous position of Russia made her classification seem unnecessary or undesirable, it was commonly assumed that Totalitarianism was a creed of the Right—a denial, that is to say, of the three traditional liberal principles of liberty, equality and fraternity. Although the Nazis, the Fascists and the Spanish Falange paid fewer tributes to tradition than the Left supposed, they had no objection to appearing in the role of critics of liberal idealism.

The pre-war democratic movement in Europe was sharply divided between its non-socialist and its socialist wings. In so far as its non-socialist wing had a specific contribution to make to the philosophy of politics (and this was not very far) it drew on the great nineteenth-century apostles of liberty and parliamentarianism. Nothing much had happened to it since Mill. In economics, its object was to resist Socialism by a combination of *ad hoc* concessions to collectivism and strategic inertia. It sought to postpone as long as possible convulsions, international and domestic, which it had little confidence of its power to avoid. It stood for peace, caution and moderation, and, in spite of the accusations commonly made by its critics, it had as little sympathy with counter-revolutionary as with revolutionary ideas.

Although various fears, notably the fear of Communism and that of bankruptcy engendered by the world economic crisis of 1929-31 and a general misunderstanding of the cause of that crisis, kept democratic Socialism in Europe on the defensive before the war, its ascendency over those who thought seriously about politics steadily increased. It had what other democratic movements had not, a political and social theory to offer. Furthermore, some of the dilemmas which that theory presented remained in the background. The problem of reconciling Socialism with Parliamentary and personal freedom, though it could never be wholly overlooked, was somewhat obscured by the fact that Russian excesses could still be regarded as belonging to a temporary phase in the evolution of Communism and as caused largely by the mistaken policies of the Western powers towards the Soviet Union in the first years of its existence. Some Socialists contended that a temporary suspension of Parliamentary government might be necessary to the realization of Socialism, but others asserted that a sufficiently powerful working-class movement could capture the Parliamentary machine by peaceful means. As for the problem of controlling economic power in a Socialist state, as it was still entirely academic, the theory that a representative Parliament by taking over all the means of production and distribution would merely be extending the sphere of life which was subject to the popular will, seemed quite satisfactory. The most serious dilemma of democratic Socialism at this time was one which it inherited from Liberalism: its dislike of power as an instrument of foreign policy was hard to reconcile with the obvious dangers to which the democracies were subject from Germany, Italy and Japan. Nevertheless, these dangers were seen as coming from the political Right; and it was the political Right in the democracies which, without sympathizing with Totalitarianism, seemed to be most indifferent to this menace. If the crash came, there seemed little doubt that those who had foreseen it, however reluctant they might have been to prepare to meet it, would gain a great deal of prestige, particularly at they might claim to have been the special enemies of Nazism and Fascism from the first. To many, the dominant issue, that between the totalitarian Right and its tepid allies and indifferent enemies on the one hand, and the forces of liberty and social justice on the other, seemed to be clearly presented in the Spanish Civil War, which accordingly acquired for them, in spite of its essentially local character, a cosmic meaning. For a while, the deep divisions in the Socialist camp could be concealed under the formula of the popular front.

Thus, before the war, European political thought was largely unconscious of the nature of the two forces which now dominate everything else, Soviet Communism and American capitalism. Within a few years of the end of the war, however, these two forces had come to provide the framework within which European political and social thinking was conducted. This is the revolution which makes the state of opinion today so fundamentally different from what it was in 1938.

Now, the totalitarian danger is seen as coming not from the Right but from the Left, and so great is the influence of labels on political thought that the effect of this in itself is revolutionary. To the lay liberal mind in Europe, Russian Communism has most of the distasteful features of Nazism and Fascism. It denies individual rights and appears to oppose the idea of a community of nations; it is the instrument of an aggressive imperialism which is suspected of unlimited ambition; and it uses cruelty as a normal implement of policy. In all these respects it closely resembles Nazism and Fascism, and the parallel is constantly emphasized in current discussion, so that in particular the discussion of international affairs often follows with a quite deceptive regularity the pattern of the pre-war controversy over "appeasement". Yet, in spite of these similarities, the fact remains that Russian Communism springs from intellectual sources entirely different from those of Nazism and Fascism. Nazism and Fascism appeared to many to be the ultimate exaggeration of the stock theories of European Conservatism—the theory of the moral need for inequality, the theory of the primacy of the nation over the individual, the theory that instinct and prejudice rather than reason are and should be the fount of political action. Soviet Communism, on the other hand, can quite fairly be represented as the ultimate exaggeration of all the stock ideas of the revolutionary tradition in Europe—the idea of equality, the idea that mankind should be organized as a single political unit, the idea that the way to Utopia is through a violent destruction of the existing social order. Before the war, it could be argued with considerable force that Communism was the logical extension of the liberal tradition in European politics, and, as such, should command the sympathy of all progressives who drew their inspiration from the storming of the Bastille. Today, much the same theory is used to justify an opposite conclusion: Dr. Yakov Talmon, in the first volume of his *Origins of Totalitarian Democracy*, has discerned the beginnings of Marxist Communism in the writings of the French encyclopaedists and the theories of the Jacobins; and Mr. Isaiah Berlin, in a celebrated series of broadcast lectures on liberty, has illustrated how the liberal passion for absolutes gets the better of the liberal passion for freedom and produces Totalitarianism.

This account of the intellectual genesis of Marxian Communism is not at all far-fetched. In the late eighteenth-century liberalism which produced the French Revolution, there were two potentially incompatible ingredients: the belief in individual freedom, and the belief in a Utopia in which all individual interests would harmonize. The second, indeed, was held to follow logically from the first; nothing short of absolute freedom would satisfy the liberal mind, but absolute freedom for all would be possible only if conflicts between personal interests could be eliminated. At first, the tension was obscured by the doctrine of the automatic harmony of interests —the theory, connected in economics with the name of Adam Smith, that the natural tendency of unrestricted competition was to produce the common good. When this idea became untenable, recourse was had to the notion of a provisional dictatorship of the *élite* which would prepare the way for a Utopia in which freedom and justice could be reconciled by educating the people in civic ideals. This notion of the provisional dictatorship played, as Dr. Talmon has shown, a considerable part in French Revolutionary thought during and after the Terror. It was always firmly tied to the idea of an ultimate Utopia, a reign of peace and virtue from which all public force would be absent. The parallel between it and the Marxian idea of provisional dictatorship leading to the withering away of the state is obvious. Similarly, the Marxian attack on property starts from liberal premises: its basis is the principle derived from Locke that a man has a right to own that which is the product of his labour; this principle, combined with the idea that the total value of any commodity is conferred by the amount of labour which goes into its production, is the foundation of the Marxist attack on all forms of interest, and of the Marxist case for the public or popular ownership of all the means of production and distribution. In Babeuf's plot for the establishment of a Communist state, the way in which the economic doctrines of the French Revolution could be made to produce Socialist conclusions was already clear. Even the idea of a class war and the special position of a "Party", conceived as the vanguard of the Revolution and the trustee of posterity, were all to some extent anticipated in French Revolutionary thought. The slow transition of Liberalism throughout the nineteenth century into extreme and even totalitarian collectivism is now a familiar theme. Even though many of the features of

Russian Communism could be found in a totalitarian régime of the Right, it is as a Left-wing doctrine, a perverse development of Liberalism, that it is now often regarded; and this impression is fortified by its propaganda, which freely appeals to the idea of liberty and to such traditional liberal causes as the rights of primitive peoples. The paradox that the passion for absolute liberty and absolute equality is the commonest source of tyranny, a paradox familiar in the nineteenth century but of which comparatively little was heard in the first half of the twentieth century, has thus gained many adherents. Equally, Communism still gets much of its support in the West from the exploitation of the old ideals of European radicalism.

The second great force of the inter-war period which was widely underrated or misunderstood in Europe was American capitalism. The potentialities of a benevolent and enlightened capitalism, which attacks poverty by insisting on production rather than concentrating directly on wider distribution, were not generally realized until Western Europe woke up at the end of the war to find that it was absolutely dependent on American generosity. Just as Communism can reasonably be represented as the ultimate extension of the liberal revolutionary tradition which has its source in Jacobinism, so the political and economic orthodoxy of the U.S.A. can be regarded as representing another wing of the liberal tradition. Like Communism, it is a cosmopolitan philosophy. Its governing idea is that the individual has natural and inalienable rights and hence that the business of public power is to protect these rights, diminishing them as little as possible in the process. The federalist form of government, the great American contribution to the world's constitutional thinking, claims two merits which today hold particular attraction: by the separation of powers, it claims to keep government sufficiently weak to prevent its becoming oppressive—a virtue which is considerable in an age accustomed to secret police and concentration camps; and it claims to provide a means of enabling communities to come together, not only in defence of their independence, but also in defence of the personal rights of their members—a virtue which is considerable in an age accustomed to continual international wars. These merits would have counted for nothing, however, if American capitalism had been unable to answer the objection that personal liberty in economics produces perpetual uncertainty, resolved periodically by crises of poverty and unemployment. The idea that it was possible to make the capitalist system work if the State co-operated intelligently with it, not restricting the freedom of the producer but, by a bold policy of financial expansion, creating new consumer demands and new outlets for productive effort, came to the rescue of American capitalism in the thirties when it was more sorely strained than ever before. It seemed to prove that, given intelligent administration, the economy could be made to be self-regulating, just as the original apostles of *laissez-faire* had believed that, in its nature, it was.

After the war, America seemed to be offering the world a "Universal New Deal". She was the only source from which the material damage done by the war in Europe could be repaired; American capitalists, it was said, were sufficiently enlightened to realize that American prosperity was bound up with the prosperity of the rest of the world. The humiliation of accepting American generosity could thus be largely offset by the reflection that it arose from a brand of enlightened self-interest, and in any case there was no alternative to accepting it. More important than all this, however, American economic doctrines were embodied in a series of international economic institutions which had the object of protecting the world for ever against the dangers of slump and the anarchy of unenlightened capitalist competition. Given universal free trade, when the time was ripe for achieving it, and bold policies of international investment, there was no reason, it was contended, why stability and prosperity should not be achieved as soon as the ravages of war were swept away. The idea that what the world needed was not discipline but enterprise seemed to many to be justified by the exhilarating spectacle of American wealth and a pathetic contrast of the Old World's poverty.

When the strength and menace of Russian Communism began to be understood, American Liberalism acquired a still greater importance: supported by American money and American military power, it supplied a doctrine with which Communism could be fought. It could show that Communism was not the quick way to build up the economy of a country ruined by war, or to lead primitive peoples along the road of material progress. It seemed even to have a recipe for the abolition of war in the idea of inter-State federation. Some liberal thinkers in Europe came near to hoping for a quick conflict with Russia, which, with the aid of what was for a while the American monopoly in atomic weapons, might produce the parliament of man. Meantime, thanks to American influence, the international ideals of pure Liberalism, the equality of nations and human rights, were laid on record in the Charter of the United Nations as the aims of all mankind.

From the first, however, various factors operated against the influence of American Liberalism after the war. To begin with, confidence in the efficacy of America's economic theories was not universal, and there was even scepticism about her ability to carry them out. The glittering prospects of perpetual economic expansion which they held out were always overshadowed by the fear of another American slump in which the rest of the world, because of its undue dependence on the U.S.A., would be involved. The essence of the Liberalism with which America was associated was the claim to liberate men from what has come to be called "power politics" but, in so far as it was used as a diplomatic weapon against Russia, it had some of the characteristics of Imperialism and these were all the more repugnant for being concealed. Furthermore, as a universalistic doctrine, it sometimes came into collision with European nationalism which had not been weakened by the war. Finally, and most seriously, obsession with Communism in the U.S.A. has lately seemed to get the better of Liberalism. The attitude of mind known as McCarthyism is not a theory of politics but a phenomenon of mass psychology which cannot be well understood outside the context of American history; but in its combination of a vague appeal to religious and traditional values with a constant appeal to mob prejudice and hysteria, it has, for the liberal mind in Europe, some of the repulsive qualities of Fascism.

Nevertheless, these two philosophies of Marxist Communism and American Liberalism have set the two poles between which European opinion has moved since the war. Political thought is invariably confused and always deals in over-simplification, but, subject to these reservations, it is possible to describe these two opposing theories in terms of two opposite pictures of a Utopian world. The Communist Utopia may be seen as a universal state founded on racial equality and rigid social justice and based on the regulation of all human activities in such a way as to produce the social good. This, broadly speaking, is the ideal which Communism presents to those who have no inclination to delve deeply into its philosophy. It is of course adapted for the purposes of propaganda to meet local requirements, and sometimes includes features, like an appeal to nationalism, which are consistent with Marxist orthodoxy only in the sense that they are recognized as necessary phases in the dialectical process and as destined, in turn, to be superseded. The common element, however, in Communist advocacy is the appeal to social justice to be achieved by the detailed subordination of human actions to the common well-being. The picture presented by American Liberalism, on the other hand, is that of a world society in which individual freedom is at its maximum, and in which the common well-being comes about through the unleashing of personal energies. This world society would find its logical constitutional expression in a universal federal state, just as its logical economic expression would be a universal customs union. While Communism, where its professions are still believed, addresses itself to a stern sense of social duty, and has something of the attraction of a secular Puritanism about it, American Liberalism opens up vistas of endless prosperity to be brought about by personal effort and adventure harnessed to the common good by the use of financial techniques which involve very little limitation of personal freedom. Both claim, of course, to be capable of supplying an immediate remedy for poverty; and, in this respect, the U.S.A. has obviously had the advantage.

To understand the European reaction to these extraneous forces which have been felt so powerfully since the war, it is necessary to consider some of the things which happened to Europe during the war. The influence of the actual experience of war on European political thought is easy to misunderstand, because it consists of a series of mutually contradictory reactions. Four sharply conflicting effects may in particular be distinguished: the war produced in Europe an immense increase of faith in the power of state action to produce social welfare; it produced a powerful reaction towards the idea of personal liberty founded on fundamental law, an idea which was more vividly understood in the light of the experiences of Nazi and Fascist tyranny; it produced an immense increase of confidence in the possibilities of international co-operation for practical ends, arising from the experience of the massive and extremely efficient machinery of military and economic co-operation between the victorious powers; and, finally, it to some extent stimulated nationalism, particularly in countries which had suffered enemy occupation and the evils of enforced migration and labour. In the last eight years, all these influences have been seen at work, their effect being to make generalizations about the state of public opinion extremely deceptive and to give a general impression of violent instability.

The origin of the faith in state action as a means of social improvement, was the success with which the victorious powers had organized their war effort at the cost of a degree of government planning which before the war would have been widely regarded as physically impossible. In Britain, where war-time government planning had gone further than in any of the democracies and where there had been no enemy occupation to give an unpleasant flavour to the idea of the state, this influence was paramount for the first five years of peace. The argument was that if the State could organize a community so effectively for war, it would be equally effective in organizing prosperity and social justice. The country was used to government by bureaucratic regulation, yet civil liberty and Parliamentary government had been maintained. Added to all this was the feeling that so great an upheaval as the Second World War would only be redeemed if victory were the occasion for a fundamental reorganization of society, and with this went the conviction that it had been the inadequacy of pre-war social and economic arrangements which had made it impossible to curb Nazism and Fascism without war. These and many other factors which it is not necessary to list here gave the Labour Party a clear and overwhelming majority in the

House of Commons for what was, to a large extent, a programme of doctrinaire Socialism. The same influences were at work, though for a shorter time and less drastically, throughout Western Europe. The theory that it was the business of government to ensure a minimum standard of welfare for all and to maintain full employment and that these functions were quite as essential as the maintenance of order and the preservation of freedom of speech, was gaining acceptance on all sides; Liberal democracy was becoming social democracy. The policies which resulted from these beliefs, systems of compulsory insurance and the nationalization of key industries, though often bitterly contested, had irresistible popular support and brought about in a remarkably short time fundamental and apparently lasting changes in the social structures of the Western European countries. On the Continent, the movement was helped for a while by the general discrediting of the political Right, which, in France in particular, had led the way in collaborating with the Germans.

It was not only as a source of benefactions, however, that the State appeared in the mind of Europe after the war. The essence of Nazism and Fascism in practice had been the exaggeration, almost to the ultimate point, of State power. Many of the social ideas which appeared in Britain during the war under the banner of militant democracy were being preached in occupied Europe by Nazi propaganda. The leaders of the collaborationist Left in France hailed Hitler's "New European Order" as a way of achieving an economically rational and socialist organization of the Continent. The extent to which Nazism exploited this Continental Socialist idealism, with its contempt for Britain and America as types of bourgeois civilization and as countries which had always lived by denying the aspiration of Europe towards unity, is seldom sufficiently appreciated. It explains, in part, the speed with which Western Europe reacted against Socialism after its immediate success in the first years of peace. All over occupied Europe the idea of the State had come to be associated, in some measure, with the apparatus of Nazi tyranny, with the secret police and the concentration camps; and to this extent the time was ripe for a revival of some of the old and simple principles of Liberalism. There was a sense in which security from the danger of arbitrary arrest, a boon taken for granted in Britain and America, meant more to those Europeans who had suffered enemy occupation than any promise of economic welfare. Social democracy necessarily involved an increase in bureaucratic power, and bureaucratic power had become connected in the minds of those who had suffered under its extreme form with tyranny.

The war had seemed to show that when national States of very different traditions were bent on some common and compelling practical object, national sovereignty ceased to be an obstacle to international co-operation. From this discovery was born the theory of "functionalism" which for a long time dominated European thinking about international politics. There were plenty of compelling tasks, such as the revictualling of the liberated countries, which might provide a strong enough incentive for international co-operation of a strictly practical kind in which constitutional and political considerations would be completely submerged. By this means, Europe hoped, for a while, to sidetrack altogether the great problem of her modern history, the reconciliation of national sovereignty with the idea of an international community. All this presupposed, however, that there would be a firm political framework in which these functional institutions could operate, a framework of continued co-operation between the great powers to whom victory was chiefly due. When it was clear that the world was not to be a unit, hope concentrated sometimes on the prospect of making functional institutions work within that part of it not controlled by Russia, and, more specifically, as time went on, on the prospect of making them function within Western Europe. In response to the ascendancy of Russia and the U.S.A., to the common experiences of war and the common troubles which followed it, it seemed to many that something like a European consciousness, stronger than the consciousness of nationality, might be evoked; and to evoke such a consciousness an international movement, the United Europe Movement, came into being and for a time commanded considerable support, mainly on the Continent.

The idea of European unity, however, had unpleasant as well as happy associations, and the fate of this movement illustrates the stimulus which enemy occupation had given to nationalism. It soon became apparent that ancient rivalries were not to be submerged in a common sense of Europe. It is clear, indeed, that the initial success of the United Europe Movement had resulted chiefly from the fact that it happened to coincide with the special interests of France after the war, because it seemed to supply an answer to the dilemma of how to reconcile German rearmament, which was needed to offset Russian power, with safety against German aggression. As soon as it was realized, however, that the European Defence Community plan would involve real sacrifices of independence, enthusiasm for it began to wane and, in France, to be succeeded by open hostility. The plan, as eventually accepted, was shorn of its federalist implications. The controversy over the Saar and that over Trieste have shown that the diplomatic revolution which has happened since the war has not been drastic enough to remove traditional causes of friction. However great the common dangers to which Europe is subject, Europe remains, in its nature, divided.

The effect of the war on European opinion about politics and

society was, therefore, to present in vivid terms a number of traditional problems: how was the passion for social justice and the
belief in state power as a means of achieving social justice to be
reconciled with the passion for liberty, both of which were strengthened by the war? How was the desire for international peace and
security to be harmonized with the desire for national independence
at a time when the world had just received equally convincing
demonstrations both of the horrors of international anarchy and of
the sufferings involved in the suppression of national independence
and the crushing of national traditions? On the one hand, Russia,
on the most favourable view of Marxist Communism, appeared to
offer social justice at the cost of an indefinite extension of the power
of the State; on the other hand, American Liberalism appeared to
offer security for personal freedom with what seemed to many
Europeans to be much too precarious a guarantee for social order.
Both Russian Communism and American Liberalism offered their
own recipes for universal peace, in the shape either of submission
to the gradual extension of the frontiers of Russia or gradual absorption into an American world. It is hardly surprising, therefore, that
almost everything which has been written or said about politics in
Europe since the war has been dominated by the wish to find what
is called "a middle way" between the extremes of American
individualism and Russian collectivism. The nearest approach to a
coherent, philosophical answer to these questions attempted since
the war is to be found in the work of the Christian Democratic
Movement. Its function has been to reconcile the aspirations of
radicalism with respect for tradition and with the liberal idea of
universal human rights. Its distinctive feature, derived from a long
tradition of Catholic social theory, has been the attempt to settle the
conflict between individualism and collectivism by insisting on the
importance of lesser social units, such as the family and the profession. The notion that individual liberty can only be realized in a
setting of small societies, the notion that the individual by himself
cannot stand up to the State, but that as a member of a group he
can make his own distinctive contribution to the common good, the
idea that the way to put a check on central government is not to exalt
the individual but to strengthen society in all its manifestations:
these principles have all played a notable part in modern European
political thought. In the writings of the Christian Democrats, like
Jacques Maritain, they have appeared purged of all association
with the defence of privilege, and their attraction has been that
they have seemed to supply a social theory at once radical and
traditional.

The astonishing successes of the Christian Democratic parties
throughout Western Europe have been largely due to local causes.
One of their chief functions was to provide a basis on which the

political Right could regroup itself. They represented those elements which accepted the essentials of the new social democracy while continuing to reject Socialism. In France, Germany and Italy these parties have developed their own characteristics, their one common feature being an unqualified rejection of Communism. In France the socialist elements in Christian Democracy have, for example, been much more in evidence than in Germany. The specific social and economic theories of the movement, its new corporatism for instance, have had comparatively little influence anywhere. The movement has espoused the idea of Europe, but even this has been tempered by its recognition of the supreme importance of the U.S.A. as the only present counterpoise to Russian power. It would thus be an exaggeration to say that the Christian Democratic movement has provided that "middle way" between individualism and collectivism for which Europe has been looking.

For a time, after the victory of the Labour Party in Britain in 1945, it seemed that Democratic Socialism might be the common European response to the challenge of Russian and American political thinking. Conceived as a combination of the social aims of Communism with the political aims of Liberalism, the theory of Democratic Socialism had obvious attractions. The Socialist movement has suffered partly from its successes. The speed with which many of its objects were achieved, particularly in Britain, and the comparative readiness with which they were accepted by people who in the past would have fought them to the last, has confronted the movement with a dilemma familiar to progressives. It must either go further along the road on which it has embarked, or it must set itself, discarding its claim to be progressive, to defend and consolidate what it has achieved. The objections to going further are formidable: the immediate tactical objection is that it would involve alienating that substantial small-propertied, lower-middle class on the support of which Democratic Socialism must depend if it is not to become a purely working-class movement. Since in most Western European countries this class includes a sufficient proportion of the electorate to enable it to hold the balance of political power, the effect of breaking with it would be to condemn the Socialist parties once again to being permanent minorities and to cast doubt once again in Socialist minds on the advantages of constitutional action. The possibility of standing still during a period of consolidation is equally unattractive, as it looks like abandoning to the Communists the role of the vanguard of progress.

Inevitably, the reaction against Marxist Communism has hit the Socialist movement, particularly in continental Europe, very hard. Marxism is an important element in Democratic Socialism in all

European countries except Britain, where Socialism has been to a greater extent developed from liberal premises and has drawn much of its inspiration from religious nonconformity. Even in Britain, however, the rapidity with which the Labour Party achieved many of its aims after the war raised the question of how far a fully Socialist economy would be compatible with Parliamentary democracy and, in the last resort, with civil liberty. It was necessary greatly to curtail the time given to debates in the House of Commons, for example, in order to provide for the immense amount of legislation involved in the Labour Party's programme. Nearly all of this legislation, in turn, gave considerable legislative power to ministries to be exercised at their discretion. It is true that Sir Winston Churchill's argument in 1945, that constitutional Socialism led inevitably to Totalitarianism, helped to lose the General Election, appearing to most people to be malicious exaggeration; but as the years went on this argument, stated in more moderate terms, secured more and more adherence, and played a large part in the eventual defeat of the Labour Party. Even the Labour leaders themselves began to realize that the accession of more and more power to the bureaucracy created constitutional problems to which Socialist thinking had so far paid too little attention.

Another factor which undoubtedly contributed everywhere in Europe to the decline in the influence of Socialism was the growing scepticism of electorates. After a while, the magical formula of nationalization lost much of its power. Serious critics, in no way opposed to the aims of Socialism, began to point out that the mere transfer of the legal right to ownership in itself accomplished very little at a time when ownership in most industries was divorced from control. The same point in a cruder form appeared in many polemical attacks on Socialism: what did it profit a miner, it was asked, to be the wage-slave of a public corporation rather than of a private employer? The private employer was at least the weaker of the two. In Britain, in particular, Socialist planning depended to a large extent on the willing co-operation of Trade Union leaders and the old leaders of capitalist industry with Government departments: this arrangement, indeed, seemed to be a condition of a smooth and constitutional transition to public ownership. Yet, it was obviously hard for Trade Union leaders, who had hitherto had the function of exacting terms from employers by organizing rebellions against them, to retain the support of the rank and file while becoming the accomplices of authority. The consequence was an outbreak of unofficial strikes, and, eventually, the growth of a somewhat indefinite heterodox movement, under the leadership of Mr. Aneurin Bevan, which served as a vehicle for radical discontent without making any discernible contribution to the solution of the new problems of Socialist theory and practice.

Yet, the most serious difficulty which Socialism has encountered in recent years has been that which is summed up in the word, now one of the commonest in contemporary political discussion, "incentives". The first question which economic thinking must answer is: What are the springs of economic action? What can be effectively employed to induce men to labour for the satisfaction of each other's needs? To this question, two broad and opposite answers have been offered respectively by liberal capitalism and totalitarian Communism. The first uses personal economic gain as the incentive for economic activity; the second, compulsion by the State. It has seemed possible to argue convincingly for both these methods, but democratic Socialism has been in the dilemma of appearing to reject them both and having no substitute to supply. It has been charged with offering nothing better as an encouragement to production than moral exhortation. This, indeed, has been used to a great extent, and much more effectively than the critics of Socialism are willing to allow; but the impression has gained ground that it is not enough, and this has done Socialism great harm at a time when unique efforts in production are needed to enable Europe to survive. The dilemma goes to the heart of Socialist theory, for one of the essential features of that theory has always been its preoccupation with the problem of distribution and its assumption that the problem of production has already been solved. After the war, Europe woke up to the startling discovery that it had not; everything conspired to make it necessary to insist on production, and to this extent Socialism seemed inadequate to the occasion.

Neither the Christian Democratic movement nor democratic and constitutional Socialism has provided that common European response to the challenge of American Liberalism and Russian Communism for which it has been fashionable to look in recent years. The present state of opinion in Europe cannot be described in terms of any one political movement or even of a series of clearly defined movements. Yet there has been, to some extent, a coalescence of different traditions, the result of which may perhaps best be described as a revival of liberal-conservative thought, with the difference that this thought has now to reconcile itself, as a condition of getting a hearing at all, to the great advance towards equality which has been made largely as a result of the successes of Socialism. These complex trends can best be elucidated by a brief examination of the present condition of the three great principles of modern European Liberalism: liberty, equality and fraternity

Before the war, the traditional assumption that the antithesis of liberty was personal power was taken for granted, and seemed to be supported by the personal adoration which the Nazi and Fascist dictators exacted from their peoples. The assumption that liberty and democracy went hand in hand, an assumption which nineteenth-century Liberalism often denied, also seemed to be firmly established. By contrast with this, the opinion has lately gained ground that the great enemy of liberty in the twentieth century is the aspiration towards social perfection; with this has come about an increasing awareness of the potential conflict between the right of the people to accomplish what they want and the right of the individual to be free from excessive control. Pressed to extreme lengths, the democratic doctrine of the mandate, which in Britain has in recent years been the subject of much anxious scrutiny, results in a form of plebiscitary democracy under which crucial decisions about public policy are taken inside the political parties before general elections, and Parliaments are relegated to the function of seeing that the executive carries out to the letter the promises made in its election programme. It seemed to many that a considerable advance towards mandatory democracy was made in Britain between 1945 and 1950, and a powerful reaction has set in since. Much more emphasis is now placed in British constitutional thinking on the ancient virtues of free discussion in Parliament. The need to emphasize the dignity and importance of the House of Commons in face of the growing power of the executive, the need to do this even at the cost of stemming the flood of legislation, is now common ground between moderate constitutionalists in all parties. This is quite compatible with recognition of the immense value of a strong executive and a disciplined legislature; how to combine these boons with freer public discussion and a more deliberate consideration of policy is a question to which no answer has been found but which is asked with increasing insistence. On the continent of Europe, on the other hand, where constitutions still suffer mainly from the weakness of the executive and from the instability of a multi-party system, the British constitution is chiefly admired for the virtue of stability. There is little temptation to follow the American example of the separation of powers, which appears to produce deadlocks in the business of government and to be ill-adapted to the needs of States which have to act quickly in response to ever-changing economic and political circumstances. For these reasons, the prestige abroad of the British constitution probably stands as high as ever; it is admired because it seems to rest on a rejection of absolutes, on a rejection, that is to say, both of pure democracy and of fanatical libertarianism.

The other aspect of the problem of liberty, how to prevent popularly elected assemblies from invading individual rights while providing at the same time for the much larger part which the State has to play in the control of society, is a constant preoccupation of political thought today. The doctrine of natural, indefeasible human rights acquired considerable prestige as a result of the re-action against Nazism and Fascism. Unfortunately, its most dramatic expression was the Nuremberg trials of alleged war criminals, which rested explicitly on the idea of a fundamental law writ in the hearts of men and taking precedence over the decrees of govern-ments. Since this noble ideal, however, involved punishing people for crimes which were not crimes when they were committed, and since there was always more than a suspicion that the most zealous of the stewards of the universal human conscience, the Soviet Union, had itself committed offences as grave as those for which its victims were to be punished, the whole conception of universal human rights acquired a somewhat squalid complexion. The failure of later attempts to agree on declarations of these rights put the whole subject in most people's minds firmly in the category of "poppy-cock". Human rights have to be realized in particular communities, and their definition is determined by local circumstances. The approach to the problem of liberty is therefore chiefly empirical, and there is great scepticism of general statements on this subject.

The theory, espoused particularly by the Christian Democrats, that the proper answer to the conflict between the individual and the State is to strengthen groups within the State has cropped up continually in political writing. It has led some Socialists to look to something like a revival of syndicalism as the answer to the question "what next?" It was the governing theme of the Conservative Party's now forgotten "Industrial Charter", brought out when the party was looking for something positive and equally pleasant to offer as an alternative to nationalization. The theory still has much influence, but as a general principle for the organization of society it evokes the scepticism aroused by most other general principles. The whole tendency of both the moderate Right and the moderate Left is now to refuse to think of liberty in any but concrete and closely defined terms: it is obvious that moderate Socialism cannot afford to deny a place to free economic competition altogether. It is equally obvious that Conservatism has to accept the framework of a State-controlled economy. The question is where to draw, by reference to efficiency and to the wishes of producers and consumers, the right line of demarcation and to find new techniques for controlling the exercise of public power and limiting it to what is necessary. The idea that liberty in industry must be thought of in terms of the worker at his bench, and liberty in commerce in terms of the con-sumer at the shop counter, the idea that liberty is a question of reconciling interests and that the reconciliation can be brought about by breaking problems down into their component elements rather than by looking for sweeping, *a priori* answers to abstract questions: these ideas have gained much prestige. It has become generally accepted that the idea of liberty contains two distinct ingredients—freedom to satisfy elementary and common human desires, like the desire for food, and freedom to take significant decisions—and that welfare cannot be discussed outside the context of liberty or liberty outside the context of welfare or either without reference to the particular circumstances of the peoples and communities under discussion.

In so far as the word "equality" was a mere symbol of the desire for a more even distribution of wealth, it carried everything before it in the years immediately following the war, and it was the banner under which social changes, many of which seem certain to be permanent, were brought about. It provoked, however, an inevitable reaction; the feeling that, under the influence of the trend of thought epitomized in the phrase "the century of the common man", mediocrity was becoming sacrosanct gained ground rapidly among all who felt themselves to be exceptional. The war had shown the extent to which society depends on exceptional men; it had also made the world rather tired of exceptional men. The charms of mediocrity, however, were rapidly exhausted, and the preoccupation with production, which did so much harm to Socialism, injured the cause of equality generally. It was obvious that even Socialism had to create new kinds of inequality, and to make positive use of existing kinds. Equality came to mean equality in the distribution of the necessaries of life; and the doctrine of the basic minimum beyond which men should be free to compete for whatever prizes were left over came to the rescue. Even this principle had to be qualified, however, as it began to be realized that inequalities, in the shape of profits, are part of the mechanism by which the basic minimum is created. "Equality of opportunity", in so far as it meant merely recognition of the economic dangers and the moral scandal of allowing exceptional talents to remain uncultivated through financial need, commanded universal assent; but even this principle has tended to share the disfavour into which all political abstractions have fallen, particularly when it is interpreted as meaning the general enforcement of some one principle of selection and the closing of all roads, save that, for example, of competitive examination beginning at the age of eleven.

Fraternity, in the sense of international idealism, has fared badly since the war. The United Nations was more modest in its ambitions than the League of Nations. Resting on the belief that collective action is impossible save with the consent of all the great powers, it sought to restrict the occasions for collective action to those on which such agreement existed, thereby excluding nearly all the occasions on which the peace of the world was in danger. The assumption that this would increase the prestige of international organization was proved unfounded, and the only reason why U.N.O. disappointed no hopes was that it aroused none, serving solely as a perpetual and a healthy reminder of what it is impossible to achieve in international politics. Before the war, European liberals had found it easy to distinguish the good from the bad powers, and to define the aim of foreign policy as the permanent ascendancy of the good ones. The distinction, though still clear, has been harder to translate into policy because of the complicating circumstance that Europe is now a junior partner in the alliance of the virtuous, and is acutely aware of her probable destiny as the battlefield in which the next war will be fought. In one form or another, the old and formerly discredited idea of "the balance of power" has reasserted itself. The notion that Britain and Western Europe might hold the balance between Russia and the U.S.A. has appeared in various forms mainly but not exclusively on the Left; those who have seen that the power with which freedom must be defended belongs mainly to the U.S.A., however, have equally been concerned to bring European influences to bear on American policy, and to make use of the help of small uncommitted Powers everywhere, notably that of India, to this end. All hope in Europe now fixes on the ability of European statesmanship to keep the peace by *ad hoc*, empirical arrangements until Russian power begins to recede. The methods of the old diplomacy are again in fashion.

Europe's response to the Totalitarianism of the Left has thus been a revival of scepticism and empiricism. The source of tyranny, it now appears, is the passion for making the world conform to abstract theories or preconceived ideas about the nature of history. The heresy of human perfectability and the faith in politics which it breeds is seen more and more as the great enemy of liberty in the twentieth century. Political thought among intellectuals who reject Communism has, therefore, taken a sharp turn to the Right. The clichés of progressive thinking before the war have been exposed to searching and often devastating criticism. Eighteenth-century liberalism, as a political doctrine, is said to have failed chiefly because of its misunderstanding of the nature of power; having begun by grossly underrating its importance, it has ended by grossly overrating its potentialities for good when wielded by the right people. It is not to Paine and *The Declaration of the Rights of Man* that intellectuals in Europe now generally turn for the answer to Totalitarianism; the idols of the age are such thinkers as Burke and Tocqueville, the apostles of a mature, sceptical and empirical traditionalism. If a liberal civilization is to be preserved, it is felt, the first requirement is that political thinking should be conducted under the discipline of reality; that it should start with circumstances and work back to principles. Absolute truths about politics there may be, but they can be expressed only in terms of particular historical circumstances. Burke's belief that there are very few things which can be rationally affirmed to be universally true has gained ground. The world is complicated, and its peace lies in a diligent search for the means of reconciling opposites and balancing contending interests. Human imperfection is the permanent limiting factor in politics; those who deny it may begin as harmless and ineffectual optimists working on the assumption that the world is much better than it is, but they end as tyrants trying to make it better by the exercise of force. Tradition, prejudice and custom are not just obstacles to progress, but the sources of what little security twentieth-century society has left to it. Such is the prevailing fashion of non-Communist political thought in Europe, a fashion which is spreading to the U.S.A. where the inadequacy of liberal rationalism is also felt acutely.

This revival of Conservative thought takes place in Western Europe against the background of a social revolution, the essence of which cannot be challenged. It is easier than it used to be to preach the virtues of inequality, but only on the understanding that the inequalities to be defended are not the old ones of pre-war society but the comparatively insignificant ones which the Welfare State has left untouched or which can be revived without fundamentally changing the character of the Welfare State. It is this which makes thinking about politics, on the whole, an uncomfortable pursuit for reflective persons either of Right-wing or of Left-wing inclination. The intellectual of the Left has seen his panaceas debunked; he has been brought to a humbler state of mind and to a somewhat wistful appreciation of the maturity and balance of the Conservative tradition. He has been brought back, by contemporary political theorists like Professor Oakeshott or Monsieur de Jouvenel, to sources which he previously ignored or despised. Nevertheless, the uncomfortable sensation remains that, for all its maturity and majesty, Conservative thought still springs from unwholesome motives. It is unpleasant for him to have to use the arguments which used to be employed to defend political and social privilege, even though they may now be employed to defend a totally different *status quo*. The Left, therefore, is often now seen escaping from the discussion of the fundamentals of politics, or searching, a little desperately, for a political theory which can be expressed in the old symbols of progressive thought but which will not involve drastic action. Equally, the political Right, while rejoicing in its intellectual triumphs, is acutely and sometimes painfully aware of how little they mean in practical terms. Conceptions like "a property-owning democracy", though they fit in admirably with the Conservative tradition, are in fact addressed primarily to the interests of the small-propertied lower middle class which now holds the political balance. To the heirs of an aristocratic tradition this class, for all its solid virtues, has few aesthetic attractions. In a community of small-property holders, thrifty, patriotic, devoted to the maintenance of social stability, there is little scope for the bold and gracious virtues which the imagination of the Conservative associates with the ancient régime. There is little scope even for the vigorous middle-class buccaneering which created the wealth which the modern State is now preoccupied with distributing. It is hard for the Conservative really to believe in the possibility of an age of achievement.

In the struggle with Totalitarianism, Democracy has now to preach not a political faith but a mature brand of political scepticsim which, whatever its merits, lacks the *élan* of Communism. This is a deficiency which both Right and Left appreciate. The commonest contemporary remedy for it on the Right is to look for faith outside the realms of politics. The familiar argument of a few years ago that the world's choice is between Communism and Catholicism was one expression of this remedy, but in so far as it involved using religion as an instrument of politics, a weapon in the cold war, it has been discredited in most places outside the U.S.A. The tendency now is for political thinkers to point beyond the confines of their subject, and leave men to seek their own salvation outside it.

BOOKS SUGGESTED FOR FURTHER READING

J. L. Talmon, *The Origins of Totalitarian Democracy* (Secker, 1952).
James Burnham, *The Struggle for the World* (Cape, 1947).
E. H. Carr, *Nationalism and After* (Macmillan, 1945).
Friedrich Hayek, *The Road to Serfdom* (Routledge, 1946).
R. N. Carew Hunt, *Marxism—Past and Present* (Bles, 1954).
Jacques Maritain, *Christianity and Democracy* (Bles, 1945).

INTERNATIONAL ORGANIZATIONS

by CHRISTOPHER HOLLIS

BY ITS TERMS of reference this essay is confined to international organizations since the last war, and indeed there is a definite distinction between the internationalism of our years and that of preceding times. Since the beginnings of civilization man has been visited from time to time by the dream of transcending frontiers, and history ever since the time of the Roman Empire has been filled with experiments of varying success in international organization. But all the organizations which flourished and died before this century—the Roman Empire, the Holy Roman Empire, the medieval Church, the Holy Alliance, the Concert of Europe and the rest—though they may sometimes have talked in terms of the world, were in fact, for better or worse, only organizations of the Powers of Western Europe. Up till the nineteenth century the contact between Europe and the other continents was still irregular and occasional. Such as it was, it was generally polemical. There was not yet any practical question of building an international organization in which European and non-European could work side by side. The nineteenth century, it is true, saw a great increase in communication between Europe and the rest of the world. But politics were still European politics. The politics of other continents were as yet little more than the conflicts for power between rival Europeans. In the nineteenth century all the Great Powers of the world were still European Powers. With the twentieth century, two non-European Powers, Japan and the United States, won for themselves the status of Great Powers. But in the first years of the century both those Powers still refused the role of World Powers. Each, by its own choice, confined its interest to the affairs of its own continent.

The 1914 War brought, it is true again, a great change. The United States, contrary to her own desire, was compelled to play a predominant part in that war and was certainly in a position to play a predominant part in the peace that followed it. It was the American President, Woodrow Wilson, who took the lead in calling for an international organization—the League of Nations—which was to preserve mankind from another war. Had the United States joined that League, as Wilson intended that she should, the story would of course have been different. But she did not join. Other non-European Powers—South American Powers, the British Dominions, Asiatic Powers—did, it is true, join. So, even in the absence of the United States, the League of Nations was not formally an exclusively European League. But it was predominantly so. It never made any very serious pretence—as, for instance, when it was challenged by Japanese aggression against China or by the Tacna-Arica dispute in South America—that it would be able to keep the peace in disputes in which neither of the parties were Europeans, and it did not in fact succeed in keeping the peace even within Europe.

The United Nations, which emerged out of the last war, is in that respect a very different body from the League of Nations. The United States never had any hesitation about joining it. The United Nations does not as yet contain all the nations of the world. But the nations that are not members—the enemy nations and some of the neutral nations of the last war—are not members because they have not yet been admitted, some of them for valid reasons and some for mere reasons of political rivalry and balance. But in theory at any rate all nations are to be admitted as soon as they qualify. There is no nation that has as yet refused to join or been expelled.

In that sense we may say that the United Nations is in theory the first truly world organization. Since, unlike the old Leagues, it cannot pretend that its members are bound together by even a nominal acceptance of the Christian religion, it has had to draw up a Declaration of Human Rights, in which are set out what are considered to be the minimum common conditions necessary for recognition as a civilized nation. It is true that means of enforcing these conditions are at present insufficient, and that many nations within the United Nations have paid lip-service to human rights but flagrantly defied them in practice; just as in the old Leagues many nations paid lip-service to Christian principles but defied them in practice. Nevertheless, with an allowance that has proved insufficient for human fallibility, hopes were high at the time of the foundation of the United Nations that it would succeed where all its predecessors had failed. If all the Great Powers, it was argued, would act together, compose quarrels among themselves and unite to prevent breaches of the peace by smaller Powers, then there could never be another war. Nor, said the optimists, was there any reason why this should not happen. The "bad" Great Powers, Germany and Japan, had been defeated and would never again be allowed the strength to threaten peace. The other Great Powers had stood together in war. Why should they not stand together in peace?

Alas, as we know, things have not worked out as simply as that. The United Nations has disappointed its most eager friends not because the membership of the Organization is not sufficiently extensive but because within the Organization the Nations have not succeeded in remaining united. The Russians, far from providing the co-operation which had been expected, have used their veto to prevent any positive policy. On only one occasion, that of the North Korean aggression, was the United Nations able to follow a clear and positive policy, and then only through the accident that the Russians happened at the moment to be absenting themselves from the Security Council, so were not there to exercise their veto. And even then the United Nations was by no means able to marshal that overwhelming physical force against aggression which would bring instant and complete victory and contain the conflict within the limits of a police action. In fact, it is realistic to recognize, as Sir Gladwyn Jebb recognized in his speech to the Pilgrim Dinner in March, 1954, that, as long as the Great Powers are divided, the United Nations cannot by itself maintain peace. Peace, if it is to be maintained, can only be maintained by other and less convenient means.

When in its constitution, as drawn up at San Francisco, a right of veto was permitted to any of the Great Powers, this concession was thought of as a concession to realism. It was argued that the machinery of collective security could be effective in restricting the punishment of aggression to a police action only if the forces opposed to aggression were of overwhelming strength: which meant in practice, it was argued, if all the Great Powers would act together. It was thought better, if there were not a unanimity of the Great Powers, not to attempt coercion. But it was of course both intended and hoped that there would be a genuine and loyal co-operation of the Great Powers and that the veto would only be invoked on rare and special occasions. Instead the Russians have from the first made no pretence of acting or of allowing their satellites to act as impartial judges of the causes laid before them. They have invariably supported the veto against any suggestion of action by the United Nations. In doing so they have purposely reduced the United Nations to impotence and have used it instead merely as a forum for propaganda. If an uneasy peace has generally been preserved in the world, it has been preserved entirely because of power politics and because of the fear on all hands of the consequences of war, and hardly at all because of the machinery of the United Nations.

The United Nations has, it is true, played its part or attempted to play its part in a number of international incidents in various parts of the world, quite apart from Korea. Its machinery was first invoked in the dispute between Iran and the Soviet Union in 1946 owing to Iran's complaint that the Soviet, contrary to the Tripartite Treaty of Alliance, was still keeping troops on Iranian soil.

Then the Soviet withdrew her troops shortly after the Iranian protest. But subsequent appeals have been less effective. To take a few instances, the attempt of the Security Council to exclude the régime of General Franco from international organizations has served little purpose except that of strengthening his régime. The guerilla attacks on Northern Greece were brought to an end not by resolutions of the United Nations but by Marshal Tito's revolt against Soviet hegemony. The British Government succeeded indeed in taking the Albanians to the Hague Court and in getting there a verdict for the damages suffered by British warships from the explosion of Albanian mines off Corfu, but it has had no success whatsoever in collecting the damages awarded to it. In Palestine the United Nations has met with perhaps its most humiliating failure. The British resigned their mandate there to the United Nations, but neither Jews nor Arabs paid any attention to the United Nations awards about the future of Jerusalem. The representative of the United Nations, Count Bernadotte, was murdered by Jewish extremists. A bloody war was with difficulty transformed into an uneasy armistice along impossible frontiers which have no prospect of survival. The patrolling of that frontier by the United Nations' Armistice Commission may have done something to mitigate the ferocity and murder there which each side has from time to time dealt out against the other, but it certainly has not done enough to prevent the situation from deteriorating so rapidly that it would indeed be a bold man who prophesied that a final catastrophe would be avoided. The Security Council and the United Nations are impotent to act, partly perhaps because public opinion throughout the world is not sufficiently interested to support action, but mainly because it is to Russian interest that the situation should remain disturbed; and the Russians therefore oppose their veto against any action. It has been impossible to find any solution of the Kashmir dispute between India and Pakistan, or of the dispute between Italy and Jugoslavia over Trieste. In China the constitution of the United Nations has not only failed to bring peace but has itself been a cause of dissension. For the British and other Governments have recognized the Communist régimes as the Government of China, while the Americans have continued their recognition of Chiang Kai-shek. As it was Chiang Kai-shek's delegates who represented China in the United Nations before the Communist revolution there, they are still received in the United Nations; and no change can be made there until the Americans agree to it. As a result, those countries which recognize the Communist régime in China are at Lake Success in the somewhat absurd position of having to sit in council with Chinese Nationalist delegates, of whose existence they have no cognizance.

Therefore, with the partial exception of Korea, it cannot be pretended that the experience in collective security since the war has been very encouraging. Such security as we have enjoyed we have enjoyed precisely because it has not been collective—because it has been very notably particular. The United Nations, like the League of Nations, if not for precisely the same reasons, has failed in giving to the whole world an organization strong enough to offer a guarantee of enduring peace, nor is it possible to see how, so long as there was enmity between the Great Powers who were the possessors of physical force, it could have succeeded. In July of 1955 the meeting of the heads of the governments of the great Powers at Geneva gave hopes of a new era of international co-operation. Whether those hopes will be fulfilled remains to be seen.

But, just as it is a great mistake to think that the League of Nations, because it failed in its supreme purpose, therefore accomplished nothing, so too with the United Nations. Under the auspices of the League of Nations there grew up a variety of specialized authorities which were able to give form to international co-operation in a number of directions. The same thing has happened with the United Nations. It may be the great cause of peace which has brought together the representatives of all the nations; but having come together, they naturally use their meeting for the discussion and arrangement of lesser topics. The nineteenth century was in general a century of easier international relations than the twentieth. Although the mechanics of transport were less efficient, yet people in that century could, in so far as passport or currency regulations went, move from country to country with a freedom that would today be inconceivable. The cynic might argue with a good deal of force that the greater the growth in the machinery of international co-operation the less international co-operation has in fact taken place. However that may be, it is certain that it is a convenience that there should be a central international organization under whose umbrella a large variety of projects of international co-operation, some of them pedestrian and non-controversial, can be grouped. We did have international postal arrangements long before there was either a League of Nations or a United Nations, and we doubtless would have the arrangements today even if there were no United Nations. Doubtless a United Nations organization is not required in order to make possible some machinery for international allocation of radio wave-lengths. Yet the existence of a general international organization makes much more convenient the arrangement of all lesser matters, and it may indeed possibly turn out that the United Nations can make comparatively little progress in its direct attack on the problem of peace but may make a much greater contribution to peace through fostering a habit of co-operation on these lesser matters, a habit which may in the end bring reward in fields far beyond those on which it was born.

The situation at the moment is that there are in existence some fourteen specialized agencies. These agencies divide roughly into two classes. Some are purely practical, and not even the most eagle-eyed can detect in their work any ideological bias. Such are, for instance, the Universal Postal Union, the International Telecommunications Union, the Inter-Governmental Maritime Consultative Organization, and the World Meteorological Organization. Useful as they are, these organizations are naturally to the general citizen the least interesting of the international organizations, but they are also the most truly international. For in the work of the purely practical organizations the Russians and their satellites have consented to take a part. From the organizations in whose policies can be detected any taint of ideology, the Russians, though members of the United Nations, have until recently remained ostentatiously aloof. In April, 1954, they showed some signs of reversing this policy by announcing their adhesion to U.N.E.S.C.O., and they rejoined the International Labour Organization of which they had been members in the old days of the League of Nations but with which they had never co-operated since their expulsion from the League at the time of their aggression against Finland. What are the motives of this new apparent co-operation and how far it will be carried still remains to be seen.

Of these organizations each has its peculiar difficulty—over and above the general difficulty of Russian abstention—and a word or two may perhaps usefully be said about the most interesting of them. First, there is the International Labour Organization. The argument for a degree of international organization of labour conditions is clear. It is more than a matter of missionary philanthropy. Cheap labour and sweated labour do not, it is true, necessarily mean low costs of production. Still they may tend to mean low costs, other things being equal; and it is often the excuse and sometimes the reason why conditions of labour cannot be improved in one country that, if such improvements were introduced, low costs in cheaper labour countries would enable them to undersell the first country and drive its goods off the international market. In order to protect themselves against what they think of as unfair foreign competition, countries resort to tariffs and quotas and import embargos. Such measures may be sometimes necessary but they are not in themselves desirable and they in turn create international ill feeling and friction and provoke counter-measures. Therefore it is a most reasonable argument that internationalism does logically imply international free trade, that international free trade is the end to which we should work, but that it is not attainable until there is some international uniformity of conditions of labour. Hence it is most logical to make an aim of the attainment of such uniformity and to establish an organization whose duty it is to work towards it.

But it must be confessed that it has so far proved easier to enunciate the aim than to implement it. Easy as it is to preach an abstract doctrine of uniformity of labour conditions, obviously in fact conditions vary so widely in different parts of the world that the imposition of any sudden uniformity would be quite out of the question. The most that an international organization can hope to do is to receive authority to impose decent, rather than identical, standards and to raise standards everywhere. But the very vagueness of such terms of reference defeats them, and national governments are not willing to be told by foreigners unfamiliar with their conditions what is decent and what is not. Therefore what has happened in practice is that considerable progress has been made, through international treaties and the like, in co-ordinating social conditions between neighbouring countries of roughly the same standards and habits, as, for instance, the Scandinavian countries or to a lesser extent the Brussels Treaty countries; but comparatively little has been done in bringing together countries whose wage-rates differ totally from one another. The small amount that has been achieved is doubtless useful, but how much it owes to the machinery of the International Labour Organization and whether or not it is a step in the direction of world free trade are more doubtful. If the countries of Western Europe should succeed in their ambition of bringing Western Europe into a single market, it is an open question whether the Western countries would be more or less likely to go forward from that to more liberal trading relations with the rest of the world.

Similarly it is reasonable enough that, alongside of the International Labour Organization, an International Trade Organization should be set up and that it should draw up a General Agreement on Tariffs and Trade. That General Agreement has met with some very vigorous criticism and the degree of practical success which it will attain has yet to be seen. The difficulty is that, while people are willing to pay tribute to an abstract ideal of world free trade, it almost always happens that at any given moment there is some one nation which for a fortuitous reason is at a great advantage over all others and that tolerable conditions of competition are only possible if some measure of discrimination is practised against that nation. Great Britain was the nation at advantage in the nineteenth century, and as a result (and not unreasonably) while Britain gave a free entry to her markets to the goods of other nations, those other nations refused to reciprocate by offering a free market to British exports. Today the nation at advantage is the United States, and this danger of excessive dependence on American goods makes other nations reasonably hesitant about the rapidity with which they are willing to move towards total non-discrimination. Unfortunately the Americans, not content with preaching such a total non-discrimination, preach it in a form which would give a special advantage to themselves. In the United States there is total free trade between the forty-eight States. On the other hand the Americans, not being a colonial people, have never had much occasion to make use of preferential arrangements. Therefore preferences seem to them much more unnatural and wicked than tariffs. They can see that it would be impracticable to demand the immediate abolition of all tariffs, but do not see that it would be impracticable to demand the immediate abolition of all preferences. As a result they put forward demands for the reduction of tariffs and for the abolition of preferences—a demand which to many other peoples who protect themselves by a preferential system seems in itself to be almost a form of pro-American discrimination.

In the same way a mistake was probably made at the time of the establishment immediately after the war, in accordance with the recommendations of the Bretton Woods Conference, of the International Monetary Fund and the International Bank for Reconstruction and Development. No fair-minded critic can fail to pay tribute to the generosity with which in these post-war years Americans have poured out money for the relief and rehabilitation of other peoples less fortunately placed than themselves. History can produce no parallel to such a record. But it was doubtful wisdom to give to the Funds power to impose fixed rates of exchange immediately after the war at a time when it was not yet possible to know what would be the proper rates of exchange. The British Government had to pay dearly for its ineffectual attempts to fulfil the obligations assumed as a part of its loan agreement.

The Food and Agriculture Organization is one whose purpose and utility is self-evident. Throughout history people have on the whole been content to leave problems of population to look after themselves. In spite of human fecundity, the enormous infant mortality meant that the population never grew with great rapidity in past ages, and, hard as such a method of natural regulation might be, there was in those times no alternative to it. Medical skill was not able to keep large numbers alive, and mortality rates themselves acted as a crude and automatic guardian of popular health. If we may judge from such tests as the surprising distances which medieval soldiers were able to march with full armour on their backs, it is obvious that our medieval ancestors must have been a very vigorous lot. The explanation is that no one who was not of vigorous health survived at all in the Middle Ages or got the chance to grow up to be a soldier. The medical discoveries of the nineteenth century created a wholly new situation in Britain and Europe. It was then for the first time possible to keep alive many babies who in any previous age would have died. At the same time breeding habits were still substantially those of previous ages. In the early part of the nineteenth century birth-rates remained by any modern stanards extremely high, while infant mortality rates fell drastically and the expectation of life increased. The population of Europe increased vastly during that century, and the Europeans, while increasing at home, were at the same time pushing out into occupation of new lands in other continents.

As long as there were new lands still to be occupied, as long as the new discoveries of medicine and science had not yet come to the knowledge of non-Europeans, so that neither were they increasing in numbers nor were they able, if conflict should come, effectively to resist the white man, these new developments brought no crisis. Our own day has seen the end of such conditions. To begin with, birth-rates in European-inhabited countries have been steadily adjusting themselves to the new death-rates until the Europeans are in sight of a stabilized population. In non-European-inhabited countries the medical knowledge is now beginning to have its effect in lower infant mortality rates, while new habits of breeding which will mean lower birth-rates have not yet established themselves. In past ages, whether humanitarians wished it so or not, nothing could be done to prevent periodic famines and plagues in the primitive countries of the world. Nothing could be done simply because communications were such that no one heard about these calamities in time and there was no way of moving vast quantities of food from place to place. With the improvement of communications—the railway and telegraph first and after them the aeroplane and the wireless—all sorts of measures are now practicable which three-quarters of a century ago were impracticable; being practicable, they present us with a moral challenge which it is not possible to ignore. One can argue in an abstract, objective way whether a high rate of infant mortality in a given country is good or bad and find arguments on both sides; but if one knows that there is a sick baby and knows how to save its life, it is not possible to refuse to save it, however uncertain the advantages of doing so. There are some obligations that are beyond argument.

Therefore the new circumstances have brought with them their new problems. The growing population of the world, the varying paces at which it is growing as between those who have hitherto been the master and those who have hitherto been the subject races, the drift of population everywhere from the land to industrialism and the cities, the constant expansion of the towns and industry into agricultural areas, carry with them dangers of grave conflict and would do so and will do so, whatever the names of the regimes and philosophies that may hold power. Experts differ from one another in their estimates of the pace both of the increase of world population and of the increase of world food production, nor is this surprising since so many of the figures must necessarily be matters of guess-work. But, whatever the precise gravity of the challenge, no one can fail to draw from it the lesson that it is important to increase in every country of the world the production of food. If we can do that, then we can perhaps increase the population of the world and lose agricultural land without involving ourselves in a food shortage and its inevitable conflict. Without that, conflict, sooner or later, seems inevitable. Therefore there can be no sane doubt that the work of the Food and Agricultural Organization, in making available to the less progressive parts of the world the knowledge and machinery which will enable it to increase its food production, is valuable.

The headquarters of the Food and Agricultural Organization are in Rome. At Geneva are the headquarters of another organization, somewhat related to it, the World Health Organization. But the World Health Organization has found itself involved somewhat more deeply in philosophical controversy than has the Food and Agriculture Organization. Of a humane ambition to improve the health of the world no one can disapprove. Even those who argue that the world is, or soon will be. overpopulated cannot sensibly disapprove of a warfare against disease. For clearly it is the special problem of our age that so many ill people are kept alive. In ruder ages they died. But, if we are not prepared to let them die, then it is vital that we make them well, if we can possibly manage it. For in a struggle to feed the world, an invalid, who must consume but cannot work to produce, is a liability.

Therefore alike on economic and on humanitarian grounds there can be no sane controversy about the desirability of the World Health Organization's warfare on malaria, tuberculosis and venereal disease. Malaria is a disease which has for centuries devastated various districts, rendering them not merely unhealthy but also unproductive; and comparatively simple remedies are all that are needed to reduce the scourge of it to negligible proportions. It is in South Italy and Greece that these measures of control have been mainly, though not exclusively, applied, through DDT spraying and other methods carried out with the assistance of World Health Organization missions. A result was that deaths from malaria in Italy, which in 1946 were 1,111, had by 1948 fallen to 4. In its campaign against tuberculosis the World Health Organization has worked through the United Nations International Children's Emergency Fund and the Danish Red Cross with its headquarters in Copenhagen. Its policy is to immunize children against tuberculosis by BCG vaccination. Over nineteen million people in Europe alone have been tested for tuberculosis under its programme and over nine million have been vaccinated.

The campaign against venereal disease has relied on the popularization of the penicillin treatment, but this campaign has led the

Organization into more controversial issues than those of malaria and tuberculosis. The desirability of curing venereal diseases is not, it is true, in itself a controversial issue, but when we move on from that to the question of what women, if any, should be sterilized and prevented from having children, we move on to a much more controversial field. The general question of birth control is more controversial still. There have been those among the delegates who have argued, "The problems of the world are very largely due to the fact that these non-European countries, whose death-rate has been recently reduced by medical improvements, still have old-fashioned large birth-rates. Therefore their population is increasing rapidly and they are pressing up against their neighbours. What more valuable contribution to peace than to teach those peoples birth control so that they may voluntarily reduce their own birth-rates!" But this line of argument has of course met with much opposition. There has been the religious opposition both of Catholics among Christians and of the orthodox adherents of other traditional religions, who have argued that birth control, or at least the use of artificial contraceptives, is forbidden by the divine law and that they cannot therefore be associated with an organization which indulges in propaganda in its favour. On a more secular plane it is argued by some that it is not at all true that the world is in general overpopulated. On the contrary, we are told, the world, taking it by and large, is underpopulated and we are still below our optimum population. Demography is a threat to peace only because the world's population is to some extent ill distributed. Nor, we are told, is it in the least true that birth-control propaganda would be likely to solve the world's demographic problems. It would be far more likely to aggravate them. Such propaganda would of its nature be more likely to have an effect among those to whom its language was familiar than among those to whom it was unfamiliar, and among the literate rather than among the illiterate. That is, it would be likely first to have its main effect among Europeans. Now the main cause of the world's trouble is not that there are too many people of European blood but that there are too few. The European proportion of the total population of the world is steadily falling. Unless they can maintain their proportion of population against the non-European, attacks on them, which will involve the whole world in conflict, are inevitable. It is all very well to say, "Teach birth control to the Indians and the Chinese", but it is by no means clear why they should want to learn its lessons. To the European it may be attractive to argue that a limitation on the number of Indians and Chinese is desirable as a contribution to peace, but what the European calls peace the Indian and the Chinese very easily call the perpetuation of unjust economic arrangements greatly to the European advantage and to the disadvantage of their own people. "Why", they very easily ask, "should we limit our numbers to please the European just when those numbers are getting sufficient to enable us to kick out the European—which is the whole object of our desire?"

So the notion that birth-control propaganda is likely to be very effective in Oriental countries is somewhat unrealistic. Such success as it did have would be most likely among the literate; and therefore even if it succeeded in checking the increase of population in those countries, it would only stop the increase of quantity by a sacrifice of quality. There would be a fall in the numbers of the educated class, to whom those nations must look for leadership. As their survival depends not so much on an absolute question whether they can ideally produce sufficient food to feed themselves as on the question whether they can organize their economy efficiently enough to sustain this larger population; since their economy has already been put into grave and inevitable jeopardy by the withdrawal of the foreign imperialist rulers which nationalism has demanded, a strong native class of educated rulers is of especial necessity to them. A measure which weakens that class will damage their chances of preserving themselves from chaos.

It is clear then that the arguments for and against a policy of birth-control propaganda are at the least balanced. That, combined with the strong religious feeling which the suggestion arouses, made it obvious that the proposal of some delegates to use the machinery of the World Health Organization for the dissemination of such propaganda was not realistic. If it had been persisted in, it must necessarily have split the organization and reduced it to impotence.

Another international organization under the auspices of the United Nations which has aroused a certain amount of controversy and criticism is the United Nations Educational, Scientific and Cultural Organization. That it is desirable that the scientific discoveries of one nation should be available beyond its frontiers is beyond argument; and, if the dissemination of that knowledge had been U.N.E.S.C.O.'s sole function, there could have been no criticism. Some might perhaps have argued that its creation was unnecessary; no one could have argued that its work was in itself undesirable. But when it sought to go beyond these somewhat negative, distributive functions, it at once entered a field of controversy. The purpose of U.N.E.S.C.O. as defined in its constitution is "to contribute to peace and security by promoting collaboration among the nations through education, science and culture, in order to further universal respect for justice, for the rule of law and for the human rights and fundamental freedoms of all". These are brave words, but it is an open question how much service to peace and international understanding is rendered by world histories and world text-books, from which by careful composite criticism all national bias has allegedly been eliminated. In education the composite work and the handbook doubtless have their place, but it is not a very important place. The world's great art and the world's great history have been above all produced by individuals, saying what they see fit to say and submitting their work to no censor. The muse is not a committee. "All things go out into mystery", and on all the great matters that vex the human soul there is not one correct and final answer which can be discovered by looking it up in the index, nor can all others be dismissed as merely incorrect. There are, it is true, degrees of variety of opinion. There are some opinions of which one can say, "I do not know if I agree with that, but it is a possible conclusion which I can perfectly understand that a man who has studied the subject might well reach". There are other opinions which bear on themselves the marks of extravagance and contradiction. From the mere fact that a man holds such an opinion one can confidently argue that he is not competent to hold opinions at all—at least in that field. Yet it is most arguable that the safest policy is one of the toleration of as wide a variety of opinion as possible. If we all say whatever we see fit, it would indeed be too optimistic to assert that truth will necessarily prevail; but at least it is more likely to prevail under a system in which falsehood is first tolerated, then laughed at and contradicted, than under any other. There are two great objections to the composite, official, professedly unbiassed, agreed productions. The one is that, if all individuality is expunged from the writing, the result is likely to be so portentously dull that nobody will read it. The other is that only mediocre writers are likely to submit themselves to the humiliation of having their work hacked about by committees. The true writer, if he cannot write freely, would sooner not write at all.

Therefore it is not very probable that U.N.E.S.C.O.'s positive propaganda for international understanding will accomplish either very much or very much good. It is a fallacy to think that you get the truth merely by eliminating differences—that truth lies in some sort of dreary Highest Common Factor of all the faiths; and the danger of U.N.E.S.C.O. is that it will tend to offer to man a comprehensive pudding of a faith, which by rejecting all that is particular in all the different faiths will in fact succeed in satisfying no one. The danger, if this prior danger be avoided, is that a cultural organization such as U.N.E.S.C.O. will collapse into doing nothing. Conferences meet in pleasant cities. The conferences have their social value, and scholars from one country broaden their minds by conversation outside the conference hall with scholars from other countries. But what goes on within the hall is all too often of little value.

A less controversial organization is the International Refugee Organization. It is one of the sad marks of our time—inevitable consequence of the new, persecuting, totalitarian State—that there are incomparably more people wandering homeless over the face of the earth than there have ever been before in history. When Woodrow Wilson coined the phrase "self-determination", he assumed that whatever happened the populations of the various districts would be allowed to remain in their homes. All that was required for them was to be allowed to make their choice of the State to which they should belong. In the long battle for Alsace between France and Germany it had not occurred to either side that there would be any question of removing the Alsatians from Alsace. But the modern dictatorships, whether of the Right or of the Left, have reduced to nonsense the formula of self-determination by themselves deciding what shall be the population which will determine itself. They remove the population that is not to their liking and substitute for it a population that they approve. This creates a situation where it is one of the most urgent tasks for internationalism to create an organization for the resettlement of these unhappy refugees. Alas, up to the present it has been found much easier to create the organization than to solve the problem. Totalitarian countries have been much more ready to expel refugees than free countries to receive them. In this, as in so many other respects, the nineteenth century was incomparably freer than the twentieth. In the nineteenth century the new countries prided themselves on keeping an open door for any who sought their hospitality, and even between the countries of Europe individuals could move freely and settle where they wished. This was an invaluable safety-valve, and it was one of the main causes of a tranquil century. The exceptional revolutionary, who had made his native land too hot to hold him, could find a home elsewhere in another land where the institutions were more to his liking; and there, most often, he was only too willing to settle down as a sober and peaceful citizen and to eschew for ever the ways of revolution. Those who were unable to find economic opportunities at home made new lives for themselves overseas. Thus during the century the new countries were able to build themselves up to strength. Had the growing number of Europeans been all bottled up by immigration restrictions, there must necessarily have been most appalling explosions. That being so, a grave blow to the chances of the world's recovery after the First World War was the American reversal of their traditional immigration policy; where formerly they had kept an open door, they now established a very vigorous control on immigration, a control which was certainly one of the main causes of the Second World War. Unfortunately in these post-war years there has been no sort of dramatic reversal of restrictionist policies whether by the United States or by any other country of the New World, and the International Refugee Organization has therefore had to do the best that it can within the very narrow limits allowed to it by national governments. Specifically excluded by the articles of its constitution from I.R.O.'s concern are not only criminals and traitors—which is reasonable, if the words be reasonably interpreted —but also all persons of German ethnic origin. Such a reservation was perhaps intelligible enough, if we recollect that the constitution of the I.R.O. was drawn up by the United Nations immediately after the German War, but it is fundamentally absurd in view of the fact that almost the most brutal of all expulsions was that of Sudeten Germans from Czechoslovakia and of Germans from the lands to the east of the Oder-Neisse line. To ask a body to solve the refugee question without solving the German refugee problem is as if one were to ask a doctor to cure half a fever but to leave the other half untouched. Even one who thinks that on general political grounds these acts of expulsion can be defended must admit the hardship which they imposed on individuals and the obligation on international authority to find a new home for those whom a hard necessity has driven from their old home. But at a time when there was greater hope of genuine co-operation between nations than has later proved justified, the International Refugee Organization was perhaps not unnaturally given the instruction that its primary task was to assist the return of refugees to their own countries. The world has not proved to be one in which refugees are often willing to return to their own countries or in which they could decently be expected to agree to a return; and the task of the organization has in fact been almost entirely concerned with finding new homes for the refugees. Only one country in the world has permitted a liberal immigration policy since the war—and that is Israel. It was of course the policy of the Jews in Palestine in the old days of the British mandate to encourage the immigration of Jews in numbers far greater than either the Arabs or the British Mandatory were prepared to tolerate. Attempted illegal immigration led, it will be remembered, to a number of harsh incidents. With the establishment of an independent Israel, immigration of Jews on a scale vastly exceeding that which would have been justified on purely economic grounds was permitted and encouraged. But even there the limit has been reached. The greater number of those who want to go to Israel have by now gone there. Even a people which is willing to accept large sacrifices in order to give a home to co-religionists has now reached a point where the economy cannot immediately receive further immigrants. It is possible that something of the first Messianic fervour has abated. So as a result, what with one thing and another, there is today, far from further unrestricted immigration into Israel, a slight balance the other way, a slight surplus of emigration over immigration.

Possibly this is a temporary condition, and possibly the tide will turn again. But, however that may be, Israel is a quite special and peculiar case in the modern world. There is no other country that has admitted immigrants in proportion to its population on anything like the scale of Israel. Nevertheless, disappointing as has been the response of the countries of the New World to the claim of the refugees, it must not be imagined that they have done absolutely nothing or that the work of the International Refugee Organization has been wholly ineffective. Nineteen countries have since the war selected persons for mass resettlement schemes. Of these, the United Kingdom, France, Switzerland, the Benelux countries and Sweden are in Europe. The rest are in the New World. Under these schemes some million of refugees have been resettled.

The work of the Trusteeship Council, which was established in order to oversee the government of colonial territories, has proved somewhat ineffective. Only a few of the members of the United Nations have colonies, and colonial powers do not take kindly to lectures on colonial morals from countries that have no colonial responsibilities—from countries, moreover, that sometimes do not grant to their own nationals the rights which they demand to be given to the inhabitants of colonies.

No attempt has been made in this essay to give an exhaustive list of international organizations or of specialized agencies working under the auspices of the United Nations, but enough has been mentioned to make it clear that, whatever the defects of the modern world, it is not suffering from a paucity of such organizations. Indeed it would be easier to argue that there are too many rather than too few, that the public is bewildered by the riot of initials with which it is confronted, that the organizations have created a pattern of intolerable complexity, and that more might have been achieved with simpler arrangements. But these are merely the organizations of the United Nations—organizations which are professedly on a world-wide basis, although, as has been said, all the nations do not as yet belong to the United Nations and all the members of the United Nations do not as yet belong to all the specialized agencies.

But there is of course quite another set of international organizations—those which are confessedly regional. Behind the Iron Curtain there is the organization, if so it can be called, by which the Kremlin dominates the nominally independent non-Russian satellite countries. This, however, is in reality a tyranny rather than an organization. But there are of course also the regional organizations of the free world. The dangers to peace in the Pacific have brought into existence the so-called Anzus Pact between the United States, Australia and New Zealand, and at the moment of writing, as a result of the more direct Communist threat in Indo-China, exploratory conversations are going on out of which it is possible that some larger defensive arrangement in that part of the world may emerge. The Arab countries, largely as a result of what they look upon as the threat of Zionism, have formed themselves into the Arab League—a league which, on paper, gives promise of the united action of all the Arab countries. Such united action has not, when tested, generally been forthcoming in practice.

But of all regional organizations by far the most interesting and important are those of Western Europe. They are of two kinds. First, there is the military alliance between the European countries and the trans-atlantic countries which promise them their support. This is known as the North Atlantic Treaty Organization. With the inclusion in it of Greece and Turkey it has stretched itself beyond any geographical boundaries that can be reasonably called Atlantic. It is in fact an alliance of all those countries in the West which can be called free and which might be threatened by an act of Communist aggression, and those who would come to their assistance if they were so attacked. Side by side with their military alliance stands their economic alliance in O.E.E.C.—the Organization for European Economic Co-operation.

Within the general boundaries of N.A.T.O. are to be found the European organizations. The two territories, it is true, do not for the moment exactly overlap. Portugal, though a member of the North Atlantic Treaty Organization, not being a Parliamentary country is not admitted into the Council of Europe. Western Germany is a member of the European Defence Community, and the European Defence Community is under N.A.T.O.; but Western Germany, unlike her partners in this community, is not herself a member of N.A.T.O. This complication is of course, as is well known, an attempt to give the Western world the advantage of German rearmament while at the same time offering the French security against the danger of a new German aggression. Sweden, with her strong tradition of neutrality, has joined the Council of Europe but will not join the North Atlantic Treaty.

But the broad pattern is clear. Western Europe, so long the proud mistress of the world, is today in a threatened and diminished condition. Threatened by Communism from the East, she has been very largely dependent for her survival on military and economic aid from America. That has been most generously given. Yet Europe has her own traditions which Europeans are unwilling to lose. Were the European countries to face the United States, each one utterly separated from all the others, totally divided and in absolute independence, no one would be nearly strong enough to hold the balance against the United States, and the whole of Europe could not hope to be more than a continent of her satellites. Therefore in the years after the war Sir Winston Churchill and other statesmen were busy preaching the gospel that Europe, if she was to survive, must forget her ancient rivalries, and unite. So long as the Iron Curtain endures, there obviously cannot be any question of union of more than half Europe. But that in most people's opinion is a great deal better than nothing. It was out of this ambition to achieve some sort of United Europe that the Council of Europe, which meets at Strasbourg, was formed.

The first decision that the Council of Europe had to take when it met in 1948 concerned the form which the European Union should have. Was the Union to be federal or functional? It was soon clear that there was not sufficient strength in public opinion in all the fifteen countries that go to make up the Council of Europe for it to be practically possible to establish in the immediate future a federal constitution for all the fifteen countries. Therefore victory in the first debates went to the functionalists. Then, those debates concluded, there arose the next question, What are these new functions which Europe can perform in unity? It was in the attempt to give a first answer to that question that M. Schumann in 1950 made his suggestion for the establishment of a supranational authority to regulate the production and marketing of coal and steel. The six Continental powers who are producers of these commodities—France, Western Germany, Italy, Belgium, Holland and Luxemburg—joined to form the community, but Great Britain, then under the late Socialist Government, did not see her way to joining. In the same way when M. Pleven, then the French Prime Minister, put forward the detailed plans for a European Army, the general idea of which had first been suggested by Sir Winston Churchill, the six Continental powers again found that Great Britain, by then under Sir Winston Churchill's Conservative Government, would not accept full membership. Despairing of the full British leadership for which they had hoped, leaders of opinion in the six countries determined to go ahead on their own and to form both a European Defence Community and a European Political Authority, or little federation. Great Britain, through Mr. Eden, fully reaffirmed the obligations which his country had accepted under the Brussels Treaty to defend France and the Low Countries against any possible future German aggression, accepted an obligation to defend the whole territory of the European Defence Community against any aggression from outside itself, and has announced the closest measures of association with the Defence Community; but he did not feel able to commit his country to joining it.

The difficulty of writing an essay on international organizations for incorporation into a book is all too obvious. The whole situation is fluid. New organizations are coming into existence. Organizations are passing out of existence. States are joining and States are leaving the different organizations. While this essay has been in composition there have been changes. There will doubtless be further changes between the delivery of the manuscript and publication; and that would have been equally true had publication taken place at any other time. We live in a world of flux, and there is no reason at all to think that any sort of general world stability will be achieved for very many years to come. But the lessons that we can draw are surely clear enough. A minimum of organizations—to work out the details of a policy on the principles of which there is general agreement—is useful. But neither a conference nor an organization nor committee can be a substitute for policy. As with the League of Nations, organizations for the preservation of peace can in practice prove dangers to peace. The League of Nations proved to be such a danger because it lulled people into a false security. They thought that a magic formula had been discovered whereby peace could be automatically preserved, and that they were freed from the normal and inconvenient obligations of vigilance. It is perhaps not altogether an evil that the organizations of the post-war world have not met with that apparent and easy success that is likely to lull us into complacency. An international organization is less dangerous when it does not run too smoothly. It then corresponds more nearly to reality.

BOOKS SUGGESTED FOR FURTHER READING

Lord Ismay, *N.A.T.O.; The First Five Years* (N.A.T.O., 1954).

U.N. Dept. of Public Relations, *World Against Want* (1953).

J. D. Warne, *N.A.T.O. and Its Prospects* (Deutsch, 1954).

Great Britain Central Office of Information, *Western Co-operation* (C.O.I., 1953).

Organization for European Economic Co-operation, *At Work for Europe* (O E.E.C. at Château de la Muette, Paris, 1954).

Council of Europe. Directorate of Information, *The First Five Years, 1949-1954* (Strasbourg, 1954).

ECONOMICS, 1900–1950

by R. F. HARROD

I. Alfred Marshall and Liberal Reform, 1900-14

ECONOMIC THOUGHT in Britain at the opening of the century was subject to the tranquillizing influence of Alfred Marshall. His ascendancy was notable, although naturally not without challenge— for instance, by H. S. Foxwell in his own Cambridge and in London by Edwin Cannan, whose sturdy self-regard would suffer him to bow to no man. But F. Y. Edgeworth, sole representative of economics in Oxford, who was Marshall's equal on the plane of severe abstract speculation, gave unstinted recognition of his leadership. In public life he was judged to be the best representative of academic thought and his views were respectfully attended to by successive Royal Commissions. There was no important challenge to his main body of doctrine. The Socialists, of course, were gathering their strength, and bent for their own reasons on the eventual overthrow of the capitalist system; but the Fabians at least were not disposed to prefer Marx to Marshall, if it was a question of analysing how wicked capitalism actually worked.

This ascendancy was partly due to personal qualities: a palpable devotion to the truth; an immense conscientiousness and sense of responsibility, leading to the polishing and repolishing of all his work and indeed to delays in publication, which in certain cases proved to be excessive; a judicial quality, a restraint and an unwillingness to intervene unless he could give the matter in question his utmost consideration; a private austerity, a certain *hauteur* and an instinctive sense of how, when one is a great master, one should act the role of great master.

This was the personal background; but what is more important to our purpose is to see how the specific character of his intellectual contribution qualified it for a commanding influence at the time. He was not a great path-breaker, like Ricardo or Keynes or even Jevons; he did indeed create certain tools of thought which have proved serviceable and durable, and he had a certain quality of impeccability and a strong sense of the limits and reservations to be attached to doctrines, so that when subsequent thought has shown the need for a qualification to some Marshallian tenet simply conceived, his admirers have often been able to show that the qualification was there in his text all the time. All this was valuable. But we are not yet at the heart of the matter. It is necessary to take a backward glance.

The genius of Adam Smith and of the British economists of the early nineteenth century consisted in their ability to sort out the vastly confusing and heterogeneous phenomena of economic life, and to introduce concepts and classifications facilitating orderly thinking. Their "system" has been criticized as over-simplified, as no doubt it was; nonetheless it was a great advance from the preceding chaos. It gave prima facie arguments in favour of individualism, and, if pushed to an extreme, these might be deemed to justify complete *laissez-faire*. The economic principles involved were intelligible with moderate study and were in fact comprehended by quite a large class of persons engaged in some form of public life. They became part of the stock-in-trade of the well-informed. As thus popularly understood, the doctrines of "political economy" became, no doubt, too rigid; yet even so their guidance was better than none, and nineteenth-century policy and administration in England were more rational than they would have been without that guidance.

Thought does not stand still. In Britain and elsewhere there were challenges to the "classical" system. On the one hand there was the view that it failed to recognize the significance of historical development, and that it claimed universality for generalizations that at most were true of a passing phase of capitalism. It must be admitted that some of the classical writers were rather narrow in their purview, but the "historical school" may have underrated the value of abstraction owing to a deficiency of intellectual toughness. There were other challenges. There were those who, finding a lack of precision at certain points in the classical thought, wanted to build systems anew from the beginning. Such were the Austrian school of marginalists and their counterpart in England, Jevons.

Marshall regarded such attempts at revolution with distaste. But his attitude to them was not one of intolerance; rather he sought to avert the evil consequences of rebellious fervour by comprehending what was valid in the rebel thought in his own system. He recognized the claims of history in principle. In regard to the marginalists he judged, I believe correctly, that much of their theory was already implicit in the older traditional system and for the rest constituted a welcome refinement. The doctrine of demand for goods and for factors of production based on their marginal utility was fully integrated with the older British cost of production theory of value in his famous *Principles*. The Austrian school continued to flourish and to thrive on controversy, and it has its progeny today. But British economists could argue that Marshall succeeded in incorporating everything that was of value in their thought without any fuss.

He laid stress on the continuity of economics and on the substantial truth at most points of the older doctrines. This attitude had a double value. Economics was (and is) a young discipline; as a science its main success so far has been conceptual and classificatory; it had not and—despite the development of statistics—still has not to its credit many laws that can be expressed quantitatively; it can do little experiment. A subject of study in this phase can all too easily become a field of fierce terminological controversies; the inexpert can mistake these conflicts for disagreements about matters of substance, and the controversialists may in their egoistic zeal themselves lose their firm grasp of the slender body of doctrine which is all that their science can vouchsafe. By such strife gains previously won may be dissipated and lost. In such a phase, skill in the choice of terms and modes of enunciating principles may require a wise sense of expediency; this does not imply any compromise with truth, for the same laws can be formulated in alternative ways. It may be wise expediency to instil and even if you can to impose—and Marshall could—what may be called a linguistic conservatism, for this will tend to curb the natural tendency of each new generation of students to mistake linguistic novelties for real contributions to the subject. And this in turn will canalize their energies into making real contributions. Marshall presented economics as a set of principles which had in the main stood the test of several generations; this might abash the tyro disposed to think it an easy matter to rewrite them. It is fair to add that in imposing this discipline Marshall was correspondingly modest about his own substantial contributions.

I have referred already to the wide diffusion in the nineteenth century of some knowledge of "political economy". This was another reason for linguistic conservatism. Facts and theories were becoming more complicated. This must put a strain on the layman. It seemed important to ensure, as far as possible, that economics should not be overlaid with technical jargon, and to dress the subject so that the politician, the administrator and the journalist should be able to retain the most essential principles within their comprehension. In this secondary aim Marshall may not have succeeded completely, but he strove hard, and he fully recognized how easily the position might slip, to the detriment of public affairs. To a large extent economic doctrine did retain its hold on the public for another generation. Marshall's more brilliant pupil Keynes did not feel these inhibitions; that there has been some loss by consequence can hardly be doubted. But whatever the proceedings of the academic world, the recent confusing changes in the real world might alone have sufficed to obfuscate the economic vision of the layman.

The synthesis achieved by Marshall must not be regarded as an isolated British product. Systems structurally similar to his were being developed abroad at the same time by such economists as J. B. Clark in America, and Walras, Pareto, Auspitz and Lieben, and Wicksell on the Continent. The minds of these eminent economists were moving in the same direction as that of Marshall, but they did not, like him, gain widespread contemporary recognition for their systems.

The older economics had a reputation for harshness, in part unfairly so; its practical maxims inclined strongly to *laissez-faire*, although its foremost proponents always allowed many exceptions. Its classification was broad and deemed handy for practical use. The Marshallian system was more refined and precise; it had been given a mathematical formulation; its assumptions were more clearly specified, and this was in itself a safeguard against the over-ready application of crude maxims. It may be well to consider how the traditional maxims stood at the opening of the present century.

The high regard for the virtues of competition and free enterprise was still, outside the ranks of Socialists, undimmed. The virtues ascribed were twofold. First, competition was held to be the only available method for ensuring efficiency and progress. Secondly, it secured for the consumer the assortment of goods he required. This was in accordance with Adam Smith's famous "hidden hand"; this conception did not of course imply some providential agency, but was a flowery description of the practical forces generated in free markets, now often referred to as the "price mechanism". The more precise mathematical formulation of the economic equilibrium, to which reference was made in the last paragraph, revealed relations which might raise doubts, expressed but not stressed by Marshall, as to the precise accuracy of those forces, when industries were subject to the laws of diminishing or increasing returns. These doubts made no immediate impact on thinking about public policy, but were to become quite important thirty years later.

Both virtues of competition, when regarded on an international scale, required, as a corollary, Free Trade. While the new century saw the beginnings of a Protectionist agitation under the auspices of Joseph Chamberlain, the leading professional economists were agreed in rejecting the arguments. The triumph of Free Trade as the official British policy, eventually supported by both political parties, had been the greatest practical achievement of the classical school. It was a notable triumph of intellect over prejudice, because Free Trade, although valid, is not an inherently popular doctrine. It was frankly based on self-interest, and, in accordance with the doctrine of Ricardo, who reduced the generalities of Adam Smith to an exact theory, its benefit to the country adopting it is independent of whether other countries adopt it or not, and of whether their

wages are high or low. But it was also deemed to be a fine example
to other nations, whose adoption of it would bring further advantages to themselves and others; and this was reckoned a good reason
for scorning to infringe the general principle in those exceptional
cases where, by self-interested calculation alone, some advantage
might be obtainable. The rigid adherence to the principle of the
open port by Britain during her period of greatest ascendancy has
not only the quality of enlightenment, but also one no less essential
to leadership, the quality of dignity, and, I would even say, of
majesty. It will long continue to stand to her credit in a survey of the
centuries. In 1900 the economists were to remain united in its
defence for a further period.

What had they to say at this time on the problem of poverty?
This has usually been near the heart of economists, for some zeal in
regard to it has often been their motive in devoting themselves to
this arduous study; if they have achieved, especially in early days,
the reputation of being hard-faced, that is because study leads to
scepticism about facile solutions.

The early school was much influenced by Malthus's views on the
population question, which led to what was known as the "subsistence theory of wages". Given the normal human tendency to
reproduction, population will increase at an insupportable and
indeed in the long run fantastic rate, unless checked by a high death-
rate, i.e. by extreme poverty. All agreed that the level of subsistence
could be raised progressively if only the birth-rate could be reduced
below its natural level. On this Malthus himself was pessimistic,
especially in his earlier phase; implying that contraception should
be repugnant to a good Christian, he doubted if moral restraint
alone would be sufficient to prevent breeding up to the point at
which poverty was inevitable. Ricardo and J. S. Mill took more
optimistic views about the possibility of restraining births. As the
nineteenth century wore on less was heard about the population
principle. Despite prodigious increases in the British population,
the standard of living had in fact been greatly improved, and there
was a disposition to relegate Malthus to limbo. This was superficial.
The forward strides in industrial efficiency and, more important,
the growing dependence of Britain on food supplies from overseas
had staved off the working of the Malthusian principle. By themselves these could only provide passing respite, for in the end, given
traditional birth-rates and the greatly fallen death-rate, Britain
would be bound to become packed full with people, like a tin with
sardines. Careful students have observed with surprise that there are
still vestiges of Malthusian views in Marshall, and have attributed
this to his usual unwillingness to break with traditional doctrine.
But on the facts at his disposal he was still right to be cautious.
What has revolutionized the situation has been the great fall in the

birth-rate; this trend had indeed begun earlier but could not yet be clearly recognized in 1900. Indeed as late as 1919 Keynes attempted to revive a population scare. The spectacular fall in the birth-rate has now for some time rendered Malthusian anxieties obsolete for Western Europe. But Malthusian doctrine, so prominent in J. S. Mill and not quite dead in Marshall, still has relevance for the poorer regions of the world where birth-rates remain high. However, Malthusian fears were no longer influencing thought about policy in Britain in 1900.

The pessimism, or perhaps one should rather say the caution, of the earlier school had a second string, known as the Wages Fund theory. This theory, which is formally correct, holds that the total amount that can be paid out in wages, wherever there is a time interval between the application of labour and the completion of a product for consumption, cannot exceed the rotating fund of accumulated savings. The practical conclusion was that the only true beneficiary of the working classes was the man who added to his savings and that neither legislation nor Trade Union action could add a penny to the total wages bill, any sectional improvements being necessarily accompanied by deteriorations elsewhere.

By the end of the century the hold of this doctrine had weakened somewhat. J. S. Mill late in life made a resounding, though not completely convincing, retraction of it. There was a shift of emphasis. What was really implied was that it would be safe to regard the wages fund—perhaps better called savings fund—as sufficiently elastic, if only higher wages could be justified on other grounds. The emphasis on demand and on the margin, initiated by the Austrian school and incorporated by Marshall and others, led to wages theory being expressed in the form that wages are the *product* of labour. Thus if only productivity could be increased, wages could be increased; this favourable situation would attract the necessary extra savings, and thus the wages fund would look after itself. Perhaps in certain circumstances the causation might work the other way round: the grant of a wages increase might improve the health and stamina, and thereby the productivity, of the wage-earner and thus create a state of affairs justifying the increase *ex post*. Or take another case. In a free and properly organized market, the wage-earner *should* obtain his whole produce as wage; but it may be that the market is not properly organized, that there is an inequality of bargaining advantage and some monopolistic element on the side of the employers, and that there is by consequence in some sense an "exploitation" of labour in which the worker receives less than his product. If in those circumstances a Trade Union comes forward and insists on higher wages or a statutory Trade Board is set up empowered to fix a minimum, lo and behold, the higher wage can be paid without adverse repercussions.

Of course these ideas must be applied with due caution. If a Trade Union too militant or a Trade Board too humanitarian fixes a wage above the product, either some workers will be thrown into unemployment or an increase of prices will follow causing a deterioration in the buying power of wages generally.

Such ideas had been weaning economists away from the rigid doctrine that the wage-earning classes must wait passively for capital accumulation eventually to pour benefits into their lap, and had been making them more receptive to the view that Trade Union action and, within carefully defined limits, state intervention might benefit the poor. Public opinion was also in a mood to form an independent judgement. It is only in the present age that we have full statistics of the distribution of the national income. Even without them it may be yet possible to form a rough and ready judgement. In the early days of the Industrial Revolution, aristocrats might enjoy a luxurious standard, but most industrialists were living hard and ploughing back their profits. Common sense might guess that there was not a large cake available for redistribution, except at the expense of savings vitally needed for industrial expansion. By the end of the century there was rather a large high-living middle class, and it seemed manifestly absurd to argue that nothing was available for redistribution to mitigate the harsh lot of the poor, which was visible enough to those who looked, and repeatedly publicized in surveys and reports. We do not have to assume that an increase in humanitarianism occurred at this time, for in the earlier days some harshness had been a stern necessity. But we need not categorically deny that the great writers of the century, whether Wordsworth, Dickens or George Eliot, had a slow-working influence in diffusing a more humane social outlook in ever-widening circles. And self-help too played its part; the Trade Unions, only efficiently organized after much perseverance and many set-backs, and the Parliamentary vote helped to push open the door, from which the heaviest bolts had already been removed.

Thus the trend of economic theory and of public opinion and the circumstances together set the scene for the experiment in economic reform of the Liberal administrations of 1906 to 1914. These were designed to bring relief to the poor. Already in the nineteenth century the State had intervened in many fields—factory legislation, education—thereby infringing the strict principles of *laissez-faire*. But the new measures went further in securing a redistribution of income on lines that would have been deemed by an earlier generation to be "contrary to the laws of political economy". The group of measures of these Liberal administrations may be reckoned as having introduced in principle what we have since come to know as the "Welfare State"; but the amounts involved in terms of pounds, shillings and pence were still small in these early stages.

The expediency of having collective bargaining by wage-earners who, as individuals, were the weaker party, was recognized by the Trades Disputes Act (1906), which gave the Unions a much more secure status and removed them from the anxiety that their collective-bargaining activities, including the withdrawal of labour, might be deemed civil conspiracies or otherwise offend against the law; some argued that the Act went too far in raising the Unions above the law. Non-contributory Government pensions for the aged were provided in 1908. A far-reaching departure was the establishment of Trade Boards (1909) empowered to impose statutory minimum wages in what had hitherto been "sweated" trades; here the State came in to prescribe and enforce a raising of standards for the poorest classes of wage-earners. In the same year Labour Exchanges were set up to provide information and increase the mobility of labour. In 1911 the great system of National Insurance was inaugurated, partly based on German precedent; it provided for compulsory insurance with State contributions against sickness and, in part of the field, against unemployment. The Shops Act (1911) provided a compulsory half-holiday. In 1912 statutory minimum wages were enacted for the important group of coal-mine workers.

These measures were accompanied by fiscal reform, also of a redistributive tendency. An attempt was made to tax the "unearned increment" of the land. The doctrine that the land was an especially suitable object of taxation descended from the early days of classical economics; crudely set out, this doctrine contains many fallacies, and, if such an impost is to be at all equitable, it is necessary to have immense patience, namely over a period of many decades, to get any substantial returns from it; this particular attempt proved abortive. More important was the introduction of the super-tax, which made direct taxation progressive—there was a death-duty precedent. Here again the important step was the introduction of the principle; two wars caused this weapon of tax collection to be carried far beyond the scale originally intended, and perhaps beyond what is wise and equitable.

II. The First World War and its Aftermath, 1914-25

The First World War led to the introduction of a widespread system of Governmental control through the economy. The question may be raised why, if free enterprise is really the more efficient system, is it abandoned in time of war. In the first place, the operations themselves place the Government in the position of a purchaser of labour and goods on a preponderant scale, and its direct interests ramify throughout the economy. Secondly, in war, speed is more important than efficiency; there is little doubt that in both wars the systems of Government interference involved colossal waste; but that had to be accepted in the interest of that speed of adjustment which a dictate can alone ensure. After the First World War the system of controls was very rapidly liquidated, and did not have a great effect on subsequent events; but the memory of it may have been an encouragement to Socialists against the dogmatisms of traditionalists who affirmed that a widespread system of controls would be totally impracticable and break down in chaos and absurdity.

There was, however, one great aftermath of the war which had a profound influence on thought and practice, namely the currency inflation. For many years before the First War, orthodoxy in this field was securely established and not subject to serious challenge. The gold standard was accepted as the best plan; even the enthusiasms of bi-metallists had abated and died; there were indeed a number of interesting developments, particularly in the provision of "gold exchange standards" for less developed regions, and Keynes's reflections upon the Indian system (1913) had seminal ideas, which were eventually to raise doubts about certain orthodoxies. Major inflations were regarded as distempers of an earlier age. One remembered the issue of *assignats* during the French Revolution, and sundry currency excesses on the American continent; but these were deemed to be self-condemned and unlikely to crop up again. But now they had cropped up. The causes were set forth by economists on orthodox lines; it was generally recognized that inflation was not merely a matter of note issue, but also connected, in accordance with already received monetary theory, with excess lending— in the interests of the smooth running of the war—by the banking system. The evils of inflation were manifesting themselves strongly, and hardly needed emphasis. They were not only seen on the domestic front in the upward spiralling of prices and wages, but also in the foreign-exchange markets. Traditional doctrine laid down that loss of internal purchasing power would be measured by a corresponding depreciation of a currency in the foreign exchanges. The foreign-exchange rates, however, did not fully measure inflation, because a world-wide process had caused a deterioration in the commodity-value of gold itself; and although the United States returned to specie payments at the old gold parity for the dollar in 1919, the dollar, and consequently gold, had much less purchasing power in terms of goods than before the war.

Where various currencies had undergone different degrees of inflation, this should be measured in their various exchange quotations against one another. The Swedish economist Gustav Cassel coined a popular phrase to express this, "purchasing power parity". The basic truth of this doctrine, and also the various modifications that have to be attached to it, was set out with a new precision. In particular it was noted that the foreign-exchange market had a strong tendency to anticipate the future, so that the countries which had not yet mastered their own internal inflationary process tended to have their currencies undervalued in foreign-exchange markets.

To English-speaking and Scandinavian economists all this was plain enough. But there were doubts in other quarters. Economic theory, although well represented in the various Continental countries, had not bitten so deep there, and it did not appear to them so axiomatic that the falling value of their currencies at home and abroad was due to their own actions in increasing the quantity of notes or bank loans. They seemed to themselves to be caught up in some kind of ineluctable process, to be the victims of irresistible pressures; they were apt to claim that the progressive rise of prices was due to forces beyond their control, and that in accommodating the amount of currency issued to the higher needs for circulation due to these higher prices, they were doing what was absolutely inevitable. The British never admitted this, and in principle it cannot perhaps be admitted. On the other hand it may be allowed that in certain cases it would not have been quite as easy as orthodoxy suggested, given the general economic circumstances, for these nations to rescue themselves from the toils of the inflationary process. It may not always be possible to draw a precise line between what is difficult and what, for practical purposes, may be reckoned impossible.

Prominent among these cases was that of Germany. This brings us to the Reparations problem. In this there were certain deep questions involved which, despite all the talk and literature, were not fully brought out at the time. The demands and the assertions of those who wanted to make Germany pay the full cost of the war were so fantastic, and the case against them so overwhelming, that Keynes was able to win an easy victory among those of well-informed opinions. Absurd Reparation demands caused much confusion in the post-war years until they were reduced to a reasonable level in 1923; the uncertainties of that period retarded the European recovery and may well have been responsible, by their disturbing effects on the social fabric of Germany, for the Second World War.

Keynes held that the Germans *could not* pay the large sums asked; the implications of this proposition were not duly considered because the sums asked were so fantastic, and the words "could not" could readily be given a rough common-sense meaning. Keynes held, not merely that the Germans could not pay these fantastic sums, but that they could not even pay much more moderate sums in excess of a certain amount. It was assumed in his argument that the payments were to be made by the normal processes of a free economy, including the heavy taxation of German citizens, and not by a coercive system under which the whole of the German economy would be rigidly controlled and a portion of its people set down to work for others by central direction. His point was that the free system does not provide means for such large adjustments as those envisaged. This contention was not strictly in line with orthodox economics. It was never put to the test or even argued out because of the rapid abatement of the demands upon Germany. But it has relevance to the problem of whether it would have been possible for the world to carry through those other large adjustments that were necessitated by the Second World War without the aid of a system of fairly comprehensive controls.

For a number of countries, including Britain and the United States, the inflationary period was over by the middle of 1920 and was followed by a period of deflation. This was a less familiar problem in the orthodox economic texts, although Ricardo had some sage ideas upon its incidence after the Napoleonic Wars. It was found that the deflationary process gave rise to some very acute evils of its own—widespread unemployment, business loss and a freezing of new enterprise.

Before the values of currencies in the countries subject to deflation had been restored to their 1914 values in terms of goods, the authorities made up their minds that deflation too was an evil and that it was not desirable to carry the process any further. The resilient United States economy was already in 1922 recovering fairly well from the deflationary bout; but the British economy remained depressed, and unemployment was greater than it had ever been within living memory, or in the records. This phenomenon provoked a train of thinking in Keynes which gave rise to the most important basic changes in economic theory in the last hundred years.

From early days one branch of economic thinking had consisted in the study of the ups and downs of trade. The British school comprised important contributors to this subject: Tooke, Walter Bagehot and, above all, W. S. Jevons. Before the war there were also notable contributions by Continental writers—Tugan-Baranovsky, Spiethoff and Aftalian—and in the United States Wesley Mitchell had begun his monumental labours. Shortly before the war in England Professor Pigou (*Wealth and Welfare*, 1921) and Mr. Hawtrey (*Good and Bad Trade*, 1912) had made contributions; and attacking the problem with sharper tools and more profound and subtle thinking, Sir Dennis Robertson published his notable volume on *Industrial Fluctuations* (1915). The period of inflation followed by deflation re-stimulated interest in the more fundamental and permanent problem of what had come to be called the Trade Cycle. In the post-war period a good deal of stress was laid on the monetary causes of fluctuations, perhaps as a natural consequence of the big disturbances in the monetary system that had taken place. There was an old tradition among monetary theorists that an ideal money ought to have stable purchasing power in terms of commodities. In the United States, Irving Fisher had recently made prominent proposals for a dollar that should be stable in terms of commodities. Now a whole host of very eminent writers concentrated their attention on the need for monetary stability—Fisher, R. G. Hawtrey, Cassel, R. McKenna, Keynes and Sir Dennis Robertson. The last-mentioned made some subtle but fundamental reservations, and presented these in a new form in his *Banking Policy and the Price Level* (1926).

England did not return to the gold standard until 1925. When she did so, she returned to the pre-war parity; she chose this rate largely for prestige reasons. Anticipation that she would do so had floated the pound up in the free markets so that the technical operation was not difficult. Keynes argued strongly that this would mean an overvaluation of sterling and have woeful consequences, but he did not get much support. He did not, however, concentrate his attention upon the undesirability of forcing the pound up to an unjustified level, but mingled his pleading with arguments against returning to the gold standard at all. He deemed that we were getting along very well in the period 1922-4 with a pound that was fairly steady, but was not absolutely stable in the foreign-exchange markets. Subscribing to the view that money should be stable in terms of commodities, he argued that the *de facto* arrangements at this time were working well and that we should take this opportunity for an experiment in a "managed" currency to remain detached for gold and to be held roughly stable in terms of commodities. After the return to gold in 1925 there was a good deal of retrospective support for Keynes's opposition to a return to the old parity, but much less for his desire to be free of a fixed gold par altogether, and some complaint that if he had not mixed the two lines of thought he might have had greater success in his advocacy of a lower parity. But his advocacy of a floating pound was destined to have far-reaching effects later.

In 1914 the United States, which had been without a central bank for eighty years, established the Federal Reserve System which was a chain of twelve central banks co-ordinated by a Federal Board. After the post-war inflation and deflation, the Federal Reserve System deliberately set itself to aim at internal monetary stability.

In the management of sterling prior to 1914 the Bank of England had had perforce to concentrate its attention in its monetary management mainly on the country's external balance of payments. In the twenties the United States had a very large gold reserve and was consequently free to concentrate attention on internal stability. This was a new departure. Its implications for the international equilibrium were not clear, but its internal objectives were entirely in line with the thinking of those economists who were urging the supreme importance of having a money that should be stable in terms of its purchasing power over commodities. The Federal Reserve experiment was thus watched with some enthusiasm, and it was hoped that we might be at the beginning of a new era in monetary affairs, in which the world should enjoy, under this American leadership, a more stable medium of exchange. For seven years all seemed to go well, but then the American slump came. Space does not allow me to examine Federal Reserve policy here; it must suffice to say that no one has been able to demonstrate that its conduct of affairs in the years 1923-9 was gravely at fault.

III. Keynes

It is well known that the American slump had a most far-reaching influence on the course of events, political as well as economic. It also had a very important effect on the course of thinking. Naturally enough it encouraged those who regarded the Trade Cycle as of central importance in economic studies. But it discouraged those who hoped to find the cause and cure of the Cycle in monetary management alone. If there had been no Federal Reserve System, the matter might have been otherwise. But the fact that this unprecedented slump occurred in a country which had in fact enjoyed the benefit of monetary management in accordance with the best ideas available, raised doubts as to the potency of this weapon and suggested that there might be more fundamental causes of oscillation than lay within the power of monetary authorities to counteract. This subject cannot be regarded as closed at the present day. In the thirties thinking took a new direction.

Some held that the great disturbances of the world slump were a delayed aftermath of those due to the First World War. Apart from the physical destruction, which was not great, there were disturbances due to the changes in the established pattern of international trade and also those specifically concerned with reparations and inter-allied war debts. Some held that these were not large enough to account for the huge dimensions of the great world slump of 1929-32. Study of the Trade Cycle revived. With the increased doubt about whether monetary mismanagement could be regarded as a prime cause, attention reverted to alternative theories, such as those advanced by the writers whom I have mentioned above, notably to theories that concerned fluctuations in the level of investment activity. While different lines of thought and different authors made their contributions to the common stock of understanding (and special stress ought to be given to Sir Dennis Robertson and to the Swedish school which had continued to flourish since the days of Wicksell), the thinking of Keynes came more and more to attract attention, both by reason of his energy and lucidity as a writer, and because his disposition was to relate his thinking about enonomic depression to more general economic theories.

In some respects his first step away from orthodoxy deserves most attention, as being pregnant with large developments. We have seen that he was particularly interested in the phenomena of deflation that occurred after 1920. He continued to advocate a more expansive monetary policy in England prior to the set-back of the return to the gold standard in 1925. But although monetary policy in the three preceding years was not as expansionist as he could wish, it would be hard to stigmatize it as a strongly deflationist policy; and yet unemployment had never been so severe. It therefore seemed that something more than monetary relaxation was needed, and he accordingly advocated *a vigorous policy of public works to reduce unemployment*. This was certainly out of step with traditional economics. According to that doctrine, economy in outlay is always a prime recipe for trouble. Public works need not be vetoed in every case, but must be judged on their merits; they are not to be encouraged, save to the extent that they can be shown to serve a really useful purpose; if anything, the balance should be tilted against them in the interest of economy; and in all cases it would be desirable if possible for them to be financed out of ordinary revenue. Keynes took the opposite view; he wanted them financed by Government borrowing. This was very disturbing to those deeply imbued with the older system of thought. A counter view was put forward which was later christened the "Treasury view". If the Government borrowed for public works, it was argued, it would merely draw funds from the capital market and reduce the amount that industry would otherwise have spent on capital account. Thus it merely diverted funds from purposes which private enterprise deemed profitable to the more problematic field of public works where expenditure might depend on the crotchets of bureaucrats; in any case no new employment would be given. While christened the "Treasury view", this opinion was none other than the age-old doctrine of traditional economics. To some Keynes's advocacy was particularly displeasing on the ground that it seemed to pander to ignorant notions of expediency and to the fallacies of public men, who could see the employment given by the public works and were too crude in their mental processes to work out how this use of funds might automatically create unemployment in another part of the economy. It seemed quite shameful that an economist of repute should lend himself to such rubbish. At the same time Keynes recommended that Britain should devote less resources to overseas investment; this seemed rather paltry.

Keynes, however, persisted in his opinion. He was deeply concerned not only to get his policy of public works implemented, but to establish its validity in the face of orthodox disfavour. He worked on this subject for a dozen years, publishing meanwhile various new presentations of his ideas; this culminated in his famous treatise *The General Theory of Employment, Interest and Money* (1936). It is not necessary to trace the evolution of his ideas, although in their various phases they had certain specific influences. But in any history of economics, however brief, some space must be given to the doctrines that he propounded in his final large volume. There is every reason to believe that, but for the Second World War and his relatively early death in 1946, he would have carried them to a further stage of systematization.

Traditional economics placed great reliance on what is known as Say's Law. This was deemed to guarantee that under free enterprise there could be no general over-production. There could only be over-production of particular commodities, and the economy had means for adapting itself so as to reduce the output of those in excess supply in favour of other forms of output. There could not be too much of everything; this not only meant that there could not be more than men had need for, but also that there could not be more in aggregate than men have money to buy. Apparent all-round saturations of the market were only temporary or frictional phenomena or, if prolonged, were due to some form of monetary mismanagement, or to some very big changes, such as those following war, to which it might take time for the economic system to adapt itself. There could be no chronic and systematic tendency for the monetary demand for goods in general to be inadequate.

The reason was that people who are paid to make goods, whether in wages, profits, etc., spend their money in demanding goods. Of course they might save some of their income. These savings were available for capital outlay. Could we always be sure that the capital outlay would be sufficient to utilize these savings, so that the demand on account of consumption and the demand for capital goods together sufficed to absorb the whole product offered? The answer to this was in the affirmative. The free system contains a mechanism to achieve this precise result, namely the rate of interest. Just as the price of wheat tends to equate the demand to the supply of wheat, so the rate of interest, that is the price paid for funds on loan, always served in the end to equate the demand for money to be spent on capital account to the supply of savings available for that purpose. If there was any tendency to excessive savings, the rate of interest would fall; whether this discouraged saving or not, it would certainly encourage capital outlay, and the fall would continue until sufficient capital outlay was encouraged to absorb all the savings, and thus to make up the total demand for goods to an equal level with the supply. The implication of this is that a free economy will tend, subject to frictions and some inevitable lags in adjustment to a new situation, to the position of full employment.

Keynes denied this tendency to full employment, and he denied the operation of Say's Law. He did not merely hold, what was obvious for all to see, that there might be intervals of grave maladjustment in which productive resources could not find the right outlet. He held that the very working of the system might in certain circumstances systematically tend to an equilibrium with massive unemployment present. To uphold this view, he was bound to deny, and did deny, that the rate of interest played the part assigned to it in Say's Law. There were two parts to this denial. First he brought to notice forces other than the demand for and supply of savings, bearing upon the rate of interest. These arose under what he called "liquidity preference". Among the various forms of assets which property owners may hold, swapping them with one another according to taste, we may concentrate our attention upon two, money and bonds. Bonds consist essentially of promises to pay money at a later date; thus money and bonds are both, in a sense, money. But money is available for use at any time; bonds represent money available for use later; thus money is more liquid. It is true that reputable bonds are not altogether illiquid. But as the rate of interest varies in the market, so will the price of bonds vary; if a man wants to dispose of bonds suddenly, without waiting for their date of redemption, he may have to realize at a loss. For many purposes a man may prefer to be on the safe side and hold ready money; bonds on the other hand carry interest. As money and bonds are both in a sense money, but bonds carry interest while money does not, this interest must be related to the one feature in which bonds differ from money, namely their lack of liquidity. From time to time property owners for various reasons desire now more, now less, liquidity. The total amount of liquidity available to them, which is the total amount of currency and bank-deposits in existence, is determined by the banking system. (On that point Keynes and the orthodox school were not in disagreement.) The rate of interest must be such as to equate the demand for to the supply of liquidity. If there is not enough liquidity to satisfy needs, some people will be sellers of bonds in the market. This will depress the price of bonds; that is, it will send up the rate of interest; this means that when the supply of liquidity is deficient, the rate of interest, which is precisely the premium for parting with liquidity, goes up.

Now suppose that there is a new force which according to Say's Law should affect the rate of interest, such as an increased propensity to save; this should cause a fall in the rate of interest if full employment is to be maintained. But it is quite possible for such an event to occur and yet for there to be no change whatever in the balance between the demand and supply of liquidity; and in that case, according to Keynes, the rate of interest cannot change; Say's Law is frustrated.

Then there is a second arm to Keynes's attack on the traditional theory of interest. By that theory the demand for and supply of savings must somehow be brought to equality; how but by the rate of interest? Keynes urged that the rate of interest did a quite different work, namely that of bringing the demand for and supply of liquidity to equality. It cannot do both at once, since the changes in the supply/demand conditions affecting liquidity may be quite different from the changes in the supply/demand conditions affecting savings. It was therefore needful for Keynes to show how on earth the demand for and supply of savings were brought to equality, since equal they must undoubtedly be. It is usually the price of a valuable that brings the demand for and supply of it to equality. Could it be different in the case of saving? What was the price paid for saving but the rate of interest?

Keynes held that there was quite a different force securing this particular equality. If investment demands, which constitute the demand for saving, proved deficient in relation to the propensity of people to save, there would be a decline of activity, employment, and income. Saving was brought to equality with investment demand, not by a fall of interest stimulating investment demand, not by a fall of interest encouraging saving, but by a shrinkage in the *source* of saving, namely a shrinkage of income itself. The volume of people's saving is not only determined by the price they can get for doing so, but also by their wherewithal from which to save. If activity and income shrink all round, saving would shrink; and it is by this painful process that saving is brought to an equality with investment when investment opportunities are insufficient to absorb all that people would be willing to save were they fully employed. Unemployment is thus a symptom of investment opportunity being deficient in relation to the propensity of the community to save. If investment opportunities are gravely deficient, and if they remain deficient, the unemployment may be very severe and remain severe; and there is nothing in the ordinary working of the economic system which tends to remove this unemployment. It is this analysis which justified Keynes in having pronounced twelve years earlier that public works would provide a net addition to employment; they increased total investment opportunity. If you raise total investment opportunity and the propensity to save remains the same, then, by a converse argument to that just supplied, the whole level of employment and activity will rise. The public works do *not* divert capital from other uses, but, by raising activity and income and saving, automatically create as much additional saving as is needed to finance them.

In the foregoing argument it was assumed that traditional theory held that Say's Law would always require full employment. It might be argued, however, that traditional theory allowed for sustained unemployment on one condition, namely if the workers, through their trade unions or otherwise, stuck out for higher wages than corresponded to their product. The natural remedy in these circumstances was to reduce wages. Keynes did not deny the principle that wage-earners cannot continue to receive more than their product. But he held that the general level of what, in the technical language of economics, are called "real" wages was not affected by trade-union bargaining, although sectional increases could be secured. If the general level of money wages was raised to an unjustified level in terms of existing prices, prices would rise accordingly and thus the general level of "real" wages would not in the event have been increased. The moral for the unemployment situation followed. If investment opportunity is insufficient to absorb what would be saved in the full-employment situation, and thus Say's Law fails, the total effective demand will be insufficient to give employment to all available labour. Only something that raises total effective demand can alter this situation. According to the traditional view just cited, if there is unemployment, money wages should be reduced, and this would stimulate employment. On the contrary, Keynes held that if Say's Law failed and there was insufficient effective demand, a reduction of wages would not increase demand, and would not therefore increase employment. The effect of a reduction of money wages would be a fall of prices, and real wages on average would be left just where they were before.

To this sweeping generalization he readily admitted that there were exceptions. Of these by far the most important is concerned with foreign trade; Keynes did not live to elaborate a complete theory of foreign trade in the light of his new ideas. If a country is on the gold standard, or has a fixed rate of exchange, then a reduction of wages might create employment—he did not deny it— by making the country's goods more competitive in world markets. As a practical proposition, however, he held that if a country had got into the unfortunate position of having wages at a higher level in terms of gold than the product of its labour justified, then, since a general all-round reduction of wages is impracticable, and a partial reduction is bound to involve great inequity, the wisest solution was to alter the foreign-exchange rate, so as to bring internal costs into line with world prices. This was the principal reason why he continued to favour flexibility in the foreign-exchange rates.

Another departure from traditional theory may be noted. We have seen that in Keynesian theory the general level of prices is somewhat flexible, responding readily to upward or downward movements in the general level of wages in such wise as to preserve the existing equilibrium of full employment or, when Say's Law was failing, the existing equilibrium of unemployment. This is in contrast with "the quantity theory of money" by which the general level of prices is supposed to depend on the quantity of money outstanding. He held that only part of existing money was used to circulate goods, the remainder being held as a reserve asset, where it satisfied the desire of liquidity. It was the amount of money available for this latter purpose that governed the rate of interest; the amount of money available for this purpose was the total amount of money in existence less that required for active circulation.

If a rise of activity or of wage-rates promoted requirements for more money in active circulation, money would be pulled out of the reserve pool; and conversely. This flow in and out of the reserve pool would have its effect on the rate of interest and so on activity and so, indirectly, on the general level of prices; but in the Keynes system the relation between the total quantity of money and the general level of prices was much more indirect than under orthodox "quantity theory" doctrine.

Thus, in Keynes's theory, money, although still playing a substantial role, no longer played the principal role in governing the tendency to inflation or deflation; this last was governed by aggregate real demand, namely demand arising on consumer account and demand arising on investment account; and to these we should hasten to add, in the light of modern conditions and fully in conformity with Keynes's own doctrine, demand arising on Government account.

Keynes's views met with, and still meet with, tough academic resistance in many quarters. But in some respects they conform rather more easily to the notions of the man in the street than did the older orthodoxy; contrary to many novelties of economic doctrine, their practical acceptance has been more rapid and widespread than their academic acceptance. During the early years of the war, the British Treasury under Keynes's influence issued a white paper setting out the main elements of the national income. This has since been greatly amplified, and widely imitated. Nations which issue no national-income statistics can hardly deem themselves self-respecting in these days. These throw light on the magnitude and trends of the main categories of demand. Study of these and kindred statistics is now a foremost method used for diagnosing or prognosticating inflationary or deflationary trends. Should demand appear excessive or deficient, consideration is given to means for operating on the main sectors of demand, whether by way of stimulation or restraint. All this line of thinking would have been totally unacceptable to the pre-Keynesian school, although it is fair to add that the minds of distinguished economists, not all of whom have accepted Keynes's complete theory—for example, Professor Pigou, Sir Dennis Robertson, the Swedish economists—were moving in a similar direction in the early twenties. According to the earlier school, it would be perfectly futile to think of stoking up total demand by such means as public works or a budget deficit. If there was prolonged unemployment, the only logical remedy was a reduction of wages. No great attention was paid to the components of aggregate demand since, by Say's Law, this was deemed able to look after itself and to give employment to all who needed it, subject to their not asking for too much pay, and subject, of course, to friction and time-lags, which might be considerable.

In regard to the role of money, there is no such sharp divergence of principle between Keynes and the older orthodoxy, but by Keynesian doctrine the role of money is de-emphasized. Earlier thinking suggested that an increase in the quantity of money would have some direct impact on the level of prices; for Keynes it might have such an impact, but only to the extent that by reducing the rate of interest it succeeded in substantially increasing demand on investment account. According to Keynes's thought banking policy still had a role to play. But he held that in certain circumstances it could not maintain full employment unaided, but would have to be supplemented by other means of stimulating investment demand.

By the logic of Keynes's thinking, aggregate employment could be stimulated by a Government equally well by (1) increasing public expenditure without increasing taxes, or (2) reducing taxes without reducing public expenditure. He was apt to stress the former recipe. That may have been partly due to his sense that a great deal more public work in Britain was required on its own merits, and that in many respects we had fallen woefully behind. But there seems to have been another cause of this emphasis. His views had, like other novel views, to overcome the imputation of being disreputable. Advocacy of public works financed by loan seemed a shade more respectable than the advocacy of a budget deficit on current account financed by loan. It is interesting in this connexion to study the Report by the Committee for Economic Development (U.S.) on Defence Against Recession (March, 1954). This committee is directed by progressive but nonetheless highly responsible and respectable American industrialists. The doctrines implicit in its recommendations are altogether Keynesian. Public works and outright remissions of taxation are both recommended as desirable measures in the event of a recession proving serious and obdurate. But there is a decided preference for the remission of taxation, leading to an open deficit on current account. Thus the wheel has swung full circle. It may well be that Keynes, in view of the great growth of the tax burden since the Second World War, would in these new circumstances have shown the same preference himself.

A few words should be said about the wider political implications of Keynes's doctrines. They have advocates and opponents both on the Left and on the Right. Some Socialists welcome them as being a thin end of the wedge, as a useful weapon for breaking down initial prejudices against State interference, as a prelude to the transition to a full-blown Socialism, in which the State shall own the means of production, distribution and exchange, and all shall be centrally planned. On this view Keynesianism is a mere stepping-stone to something better. Other Socialists, who have grown doubtful of the virtue of universal nationalization, are Keynesians in a more genuine sense. While seeing the need for more State interference than is necessarily implied by his doctrines, they nonetheless welcome them as genuine methods of overcoming some of the outstanding evils of capitalism of the old order. But those of the political Right-wing in whose minds the fearful tragedies of the great depression have had influence, and who have had the sense that all was not well with capitalism and perfect *laissez-faire*, have also welcomed Keynes's doctrines as holding out the hope of preserving all that is best in an individualist economy by a means of central guidance within strictly circumscribed limits. Only those who pin their faith to complete *laissez-faire*—but these are now in an extreme minority—maintain strong opposition to Keynes. I should add that there is also a quite widespread hostile prejudice, especially in the United States, among those who are altogether ignorant of his authentic views.

Certain other developments in economic thought during the inter-war period must be recorded. One was the growth of the doctrines of "imperfect competition". It will be remembered that the theory of the equilibrium of prices and output was receiving a stricter mathematical formulation at the turn of the century. This formulation implied a more precise concept of competition than was intended by the authors who used that word in an earlier age. The mathematical analysis could be used to show that competition, working through the price mechanism, secured what might be regarded as an ideal arrangement; this was Adam Smith's "hidden hand" reduced to precise terms. But then certain anomalies appeared. Marshall had suggested that industries subject to increasing returns ought to be given some special stimulus or bounty. This led to a more precise analysis of the working of increasing returns, to which Professor Pigou made his contribution; this in turn led to a re-examination of the notion of competition. It transpired that in the equilibrium equations, competition had to be given a certain form, which was later christened "perfect competition". It also transpired that in a large range of economic activity, commonly dubbed competitive, including most of manufacture and distribution, competition was by no means perfect in this sense; but where competition was not perfect, the price mechanism did not always lead to an ideal result. Accordingly a substantial body of doctrine was developed, constituting generalizations about what happened where competition was short of perfect, which really comprised all cases where an individual could not sell his output in an organized market at a price unaffected by his own contribution to it. Quite a systematic and interesting body of opinion was built up. There may have been some tendency for the aberrations from the ideal thus disclosed to add to the doubts of those who were disposed to criticize free enterprise.

Although the doctrines of imperfect competition were fairly clear, they had to make some rather drastic assumptions about how business-men behave. Some of these assumptions have since been criticized, and the subject has been further developed since the war. In this more recent work, doubts have been raised whether the distorting effects of "imperfections" of competition are as great as had previously appeared in the first flush of enthusiasm of those propounding the new doctrines.

The other important development in the inter-war period was the growth of what is called econometrics, under the influence of such distinguished pioneers as Dr. Ragnar Frisch, Dr. Tinbergen, and Dr. Kalecki. Hitherto economic doctrine had consisted of a body of laws or tendencies stated in qualitative terms only, and often in forms that were difficult, if not impossible, to verify. Indeed many so-called laws are not properly generalizations at all, but truisms or self-identical propositions, which may nonetheless throw light on the working of the economic system. Economists had often been experts in their knowledge of statistics, but the statistics mainly served the purpose of historical or geographical description or, if brought into relation with economic laws, were used for illustrative purposes only. It was the ambition of the econometricians to change all this, to formulate economic laws in terms which could be statistically verified, and to make a vigorous onslaught on the statistical series available, in order to make them answer the question whether certain laws were true or not. New techniques were devised; Trade Cycle study appeared an especially good field for the use of econometric methods. This approach presents formidable problems, and it cannot yet be said to have led to authenticated generalizations of first-rate importance; but perhaps some negative results may be credited to it. These methods are still in their early stages, and there is little doubt that a great future lies before them.

IV. The Second World War and its Aftermath

The Second World War ushered in a new period of economic control, considerably more intensive and all-pervasive than that of the First. Once again the prime reason for resorting to a controlled system was the priority that the situation required to be given to speed as against economy and efficiency. For Britain the crucial control was that concerned with imports. The absorption of shipping for military purposes and the great lengthening in the time of each ship's voyage and turn-round, together with the loss of shipping, a minor factor at first but becoming more important later, reduced the availability of ships far below the need for importation. Food and materials were thus in short supply; if this had been looked after by the "price mechanism", there would have been a danger of acute inflation, towards which other forces also were working; furthermore, with the reduction in the size of the "real" national income—that is, the quantity of foods and services available for personal consumption, it was desirable that a much larger share of it should go to the poorer sections, so that their standard of living should be sustained; at a time when all were called upon to make what sacrifices they could, it was thought that the richer and middle sections should bear the main economic burden; such a redistribution could hardly have been effected quickly through the workings of a free system. Food shortages were looked after by price control and rationing; material shortages by central allocation in accordance with priority. The last-mentioned was an extremely crude system, but may be deemed to have been carried out efficiently considering the very defective nature of the system as such. Free wage bargaining was maintained in Britain, while restraint was urged and displayed; with this in view prices were kept down by subsidies which served to fill the gap between the prices that had to be paid for imports and those which it was desired to charge in the shops, and also to stimulate domestic agriculture. Vast Government expenditures naturally set up an inflationary tendency; more was covered by taxation than in the First War, but large-scale borrowing also had to be relied upon. The Keynes doctrine, that interest rates could be kept low by creating a sufficient amount of liquidity, was put into effect. Inflation, in the sense of excessive aggregate demand, was reduced by disallowing all forms of new investment other than those required for the war, while the tendency to spiral was reduced by the price controls and the wage restraints already mentioned.

After the war, the United Kingdom maintained a system of fairly intensive control. The real intention behind this will probably continue to be judged ambivalent. The Labour Party was in power for the first time; no one knew, and perhaps it did not know itself, how far it was still committed to the full Socialist doctrine of the eventual nationalization of the means of production, distribution and exchange. It inherited from war-time a very comprehensive system of state control, and it was naturally not inclined to dismantle this. The forms of control were determined by war-time needs, and were no doubt different from those which would have been adopted by a Socialist Government fresh to power and devising by the light of its inner consciousness the first steps towards a

Socialist Utopia. Many Socialists no doubt hoped that the *de facto* system of control would be consciously transformed into a first phase of Socialism, from which to advance further to a fully planned economy. Others may have abandoned the fuller aims and have been converted to the idea of a "mixed" economy, partly shaped by the kind of controls already in existence, and partly by the ideas of Keynes, but flavoured with a larger spice of nationalization than he would have desired. It does not follow that all non-Socialists were opposed to the maintenance of the controls. To some extent, the war-time conditions that made the controls expedient were still present. The shipping shortage was in due course relieved, but was succeeded by an acute imbalance of international payments which seemed to require drastic restrictions on imports; and these would continue to have widespread implications for the economy as a whole, setting up the need for rationing, material allocations, etc. High Government expenditure overseas and expenditure on reconstruction at home maintained effective demand at a high level, which could easily lead to vicious inflation. A disturbingly large amount of inflation occurred despite the controls. This mixture of motive makes it difficult to interpret the post-war phase of British economic policy in the light of any particular doctrine. Meanwhile there was a considerable extension of those measures which were first initiated in the 1906-14 period and are sometimes thought of as constituting a "Welfare State". Lord Beveridge who played a notable part in the earliest days in the inception of the system and had since been associated with it in various ways, produced a comprehensive survey during the war on the need for a great extension; and his name has in consequence been justly associated with the system. While in some minds the "Welfare State" is associated with a Socialist philosophy, it could also be claimed that it was in the Liberal tradition.

In the United States the controls were quickly relaxed. This was also true of Belgium. In France they were retained for a longer period, but, partly owing to temperament and partly to the mentality engendered by occupation, when it might be patriotic to evade controls rather than the other way round, the post-war controls were far less efficient than in Britain. The Scandinavian countries and Holland maintained "mixed" economies. Western Germany was subjected to the controls involved by occupation, but after her "currency reform" took rather decided steps in the direction of a free economy. Generally, after the first post-war quinquennium, there was a marked tendency to economic Liberalism in Europe; and in this Britain joined, although more tentatively and with greater reservations, particularly after the accession of a Conservative Government in 1951.

Thus it is difficult to relate the course of events very closely to any one trend in economic philosophy and doctrine. The requirements of expediency from time to time took charge and systematic thinking was in abeyance. There was, however, much new thought on economic policy in relation to international economics. This occurred while the war was still proceeding, and was largely due to American initiative. The aftermath of the world slump had involved a considerable growth of restrictionism in international trade, and in the case of Germany this was not unconnected with power politics. The Americans hoped that victory, when achieved, might be made the occasion for a return of economic liberalism in the international field, and suggested to the British that obligations due under Lend-Lease arrangements should be written off if they joined with the Americans in giving a lead to the free world in this direction. The British entered with some enthusiasm into these discussions, but, while not averse from a greater degree of liberalism, stressed that some measures of concerted policy between the nations were needed to prevent the post-war recurrence of disasters such as the slump of 1929-32. They also had in mind that the great difficulties with which they, and other countries of Europe, would be faced after the war might present obstacles to an easy return to international liberalism. The discussions were also perplexed by the great American dislike for the system of Imperial Preference, which was of old standing, but in which the British themselves had played little part before 1932; on the British side the policy of Preference had come to be supported by sentimental as well as economic considerations.

In the discussions that took place, Keynes played a leading part, and his thoughts about the causes of depression had influence; some of the American participants were already subscribers to Keynes's doctrines on this topic. The results of the discussions were embodied in an agreement subscribed to by a large number of nations (some, however, only represented by Governments in exile) at Bretton Woods (1944). In consequence the International Monetary Fund and the International Bank for Reconstruction and Development were established when the war was over. The former of these institutions was set up to supervise a world monetary system: the different nations agreed to maintain fixed pars of exchange which could, however, be altered from time to time should a "fundamental disequilibrium" arise. To facilitate the system, a central Fund was set up to which all the nations subscribed, which would constitute a pool of resources that could be drawn upon to tide nations over temporary difficulties. Some held that this would also play an important part in the event of an onset of world depression. In such a case, nations are liable to resort either to deflation, which by Keynes's doctrine only tends to intensify the world slump, or to a restriction of imports, which is essentially beggar-my-neighbour in a time of slump, or to both. The hope was that the Fund would eliminate or reduce the need for the adoption of either of these undesirable expedients. It also embodied a provision, known as the "Scarce Currency Clause", which was designed to put some of the responsibility for redressing an imbalance in international trade on creditor countries. This was a concession by the Americans who were deemed by others to have failed in the period before the war to take measures appropriate to a creditor country for reducing international disequilibrium. The International Bank was designed to re-stimulate the flow of international investment which had sorely languished after the world slump. There were also discussions for internationally held buffer stocks, which might reduce the excessive oscillations in the prices of primary products; but these came to nothing. All these plans and measures might be deemed expressions of the philosophy that holds that central management and policy are required to preserve capitalism from its recurrent tendency to depression and to maintain an international equilibrium of payments. The British were willing, not altogether without misgiving, to take American agreement to these plans as sufficient earnest of good intention to justify them in co-operating in bold measures to reduce restrictions and discriminations in international trade; these were embodied in the proposed International Trade Organization, which was, however, never implemented, and then, in a modified form, in the General Agreement on Trade and Tariffs.

While these various institutions have come into being, it cannot be said that the general plan for combining concerted action on an international scale to secure a trade balance and full employment on the one hand with a great abatement of restrictions of trade on the other has been implemented. Post-war dislocations have proved much larger than was anticipated. Restrictions have been severe; these have included discriminatory restrictions to which the Americans from the beginning took particular exception. It had been hoped that the convertibility of currencies, in accordance with the pars established with the International Monetary Fund, would be achieved within a five-year period. This has not been realized. Currencies have been "inconvertible" in a new sense. In the old days a "convertible" currency was one that was redeemable at will in gold, or in some other gold-convertible currency; "inconvertible" currencies were not so redeemable, but could always be legally sold at a discount in free markets. Inconvertibility in the new sense has involved restriction even on the right to sell at a discount. Sterling in particular, which is a currency of world-wide use, has had a complicated history, various different kinds of sterling having come into existence, entailing different privileges for their owners in regard to their rights to convert or to transfer. After the war, all the nations experienced an intense imbalance of payments *vis-à-vis* the U.S. dollar, and old-fashioned measures of commercial policy did not appear sufficient to restore this. This has been one important cause of the various brands of inconvertibility and of commercial restriction. The problem was temporarily eased, but not solved, by very generous aid granted by the United States to other countries. The difficulties have gradually become less formidable. It is hoped that the world may yet move towards some system not dissimilar from that envisaged at Bretton Woods, but by much slower stages than was anticipated.

In 1950 the countries of Europe, which were then enjoying the full benefits of Marshall Aid and seeking to put it to its best use, set up the European Payments Union, whose principles were in some respects not dissimilar from those of the International Monetary Fund. It was markedly dissimilar in one respect, however, in that it came into full and active operation and has served greatly to reduce the impediments to trade inside Europe. British membership had the result that the sterling area was included in the mechanism of payments set up; Europe and the sterling area together form such a wide region as to make this experiment a very notable one.

The great complications resulting from various kinds of inconvertibility and of foreign-trade restriction, as well as those pertaining to attempts to control or repress domestic inflations, require corresponding developments in the theory of international trade and of inflation. Events have moved quickly, and it cannot be said that theory has kept pace with practice. Expediency has ruled; at times it has been wise and evolved apter remedies than theorists might ever have thought of; but in some respects lack of theory has been harmful; failing the guidance of general principles, policy has often been short-sighted, sometimes one might even say blind. The situation remains fluid, and policies and institutions are likely to undergo much further adaptation in the near future. It may quite well be that economic historians will never be able to give a coherent account of the true causes and effects that were operating in the international economic field in the period 1945-54.

Meanwhile the number of economists and the volume of high-class economic literature have been growing rapidly, and economists of undoubtedly distinguished intellectual ability have gained reputation. It is not clear, however, that there has been important progress in fundamental theory. We have noted that at the turn of the century "the principles of political economy" were restated with far greater precision in the formulation of equations determining a "static equilibrium". Recently these doctrines have been restated with a still greater degree of refinement. There has been a desire to get away from the notion of an abstract "utility" with its doubtful philosophical implications and unamenability to precise measurement. Immense efforts have been directed to stating basic postulates with the utmost precision and freeing them from all assumptions that cannot be warranted by the strictest logic. Econometric studies have been further advanced. In the older economics "static" and "dynamic" elements were intermixed, perhaps confusedly; in the refinement of static theory at the end of the last century, dynamic elements tended to be lost sight of. Recently attempts have been made to formulate a precise body of theory, which should constitute a system of dynamic principles. These efforts are still only in an early stage, but it is hoped that an important body of theory and doctrine will in due course emerge.

In fine, the rapidity and bewildering complexity of recent changes have tended to outpace the powers of systematic study. Nonetheless, on the theoretical side, a large amount of highly intellectual and subtle work has been done. It cannot be said that there have been new seminal ideas of a fundamental character. But the subject is in movement, and the position is therefore hopeful. In regard to the application of theory to policy and practice, the availability of national-income statistics, subject to continued improvement, has been much the most important development. For the rest, the development of a body of settled doctrines of applied economics is likely to proceed more quickly when the commotions and the tempo of change that are the aftermath of the Second World War cease to be so violent.

BOOKS SUGGESTED FOR FURTHER READING

A. Marshall, *Principles of Economics* (Macmillan, 1870 and subsequent editions).

J. M. Keynes, *General Theory of Employment, Interest and Money* (Macmillan, 1936).

J. E. Meade, *Economic Analysis and Policy* (Clarendon Press, 1936).

R. F. Harrod, *Life of Keynes* (Macmillan, 1951).

Worswich and Ady (ed.), *The British Economy, 1945-1950* (Clarendon Press, 1952).

National Income and Expenditure, 1946-1952 (H.M.S.O., 1953).

INTERNATIONAL ECONOMICS

by DR. THOMAS BALOGH

I. Introductory

INTERNATIONAL economics in the first half of the twentieth century were dominated by the break in the fundamental unity of the world and the rise of two sharply polarized social and productive systems each of which was all but controlled by a giant. Not since the apogee of Imperial Rome has any one sovereign community in the Western World risen to a position of such overwhelming superiority as the United States. Even Britain at the time of her industrial and commercial supremacy a hundred years ago never achieved such preponderance of power. At the opposite pole the Soviet Union has an even more crushing command. She has, with hardly any outside help, in twenty-five years of savage effort not merely transformed herself from a mainly primitive peasant economy into the second largest industrial Power equipped with everything from jet engines to hydrogen bombs, but initiated a completely new system of economic organization at fundamental variance with what was before. By her exertions she has proved the possibility of the conscious planning of national economic destinies. The vast effort required and, the constant fear of armed attack led to policies—indeed to the rise of a whole system—of repression which evoked apprehension, disapproval and hatred abroad.

Behind these struggles and antagonisms there looms in both political spheres the fundamental problem of dealing with agriculture, of transforming primitive farming into an efficient provider of food for the growing population of both East and West. The old Malthusian problem of over-population and the forcing-down of living standards is once more posed for the majority of the human race. After the rapid expansion of the nineteenth century into the still available empty spaces the problem is one of increased production. Curiously enough only in the United States was a successful beginning made in tackling the expansion of agricultural units into large-scale and scientific food-factories. Even there political pressure of the large numbers of small farmers has created an almost insuperable domestic economic problem. Yet nothing has raised the issue of the inequality in the international distribution of wealth, of the poverty and despair of the great majority more acutely than the success of the United States during two wars in laying the foundations of a secure material basis of existence so sadly lacking elsewhere.

Finally, the twentieth century brought about the ruin of the power and role of Europe, that small, over-populated peninsula off the Eurasian mainland and the adjoining scattered islands. History, at least official history, until 1914, was a history of Europe; and the fact that local feuds in Europe brought time and again wars and ruin to remote parts of the world shows sufficiently her complete dominance. After the two attempts—both all but successful—of the most central and potentially most menaced, and therefore most aggressive of its nations, Germany, to dominate the world, Europe is left powerless, stretching between the giants, unable to defend herself, yet still the most important single strategic area in the world, the possession of which would instantaneously give the Soviet Union even industrial preponderance over the United States. This combination of powerlessness and importance is one of the most perilous features of the day.

All these revolutionary changes have not yet had time to work themselves out. Their magnitude and violence have inevitably created a political and social fluidity and produced spots of vacuum of organized force which might at any moment result in shifts of power that would assuredly evoke a conflict imperilling progress, if not existence. The lessons of the past decades have not yet been fully assimilated, though they point towards ways in which social tensions could be diminished and the peril of armed civil and international clashes thus lessened. In the following, these lessons will be explored and some tentative conclusions put forward on the desirable, and on the possible, directions of further development.

II. The End of an Epoch

This revolutionary overturn of all settled international relations and institutions came unexpectedly. To the Edwardian member of the great centre of international capital, London, nothing could have appeared more stable than that supple and successfully working mechanism, uniting the economic destinies of the whole known world. It was, after all, the logical culmination, the crowning achievement, of centuries of evolution.

The concert of the Great Powers of Europe had come to deal successfully with several threats to peace; a balance of forces had been established in which none of the Great Powers was able to claim unchallengeable predominance. If Imperial Russia was more populous than the rest, she was industrially backward. The increasing strength of Germany was, as yet, not of a different order of magnitude from that of France. And the financial paramountcy of Britain was counterbalanced by her vulnerability through greater dependence on overseas supplies. No power outside Europe counted for much, though the U.S. had challenged Spain, and Japan Russia, and in both cases the Europeans were roundly defeated. A general conflagration—in contrast with limited, sharp conflicts of interest—seemed unthinkable.

If peaceful development seemed assured on the political plane, the economic achievements were equally remarkable. The lugubrious predictions of the classical economists echoed in much sharper form by Marx and his disciples, predictions which had been remarkably confirmed in the first half of the nineteenth century, were visibly confounded. A notable rise in the standard of life of the masses had taken place, especially in the last quarter of the century. The Malthusian devil seemed, if not altogether exorcized, very much weakened: the birth-rate was beginning to fall. If social inequality was extreme, measures to mitigate the consequences of individual misfortune were spreading—had not Sir William Harcourt already in 1892 avowed that all were Socialist? The rich were no doubt very rich—but, as Mr. John Maynard Keynes put it in one of the best flights of his pen,[1]

> If the rich had spent their new wealth on their own enjoyments, the world would long ago have found such a régime intolerable. But like bees they saved and accumulated, not less to the advantage of the whole community because they themselves held narrower ends in prospect.

As investment increased so did productivity; wages rose and could eventually be expected to rise even relatively to profits. Equality—at any rate as much equality as was compatible with incentive to hard work and ingenuity—would be attained by organic growth, without violence.

Nor was this vista restricted to one country. London was at the centre of a world-wide web. The households of Europe, indeed of all the world, benefited from the universal exchange of goods. By specializing in the production of those goods and services for which it was relatively best fitted, each country benefited itself and the others. Even if a country were more efficient in most productive pursuits than all others she would gain from trade if she concentrated on the production of goods in which she excelled most: she could obtain more of the other commodities by exchange than by frittering away her own efforts. One of the most important determinants of this relative aptitude of a country is the abundance

[1] J. M. Keynes, *The Economic Consequences of the Peace* (Macmillan, 1919), p. 16.

of resources needed for production. Plentiful land is obviously an advantage for specializing in agriculture, a large supply of labour for producing goods which demand more human application. By specializing on the production of such goods, however, the demand for these abundant—and therefore relatively cheap—resources would increase and thus trade between countries would tend to equalize income internationally, even without migration. Harmony *between* as well as *within* countries would thus be promoted.

This benign influence would be much strengthened by the movement of labour and capital. In the decades before 1914 the over-population of Central, Eastern and Southern Europe was relieved by the vast migration to North and South America, while Ireland and the British Isles were provided with outlets beyond America in the Pacific Dominions. This relieved the pressure on wage-levels in Europe and made possible the phenomenal development overseas.

The movement of capital was equally smoothing the way for a general upsurge in all parts of the world. It flowed from areas of relative affluence to the peripheries, where it relieved a shortage that commanded usury levels of interest at 20, 30 or 50 per cent. or even more a year. And England effortlessly and naturally became the centre of this world-promoting evolution. Her foreign investments were vast—some £3,000 million (equivalent in terms of present purchasing power on international markets to some £12,000 million). The income from them—some £200 million per annum—was sufficient to pay for a third of her imports, an income equivalent to some £1,200 million today if the same proportion of imports were to be covered. Yet practically the whole of this income was reinvested abroad: between a third and a half of the national savings of Britain in the last decade before 1914. France and Germany also expanded their foreign assets vigorously.

If the U.S. at present were to (or could) follow Britain's example, she would have to invest abroad some $15,000 million per annum. This represents a multiple of the amount recommended by the U.N.O. Expert Committee on the "Measures for the Economic Development of Underdeveloped Countries", an estimate which was promptly dismissed by official opinion as utopian dreaming and a wild exaggeration of the needs of those countries. Indeed such a flow of capital would be equivalent to something like a sudden *doubling* of its total supply for the rest of the non-Soviet world. But more of this anon.

Such comparisons have at times been used to extol the virtues of Britain and to suggest that the United States has failed to live up to the demands of her new role as creditor and dominant country in the free world. This reproach lacks all sense of balance. No conscious policy was pursued by Britain in helping the world except, perhaps, the rather belated abolition of the Corn Laws. The facts that there had been no considerable interruption in the peaceful evolution of the world economy and that Britain was a small island reaching outwards for supplies were at the roots of the smooth evolution of the nineteenth century. British statesmen and financiers of that period and of the beginning of the twentieth century would have laughed out of court any suggestion that richer or dominant countries had any responsibility for the weaker, or should come to their succour even to their extent that a rather Conservative member of the American Republican Party would now deem morally right, or at least opportune.

The evolution in the latter part of the nineteenth century gave solid hope for a progressive amelioration of the condition of man. No doubt the British and the lesser international financiers not merely participated in the growing prosperity but reaped huge monopoly profits (though the losses through default and failure were also considerable). No doubt the inequality remained crying, especially internationally; no doubt the peripheries were shaken by periodic financial upheavals which spelt ruin and hardships, while the cyclical fluctuations in the economic activity of the centre were mitigated by international trade; no doubt Britain let the poor countries carry her gold reserves through the admirable mechanism of the London Discount Market and charged rather high interest for this favour. Yet progress was astonishing, and on an astonishingly broad front.

TABLE I

MANUFACTURING CAPACITY[1]
(World = 100)

	U.S.	U.K.	Germany	France	Russia (U.S.S.R.)
1870	23·3	31·8	13·2	10·3	3·7
1881–5	28·6	26·6	13·9	8·6	3·4
1896–1900	30·1	19·5	16·6	7·1	5·0
1906–10	35·3	14·7	15·9	6·4	5·0
1913	35·8	14·0	15·7	6·4	5·5
1926–9	42·2	9·4	11·6	6·6	4·3
1936–8	32·2	9·2	10·7	4·5	18·5
1950[2]	43·0		33[3]		14·0

The complete industrial domination by Britain was, moreover, avoided by the commercial protectionism of the peripheries, which enabled countries such as the U.S. and Germany to start on a career of intensive economic development, however strenuously

[1] From League of Nations, *Industrialization and Foreign Trade* (1945), p. 13.
[2] From F.A.O., *European Agriculture* (1954), p. 3.
[3] This figure represents the total for Western Europe.

such "mercantilism" was denounced by the strict canons of English classical economic laws. Nor was the productive technique on so large a scale or necessitating such large investment as to prevent the expansion of new export industries in the weaker countries. Indeed, as Table I shows, the United States, and subsequently Germany, soon surpassed Britain in industrial output (though not in financial or trading strength).

Perhaps the most eloquent proof of this progress in the West was the subtle, unacknowledged but, all the more for that, far-reaching transformation of the international Socialist revolutionary movement into a Parliamentary reformist organization willing, indeed eager, to co-operate (at least clandestinely) with the Powers That Be. For all their Marxist slogans the great majority of the Western and Central European Socialists were rapidly becoming reconciled to the Liberal capitalist system, which showed increasing appreciation of the strength of organized Labour and willingness to give its leaders a due place in the State organism. The very fact that only their Russian comrades remained "untainted" by Reformism (or at least the majority—the right-wing Mensheviks being quite willing to compromise even with the Tsar) shows the extent of the success achieved by capitalism in contrast to the period just before 1848.

III. The Prelude to Catastrophe

The First World War shattered the basis of this precarious balance. No doubt the armed conflict itself was merely a culmination of certain basic trends which had menaced the harmonious growth of the world economy. But even if it only speeded up a process which would have taken place in any case, the very fact that the development took place abruptly, without giving a chance for either physical or intellectual readjustment, made a difference not in degree but in kind.

Much the most important consequence of the war was to set off the United States on her vast expansion. In contrast to this effervescence, which increased American national real income per head by some 50 per cent. in the fifteen years up to 1929, there was a fall in all other main industrial countries which could only be made good in slow and painful stages.

But it was the weakness of Britain and the obstinate refusal of her financial rulers to recognize the change which in the end undermined the effort at reconstruction. Britain had suffered little physical damage during the war. She had lost her traditional markets. The problem of readjustment to these changes in Britain's trading position would in any case have posed very difficult problems. Its solution was prevented by an unfortunate combination of free trade and deflation pursued with dogged obstinacy by the

Treasury and the Bank of England with the approval of the over-whelming majority of academic economists. Keynes and his friends cried in the wilderness.

It would almost certainly have proved impossible to restore Britain's traditional exports. For the establishment of new industries with a chance of survival and expansion, an atmosphere favourable to investment was needed, and some security until these industries were firmly established. In the face of this awkward position it was decided to restore the pound to its old parity with the dollar through a policy of calculated deflation. Viewed from the point of view of financial interests something could be said for this policy. But it rendered a rapid adaptation of the country's productive structure to contemporary demands impossible: investment stagnated, and mass-unemployment did not disappear for two decades.

Equally dangerous policies were pursued in the war-ruined countries of Europe. An immense foreign debt was accumulated—partly to pay reparations and war debts to the U.S. So long as this process of borrowing continued, demand remained high and great prosperity reigned. But it could not continue indefinitely: the debt was mounting faster than income.

Already in 1927 this somewhat unstable prosperity threatened to collapse because of the monetary pressure on Britain. A new lease of life was given to the boom by the success of Mr. Montagu Norman in persuading the American financial authorities to help him out by initiating an explosively expansionist cheap-money policy. Foreign lending, especially at short term, revived. Inevitably the policy also caused a fantastic boom on the Stock Exchange. The Stock Exchange profits increased demand for goods and services. And the increase in demand stimulated new Stock Exchange gains: another fundamentally unstable position was created.

The Federal Reserve soon saw itself constrained to restrict credit generally in order to limit speculation. At first this proved ineffective. Stocks continued to boom for another eighteen months, though business began to droop somewhat earlier.

The position abroad, however, was rapidly aggravated by this reversal of cheap money in New York. First Britain, the middleman, was put under pressure for repayment. The bank-rate went up to 6 per cent. In consequence her own clients and especially Germany also began to feel the draught. As repayments had to be made to the creditors, demand for imports was cut down, and efforts were made to increase exports to obtain foreign exchange. Soon most countries were engaged on a mad round of beggar-my-neighbour measures, all wanting to pay and none willing to receive, as receiving (in the shape of imports) would have meant unemployment. Deflation became general and was severely aggravated by the smash on the New York Stock Exchange which ruined large numbers and thus cut demand severely. There was no end in sight to this cumulative bankruptcy.

It is as fascinating as it is futile to speculate what difference an early victory of the monetary reformers would have meant to world economy and politics. Would Keynes, by combating unemployment successfully, have been able to defeat Hitler's attempt at power? Would the old world-balance have been maintained with Europe continuing to play a predominant role? Or was the mismanagement of monetary affairs merely the trigger which brought on or accelerated an inevitable political trend?

Be that as it may, the total dominance of economic orthodoxy in the crucial period of 1931-3, when there was still time to save a complete collapse of the reconstruction of the 1920's, the refusal to permit Government intervention to relieve the paralysis of the economic system, made it inevitable that recovery, when it came, came piecemeal, on a national, and mostly on a nationalistic, basis. The world economy remained shattered even before the outbreak of hostilities finally broke it into all but hermetically sealed parts.

Britain was the first to recover. Here the crisis of confidence led to the fall of the Labour Government (which did not know how to impose exchange restrictions) and to a depreciation of the pound. The relief provided in the export industries was instantaneous, but it was quite unnecessarily counteracted by a savage two-fold deflation: by both ruthless restriction of credit, and a cut in the salaries and benefits of those least able to bear the sacrifice, the unemployed and the teachers. The difficulties of foreign nations, especially in Europe, were, on top of these cuts in British demand, further aggravated by the imposition of a fairly harsh system of tariffs.

The restriction of imports stimulated investment: new factories were built to produce the goods hitherto imported. Credit was at last relaxed. A building boom got going, stimulated by the fall in the cost of living—a consequence of the collapse of commodity prices abroad. By 1936-7 industrial production for the first time surpassed the high mark of 1913. It was a remarkable achievement, but it could have been done more quickly and with much less damage to other nations.

The American experience was at once much less happy and more inspiring. The do-nothing tactics of President Hoover led to an increasing spread of bankruptcy. As more and more property, shares, houses and land came under the hammer, their value fell away and more people were drawn into the vortex. Though attempts were made to mobilize public credit to help, the avalanche gathered speed and, on the day of the inauguration of the Democratic leader Governor Roosevelt as President, all banks closed down. The U.S. was paralysed.

There followed an epic fight to re-start economic life, an epic which the protagonists of *laissez-faire*, of do-nothing, are desperately anxious to forget. The dollar was depreciated, and the prices of primary products raised. An attempt was made to organize industry and labour to avoid competitive wage and price-cutting. Social security measures protected the innocent victims of individual mishap and social misfortune. Public works, including the massive Tennessee Valley reclamation scheme which transformed one of the most blighted areas of the Union, were started to fight unemployment and develop the vast resources of the country. Banks were guaranteed and re-started. Public utilities were controlled. Massive credit facilities were granted to house-owners. Yet, such was the furious distrust in the propertied classes of the President who undoubtedly saved their existence, that private investment languished and full recovery was prevented until the war. Roosevelt, after 1938, lacked adequate Congressional support to impose his will and attain full recovery.

Continental countries lacked rulers with sufficient self-confidence and elasticity. Thus the Anglo-American torrent of deflation was redoubled there to "safeguard" the gold reserve, and the maximum damage ensued. The intellectual dictatorship of the extreme Liberals was unbroken throughout the depression, and the depression therefore could not be checked. In France, the crisis merely meant a strangulation of development, not actual collapse. The country never again recovered during the years before the war. Even the victory of a Popular Front did not lead to a solution of the economic problem, despite the belated devaluation of the franc. France entered the war-crisis disillusioned, torn by class dissension and materially weakened.

The hesitant and half-stagnant recovery of the main industrial countries left most primary producers in a parlous state. Though several schemes were tried to lift, or at least to stabilize, the prices of primary products, they were even at the height of the frustrated recovery of 1937 more than 10 per cent. worse, relatively to those of manufactured products, than before the depression. This, in the main, explains the extraordinary success of the German drive for economic dominance in the peasant countries of Eastern Europe.

It was the catastrophe which overwhelmed the democratic Weimar Republic that was to drag the world into the Second German War and the final ruin of the power of Europe. As unemployment increased, so did the votes for Hitler. The respite on reparations given in 1931 to the last democratic Chancellor, Brüning, did little to relieve the situation. As the foreign position worsened, the uneasy brilliance of the first German economic miracle, dependent on U.S. loans, faded. Yet, after democracy had been crushed by the intrigues of the military, the success of the

Papen Government in cutting down unemployment and Nazi votes showed how little wisdom would have been sufficient to safeguard the Weimar Republic.

The orthodox illusions which led to the victory of Nazism also prevented a correct appreciation of the magnitude of its threat. Inflationism and monopolistic restrictionism were the pejorative terms with which the Nazi danger was fought (and not much else). Even in the year after Munich the rearmament expenditure of the West, held back by economic, especially monetary, considerations, was but a fraction of Nazi war supplies. Yet the Nazi "miracle" is easy to understand. Internally a massive expenditure on roads, barracks and armaments completely absorbed unemployment. The consequent increase in demand of the newly employed was kept in check by freezing wages and prices and severe taxation. Massive controls over imports prevented any deterioration of the balance of payments through an increase of foreign purchases. Exports were stimulated by direct measures and political influence in primary-producing countries was secured by concluding bulk-buying agreements at a time when Western demand for such goods was still very low.

The first successes of the Russian experiment in economic planning also stand out. Yet that experiment could not have started at a less propitious moment. Russia had to rely on the export of primary produce to obtain the basic machinery to prime the pump of industrial construction. At the very point of launching the first of a series of industrialization plans these prices collapsed. More and more had to be squeezed out of the peasant in order to obtain a shrinking amount of machinery from abroad. And the increase in Soviet production was slow in maturing.

In order to overcome the difficulties encountered with the peasants, a wholesale collectivization of land was launched. The result was an appalling agricultural collapse. There was widespread famine in rural areas, apart from the suffering caused by the deportation of the richer peasants.

The collectivization, however, made possible an increase in the supplies available to towns; it thus laid the foundation of the success of the drive for industrialization. This was momentous: there can be no doubt that industrial production grew at a pace unparalleled even during the explosive expansion of the United States. As Table I shows, within a decade or so the Soviet Union, starting from a primitive state, emerged from the ordeal as the second largest industrial Power in the world. The technical and economic achievement of the Soviet was soon amply confirmed by the Russian capacity to resist the German attack. Even the wholesale slaughter of their administrative and technical *élite* in the late 1930's did not altogether stop expansion; it was merely reduced to a level roughly equal to that of the best years of the non-Soviet world.

IV. A False Utopia and the Cold War

The attempt at re-creating "liberal" world economy, i.e. a world economy dominated indirectly, through "free" markets in goods and capital, by one or more powerful industrial countries, had failed in the depression. The war confirmed this disintegration and even further distorted the structure of the individual regions and their relations to one another. The United States had already in the twenties obtained a very substantial lead over the other units of world economic system. The failure of her recovery in the thirties was followed by an immense expansion during and after the war. Productive capacity, which had slightly contracted in the previous decade, doubled between 1939 and 1952 and has since increased by another 20 per cent. (Yet an increasing part of the investment served to modernize rather than to expand industry.) All this was achieved in a period when consumption steadily expanded; even at the height of the war it was fully a fifth higher than in the last pre-war year. And the Government spent on the war and cold war $759·7 billion at 1953 prices. Truly the miracle of the widow's cruse worked overtime. It was steadily and steadfastly doubted by the orthodox who, with the same obstinacy with which they had expected a turn to the better round every corner during the depression, now spied bankruptcy and runaway inflation everywhere. The nation in fact waxed richer and more self-sufficient every year.

The U.S. became the dominant power of the non-Soviet orbit. Nor is this all. The explosive growth of the country posed novel problems for the rest of the non-Soviet world. American progress tended not merely to displace violently the older and less perfect supplies, to the detriment of the old producers; it also enabled American producers to offer attractive short delivery periods and favourable credit conditions. The advantage of the vast scale of U.S. enterprise was complemented by Government agencies helping exports (e.g. in agriculture) often by subsidies or sales at a loss. All this meant that America's competitors were thrown severely on the defensive, and the very existence of their potentially most profitable industries was menaced.

The American experts and (under their influence) public opinion seem to have been genuine in hoping to improve the economic position of the war-devastated countries by enforcing the interplay of market forces internationally, even though the most forceful of these experts, Mr. White, has since been accused of treasonable conspiracy. What was astounding was that practically all British economic experts and politicians shared this view. No country had benefited more by the nineteenth-century type of division of labour than Britain. No country was, therefore, more severely hit by the economic consequences of the Second War, and less in a position to be exposed to the blast of uncontrolled markets. Her foreign wealth, attenuated by the effects of the long depression, had to a large extent been liquidated to cover the vast deficit in her trade balance caused by single-minded concentration on the war. The condition for a successful return to the pre-1914 "rules of the game" were lacking the world over, but no country would be more menaced by their enforcement than Britain.

The representatives of both the U.S. and Britain seem to have been oblivious of the magnitude of the structural changes wrought by the war. They thought in terms of a rather short period of reconstruction followed by a transitional period (equally short) of readjustment. After that the world could return to "normal", which was envisaged as a conscious restoration of the pre-1914 system of markets with only scant allowance even for the existence of the Soviet system, of which State monopoly of foreign trade was one of the essential pre-conditions. It was thought quite erroneously that the Nazi economic system had caused the aggression of Hitler and not the other way round, and that the bilateral agreements concluded by Dr. Schacht were in some way an especially devilish type of aggression rather than an expedient permitting two countries to trade with one another despite instability elsewhere. A moral fervour overcame most of the American and many of the British experts, and the sway of the free-market forces was in some way taken as a moral "good", as an ultimate aim to be striven for at almost any cost.

The Atlantic Charter in its fourth Clause provides the economic objective for post-war:

> FOURTH, they will endeavour, with due respect for their existing obligations, to further the enjoyment by all States, great or small, victor or vanquished, of access to the trade and to the raw materials of the world which are needed for their economic prosperity.

To give effect to these aspirations a number of conferences were held. An imposing framework of international institutions and agreements emerged. The U.N.O. Economic and Social Council was to take general charge. Under it the Food and Agricultural Organization established at the Hot Springs Conference was to increase production and consumption and to stabilize prices.

A further great Conference was held at Bretton Woods to organize the post-war monetary system on a basis designed to maintain full employment and stimulate international investment. It dealt therefore with the central problem of international stabilization and equalization of wealth. Unfortunately, the idea of establishing a truly international Central Bank was ruled out. This would have worked on the model of a national note-issuing Bank (e.g. the Bank of England) and would have had unlimited power to provide liquid funds to countries which got into difficulties not through their own fault but because an international depression suddenly robbed them of their markets. All actually achieved was that an International Monetary Fund was created by common subscription of the participating countries. It was insufficient even to re-establish the pre-war real value of the gold reserves of the countries outside North America. The use of this Fund by members in difficulties was moreover hedged round with conditions, and, in fact, made dependent on U.S. consent.

The longer-term problem of re-starting international investment so as eventually to equalize wealth and income the world over was tackled by creating an International Bank for Reconstruction and Development. In this instance too the basic idea, sound as it was, was frustrated by the insufficiency of the means and the severe conditions restricting the eligibility of borrowers. Each project had to be self-supporting, and it is unlikely that in times of greatest need, in a slump, many could satisfy this condition. On the other hand, in poor countries only the simultaneous start of many projects would make each profitable, as only a general rise in income would enable the products to be sold.

If the means provided were rather scant, the obligations of the members were very strict. They were to refrain from discriminating against any of their fellow-members, they had to abandon all restrictions on foreign payments (except on capital exports). Bilateral payments arrangements and other devices making possible the maintenance of demand in the teeth of a U.S. recession were outlawed: there could be no long-term planning of imports and exports; they had to be bought in the cheapest (i.e. the most depressed) market.

These draconic rules were complemented by a corresponding definition of good-neighbourly behaviour in commercial relations. They could not avoid hampering or even preventing poor countries from maintaining or restoring the balance in their trade without having to cut their prices and incomes unnecessarily. No regulations were devised, however, against those practices by which a rich country could secure advantages on foreign markets, such as loans or general subsidies.

Poorer and smaller countries would have been gravely handicapped by these rules given even the avoidance of a depression, as they would have had to forgo any longer-term planning of their foreign trade and internal development—the only way in which the advantages accruing to those of their competitors who based their mass-production techniques on the existence of vast and well-protected internal markets could have been offset. As Britain was in urgent need of assistance after the end of the hostilities these rules could have been imposed on her even if her experts had not wholeheartedly shared the U.S. point of view.

Yet in the immediate post-war period an experiment—modelled on Lend-Lease—was started which could have provided a solid and hopeful basis for further action. This experiment, the United Nations Relief and Rehabilitation Administration, was charged with dealing with the immediate distress found in the liberated territories. It was financed by the countries which had not been under enemy occupation, in proportion to their national income—a completely novel and juster way of sharing burdens between Allies. It proved a great success: reconstruction was speeded up and hardship very much mitigated. Without it, famine and disaster could not have been avoided in a large part of Europe. Three times in the short post-war period recourse was had to this type of solution—without the lesson being learned.

The problem of the rest of Western Europe was not dissimilar to that of Britain. If the immediate position on the Continent was much less favourable—because of the appalling physical destruction in most countries—the medium-term prospect seemed more favourable. None of the Continental countries depended to the same extent on foreign trade, and (apart from the Netherlands, which lost Indonesia) none had suffered such losses in foreign income.

The success of the first attempt at reconstruction with the help of U.N.R.R.A. was remarkable. Production, which had sunk to half of pre-war output at the end of hostilities, was (outside of Germany) back to the pre-war level early in 1947. Agricultural output, the collapse of which was so much responsible for hardships and the dependence on the U.S., rose by a quarter in one season (though at that time it barely surpassed three-quarters of pre-war). After the First War, production outside Germany had not shown similar recovery until 1924, i.e. the recovery had taken four years longer.

In 1947, however, partly because of the severity of the winter, partly because of the premature decontrol on the Continent (and to a lesser extent even in Britain), production and the balance of payments began to show signs of deterioration. The British Government did not heed the warnings (in which even American experts unexpectedly joined), and resolved to restore the convertibility of sterling into dollars and play the old game.

The result was catastrophic. The whole of the U.S. loan—which was to have sufficed to pay for the supplies needed for reconstruction in the transition period of four to five years—was used up in a matter of weeks. When this was exhausted, the British Government at last began to try to build up an administrative machine to co-ordinate economic policy at home and to secure balance in her foreign payments.

Nevertheless, it was quite clear that unless substantial help was granted and Western Europe was allowed to control the seemingly insatiable demand for dollars, she would have to undertake a harsh cut in her income and face severe unemployment in order to cope with the position. The post-war plan to turn the clock back to 1914 had obviously broken down. An attempt to implement it would obviously have endangered the existence of the West.

The solution of these difficulties was due to a new element in the international political situation which was to assume dominant importance in the next few years. This new element was the growing antagonism of the two giant States which were left dominant, each in its own sphere, after the conflict which shattered the strength of Europe. The Potsdam Agreement of the summer of 1945 represented the last flicker of understanding with the Soviet. Already in 1946 severe strain was experienced between the war-time allies. The Americans resented the attacks of the Communist parties on U.N.R.R.A. and the simultaneous steady increase of their share in its total burden (in the end 77 per cent.) and were exasperated by the deterioration in the political position in Eastern Europe. They were, obviously, far from realizing that even this proportion did not quite adequately express their relative ability to bear sacrifice. Whether or not the political or economic exasperation was the main cause of the demise of U.N.R.R.A. is difficult to decide. But wound-up it was in Europe in 1947, and soon afterwards in Asia too.

The Moscow Conference, which tried to arrive at some definite agreement on Germany, broke down, and American hostility to the Soviet became open. The American origin of the Morgenthau plan for destroying Germany as an industrial power was forgotten—a plan the partial implementation of which had prevented a speedy restoration of the vanquished and a utilization of her resources and skill to repair the damage she had inflicted on Europe. The erstwhile enemy rapidly advanced into the position of a prized potential ally.

When therefore it became clear that Europe was drifting into a crisis, the invitation to the Soviet Union to participate in the Paris Conference on European Economic Reconstruction was hardly conducive to making Congress, dominated as it was by Republicans, amenable to granting a generous unilateral contribution. The brusque withdrawal of Molotov opened the doors to help for Western Europe. The acceptance by the U.S. Congress of the European Recovery Programme initiated by General Marshall represented a fundamental departure in economic relations between sovereign countries in peace-time (though it was similar to war-time arrangements such as the English subsidies in the nineteenth century or Lend-Lease and U.N.R.R.A.). Immediate need rather than ability to repay, or the possibility of profitable investment, was made the criterion of economic relations between the dominant and the peripheral countries. Long-term investment programmes for making Europe more self-sufficient were to be submitted to the Organization of European Economic Co-operation.

In the meantime U.S. emergency help was given to tide over the immediate crisis in the European countries. Part of the U.S. help was, moreover, devoted to easing the blockage in trade created by the lopsidedness of the balance of payments of Western Europe; while a few countries (e.g. Belgium, Italy) were general creditors, most others were forced to extreme restrictions, having exhausted their liquid reserves. This easing of inter-European trade meant a sharp discrimination against the U.S. exports, as the latter continued to remain severely restricted. The investment plans, had they been successfully implemented, would have had the same result. Finally, the American Economic Co-operation Administration took an active hand in joining the Sterling Area to a comprehensive European payments system—against the strong resistance of the Bank of England and the Treasury, which still had not learnt to appreciate the immense advantage conferred on British export industries by these arrangements. Thus the American Government was actively supporting by large unilateral grants discriminatory actions against her own nationals. Surely a more complete change in attitude has never been experienced. Unfortunately, European officials and Governments had so firmly committed themselves to a return to the uncontrolled sway of markets that this unique opportunity was to some extent wasted. They could not acknowledge the magnitude of their mistakes.

The short-term success of the new approach was striking: production in Europe expanded in the following eighteen months by over a fifth. By 1950 it had expanded to 21 per cent. above pre-war levels. Agricultural output, which had been lagging behind, also recovered. Equally impressive was the performance in the international field. The visible adverse balance of the Western European countries with the rest of the world fell from some $6 billion p.a. in 1947 to $4·2 billion in the second half of 1948; this achievement is the more remarkable in that consumption standards improved substantially and investment expanded simultaneously.

The long-term plans of the Western European countries initiated by the U.S. were to have stabilized and extended this recovery. The weakness of the approach was that it did not offer any incentive to individual member countries for increasing investment and holding back consumption. Indeed the more a country tried to rely on its own efforts the greater was the danger that its share in the total aid would be cut. Nor did the Europeans try, or the Americans insist on, an effective co-ordination of European investment plans; and thus a unique opportunity was lost of increasing productivity and competitiveness. Finally, far from having regard to the relative wealth of the countries aided, the immediate political end of the plans plainly manifested itself: in order to still immediate discontent the existing maldistribution of wealth in Europe was accepted. The richer areas received most of the money. Much the same applies to aid granted by the U.S. to other countries. Out of $45·5 billion total aid actually delivered[1] in the nine years, $33·1 billion went to Western Europe (or rather O.E.E.C. and Jugoslavia), and Asia received $10 billion, of which most was concentrated on Japan, Philippines, Formosa and South Korea. The rest of Asia received a few hundred millions, South America practically nothing.

Nor was the victory of the new approach final. No sooner had conditions in Europe improved than heavy pressure was brought by the U.S. to enforce a freer entry of American goods and to relax controls over foreign payments. Nor was there much need for this pressure. British and Continental experts and politicians were all drawn towards this easy and popular course. Yet it was soon to be demonstrated premature.

When U.S. economic activity suffered a sharp check in 1949, prompt measures by President Truman limited its internal effects on income and demand, and soon halted and reversed the fall even of production. Internationally, however, the action of the American Government was far from being as enlightened or successful. It forced a sharp devaluation of European currencies. In this way much of the effort at reconstruction, and at assuring a more equal distribution of world income, was wasted: the devaluation necessarily led to a sharp relative fall in the value of European products and labour. No sooner was devaluation carried out than the American domestic scene improved and with it her demand for foreign goods.

Yet even this lesson was insufficient. In 1950 yet another retreat was made towards the earlier dogmatic approach. Aid to Britain was ended and further decontrol insisted upon. It is probable that this retreat would in any case have led to a crisis. But a crisis was made inevitable by the violent twist given to international political and economic relations by the outbreak of hostilities in Korea, and, even more sharply, by the Chinese intervention that defeated General MacArthur's impetuous thrust to the Yalu River.

----

[1] Over $60 billion were voted or almost $6 billion p.a. While still relatively less than the pre-1914 European investment abroad this flow begins to reach the same order of magnitude.

Rearmament, hurriedly decided upon, invigorated U.S. economic activity. Production increased by some 40 per cent. in less than four years to the next peak in 1953. Though U.S. expenditure on arms increased by some $35 million (equivalent to the total national income of Britain at current exchange rates), consumption rose by slightly *more* than that, and even private investment expanded. All fears of those who dreaded inflation even more than they dreaded Stalin, and who predicted bankruptcy, were triumphantly overborne by the flood-tide of U.S. production.

Once more insufficient attention was paid to the relative capacity for bearing the new burden. In sharp contrast to the U.S., Britain

TABLE II

ANNUAL INCOME PER HEAD IN VARIOUS COUNTRIES IN 1938

	Income	*Countries in group*	*Population of group in 1938 (millions)*
I.	More than $500	Australia, New Zealand, United States.	138
II.	$400–$500	Sweden, Switzerland, United Kingdom.	58
III.	$300–$400	Canada, Denmark, Germany, the Netherlands, Norway.	95
IV.	$200–$300	Belgium, France, Ireland, Luxemburg.	53
V.	$150–$200	Argentina, Austria, Chile, Czechoslovakia, Finland, Hungary, Spain, Yugoslavia, Union of South Africa.	91
VI.	$100–$150	Albania, Algeria, Bulgaria, Iceland, Italy, Morocco, Newfoundland, Panama, Puerto Rico, Tunisia, Uruguay, Venezuela, U.S.S.R.	247
VII.	$75–$100	Cuba, Ecuador, Greece, Jamaica, Japan, Palestine, Paraguay, Poland, Portugal, Roumania.	147
VIII.	$50–$75	Belgian Congo, Brazil, Colombia, Egypt, Mexico, Peru, Turkey.	118
IX.	Less than $50	Bolivia, Ceylon, China, Dominican Republic, El Salvador, Guatemala, Honduras, India, Netherlands Indies, Korea, Philippines.	950

Note: This table is based on Woytinsky and Woytinsky, *World Population and Production* (1953), pp. 389-91. The population of the countries listed is just under 1,900 million, out of an estimated world population in 1938 of 2,180 million. The countries not included in the table, e.g. Burma, Indo-China and the greater part of Africa, would come towards the bottom of the income scale, thus heightening the contrast between the few rich and many poor countries.

and France assumed obligations which necessitated cuts not only in current consumption but even in investment. Yet productive investment in Europe was already a fraction only of the American level. Thus the future competitiveness and the standard of life of Europe were once again endangered.

Under the impact of renewed financial crisis in Europe U.S. policy once more veered round. The Economic Co-operation Administration was transmuted into the Mutual Security Administration. Apart from military and economic aid, expenditure of and on American troops abroad steeply increased. In addition, the Americans placed orders in Western Europe for supplies for themselves or for their Allies; and as agricultural surpluses piled up in America, special allocations of these were also made. For the third time in the post-war period this return to the principles of U.N.R.R.A. and Marshall Aid restored a better balance between the U.S. and her allies. Economic expansion in Europe was resumed, and it did not falter even when the U.S. expansion came to a halt in 1953.

If the progress of what might be termed the middle-income-range countries was unsteady and hardly sufficient to bring about a better balance in the world economy, the development in the poorer areas comprising the vast majority of the population of the non-Soviet orbit was calamitous. It is problematical whether total real production *per capita* outside the Soviet Union in 1950 was higher than in 1913 or even in 1900. Moreover, far from abating, this tendency seems to have been *accelerated by the Second World War. Food production in most under-developed areas has lagged sharply behind the increase in population.* The increase of the world's food supplies was until 1950 almost entirely concentrated on North America and was probably one of the explanations for the continuous acute dollar shortage experienced in the post-war period. Even within the medium range of average national income, e.g. in Western Europe, such increase in

TABLE III

FOOD PRODUCTION PER HEAD
(1934–8 = 100)

	1951/2	1952/3[1]
North America	114	118
Oceania	86	84
Western and Southern Europe	103	103
Latin America[2]	91	96
Near East	102	107
Far East (excl. Chinese Mainland)	82	82
World[3]	98	100

Sources: F.A.O. *The State of Food and Agriculture* (Rome, 1953).

[1] Provisional.   [2] Excl. Argentina, 108 and 107.
[3] Incl. estimates for the Soviet World.

production as there has been is due to the spectacular advances in the U.K. rather than to a recovery in the poorer areas (there has been a fall in production *per capita* in both Spain and Italy).

Surprisingly enough, much the same was true of the progress in industrial output. Outside the Soviet orbit it has been almost entirely concentrated in the *rich* areas. Industrial production outside the Soviet Union in 1952 was only four-fifths higher than in 1938. In the U.S.—which represents all but one-half of the total—the advance is $1\frac{1}{2}$ times the output in 1938, and so it is in the richest members of the Commonwealth. In Western Europe the advance was only 35 per cent. (France only just managed to catch up with its 1929 output). *In the poorer areas of the non-Soviet world the increase was only 10 per cent. as against an expansion of population of 20 per cent.*

It should be noted that this relative and absolute impoverishment of these countries took place despite several exceptionally favourable circumstances: the real value of their pre-war debt was diminished, and during the war they accumulated large reserves on which they drew sharply. Moreover, the price of their exports also increased relatively to that of their imports.

Thus the future is not encouraging, though determined steps have been taken even outside the Soviet orbit to increase production by deliberate Government policy, and this change in attitude attained considerable success in certain key areas (e.g. India). Despite these efforts something like two-thirds of the total productive investment of the non-Soviet world remains concentrated in the U.S. and the rest is all but totally absorbed by the middle-income-range countries. Investment in the under-developed territories in 1950 was estimated by the United Nations experts at $5 billion, or a small fraction only of the provision of capital in the U.S. for a population less than a tenth of the poor areas. It has since increased, but not sufficiently to change the tendency towards a growing inequality in the distribution of wealth and income. Indeed it is to be feared that in certain important under-developed areas a steady actual impoverishment is inevitable. Medical improvements are likely to lead to a continued increase of the population far outstripping the increase in capital and in the capacity to maintain an already insufficient material standard of life.

The sombreness of the political outlook is aggravated by the fact that the division between the rich and the poor is also a racial division. It is on the whole true to say that only white populations have grown richer while most, if not all, of the coloured ones have been subjected to impoverishment (though there has been some economic progress in South Africa and in some of the African colonies as well as in India and Japan). The desperate political consequences of this development can hardly be disputed.

Developments in the Soviet orbit, though not free from sharp set-backs in some fields, especially agriculture, have given further proof of continued and ferocious energy in expanding national productive capacity. All indications suggest that the economic achievements of the Soviet which have been neglected by Western military and diplomatic strategists will pose awkward problems for the West. A correct appraisal in the West, and especially in the U.S., of the Soviet economic system and its potentialities has not been easy. All our traditions revolt against acknowledging its tremendous dynamism. Success in the economic field could surely not accrue to a system so cruel and despotic: it must be reserved for Free Private Enterprise and for the Rule of the Law. That economic success might not in itself be a sufficient proof of moral excellence seems to many authors too disturbing a thought.

After correction for overstatements, all evidence seems to indicate that national output in Russia, which could hardly have been more than two-thirds of pre-war in 1946, by 1950 exceeded pre-war levels. Since then progress has slowed down, but it seems probable that the increase in total Russian output is of the order of magnitude of at least 6 to 7 per cent. compound per annum. It might well be higher, possibly as high as 9 per cent. The rate of growth of manufacturing production alone seems to have been substantially higher, possibly as high as 11 per cent. In other words Russian production doubles every twelve years or so. This compares with an increase of American manufacturing capacity of roughly 5 to 6 per cent. compound per annum between 1946 and 1953, and with a British increase of about the same order of magnitude until 1950 and again in 1953-4. Over-all production in the West increased much less—between 3 and 4 per cent. This means that Russia will, in a decade or so, obtain a substantial *absolute* preponderance over Western Europe unless energetic action is taken by the West.

TABLE IV

POPULATION AND PRODUCTION IN THE SOVIET UNION
AND WESTERN EUROPE IN 1951

	Unit	Soviet Union	Western Europe[1]
Population (end of year) . .	Million	207	207
Coal and lignite output . .	Mill. tons	281	530
Electricity generation . . .	Bill. Kwh.	103	196
Oil consumption . . .	Mill. tons	42	56
Crude steel production . .	Mill. tons	31	51
Cement production . . .	Mill. tons	12	41
Cotton cloth production . .	Thous. tons	556	987
Refined sugar	Mill. tons	3·0	4·3

[1] Belgium, France, Italy, Luxemburg, the Netherlands, the United Kingdom and Western Germany.

Despite the heavy investment which this expansion entailed, consumption in Russia has been continuously increasing since 1946 —some 5 to 7 per cent. p.a. on the average. The last Five Year Plan, and recent Budgets, seem to represent a change in policy in this respect even though some vacillation has occurred after the resignation of Malenkov: the share of investment going to light industry, building, public utilities and agriculture seems to have been substantially increased.

Soviet planning, especially in the peripheral areas, e.g. Hungary, has been guilty of gross blunders, waste and cruelty. Much effort has been misdirected and a frightful psychological strain imposed. But the material achievements are real, and worth pondering upon if an effective answer is to be found.

V. The Outlook for International Economics

The bright hopes of the nineteenth century for uninterrupted and peaceful progress towards greater equality in opportunity between nations has been sadly disappointed. The gloomy prediction of Marx that the rich would become richer while the poor would suffer ever greater hardship has unfortunately been vindicated on the international scene. In glaring contrast is the complete defeat in the advanced industrial nations of this, his main justification for revolutionary action. Inequality in wealth and opportunity has not increased in North-West Europe or North America. It has been kept in bounds by strong collective action, by steadily progressive taxation and by the provision of social services. It is the absence of such collective balancing action which has been responsible for the failure to achieve a better distribution in welfare between countries. The forces which operated to bring about some sort of equalization in the nineteenth century were paralysed by the two wars and the intervening period of economic instability which meant penury for the poorer areas.

Nor is this all. The rapid technological change which demanded an ever increasing scale of investment has meant that progress in the advanced countries in many cases has turned to the detriment of the less developed territories. Moreover, the growing discrepancy of income between countries has set in motion forces which, if left unchecked, will tend to aggravate their own cause. The rapid development of ever new consumers' goods and aggressive salesmanship stimulate demand. In poorer areas where savings are insufficient, it is suicidal to permit an increase in conspicuous spending on imported "new" consumer goods. The growing awareness of the masses of their wretched condition in wide regions raises in any case difficult problems for democracy. The contradiction between the need to save and invest and the need to allow an increase in the wretched standards is sharpened by conspicuous waste of the upper classes. The optimistic outlook of the nineteenth century is no longer justified under modern conditions.

There is yet a further and possibly more important problem. In the years since 1945 economic activity all over the world has been strongly sustained by the scarcities inherited from the war, by the need to make good the destruction. In 1949 the American Democrats, by their timely if wholly unorthodox measures, prevented the fall of production from engulfing the world in a real slump. Afterwards, the mounting demands of the cold war provided fuel for expansion. But the needs of the consumers have in the last few years been increasingly fulfilled. Armaments expenditure is likely to contract unless there is a hot war—an increasingly unlikely immediate risk. Yet the whole U.S. economy is geared to high investment, i.e. to a continuous expansion of demand. Without it production would decline. Even though a collapse, such as in 1929-31, is most unlikely to be permitted, the recent victory of orthodox economics in the whole Western World might well discourage timely measures. Even the abrupt reversal of the orthodox deflationary monetary policy in the U.S. in 1953, and the seemingly effortless recovery from the recession of 1953-4, offer no security that effective action will in future be undertaken to prevent U.S. development from endangering the stability of the rest of the world. The poorer countries must keep their liberty of action.

Nor can it be assumed that private foreign investments—on which there is an ever-growing reliance—can bring about a better distribution of wealth. It has been on an insignificant scale since the war because the favourable basic situation of the nineteenth century no longer obtains. Only an over-all plan evolved for poorer communities as a whole, and resulting in a sharp increase in incomes, can break this vicious circle.

The typical under-developed country even in the more recent past has only attracted capital for the exploitation of primary products, through plantations or extractive enterprise. This has helped the poor area relatively little, while profits flowing to the rich areas have been formidable—in the case of the U.S. post-war investments all but 20 per cent. per annum on the average.

Independent experts appointed by the United Nations have estimated that merely in order to keep step with the increase in population some $19 billion of investment would be needed annually in the poor areas of the world. These areas would hardly be able to accumulate more than between a quarter and a third of this sum. The rest, some $10–14 billion, would have to come from the rich areas. Their report was denounced as unrealistic. Yet if their calculations are correct, such an investment would still leave the under-developed areas lagging well behind the industrial countries. Thus there would still be an appalling danger from exacerbated feelings and racial resentment. And, indeed, the flow of investment they aim at is, *relatively*, smaller than that achieved in the early years of the century.

Now it may well be that a greater effectiveness could be achieved from capital investment in under-developed territories (though it is increasingly clear that a vast part of the investment would be for completely "unproductive" purposes such as schools, etc.). Even so the discrepancy between the requirements and availability is shocking. Nor could the investment be managed by private capitalists. The social and political consequences of such a vast accumulation of absentee American ownership could not be other than disastrous.

How, then, can we deal with the twin problem of international instability and inequality?

The lessons of the past decades are conclusive and not in the least discouraging, except perhaps to those who are blinded by partisan dogmatism and reject all collective action as "communistic". We must apply the same methods on the international plane as have been so successful in the U.S. and North-Western Europe: we must banish the socially destructive consequences of the free sway of markets by planned international redistribution of wealth. Nor should it be forgotten that immense advance in this direction has already been made, and that it was the United States which carried the main burden of that advance.

Whenever and wherever the common-sense approach was adopted of helping those who needed help, as it was under U.N.R.R.A., under the Marshall Plan, or even under Mutual Aid and the shockingly mutilated Fourth Point Programme of Mr. Truman, immediate and unhoped-for results were achieved. Even the limited success of the International Bank was (within its insufficient framework) an important proof of the possibilities. It is the stubborn refusal to learn the lesson of the past (not least by the rulers of countries which, like Britain, would in all probability benefit most by its acceptance) that has been responsible for much of the repeated discomfiture of the world. The Western World is at the threshold of ability to banish want if only its productive capacity is used fully and for the socially most urgent purposes.

Fortunately the twin problems of development and stability are interrelated. The threatened exhaustion of markets and decline of demand in the richest countries of the world is due to the vast and increasing saving in those countries for which no investment outlet can be found. If measures are taken to support the less fortunate territories of the free world by calling on the richest; if the internal triumph of the progressive movements in equalizing wealth and opportunity in the rich industrial countries, which defeated the Marxist prediction of the growing impoverishment of the masses is translated into international relations: this will automatically lessen the danger of a slump in these prosperous countries.

There are, of course, some acute political difficulties. First of all, it would be absurd to expect the U.S. to shoulder the whole of the burden. An obviously fairly shared and international scheme is required. Equally obvious are the difficulties encountered through the unequal distribution of income in the poor areas. Though the *average* standard of life is admittedly wretched in most poor countries, *some* people there are exceedingly rich, much richer than the average in the richest areas; and it is the richest in the poor areas who are bound to benefit most from any aid unless novel steps are taken. A common-sense arrangement, including sharp taxation of the rich and land-reform, ought to create a sufficiently equitable situation to be tolerable for those countries which have to provide the aid.

Fortunately, the basis of such a solution already exists. What needs doing is, first of all, the transformation of the International Monetary Fund into an International Central Bank capable of assisting countries which get into difficulties because of depression elsewhere. This would enable the stabilization of expansion in the free world. A solid model for organizing international economic development has been provided by the constitution of U.N.R.R.A., sponsored by Roosevelt, and by President Truman's Marshall Aid and Fourth Point: the former representing unilateral aid, the latter sharing technical knowledge. The existing International Bank for Reconstruction and Development ought to be strengthened and transformed into an International Investment Board capable of making free grants and not merely loans. Such a Board has been sponsored by the Economic and Social Council of U.N.O. (S.U.N.F.E.D.), and U.S. contributions to it have been advocated by an official U.S. Government Committee (the so-called Gray Report). This Board should be alimented financially by the assignment to it of basic quota contributions from all richer areas, depending on the *current income* of all members, as well as of a further quota equivalent to a *rising* proportion of the *increase* in the national income of the richer areas. Thus the progressive principle of contribution could be adopted without demanding too great a sacrifice by the richer areas.

The investment programmes which the Board should underwrite must not be selected necessarily or narrowly on an economic basis. They should consist of a judicious mixture of two general aims: on the one hand they should attempt a planned increase of productivity in large regions by stimulating rationalization and co-ordination of economic plans; on the other hand, the establishment of minimum standards of health, education, communications and public utilities, the latter primarily irrigation and connected electrification schemes, should be envisaged to prepare the poorest countries for an eventual participation in plans of the first type. Need and economic progress should be the twin criteria. The least indigent beneficiaries should be required to undertake to contribute a rising proportion of the increase in their income consequent on the initial grant (or loan) by the Board.

A flow of funds eventually rising to at least $8 to $10 billion per annum should be aimed at. The automatic expansion of the scheme through the increase in world real income would carry it at a steady rate towards much higher figures, unless it were modified in the light of new circumstances and experience. The expansion of the scheme should be gradual because its success would seem to require a vastly increased supply of technical and managerial staff of high competence, and their education would take time.

The redistribution of wealth, the stimulation of large investment schemes in under-developed areas, would diminish the need for protective measures aimed at excluding exports of the most developed areas in the world. It would not altogether eliminate such measures for some time: even if aid were provided through collective action, the greatest benefit could only accrue to the poorer countries if they were enabled to overtake by stages the dominant economy of the Western World, the U.S., in technical ability. This, as we have seen, would only be possible through conscious regional planning, protected and stimulated by discriminatory preferences within the region for each other's produce (just as the States forming the U.S. grant preference to each other). When technical development had substantially bridged the gap, these protective measures could be slowly removed. A premature dash to "free" markets, convertibility or non-discrimination would perpetuate the present inequality and insecurity because it would amount to unilateral abolition of protective measures by the poorer areas without any countervailing concession by the richer countries. It would, therefore weaken the West in its efforts to meet the challenge of Soviet planning.

There can be no question that technical progress has enabled the Western World, if not to banish want, to initiate a sufficiently obvious and speedy economic progress to fire the imagination and secure the political stability of those marginal areas where poverty and despair has led to the rise of powerful communist movements. If the West fails, the example of Russia, and perhaps even more of China, will, within a measurable time, exercise an increasingly great attraction for peoples whom the individualist economic system has failed to help substantially and sufficiently quickly. We may deplore the consequential loss of personal liberty and choice, but we must admit the attractions to these areas of a system which has transformed Russia within a generation, and which has successfully dealt with the racial issue.

In the years before 1951-2 support for the suggested methods of meeting the Soviet challenge on its own ground had made substantial headway. Since then, the almost exclusive preoccupation with military preparations on the one hand, and the revival of economic orthodoxy, of fears of budgetary bankruptcy (in the midst of unparalleled prosperity) on the other, have thrown the Western World back from the high level of insight reached by the U.N.O. experts and by President Truman's advisers. It is to be hoped that this reaction against an international re-distribution of income and wealth will be transient only. The possible easing of the political tension might and ought to be the basis of a more constructive attitude. It would be disastrous if it merely led to efforts to cut arms-expenditure and taxation simultaneously (especially taxation falling on the richer classes) in the most prosperous areas, and thus aggravated the inequality in living standards internally and internationally, and increased the threat to economic stability. The advocates of the unfettered market economy, as in the 1930's, might well then end by losing us the precious economic lead we still possess over the Soviet orbit by enforcing restrictive economic policies in their fear of "inflation".

BOOKS SUGGESTED FOR FURTHER READING

H. Arndt, *The Economic Lessons of the 1930's* (Chatham House, 1944).

P. T. Ellsworth, *The International Economy* (Macmillan, New York, 1950).

Donald Marsh, *International Trade and Investment* (Harcourt Brace, New York, 1951).

A. Bergson (ed.), *Soviet Economic Growth* (Peterson & Co., Evanston, Illinois, 1955).

National and International Measures to Maintain Full Employment (U.N.O., 1950); *Measures for the Economic Development of Underdeveloped Areas* (U.N.O., 1951).

Thomas Balogh, *The Dollar Crisis* (Blackwell, 1949).

WORLD RESOURCES

by LORD BOYD-ORR

I.

MANY PEOPLE are beginning to wonder whether our civilization can survive the impact of modern science. Even if it can be saved from sudden destruction in a Third World War with hydrogen bombs and biological weapons there remains the question of whether and how soon the natural resources of the earth, upon which this highly developed mechanical age depends, will be exhausted.

This is a question which did not worry ancient civilizations with their small populations and non-industrialized way of life nor even later ones with a highly developed social and political structure. From the beginning of the Christian era until the seventeenth century the demands made on the earth's resources were limited to food-producing land and forests and were only local and small in proportion to the whole earth. The total human population was small and for long periods static and at other periods increasing very slowly. As late as the seventeenth century it was less than a fifth of what it is today. About 90 per cent. of the population were engaged in food production and the only shortage they feared was of food due to bad harvests. In the seventeenth century, however, there began the new age of technology, with its mechanization which developed slowly until the nineteenth century, when with the steam engine and other inventions, mechanization with its increasing demands on natural resources began to develop at an ever accelerating rate.

Since the beginning of the present century science and technology, giving increased capacity for production with correspondingly increased rate of consumption of natural resources, have advanced more than in the previous 2,000 years. At the same time there has been a parallel increase in the rate of growth of population. The increase per annum is today more than 200 times greater than the average increase per annum from A.D. 1 to 1600. The rapidly increasing consumption of resources per head combined with an equally rapid growth of population makes the rate of exhaustion of natural resources a matter of vital concern.

Some believe there is no hope for the future, unless the present rate of growth of population can be stopped by birth control. Others believe that with modern science the earth can be made to support as many inhabitants as it is ever likely to have. Though even the wisest cannot foresee what the future will hold in this rapidly changing world, it is of interest to examine the facts so far as they are known and to speculate on the kind of world our grand-children will inherit.

Of the factors which will decide how long the resources of the earth will last, the most important are the size of the population and the rate at which the consumption per head is increasing. The next most important factor is the food supply. If it fails to keep pace with population, the gloomy predictions of some writers, that civilization will collapse in a fierce fight for food to decide which type of people and which races will survive and which die, are going to be fulfilled. Less essential, though of supreme importance in deciding how long the Western highly industrialized and mech-anical way of life can continue, are the supplies of raw materials for manufacturing and energy for power-driven machines. Finally, even of greater importance are the resources of human intelligence needed to adjust the structure of human society to this new age of science, and its way of life to what can be supported by available natural resources.

II. The Demand on Resources

(a) Size of Population

Fairly accurate figures are now available for about two-thirds of the world population. For the remaining third only estimates can be made. The further back we go, the lower is the proportion estimated and the wider the margin of error. The figures given by different demographers are, however, in fairly close agreement, and those of any expert are good enough to show the trend of population growth. Round figures are sufficient for the present purpose.

As is the case with other species of animals the size of population is limited by the food supply. Before the beginning of agriculture about 10,000 years ago the total population probably did not exceed one million. With an increase in the food supply as agricul-ture spread there was a corresponding growth of population. By A.D. 1 it may have been about 275 million, of whom there were, in millions, 100 in India, 70 in China and 54 in the Roman Empire, which had a census in 5 B.C. These are the areas where agriculture was developed. By 1600 the population had reached about 450 million. Until that date the rate of growth had been slow; from 8000 B.C. to A.D. 1 less than 30,000 a year, and from A.D. 1 to 1600 about 100,000 a year. From 1600 onwards the population has expanded at an ever accelerating rate. Today it is about 2,500 million with an annual increase of a little over 35 million.

The most obvious reason for the sudden increase in the rate of expansion which began first in Western Europe in the sixteenth century was the advance in technology which followed the Renaissance. This led to an increase in the food supply by improvement in agriculture, and to the better control of disease. Western Europe had the additional good fortune of food imported from the new continents. An example of the rate at which a population can increase under favourable conditions is given by England and Wales, the population of which shot up from 9 million in 1800 to 33 million in 1900. To get a true picture of the rate of increase there should be added to the 33 million the numbers who emigrated to North America and elsewhere and their descendants, less the relatively small number of immigrants. In the third quarter of the nineteenth century people were leaving Britain at the rate of over 100,000 a year. If the whole world population had expanded at the same rate, the population of 1600 million in 1900 would have been between 3,000 and 4,000 million.

The alarming feature of the present position is that the technical knowledge which initiated the phase of rapid expansion in Europe has spread to all continents. In Japan, the first Asiatic country to adopt Western technology, the population rose from 35 million in 1872 to 83 million in 1950. All other countries in the world are now adopting modern technology. The process is being helped by United Nations specialized agencies, e.g. The Food and Agriculture Organization, The World Health Organization and U.N.E.S.C.O.; and also by the United States technical aid programme and the British Colombo Plan. Provided the food supply can be stepped up enough, the expansion of population in these undeveloped countries may be more rapid than in European countries in the nineteenth century, because the means of eliminating killing diseases, one or more of which afflict 80 per cent. of the populations with the highest death-rate, is now much more efficient. Thus, for example, malaria can be eliminated by spraying with one of the new insecticides. Wide areas have been completely cleared. Protection against tuberculosis, the white scourge of India and other countries, can be conferred by inoculation. In India 170 million young people are being inoculated. Yaws can be cured by a shot of penicillin. Intestinal infections and infestations can be prevented by modern sanitation. All these measures are now being applied to some extent in practically every country. In Europe, the United States and the British Dominions, where preventive medicine has been applied and hunger abolished, the average length of life is nearly seventy years. In Asia, Africa and South America, where it is beginning to be applied, the average is only thirty to forty years. But in areas in these continents where it has already been applied the fall in the death-rate is so great that it is estimated that the population will be doubled in less than thirty years. It is estimated that at the present rate of expansion the world population will reach nearly 4,000 million by 1984. That is double the number in 1939.

That rate of growth is no greater than what took place in Europe in the nineteenth century. If, however, preventive medicine, which is much more efficient than it was in the nineteenth century, were vigorously applied in all countries there would be an unprecedented explosion of population. A striking example and warning is given by what happened in the suburbs of Georgetown in British Guiana, when by the application of D.D.T. the infant mortality rate fell, between 1947 and 1949, from 350 to 67 per 1,000, with the result that the population is increasing at a rate which if continued would double it every seven years. A similar sudden increase in population, though not to the same degree, has taken place in other areas. Wherever there is such a high infant mortality rate (which is the case in half the population of the world) the elimination of preventable disease may lead to a doubling of the population in less than thirty years.

It is obvious that if the expansion of population continues indefinitely, it will end in a fierce struggle over the earth's diminishing resources. To avoid this disaster, the birth-rate must be reduced. The International Planned Parenthood Federation and other organizations are carrying out a vigorous campaign for birth control. Pandit Nehru has sponsored a great national movement in India, and some other governments approve of education on preventive measures, at public health centres. There are, however, religious objections to the use of preventive measures, and there is the further difficulty that the highest birth-rate is among poverty-stricken, ignorant people, difficult to reach with the necessary education. Then, some governments are anxious to increase their population. Russia, for example, offers valuable prizes to mothers of large families. Under these adverse conditions it will be a long time before the commendable efforts to get a falling birth-rate to equal the falling death-rate will be able to stabilize the population.

A study of population growth since the earliest times gives grounds for hope that world population will ultimately be stabilized. There are three main phases of growth: the first with a high birth-rate and a high death-rate nearly equal, with resulting slow growth. In this phase the expectation of life at birth is short. In England until the seventeenth century it was only about thirty years—nearly the same as today in Asia, Africa and most of South America.

In the second phase, under conditions more favourable to survival (especially control of preventable diseases and more food), the death-rate falls without any corresponding fall in the birth-rate, and the population shows a rapid increase. In this phase expectation of life lengthens. It is the phase through which Europe was passing in the nineteenth century, and by the end of the century expectation of life under such favoured circumstances had reached nearly fifty years. Now the same phase seems to be in full swing on a world-wide scale.

In the third phase, with a further rise in the standard of living and better education, the birth-rate falls to or below the replace-ment rate, and the population becomes static or may even begin to decline, with a further increase in the expectation of life of the individual. Western European countries after their explosive phase in the nineteenth century, entered this third phase early in the present century. The following figures for England illustrate the slowing down of the rate of growth.

								Rate of increase per 10,000
1871–80	.	.	.	.	.	.	.	140
1901–10	.	.	.	.	.	.	.	118
1931–40	.	.	.	.	.	.	.	27

Even though total numbers were still increasing in 1931-1940 the factors causing a decline were operating. The following figures for the United States illustrate the tendency for the percentage of old people to increase when the death-rate falls faster than the birth-rate.

			1860	1900	1940	Estimate 1980
Percentage over 65	.	.	2·7	4·1	6·8	14·9
Percentage under 20	.	.	51·2	45·3	34·5	26·0

In England, it has been estimated, by 1980 a fifth of the population will be old-age pensioners, i.e. men over 65 and women over 60. But these old people make little or no contribution to the birth-rate, which depends on the number of women between say 15 and 45. Between 1921 and 1936 the number of females in England increased by 7 per cent. but the number of girls under 15 decreased by 14 per cent. These are now the women between 20 and 35, the period of greatest fertility.

Rate of growth of population is determined by the net reproduc-tion rate, which is based on the proportion of women of childbearing age to the total population and the average size of families. A rate of 1 indicates stability, above 1 increase, below 1 decrease. In England in the 1880's it was 1·52. By 1937 it had fallen to 0·78 and in the late 1940's it was estimated that the population of 45 million might fall to 31 million by 1975. The population of all Western European countries were following the same trend

and there was talk of "race suicide". But this downward trend
has not continued. During and after the last war, in countries
where the birth-rate had been falling rapidly the rate has
risen. In fourteen countries where the average rate had fallen
from about 26 in 1915 to 17 before the last war, it had risen to 23
in 1947. The United States population has grown as much in the
last 4 years as it did in the ten years 1930-40. It is impossible to
say whether this post-war increase indicates the beginning of a
new growth phase of populations which were on the decline, or
merely the usual temporary increase which takes place after wars
and in this case is magnified in proportion to the size of the last
war and perhaps also to the emotional upset due to the fear of
another war.

However that may be, there is reason to believe that if all nations
could reach the standard of living and culture of countries where,
before the last war, populations had begun to decline, the alarming
rate of growth of world population would be slowed down and
ultimately reversed. If that view be right, the policy of the wealthier
countries should be, not to stop giving aid to the poorer countries
in controlling diseases and developing agriculture until famine and
disease have reduced the population (as has been suggested), but
rather to increase the humanitarian efforts of the United Nations
and American and British Agencies referred to above. As Notestein,
one of the leading authorities on the subject, has said ". . . only in a
society in which the individual child or adult has a reasonable
chance for survival in healthy life, will develop that interest in the
dignity and material well-being of the individual essential to the
reduction of fertility". He therefore believes in directly fostering
public health as part of the programme required to reduce growth
potential. It will be a long time, however, before that work, plus
propaganda on birth control, slows down the birth-rate to the
replacement level. In trying to estimate whether natural resources
will be able to support the population of the future it would be wise
to assume that by A.D. 2000 it will reach about 5,000 million.

(b) Consumption of Resources per Head

We have dealt at some length with the size of the population
because if it were to continue to expand at the present rate the
human family would ultimately be bankrupt. Of equal importance
with the number of people is the rate of consumption per head.
This is increasing faster than the growth of population. Thus, for
example, world production of iron has increased from 12 to 163
million tons per annum since 1870. Of 80 billion tons of coal produced since it began to be used in appreciable amounts in the
seventeenth century, 60 billion have been used since 1900. Consumption per head is now highest in the United States, where the

amount of metals and mineral fuels used since the First World War is greater than the total amount used in the whole world in all history before 1914; and it is anticipated that the demand for energy and metallic minerals will in 1975 be nearly double what it was in 1950.

The whole world is now in a phase of rapid industrial development with an accelerating rate of consumption of non-replaceable fuel and other minerals. In spite of the destruction caused by the war some European countries have already increased their industrial production by over 50 per cent. since 1945. Countries which were primary producers with peasant populations are now becoming industrialized, because they realize that the standard of living is roughly in proportion to their industrial output and also because with modern weapons industrial potential is more important than man-power. In countries which have lagged behind in industrialization the rate of increase can be faster than in the developed countries. In the U.S.S.R. since 1945 production of coal and of steel has nearly doubled and production of electricity nearly trebled. By 1960 the U.S.S.R. may have pulled ahead of Western Europe.[1]

Rapid industrialization seems now to be the economic policy of all countries, some of which, like the Argentine, Australia, Eastern European countries, and even food-deficit countries like India, Pakistan and China, are tending to sacrifice agriculture for industry as England did in the latter half of the nineteenth century, and as the U.S.S.R. did until the change of régime after Stalin's death.

As the standard of living rises with industrialization, consumption per head of agricultural and forest products rises, more cotton and wool are needed for clothing and home furnishings. More wood is used for housing, furniture and other things, including newsprint, the consumption of which has increased at a fantastic rate. In the United States a single issue of one New York Sunday paper costs 20 acres of timber.[2] Consumption of the more expensive foods, which make a bigger demand on land than cereals, increases. In the United States, with full employment and good wages during the last war, consumption per head of milk, eggs and meat rose 15 to 18 per cent.

Of all the earth's resources by far the most important are those which can produce food. The ill-nourished two-thirds of the world's population are now realizing that sufficient food for their needs can be made available. If this is not done there will be unrest and revolution as occurred in France in 1789, in Europe in the hungry forties, and as is now occurring in the poverty-stricken colonies of the

[1] Wincolt, *Financial Times* (London, March 16, 1952).
[2] Roberts, *The Estate of Man* (Faber and Faber, 1951).

European empires. On the other hand, with an abundant food supply the human family could carry on in comfort even though some of the other resources were exhausted. The Greeks had a high level of culture, intellectual attainment and presumably satisfaction with life without industrial goods like motor cars, jet planes or atomic and hydrogen bombs, which make the largest demands on the earth's resources of materials and energy.

III. Food Needs and Resources

There are two aspects of the food problem. Food can be regarded as in the same category as any other trade commodity, to be produced and sold for profit with the supply regulated to the economic demand. This is the principle on which farmers conduct their business, and rightly so. On any other principle they would become bankrupt. What suits the farmer is a world scarcity with a sure market at a remunerative price, as occurs during wars. According to that view there is today too much food in the United States, where stocks have accumulated to the value of 6,000 million dollars, too much wheat in Australia and too much rice in Burma.

The other view, that of the consumer, is that, food being a daily necessity for life, the supply should be sufficient for the needs of all people. According to that view there has never been sufficient food in the world. Even after normal harvests there was scarcity before the next harvest, and after a bad harvest there was famine, sometimes on a large scale like that affecting India and China in 1876-8, when 14 million perished. Famines were not limited to Asia. Until the nineteenth century they were almost as common in European countries. These famines, occurring almost every decade in some part of the world, were merely acute forms of the continuing and nearly universal world food-shortage.

Governments in their own interests have been forced to try to maintain the food supply, because hunger leads to social unrest and the danger of revolt. The older civilizations carried out irrigation and food-storage projects. In modern times all governments in advanced countries have assumed responsibility for the national food supply, and have promoted increased production by agricultural research and education. They have intervened in acute shortages, as the U.S.A. did in the 1930's with its food stamp plan; and have supported agricultural prices in the interest of both consumer and producer. The assumption of the responsibility for seeing that everyone has sufficient food has reached its highest expression in the United Kingdom where, beginning in 1935, a food policy based on nutritional needs was evolved. Subsidies amounting to over £400 million were provided to bridge the gap between the price the farmer needed for a reasonable profit and that which the poorest could pay, with in addition free or cheap supplies of milk and vitamin-rich substances for special cases. Today the large food-deficit countries containing half the population of the world have five- or ten-year national plans to increase food production to provide sufficient for the people.

This sense of responsibility for the food supply has passed into the international sphere. In 1938, under the auspices of the League of Nations, representatives of twenty-two nations met in a conference to consider ways and means of increasing the world food supply to meet human needs, and the social and economic advantage which would accrue from such a policy. The war put an end to that movement, but in 1944 President Roosevelt called the Hot Springs Conference to consider how the nations could co-operate to abolish hunger and at the same time raise the standard of living of peasants many of whom through poverty were short of food. From that arose in 1945 F.A.O. (The Food and Agricultural Organization) to which more than sixty nations now adhere. That Organization in 1946 set up the International Emergency Food Council consisting of the representatives of the thirty-four most important food-exporting and importing nations, to deal with the post-war food shortage. It took charge of food exports, allocating available supplies to different nations in accordance with their need, prevented prices from rocketing owing to the scarcity, and promoted all-out efforts to increase production. For the first time in history the nations co-operated on a world-wide scale to ensure that people had food.

So soon as that temporary Council had been set up, the then Director General submitted to all governments a permanent world food plan to be carried out by the co-operation of all the Agencies of the United Nations including the World Bank for Reconstruction and Development. Though the majority of the nations were in favour a few refused to co-operate. F.A.O., however, continues to work to the limit of its funds and authority for a food policy based on human needs; and the U.K. and the U.S.A. are supplementing the work of F.A.O. by the British Colombo Plan and the Truman Technical Aid Plan (Point Four). That development of international co-operation in the last twenty years is a remarkable achievement which warrants the hope that in the not too distant future nations will co-operate in a world food plan. This plan, by providing sufficient food for all, will go far to allay social unrest and revolution in the countries where the masses are ill-fed and poverty-stricken; it will organize the great projects needed to produce sufficient food and bring about a big expansion of the world market for industrial products, thus preventing unemployment and economic distress as the market for armaments declines; and it will stabilize world prices within limits at levels fair to producers and consumers. This last can be done by building up a reserve to equalize good and bad harvests and prevent the violent fluctuations in world prices which are bad for trade.

I have referred to the growth of the movement for international co-operation in a world food plan because, as will appear later, the only hope of producing sufficient to meet the needs of the growing population lies in the joint action of the highly industrialized countries and the under-developed countries—and also because incidentally the rapid development needed would go far to create a rapidly expanding world economy to balance the rapidly increasing industrial potential. The large number of water-control projects like the T.V.A. of the United States, the vast quantities of agricultural equipment, the building up of secondary industries which modern agricultural needs, the great reafforestation projects needed to prevent soil erosion, and the means of food storage and transport would provide a market for the output of the heavy industries for many years ahead; and as the purchasing power of the 60 per cent. of the world population engaged in agriculture increased with increasing output there would be an equally rapid growth of the market for consumer goods. Such a world food plan would provide a long-term investment which would ultimately yield dividends, as the increasing wealth of the undeveloped countries enabled them to begin to pay interest on the credits needed for development of their resources. Further, in the opinion of the writer, the only alternative to the nations co-operating in groups to apply the great powers of modern science to the piling up of armaments (which, if continued, will eventually explode in another war) is their co-operation in applying them, to their mutual advantage, in order to develop the resources of the earth, beginning with food.

(a) The Amount of Food Needed

The average energy requirement to maintain body heat and muscular activity is between 2,500 and 2,600 calories. Less is needed to maintain body heat in warm than in cold countries, though with better housing and central heating the difference between hot and cold countries has decreased. And in the highly industrialized countries where the machine has replaced the muscle for physical work, the amount needed for muscular activity has decreased. In addition to energy, the body needs an average of about 70 grams of protein, plus vitamins and minerals which are supplied by the more expensive foods the consumption of which rises as purchasing power rises.

According to F.A.O. estimates in 1936, the average pre-war intake for the whole world was 2,460 calories. But this was ill-distributed. About 440 million had about 3,000 or more calories, while about 1,230 million had less than 2,500 calories. In 1947/8 the average world-intake had fallen to 2,210 calories, and 2,000 million people had less than 2,500 calories.

As income-level falls, the diet consists more and more of carbohydrate foods which are the cheapest satisfiers of hunger. A low-calorie intake is associated with a deficiency of the more expensive protein and vitamin-rich foods. In 1948/9 the number of people getting 70 grams of protein or over had fallen from 680 million in 1936 to 480 million, while the number with less than 70 grams had risen from 1,010 to 1,830 million. The fall in quantity was evidently accompanied by a deterioration in quality.

From the end of the last war till 1952 the world food position was getting worse. Population had increased by 12 per cent. while food production had increased by only 9 per cent. In 1952/3, however, food production kept pace with population increase. If with good harvests this improvement in the food position of the world continues, the total world food supply will soon be back to the pre-war level; but the distribution is worse. Owing to lack of dollars a large part of the supply which might be exported consists of an accumulation in the United States to the value of 6,000 million dollars.

In view of these figures we may take it that the food position of the world today is no better than it was before the last war, when it was estimated that two out of three people in the world were ill-fed; and that, taking account of the anticipated increase in population, the assumption that world food supplies would need to be doubled in the next twenty-five years to provide sufficient for health for everybody is approximately correct. That raises the question whether world food resources can be made to yield that increase.

(b) World Food Resources

The rapid growth of population in Europe in the nineteenth century was made possible partly by the improvement in agriculture, giving a bigger yield per acre, but mainly by the import of food from the new continents—the Americas and Australasia. Today there are no new continents to add to the food-producing land. On the contrary the area of fertile land has decreased by soil erosion. This occurs when the trees and other vegetation which act as a sponge, retaining the water after rain, have been removed, and the water after heavy rains runs off the denuded surface, carrying with it the fertile soil; or in a drought when the fine particles of soil are carried off from land bared of its vegetable covering by cultivation or overgrazing. This has occurred since the first city grew up. The forests were cut down for building, for fuel and for smelting metals; and the land was overcultivated and overgrazed to provide food for the growing population. From early times until the seventeenth century the centre of power and population moved west through Asia Minor, Greece, Rome and Spain, leaving behind destroyed forests and impoverished lands unable to support the large population they had at their prime—unless, as in the case of Greece and Rome, by importing food from colonies and conquered lands.

In the United States, about a fourth of the once-fertile land has deteriorated through erosion. It has been estimated that of the original nine inches of topsoil about a third has been washed away or blown away.[1] This loss of fertile land, which is worst where the pressure of population on the land is greatest, is taking place in nearly all countries except Egypt, whose soil is renewed every year by the deposit of silt in the flooding of the Nile, and those of north-west Europe, which is protected by a sufficient and equitable rainfall and by conservation methods of agriculture. Something like half of the original fertile land of the earth has been lost since the city-state made its increasing demand on the surrounding lands. As Hyams says, ". . . the first step towards civilization is soil exploitation".[2]

The interest in soil erosion which began by the alarm caused by the "dust bowl" in the United States about twenty years ago, together with the interest in the accelerating rate of growth of population, revived discussion of the theory of Malthus (1798). He asserted that as population increases in a geometrical ratio and food production in an arithmetrical ratio, food supply can never catch up with population unless there is a check on population growth. Malthus, however, could not foresee that, with the advance of science, the increase of the food supply can proceed not arithmetically but by sudden leaps, as is the case in other fields—for example, the increase in the energy supply by the invention of the steam engine, by the discovery of petroleum, and by the internal combustion engine, and the release of atomic energy. The same applies to agriculture, though not in such a dramatic way. The breeding of the Marquis wheat with a shorter time of growing and ripening enabled the wheat belt of Canada to be extended north. A method of treating seeds before planting discovered by the Russians had a similar effect. New methods of controlling diseases in plants and farm animals, if universally applied, would make a big increase in yield. The discovery of extracting nitrogen from the atmosphere and using it as a fertilizer has enabled the yield of pastures in the United Kingdom to be doubled by progressive farmers. In India, the Japanese and Chinese methods of growing rice which have been recently tried in experimental areas show that in proportion to the amount shown the yield can be increased several times.

The rate at which the food supply could be increased, by methods

[1] Bennet, Chief of Soil Conservation Service, quoted by Harrison Brown, *The Challenge of Man's Future* (Secker and Warburg, 1954).

[2] Hyams, *Soil and Civilization* (Thames and Hudson, 1952).

already in practice on the best farms in all countries, was demonstrated during and after the last war. Then, by the incentive of a guaranteed market at a remunerative price, food production in the United States increased by about 40 per cent., in spite of the loss of land by soil erosion, and in the United Kingdom (where agriculture was already at a high level of efficiency) by about 50 per cent. It has been estimated that if production on all the land already under cultivation were brought up to the level of the most efficient in each area, the world food supply would be doubled.

Soil erosion can be stopped and much of the lost land reconditioned by reafforestation and water-control projects to transform the destructive power of floods into electricity and use the water for irrigation. These long-range projects are being carried out in the United States, Russia, China and other countries. Probably the most spectacular, though on a small scale, is what is being done by the Jews in Israel. With modern engineering and agricultural science the devastated lands can be reconditioned to set wider limits to the food resources of the world.

Food-production resources are not confined to land. Production of both salt- and fresh-water fish could be increased. Nearly 98 per cent. of the fish caught are in the Northern Hemisphere. The lowness of the amount got from the Southern Hemisphere is probably due to the fact that fishing has not been developed by modern methods. Fish culture in flooded rice fields and in other inland waters could be greatly expanded.

In addition to the traditional methods of food production from land and sea, we now have new methods devised by chemists. Food can be produced from wood-waste. In the last war Sweden produced from wood large quantities of food for animals and men. Yeast in solution of sugar and mineral nutrients can produce edible protein. A pilot plant in Jamaica is now in operation. Using the sugar produced on an acre of land in the tropics a ton of protein could be produced. That is more than twenty times the average amount produced by beef cattle on an acre of pasture. Research work in California on the production of food by the alga chlorella has now reached the stage when production is being tried on a practical scale. Theoretically it can give much higher yields of a high protein per acre of water-culture than can be obtained by agricultural methods from land. Chlorella has been found suitable for chicken-feed. Feeding tests with animals and humans suggest that algar and plankton consisting largely of salt water algae could be produced as a high protein food in great quantities. With such means of food production any shortage of food occurring is due neither to the lack of knowledge nor to the niggardliness of nature.[1] The advance of technology has laid the spectre of Malthus, which

[1] Brittain, *Let There be Bread* (Simon and Schuster, New York, 1952).

was very real in his day. The obstacles to increasing production and to adjusting distribution so that all the people in the world may have sufficient for health are social, economic and political in character.[1] Interesting though these be, they are outside the scope of this essay.

IV. Resources Other than Food

Increasing food production to satisfy the needs of the people in the world fifty years hence, which, in this rapidly changing world, is as far ahead as it is worth planning for, will make big demands on both energy and mineral resources. If, as was estimated in 1946, pre-war food production would need to be doubled in twenty-five years to provide sufficient for the health of the anticipated size of population, it would need to be nearly trebled by A.D. 2000. As was noted above, this would require enormous quantities of industrial products with corresponding demands on energy and minerals. Then as the people of the undeveloped countries come to have sufficient food for full health and vigour, they will want and ultimately get a standard of living more comparable with that of industrialized countries. This will mean further big demands on energy and minerals.

Some writers have based their estimates of the size of population the earth will support on the area of land which could be cultivated. As a matter of fact, with modern technology the limit of food production is determined more by available industrial potential than by available land. Even if one considers only future requirements for agriculture and for the production of food and clothing, it is necessary to take account of energy and mineral resources.

V. Energy Resources

Of all resources, other than food, energy is probably the most important, because with sufficient energy the supply of metal and other mineral materials can be maintained by the extraction of ever-lower-grade ores, and the diminishing resources of other materials can be offset. Primitive man's only source of energy was the food he ate, giving him probably less than 3,000 calories per head per day. The earlier civilizations developed the use of wind- and water-power, and, for domestic heat and for smelting metals and firing bricks and lime, wood—which continued to be the main source of exhaustible energy until late in the seventeenth century, when coal, supplemented by petroleum at the end of the nineteenth century, became the main source of energy in industrialized countries. In the United States, according to Harrison Brown,

[1] Boyd-Orr, *The White Man's Dilemma* (Allen and Unwin, 1953).

consumption is about 160,000 calories per head per day, the proportion from different sources being

Coal	37·7 per cent.
Petroleum	35·6 ,, ,,
Natural gas	18·4 ,, ,,
Water power	4·6 ,, ,,
Wood fuel	3·7 ,, ,,

(a) Non-Renewable Sources

There are immense quantities of coal in the earth. Estimates of the amount which can be made available depend on the thickness of the seam, the amount which must be left in the workings, the depth of mines which can be worked and the availability of sources, such as those in Northern Siberia. The main supplies are in the United States, which has more than half the estimated world reserves, and in Europe, the U.S.S.R. and China. Estimates of how long easily available supplies will last vary widely, but there seems no likelihood of a coal shortage in the present century. China's supply may run out within a hundred years. Optimistic estimates give the United States a thousand years' supply. The United States is also fortunate in petroleum, with a third of the known world's resources; but it is producing three-fifths of the world's total industrial output and is already a net importer of petroleum and petroleum products. Even if known reserves be doubled, they will be exhausted in the United States in about 30 years, in Russia and Venezuela in about 40 years, and in the Middle East in about 100 years. Further supplies, however, can be extracted from coal and shale.

Energy from atomic fission at a cost of about 25 per cent. above power from coal is now beginning to be used. The biggest deposits of uranium are in the Congo and Canada. But according to Mezerik,[1] at the present rate at which it is being used for bombs, no rich deposit will be left after about 30 years. Bertrand Russell has made the caustic comment: "The supply of uranium in the planet is very limited and it is feared that it may be used up before the human race is exterminated." Uranium and thorium, however, are widely distributed though in low concentration Though an increasing amount of nuclear energy will become available, the main sources of energy will, for a long time, continue to be coal and petroleum.

The length of time that the non-renewal sources of energy will last depends of course on the rate of consumption. According to Harrison Brown,[2] the United States uses the equivalent of 8 tons of coal per person per year, Europe about 2·5 tons, compared with

---

[1] *Pursuit of Plenty* (Harper, New York, 1950).
[2] *The Challenge of Man's Future* (Secker and Warburg, 1954).

less than 100 lb. for Asia. Taking account of the increase in population and the increased consumption per head, total consumption in the United States may be doubled by 1970. In other countries now in the race for industrialization the rate of increase may be greater. In the U.S.S.R. coal production is said to be doubling every five years. In other countries being industrialized consumption may double every ten years. It is obvious that this great accelerating rate of increasing consumption of non-renewable sources of energy per person, together with the rate of increase of number of persons, will ultimately lead to an exhaustion of easily available sources. If the human family does not change its way of life, the machine civilization will either blow itself up or burn itself out, to be followed by a more agrarian way of life.

(b) Renewable Sources

Considerable amounts of energy can be obtained from wind- and water-power. In North America, where about 40 per cent. of the "steady" water-power has been developed, sufficient is supplied to give the whole population nearly a quarter of one horse-power per head. That is only about a seventh of what the U.S.A. derives from coal and petrol, but it is more than what the greater part of the population of the world exists on. If the steady power were increased by reservoirs to use all the available water— a vast project—the present world water-power could be increased about twenty times. With full development the main sources would be in Africa and Asia, which between them would have about two-thirds of the total world supply. Wind-power is of value especially for pumping water in sparsely populated areas where fuel costs are high. In the last twenty years large units with improved designs have been developed in the United States, in Great Britain and also in the U.S.S.R. A recent survey has shown that the development of wind-power in Great Britain could effect a saving of 2 to 4 million tons of coal a year. That is little more than what is produced in a week.

Until the seventeenth century, except in China where coal was used a thousand years ago, wood was the main source of energy. It still supplies 3·7 per cent. of the energy used in the United States. In countries where other fuels are expensive it is still the main fuel for heating and cooking. In the past, forests were cut down without any adequate measures being taken for replanting. In the lands of the older civilizations from the western end of the Mediterranean to the east of China the forests were destroyed with resulting soil erosion which changed much of what was once fertile land into barren desert. Our modern civilization has continued the process of destruction. In the last hundred years the greatest destruction has taken place in America. Tom Gill has given a graphic description of vanishing forests and resulting soil erosion in Mexico.[1] In the United States the original virgin forests covered about 40 per cent. of the land. Today they cover only about 7 per cent. The destruction continues. In the Annual Report of the Forest Service, 1947, it is stated that the estimated stand of saw timber decreased by 44 per cent. between 1909 and 1945. Cutting still goes on in excess of planting.

It is estimated that about a third of the primeval forests of the world have been destroyed, but there are about 5½ million square miles of accessible timber. If all this were under the skilful management practised in Sweden it could supply energy equivalent to 5 billion tons of coal a year, which is more than the present total (non-food) world consumption. Much wood is of course needed for constructional timber, paper pulp and many new industrial uses. A number of countries are now beginning to adopt proper forest management; but so far, less than a fifth of the forest land is receiving the attention it needs to prevent destruction.

Certain food crops, e.g. potatoes, corn and sugar, which can be converted into power alcohol, could yield more energy per acre than forests. Alga could yield more energy than any field crop, but the cost would be about twenty times that derived from coal. Solar energy could be directed by focused mirrors to concentrate the sun's rays. In India where, to the detriment of the soil, cow dung is used for cooking, experiments are being made to devise cheap reflectors for cooking. It is estimated that by the use of solar machines one acre of land in Arizona would provide sufficient power to support fifteen persons at the high level of consumption of the United States. The cost of trapping solar energy direct would however be high on account of the heavy capital expenditure needed.

From this brief review it appears that in the not too distant future energy derived from irreplaceable mineral sources will become scarcer. This exhaustion may ultimately slow down the present tremendous rate of industrial expansion. On the other hand, renewable sources of energy from vegetation, wind- and water-power and direct use of solar energy can, if developed to the full, provide sufficient to maintain in reasonable comfort a world population much larger than the present one.

VI. Mineral Resources

The advance of civilization depended on the discovery and use of metals, first copper then bronze, the main constituents of which are copper and tin. About 1000 B.C. man learned to produce metallic iron from ores, a more difficult process than producing

[1] *Land Hunger in Mexico* (The Charles Pack Forestry Foundation, Washington, U.S.A., 1951).

copper. As iron ore is more abundant than copper or tin the use of iron increased rapidly. Technical developments making possible modern methods of extraction of iron with coal made possible the Industrial Revolution.

The earth contains enormous quantities of iron, which is the basis of industrialization. But the sources of easily available iron in the industrialized countries are becoming exhausted. In the United States, where 14 tons per person are produced to yield the 8 tons of iron and steel used, reserves of ore with 50 per cent. of iron will be exhausted in about 15 years and reserves of above 35 per cent. in about a further 25 years. Before all countries have become industrialized, easily mined ores will be exhausted and lower grade ores will need to be used. But there is so much iron in the earth that with sufficient energy and coal for extraction of ore and smelting there need be no sudden collapse of industry, though costs may rise.

Copper is being exhausted more rapidly than iron. In 1900 the average content of ores being mined in the U.S.A. was 5 per cent. Today it is not more than 1 per cent. The shortage can be relieved by substituting other materials in some of the processes for which copper is used. Aluminium can be used in a number of ways, but it will be difficult to replace copper for transformers and other electrical equipment. This is one of the earth's resources the exhaustion of which may impede industrial expansion, unless substitutes can be devised or very low-grade ores processed at greatly increased cost.

The known world reserves of lead which can be got by existing methods are estimated to be about 100 million tons, which at the present level of consumption will last about 70 years; but the rate of consumption is increasing. The U.S. President's Materials Policy Commission estimates that the consumption rate of 1·2 million tons in 1950 will rise to 2 million in 1975. An even faster rate of increase in consumption may take place in other countries undergoing rapid industrialization. As the supply decreases more care will be taken to recover scrap lead, and less of the mineral will be used in processes such as lead paint (from which none is recoverable).

The situation with regard to zinc and tin is somewhat similar to that of lead. World reserves of manganese, large quantities of which are used in the steel industry, are sufficient to last for many decades; but ultimately low-grade ores will need to be processed, with higher costs. About half the world's reserves are in the U.S.S.R., which has stopped exporting. Magnesium is found in several different kinds of ores; but though these may be exhausted there is an abundant supply of sea-water at a concentration of 0·13 per cent. from which it can be extracted by a series of simple processes. The present cheap sulphur production will end in about another 25 years, but supplies can be got, at higher cost, from large deposits of calcium sulphate which are widely distributed. Deposits of nickel, chromium, cobalt, molybdenum and tungsten (used for steel alloys and other purposes) are widely distributed; and total world supplies of relatively rich ores are sufficient for the immediate future, though in a few decades resort will of necessity be made to low-grade ores.

New industrial processes will make new demands on some minerals and find substitutes for others becoming too expensive. Thus, for example, fluorspar is now being used in increasing amounts for new types of plastics and other purposes; and if a cheap process can be devised for extracting titanium, which exists in ample amounts and has excellent properties including lightness and strength, large quantities will be used.

Though the rich sources of important minerals are being exhausted there are further large supplies in low-grade ores. It is unlikely, therefore, that there will be a sudden stop of any branch of industry owing to lack of raw material; but the cost of extraction and processing will rise as the percentage of recovery falls, in which case the limiting factor may be not the amount of any material in the world but the amount of energy needed to get it.

VII. Distribution of Resources

The industrialized Western nations have drawn both energy and material resources from whatever part of the earth they were to be found in. This they were able to do by using their military superiority in occupying the areas they wanted, and by their technology in developing natural resources. But the military and economic domination of the earth by the white man seems on the decline. Resentment at the power of the white man, which was smouldering before the First World War, has broken out into open revolt, with intense nationalism and anti-imperialism. We are witnessing the decline and fall of the European Empires which held their foreign possessions by military power, and it is doubtful how long the economic power of foreign investments will combine to control resources in former colonies which are now acquiring the technical knowledge to enable them to work their own resources. There are many potential Moussadiqs among the thousands of Asians and Africans who have received a university education. The political independence of the colonies is liable to be followed by a move to nationalize their resources, part of which they will want for their own industrialization; for the remainder they are likely to demand a price which will give the native producer the same standard of living as the worker who uses the raw material in the Western countries. This would profoundly affect the industrial development of countries depending on foreign imports of raw materials. The United States, which was once a raw-material surplus country, is now a raw-material deficit country. Of more than a hundred mineral materials used, it is dependent entirely on imports for about a third of them and partly on imports for another third.[1] Control of the sources of mineral materials throughout the world is as important for the United States, in view of its anticipated development, as the trend of ideology that colonies and other States will adopt when they gain political and economic freedom. In international affairs, politics and control of rich sources of raw material cannot be entirely dissociated from each other.

VIII. Conclusion

The rapidly rising tide of world population with its increasing demand per head for energy and materials seems to threaten us with the exhaustion of the earth's resources upon which our Machine Age depends to support its way of life. But there is no reason to fear that our civilization will suddenly collapse as some source of energy or material is exhausted. The problem has been recognized and is being studied by individuals and by committees of experts appointed by governments, such as the Paley Committee appointed by President Truman, and by the investigation by Palmer Putnam under the auspices of the U.S. Atomic Commission, and by an international commission appointed by the United Nations. Mankind has taken thought for the future and, realizing the position, can direct the development of civilization so that there is no sudden break in its progress, provided there are leaders with vision and high moral purpose as well as intelligence able to control the powers of modern technology and direct them to constructive ends for the benefit of the whole human family.

The danger is not so much that the Machine Age will collapse through exhaustion of resources as that it will through lack of intelligent leadership destroy itself in war by the enormous powers it has developed from its resources. If war can be avoided there will be time for new sources to be discovered and for science to find substitutes for those being used up.

Even if some irreplaceable resources of energy and material were exhausted it would still be possible for a world population of two or three times the present size to have sufficient food and other physical necessities of life and sufficient energy and material from renewable sources to support a higher level of physical and spiritual well-being and of culture than any previous civilization has attained; though we might need to get along without jet planes and hydrogen bombs and with fewer blast-furnaces and huge factories producing things not essential for a life of physical comfort and high spiritual and intellectual attainment. The kind of world our children will

[1] *Report of U.S. President's Material Commission* (Political and Economic Planning Summary, London, 1952).

inherit depends less on its material resources (which can be made ample for their needs) than on whether, by the spread of education with freedom of speech and expression, there can develop a well-informed, world-wide public opinion which will force governments of all countries to co-operate in developing the resources of the earth for the common benefit of all mankind.

BOOKS SUGGESTED FOR FURTHER READING

Palmer Putnam, *Energy in the Future* (Van Nostrand, 1953).

Harrison Brown, *The Challenge of Man's Future* (Secker and Warburg, 1954).

Mezerik, *The Pursuit of Plenty* (Harper, 1950).

Rosin and Eastman, *The Road to Abundance* (McGraw Hill, 1953).

Lord Boyd-Orr, *The White Man's Dilemma* (Allen and Unwin, 1953).

The Work of F.A.O. 1950/51 (F.A.O. Office, Rome); *The State of Food and Agriculture 1955* (F.A.O. Office, Rome).

SOCIAL AIMS OF THE CONTEMPORARY STATE

by François Lafitte

I. What is the Welfare State?

(a) State Management of the Economy

THE "WELFARE STATE" is an imprecise term, of uncertain origin, which came into use in Britain round about 1948. Its use marked a recognition that there had occurred after the war a decisive change in public social policy. The nation had adopted wider aims.

The change can be summed up by saying that the State has now permanently assumed a strategically decisive position in the nation's economic life, such as it never before held save during the two world wars; that its dominance of economic affairs is due mainly to social rather than economic or military reasons; and that this has come about because social policy has, by general agreement, adopted "universalist" aims.

State outlay[1] claimed successively higher shares of the national output during the Boer war and the first and second world wars. Though the State's demands diminished when armed conflict ceased, public outlay settled down after each war in turn at a permanently higher level than hitherto. Between the world wars taxes in Britain seldom exceeded a fifth of the nation's economic output.[2] In 1950 (before the Korean war) and again in 1952 (when rearmament was under way) taxes were equivalent to a third of national output.

About a third of the money raised by taxes is simply taken from one set of citizens in order to be passed on to another, in the form of pensions, interest on loans, subsidies and other "transfer expenditure". The rest is spent in ways which involve a direct use by the State of a portion of the nation's "real" economic resources. Some is devoted to repairing, renewing and extending publicly owned buildings and other capital equipment ("gross investment"),

---

[1] For convenience "State" is used to indicate collectively both the central Government, the (wholly Government-managed) compulsory insurance scheme, and all local authorities spending publicly levied funds. "Taxes" likewise comprise central government taxes, compulsory insurance contributions, and local rates.

[2] Measured at market prices (see concluding note).

but the bulk goes on public purchase of goods and services (public "current consumption"). Of all goods and services currently consumed by the nation,[1] the State's share was only a sixth in 1938, even though that was a year of incipient rearmament. In 1950 the State took a fifth; in 1952 and 1953 very nearly a quarter.[2]

In investment on fixed capital goods the public sector in 1952 actually exceeded the private sector. The latter accounted for 45 per cent. of investment, while the State was responsible for 35 per cent. and the public corporations managing nationalized industries for the remaining 20 per cent. Social capital, chiefly housing, took well over a quarter of all investment; and well over three-quarters of all new social capital was publicly provided. Defence claimed under a twentieth of all investment. In the rest of the field (industry, agriculture, transport and trade) the public sector, including public corporations, accounted for two-fifths.[3] The State also influences the economy far more than in the past by regulation—of foreign trade and exchanges, private investment, building, rents, supply of various materials, and much else—and by the types of taxes imposed on business and consumers.

The last war accomplished the "Keynesian revolution" in economic thought and perfected methods of managing the entire economy for accepted public purposes. The new economic engineering had originally been advocated not with war but with the great depression of the 1930's in mind. It was concerned with positive action by the State—by budgetary, credit, and other controls—for maintaining the balance and full working of the whole economy, as distinct from merely balancing the State's own income and outlay. The war acted also as a forcing house of thought about social policy,[4] precipitating what may be loosely called the "Beveridge revolution". When conflict ceased, the same methods of economic engineering were applied to establishing a Welfare State, and then, after 1950, to attempting to maintain a rearmed Welfare State.

The purposes of economic management include promotion of industrial and agricultural development, regulating the balance of overseas payments, and, latterly, securing rearmament. But above all public opinion looks to the State to secure "full employment". In the economic field this is what is distinctive of the Welfare State—that the Government is pledged, as past governments never were, to

---

[1] Measured at "factor cost" (see concluding note).

[2] Equal to 20 per cent. of the nation's *total* real resources, whether used for consumption or capital investment, against 15 per cent. in 1938 (see Table III).

[3] In 1953 and 1954 the social element in investment was appreciably enlarged by the expansion of house building; and a larger, but far from predominant, share of house building was left to private investors.

[4] See the volumes of the official war history on *Problems of Social Policy* by R. M. Ti†muss (H.M. Stationery Office and Longmans, 1950) and *Studies in the Social Services* by S. M. Ferguson and H. Fitzgerald (H.M. Stationery Office and Longmans, 1954).

preventing a recurrence of the plague of unemployment.[1] The purpose behind this pledge is social more than economic. That is to say, if the quickest way to enlarge the community's total wealth and general standard of living would involve economic risks and changes enlarging inequality of incomes or diminishing the economic, occupational or geographical security of individuals, then the State is tacitly expected to prefer fairness, uniformity and stability, even at the price of a slower rate of economic advance. Full employment is wanted not chiefly as a means of adding to wealth but in order to avoid the social tragedy of worklessness. "The greatest evil of unemployment is not the loss of additional material wealth . . . There are two greater evils: first, that unemployment makes men seem useless, not wanted, without a country; second, that unemployment makes men live in fear and that from fear springs hate".[2]

Even nationalization of fuel, power and transport seems to have been undertaken more for social than for strictly economic reasons. Social motives in taxation are stronger than ever before, alike in the way taxes are spread, in the purpose of some taxes (such as the steep post-war death duties), and in the use of taxes in conjunction with consumer subsidies and rent control for modifying the pattern of consumption in socially rather than economically desirable ways. Taxation has become a main instrument for redistributing the unequal incomes derived from economic activity.

(b) Social Universalism

In State expenditure the key position of outlay for social purposes is obvious from Table I. Its importance is, indeed, exaggerated by observers who contrast social outlay merely with spending on defence. It is fairer to add to the latter the chief public bills directly attributable to past wars—war-damage payments, interest on war borrowings, and war pensions. Table I compares social outlay (excluding war pensions) with war outlay in this wider sense.

Even with this adjustment the new importance of social spending is unmistakable. In 1950, when the threat of war still seemed to be receding, public current outlay on non-war social services ("social outlay" in the table) was the biggest single item, representing 12 per cent. of the gross national product (at market prices), against 10·9 per cent. for war outlay. In 1938, on the other hand, despite a proportionately much heavier charge for unemployment, social

[1] The Conservative Chancellor of the Exchequer told Parliament in his 1954 Budget speech that "the aim of the Budget must always be to maintain the balance of the economy as a whole"; and that his party, no less than the Socialists, accepted the responsibilities defined in the all-party declaration of 1944 "to keep up employment and, with due regard to the balance of payments, to use our resources to the full".

[2] Sir William Beveridge, *Full Employment in a Free Society* (Allen and Unwin, 1944).

outlay claimed only 8·6 per cent. of national output, against 10 per cent. for war expenditure. If food subsidies are included—and the case for so doing was very strong before 1953—then the preponderance of the social budget in 1950 was even greater (14·5 per cent. of national output). By 1952, however, rearmament had enlarged the war budget while economies (especially on food subsidies) had reduced the social budget. The two budgets were virtually of equal size, each requiring about 13½ per cent. of the national output and together absorbing 83½ per cent. of the State's entire outlay on current account. When—if ever—Britain can again count on peace in the world, it is clear that social spending will rapidly become by far the main element in public outlay.

The new dimensions of the social budget are due to the fact that public social services are now in aim, though by no means always in practice, comprehensive and universalist. They are intimately concerned with the personal welfare of every citizen, not merely as in the past with the needs of special groups of citizens distinguished by criteria of status, such as destitution, income, occupation, or economic class. This universalism is the essence of the Welfare State. It marks a revolution, still in its very early stages, in the assumptions underlying social policy.

The Welfare State assumes that all citizens, not merely the abnormal, the poor, or the lower classes, have certain social needs which cannot be satisfactorily met from their personal earnings, from private or commercial services, from charity or voluntary clubbing together. It assumes that these needs—for education, medical care, income during illness and retirement, and much else— are best provided for by publicly organized services available to all by virtue simply of their citizenship; just as roads, fire brigades and other communal facilities are used by all citizens. It assumes that for nearly all citizens the public social services, rather than the market or voluntary services, will be the normal way of securing the requisite satisfactions.

It assumes that the State must see to it that all important social needs "from the cradle to the grave" are adequately provided for, either by public services or by public support and supplementation of voluntary facilities. In principle the Welfare State, far from viewing its social services as a regrettable burden, wants its citizens to use them for their own betterment or convenience, and strives to improve the services offered. It seeks to remove the causes of avoidable distress, above all by preventing unemployment; but it does not expect thereby to make social services less necessary but rather, by needing to spend less on relieving avoidable poverty or illness, to have more resources for constructive services such as education.

The Welfare State is an international, not a specifically British or a specifically Socialist phenomenon. The United Nations Charter pledges all member States to promote "higher standards of living, full employment, and conditions of economic and social progress". The Universal Declaration of Human Rights proclaims that "everyone has the right to a standard of living adequate for the health and well-being of himself and of his family, including food, clothing, housing, and medical care"; and that "everyone has the right to education. Education shall be free, at least in the elementary and fundamental stages. Elementary education shall be compulsory. Technical and professional education shall be made generally available and higher education shall be equally accessible to all on the basis of merit."

These are not empty words, at least in western and northern Europe, Britain and the English-speaking Dominions, or in the U.S.A. In all these countries the Welfare State is gradually emerging, though in very varying forms. In few is it yet far advanced. Yet even in the richest of them, the U.S.A., which might be thought to have least need for public social services and which tends to equate the Welfare State with "Socialism", the development of publicly financed services on a basis of citizenship has gone much farther than is commonly supposed, especially in education and

TABLE I

STATE CURRENT SPENDING (U.K.)

	1938 £m.	1950 £m.	1952 £m.
Consumption Outlay			
War	337	812	1,457
Social	233	832	951
Other	202	423	478
	772	2,067	2,886
Subsidies			
Social	24	145	176
Food	—	324	274
Other	14	77	57
	38	546	507
Payments			
War: (1) Debts and damage	194	533	572
(2) Pensions	39	80	85
Social	233	596	731
Other debts and payments	106	263	312
	572	1,472	1,700
Totals			
War outlay	570	1,425	2,114
Social outlay	490	1,573	1,858
Food subsidies	—	324	274
Other outlay	322	763	847
	1,382	4,085	5,093
Gross National Output			
(at market prices)	5,717	13,131	15,605

social security. Well developed social services, public or voluntary, are seldom found except where there is a high degree of economic prosperity, for nations usually have the social services they can afford rather than those they need. Hence it is almost exclusively among the score of nations at the top of the economic scale that the beginnings of the Welfare State are to be observed. In most of these advanced countries social spending has reached levels comparable with that of Britain. Among them the tendency to universalism in social policy seems to have gone farthest in Britain, Scandinavia, New Zealand and Australia.[1]

TABLE II

THE PUBLIC SOCIAL BUDGET
(included in Table I)

	1938 £m.	1950 £m.	1952 £m.
Consumption Outlay			
Health care	67	465	495
Education and child care . . .	113	266	340
Welfare	39	53	62
Employment	1	16	16
Environmental, etc.	13	32	38
	233	832	951
Subsidies			
Housing	23	73	88
Nutrition	1	61	75
Pensioners' tobacco	—	11	13
	24	145	176
(Food)	—	(324)	(274)
Payments			
Insurance benefits	154	384	470
Family allowances	—	64	80
Assistance	74	92	123
Education and training, etc. . .	5	56	58
	233	596	731
(War pensions)	(39)	(80)	(85)
Totals			
Social outlay proper	490	1,573	1,858
Food subsidies	—	324	274
War pensions	39	80	85
Social outlay in broadest sense . .	529	1,977	2,217

[1] The variety of forms of social provision is striking. France spends proportionately less than Britain on health services and French social-security schemes are not yet universalist, save for family allowances. Yet when social-security payments are related to the sum total of personal incomes in either country, payments in France represent a redistribution of income proportionately double that effected in Britain. This is mainly due to the very high level of French family allowances. A nearly similar effect is achieved rather differently in New Zealand. Social payments there are mostly conditional on a means test, but the standard of income guaranteed to those with insufficient means is extremely generous.

TABLE III

SHARE OF REAL NATIONAL PRODUCT[1] APPROPRIATED
FOR STATE CONSUMPTION

Social Outlay	1938 %	1950 %	1952 %
Health care	1·3	3·8	3·5
Education and child care . . .	2·2	2·3	2·4
Other services	1·0	1·0	0·8
	4·5	7·1	6·7
Defence Outlay	6·4	6·9	10·3
Other Outlay	3·9	3·5	3·4
Total	14·8	17·5	20·4

II. The British Welfare State

The British Welfare State is instructive for several reasons apart from the fact that it is one of the most advanced expressions yet attempted of a universalist social policy in a free society. In Britain some of the aims of the universalist approach have been most logically argued and pursued, and many of the problems it raises can be seen in extreme forms. And the British attempt has been launched in—and has contributed greatly to—conditions imposing probably the heaviest burden of taxation borne by any advanced country in the world.

The British Welfare State pursues its aims partly by regulation but mainly by public spending. Three types of public spending can be conveniently distinguished and are shown in Tables I and II for both social and other public outlay. The first type of spending is when the State itself appropriates economic resources for current "consumption", using staffs, goods and materials—for instance, in schools, medical care, welfare work, the army, or street cleaning—which would otherwise serve possibly quite different uses in the private sector of the economy. The second and third types of public spending are schemes for transferring income or purchasing power from one set of private consumers to another.

One group of redistributive schemes operates by direct payments. On the social side the bulk of these payments go to individuals, as pensions, family allowances, scholarships, or assistance; but some payments go to voluntary institutions independent of the State, such as universities, as grants towards the cost of socially valued work. The other group of redistributive schemes, for subsidized private consumption, is intermediate in effect between social payments and public-consumption outlay. Instead of adding to the

[1] Gross output at factor cost.

freely spendable income of the benefited citizen, it reduces the price of particular goods or services (milk, accommodation, legal aid) that he buys for himself in the market. This is done to stimulate his consumption along certain lines.

The bulk of State spending, whether on social or non-social objects, is on current account in one or other of these three categories, and is almost wholly financed from taxation. The social services also need buildings and other capital equipment, while the State itself provides a large proportion of new dwellings. Much of this social investment is financed from loans rather than taxes. Some of it (e.g. schools and hospitals) sets up no returning flow of income to the State, while the rents received for publicly owned dwellings are deliberately fixed at an unremunerative level. The annual capital charges for social-service equipment therefore become part of the current cost of social services, and public losses on housing become public subsidies to tenants' rents.

(a) Physical Planning and Housing

The British Welfare State intends much more than it has yet achieved. Fulfilment of its present aims will require a generation of economic advance in peaceful conditions. Public regulation of the nation's physical environment has been extended since 1948 far beyond what is needed for general hygiene, prevention of epidemics or accidents, control of fire risks, or good neighbourliness in the use of land and buildings. The aim now is gradually to secure a refashioning and orderly territorial regrouping of industry and of the whole physical equipment of town life. In principle no one may alter the (non-agricultural) use of land or buildings in any significant way, or undertake any important construction, without the State's permission; and the State may require alteration of existing uses in the public interest. Comprehensive town and country planning deliberately overrides the market in land and buildings in order to guide, if necessary to promote, physical development along socially approved lines.

Permission to develop or re-develop is granted or withheld in accordance with the local "development plan" in which each city and county tries to present a broad picture of the location and character of desired development and land-use over the next twenty years. All new building is guided by such plans, which specify zones for different purposes (agriculture, open space, housing, commerce, industry, etc.), prescribe densities and impose controls of other sorts. At regional and national levels official policy attempts to co-ordinate local plans; to decide which towns to expand or restrict; and to control the location of new industrial undertakings, the tendency being to "bring work to the workers" (even to the point of subsidizing industries willing to settle in "development areas"), rather than to oblige workers to migrate from decaying to expanding urban areas.

British community and territorial planning excites the admiration of most other countries. The conceptions inspiring it are magnificent and the results in the long run may well be fine. But, on this comprehensive scale, it involves vesting great discretionary powers of control in the hands of authorities with little sociological and economic experience to guide them in the new art of consciously re-designing the physical apparatus of urban life. Bureaucratic pettiness in controlling private development, coupled with unrealistic grandeur in public projects, may well inflict losses on the community (through frustration of private enterprise and wasteful public use of resources) as great as the eventual indirect savings that planning promises to derive from well designed and uncongested cities. The chief purposes of planning are social: progressive removal of the blemishes left by the formerly uncontrolled growth of towns and intensified by the expansion of motor transport—squalor, overcrowding, indiscriminate mixing of housing and industry, traffic congestion, disappearance of urban open spaces, decay of inner city areas, unchecked suburban sprawl, submergence of fertile land, spoiling of beauty spots.

One major object is to improve, and where necessary enlarge, the nation's stock of dwellings. Perhaps a quarter of these are industrial workers' dwellings built before 1880, crowded in mean streets, falling in their old age far below contemporary standards of tolerance. Local authorities now have a duty to watch over and interfere with most aspects of the housing of their communities. They must see to it that the quantity and quality of accommodation are sufficient for all needs, with the general aim of securing "a separate dwelling for each family". They must compel private owners to keep dwellings in a fit state and may assist them financially with repairs or improvements. They can themselves take over and modernize useful old property. They must pull down slums—or make them tolerable pending demolition—and provide new dwellings for their inhabitants. They build houses and flats of their own for the use of most sections of the community; they have special responsibility for securing accommodation for the overcrowded, the old, the tuberculous, the homeless and other special groups; and they are expected to allot their dwellings to those with the greatest "housing need".

Policy under Labour rule from 1945 to 1951 stressed new house building by local authorities to the detriment both of private building and of the proper maintenance of existing dwellings, which had been perforce neglected during the war. The standards prescribed for new municipal dwellings were unprecedentedly high —including in the early years two water-closets in each house with three bedrooms or more; resources were rather lavishly used, while building productivity was poor; so that house building was slow and costly. Under Conservative rule after 1951 the volume of house building was expanded by over 50 per cent., the design of municipal dwellings was simplified without sacrificing essential standards of space and amenity, private building was given more scope, productivity and the pace of building improved. In 1954 local authorities were launched into the beginnings of a campaign to repair and improve neglected dwellings and to patch up or replace slum property.

But the State retained its predominance in new building. Little more than two-fifths of the new dwellings started in the first half of 1955 had been commissioned by private interests. In the nine years following the end of the war 1,500,000 out of 1,800,000 new dwellings (including temporary prefabricated bungalows provided under a State emergency scheme just after the war) were publicly provided, compared with about 1,500,000 out of 4,000,000 new dwellings built between 1919 and 1939. By 1954 at least one family in five was a tenant of the State, against one in eight in 1939 and under one in a hundred in 1914.

(b) Rent Control and Subsidies

This gradual replacement of the private by the public landlord is chiefly due to the inability of the private investor to provide dwellings that are simultaneously of the quality insisted on by public policy and also within the rent-paying propensity of the poorer half of the population. That inability is in part due to insufficient effective demand (even in a fully employed community) on the part of the poorer consumers in a period of high building costs. It is even more due to a control of private rents so stringent and so prolonged as to deprive the private landlord of any reasonable reward for his trouble and even, very frequently, of the means of keeping his property in good repair. From 1939 until 1954 it was illegal to raise the rent of almost every privately owned dwelling, and it was (and remains) extremely difficult to remove any tenant who insisted on staying. The wholly artificial structure of private rents fostered a wasteful use of accommodation, so artificially exaggerating the housing shortage; contributed powerfully to the neglect and premature decay of useful dwellings; and, by obliging owners in effect to subsidize tenants, created a generally false standard of expectations in housing. Rent (including local rates) fell from 11 per cent. of the average family's outlay in 1938 to 7 per cent. in 1952. The mass of people became accustomed, in a world of transformed costs and incomes, to expecting good accommodation at something like pre-war prices. Even the first tentative step taken in 1954 towards allowing higher rents was intended only to give owners an addition barely sufficient to pay for repairs at post-war prices, and was conditional on repairs actually being done.

Municipal house rents have to be subsidized in order to permit or induce the poorer badly housed families to become public tenants. Very heavy subsidies now have to be paid, since tenants inevitably contrast the rents of municipal dwellings built at heavy post-war costs with the still mainly pre-war rents of privately owned dwellings. The amount of public rent subsidies is determined in a somewhat curious fashion and their distribution among subsidized families is even more curious. In 1938 the average rent of the typical municipal house happened to be one-tenth of the average man's earnings in industry. After the war Labour and Conservative governments in turn decided that the total public outlay on subsidies should suffice to permit the rents of post-war municipal houses also to *average* one-tenth of earnings—although the typical dwelling now to be subsidized was in every way markedly superior to, and larger than, the typical pre-war dwelling, and was no longer reserved for a "working-class" tenant with a possibly high risk of unemployment.

The national rate of subsidy is determined from year to year by calculating the gap between the total cost of new housing and the income to be expected if rents are fixed on this 10 per cent. basis. For each new dwelling the annual subsidy, shared between government and municipality, is paid to the local authority's housing account, to which the local authority may, if it chooses, pay an additional subsidy, at its own expense. The account also receives subsidies, differently calculated, for dwellings built before the war. These funds form a pool which each municipality may distribute as it thinks fit among its own tenants. Many authorities spread the subsidy fairly uniformly over all their dwellings, so that rents vary with size and quality of accommodation provided rather than with cost of construction of particular dwellings. Until 1954 relatively few local authorities were willing to adjust rents—and therefore the degree of subsidy—according to the financial means and needs of tenants. By then, however, pressure of costs had begun to enforce a spread of "differential rent" schemes.

Means and needs among public tenants vary far more widely than before the war, since tenants are taken from much wider sections of the community and are chosen according to urgency of "housing need", a test from which rent-paying capacity is deliberately excluded. Thus there is no clear relation between a tenant's capacity to afford rent and the size of the rent subsidy he receives. The family with several earners and a joint income sufficient to afford a car, a television and other amenities may enjoy as large a subsidy as the poor family with several children and an irregularly employed breadwinner.[1] Some poor families have to refuse municipal dwellings altogether because the local authority does not concentrate its subsidies on those with the lowest rent-paying capacity. There is probably no other country where the two distinct problems of granting a public tenancy and granting a public rent subsidy are so thoroughly confused, with the consequence that public outlay on rent subsidies is determined not by the amount of poverty among tenants but by the rate of building of municipal dwellings.

(c) Nutrition Subsidies

Housing subsidies and private rent control (transformed from a reasonable protection of tenants, as it was from 1918 to 1939, into a compulsory subsidy at landlords' expense) are examples of the social influencing of consumption. The nutrition subsidies are a further example. To expectant mothers, babies, and children below school age the State offers free (that is, 100 per cent. subsidized) cod-liver oil or vitamin A and D tablets, and, at heavily subsidized prices, concentrated orange juice and a daily supply of milk. Orange juice and milk are free to those who cannot afford to pay; and a free daily drink of milk is also offered to every child at school (including private schools).

The majority do not in fact bother to obtain their welfare foods,[2] but the milk scheme is highly successful. Since the small charge for milk at school was dropped in 1946, nearly nine in every ten children drink their daily third of a pint. The subsidizing of milk (for the general public as well as for mothers and children, though in lesser degree) has vastly increased consumption, from 21·1 gallons a year a head of the population in 1938 to 33·3 gallons in 1952. It has possibly effected a permanent change in public taste and has certainly helped produce a remarkable improvement in the health and physique of children. Half the milk consumed by large families (whose nutrition is still a problem) is supplied by the welfare schemes, and it contributes greatly to the still deficient calcium and protein in their diet.

A minor social revolution has increased the proportion of children eating midday meals provided at school from 3 per cent. before the war to 45 per cent. (1953). Apart from its nutritional importance,

[1] In 1953 the borough of Stoke Newington (London) decided to charge unsubsidized rents for dwellings let for the first time and to grant subsidies according to need to tenants unable to pay in full. Of 243 tenants so charged, 47 got no subsidy at all while 14 were granted exceptionally large subsidies. The council's housing manager reported that some applicants refused unsubsidized tenancies because, if they had to pay "all that rent", they said they might just as well buy houses of their own (*Municipal Journal*, September 25, 1953).

[2] Professor A. Moncrieff believes that the disappearance of rickets in Britain has in fact been effected mainly by compulsory addition of vitamins to all margarine and dried milk (*Child Health and the State*, Oxford, 1953).

especially for the poorer families, the school dinner is socially convenient, both for the growing proportion of pupils who make long journeys to school and for mothers needing a midday break or going out to work; and its educational value is appreciable. A school dinner costs (1953) about 1s. 6d., of which roughly half represents the cost of premises, equipment, staff and fuel. The charge to parents is usually 9d., the approximate cost of the food alone (probably more than a fair number would spend on feeding a child, less well, at home); but nearly 10 per cent. of the children, coming from poor homes, get their meals free.

The original plan was to extend this service until the great majority could eat at school—and then make the meals free for all. With this promise family allowances well below the rates recommended by the Beveridge report were justified. By 1949 the Labour Government felt obliged to stop the further provision of canteens and kitchens at existing schools, as distinct from new schools, which are invariably equipped for meals. Five years later it was clear that school building would be heavily strained simply to keep pace with the greatly expanded number of children passing through the schools in the 1950's. There could be no hope of completing the school meals service until some time after 1960, when pressure would at last slacken. Universal provision of free dinners at school is an aim the Welfare State has been forced to abandon, or at least postpone for perhaps two decades.

(d) Tobacco and Food Subsidies

A more peculiar social subsidy resulted from the decision taken in 1947 to remit part of the tax on tobacco purchased by pensioners. Any pensioner can apply through the Assistance Board (though there is no means test) for a book of "tobacco tokens" worth 2s. 4d. a week. Well over 2,000,000 pensioners take advantage of the subsidy—including some who resell their cheap tobacco—and it costs the State as much as it spends on maternity and infant welfare.

This subsidy is not a deliberate expression of social policy but an accidental feature—or blemish—of the Welfare State, a consequence of pensioners' protests against the raising of the tobacco tax to unprecedented heights. Equally accidental were the biggest of all the subsidies, those applied to a wide range of foodstuffs (including milk) sold to the public at large at less than market prices. These *general* food subsidies had virtually nothing to do with nutrition policy. They originated in war-time measures for preventing inflationary increases in wages, at a time when the supply of goods that wages could buy was dwindling. Subsidies were then applied to food, clothing, footwear and other goods in order to keep the cost-of-living index (rather than the cost of living itself) steady, in return for trade-union agreement to resist pressure for higher wages.[1] After the war the Labour Government concentrated these subsidies on food and continued to use them for the same anti-inflationary purpose— in return not for a promise but for an increasingly vain hope that the unions could be persuaded not to force earnings up faster than production.

In these circumstances the cost of subsidies rapidly soared to unprecedented heights, requiring in 1948 as much as was spent on all social-insurance benefits and family allowances. Results did not justify the vast expense. Inflationary raising of incomes was not prevented. Artificially cheapened food prices (like artificially cheapened rents) strengthened the "illusion of unlimited resources" —the idea that men could enjoy a good standard of living in the immediate aftermath of Britain's most destructive war without any undue effort to earn it.

Subsidies are best used differentially to help *selected* "economically weak" groups (such as old folk or children) to increase their deficient consumption of socially important products. The food subsidies, however, were applied indiscriminately to the whole body of consumers. Huge sums were spent, moreover, on artificially cheapening, not expensive "protective" foods, but carbohydrate foods like cereals, potatoes and sugar, consumption of which needed no stimulating. The poorest sections of the community were of course incidentally benefited. In 1950 83, instead of actually 17, citizens out of every 1,000 in York would have fallen below Mr. Rowntree's poverty line had all food subsidies been abolished.[2] But the remaining 917 in every 1,000 were also having their food subsidized even though, unsubsidized, they would have remained above the line. A fraction of the money spent on the 917 would have sufficed, if subsidies were withdrawn, to maintain or improve standards for the 83.

After 1948 it became increasingly clear that the general subsidies ought to be cut and the loss made good to groups needing social protection by equivalent increases in pensions, family allowances and other services specifically designed to maintain their consuming power. The Labour Government itself began the process of cutting subsidies, if only because imports of subsidized foods such as meat could not be increased sufficiently to make rationing unnecessary without further increasing the bill for subsidies. But there was powerful resistance from those Socialists who saw in the subsidies a

---

[1] Maintaining consumption standards among the weaker groups of the community—soldiers' families, pensioners, the sick, very large families—became no more than "one minor aim of policy", say Professor Hancock and Miss Gowing in *British War Economy* (H.M. Stationery Office, 1949), a volume of the official war history. Another volume, R. J. Hammond's *Food: 1. The Growth of Policy* (H.M. Stationery Office and Longmans, 1951), gives a detailed account of the development of cost-of-living subsidies.

[2] B. S. Rowntree and G. R. Lavers: *Poverty and the Welfare State* (Longmans, 1951).

new and indispensable instrument (which they had not thought of before the war) for redistributing income. In 1952 the Conservative Government took the first decisive steps both in cutting subsidies and taxes and in compensatory increases of social payments to special groups. Up to 1952 the mainly social character of the subsidies is apparent, for their main effect was to enable consumers to buy food at less than market prices. By 1954 the still large remaining subsidies were assuming a different character, becoming increasingly a device to enable farmers to earn more than market prices for their produce. Further reductions of subsidies now depend chiefly on future agricultural and economic policy rather than on social policy.

(e) Social Security

Subsidies of all kinds in 1952 still accounted for a fifth of the social budget, against only a twentieth in 1938. In the schemes for redistributing income by direct social payments (taking over a third of the social budget) the changes have been less marked and less controversial. Most social payments are made by the social-security services—national assistance for those whose income fails or falls short of subsistence needs; national insurance giving payments, without a means test, in contingencies when normal income usually ceases; and family allowances, whereby the community shares with parents the cost of rearing children.

Nationalized assistance has broken completely with the age-old traditions of local Poor Law assistance. The citizen in need, if precluded from work or unable to find it, now has a right to financial help provided his resources (if any) fall short of his minimum needs. The standard of subsistence need guaranteed—representing the smallest income society thinks people can be expected to live on—has been much more liberal since 1948 than ever in the past. The former legal duty of a wide range of relatives to contribute to the support of a person without means has been abolished. The husband has a duty to support his wife and *his* children (under sixteen), and the wife a duty to support her husband and *her* children. But that is all. And the means test applied is restricted to the resources of husband and wife and immediate dependants, and must disregard in part certain forms of savings or income (e.g. private superannuation or sick pay) they may be receiving.

It was intended (as proposed by the famous Beveridge report) to reduce recourse to assistance to a minimum by providing a system of payments, sufficient to live on, which the citizen could count on as a right, without having to prove financial need, during illness, unemployment, widowhood, retirement and other contingencies. To this end compulsory insurance (financed partly by special contributions and partly by general taxation) was extended to cover all citizens;[1] and the range of payments was extended to provide (1) retirement pensions (subject to ten years' insurance for those not previously covered), widows' and orphans' benefits, and maternity and death payments for all; (2) sickness payments for all gainfully occupied, and (3) unemployment and employment injury benefits for all working for employers. In addition, family allowances (financed from general taxation) were introduced. This step was taken because the impossibility of varying a man's earnings with the size of his family, coupled with society's refusal to allow children to work at least until the age of fifteen, was a major cause of poverty among the larger families. It was known too that before the war many large families among the less well paid workers could derive a bigger income from unemployment pay (which had to recognize the needs of dependants) than from wages (which did not). No allowance is paid for the first child in a family, because wages are almost invariably adequate for the one-child family.

Some advanced countries, such as Australia, New Zealand, Norway and Denmark, rely entirely or mainly on assistance (conditional on proof of financial need) to meet many of the needs Britain attempts to cover by insurance. Yet the British aim of "insurance for all normal needs", with assistance in reserve for abnormal cases, seemed modest enough. For British social insurance seeks to provide, not payments proportional to normal earnings (as in many other countries), but flat-rate benefits simply sufficient, on average, for minimum subsistence needs. Given these aims, it is nevertheless remarkable that the social-security budget should be so small. So far it has effected a smaller annual transfer of income within the community than is represented by interest payments on public debts or, up to 1950, by State subsidies of all kinds. In 1938 there were 2,935,000 old or widowed insurance pensioners in Britain, but in 1952 no less than 4,640,000. In 1938 there were no family allowances, but in 1952 these were paid for 4,840,000 children. In spite of this increased load of old and young, social security payments, which represented 4·5 per cent. of the total of personal incomes in 1938, amounted to no more than 5·3 per cent. in 1952 and 5·6 per cent. in 1953.

The smallness of this change was in part due to the fact that there were respectively only 415,000 and 280,000 unemployed workers in the latter years, against 1,700,000 in 1938. But it is also evidence of the erosion of social-security standards by persistent monetary inflation. Table II depicts the finances of a Welfare State operating in conditions of continually rising prices and money incomes, in which merely to keep pace with costs involves continual upward revision of the figures for social outlay. In some countries this

[1] Though self-employed or non-employed persons with very small incomes may obtain exemption.

revision is effected automatically for social security, because contributions and benefits are fixed proportions of earnings, rising or falling with them. In Britain insurance and family-allowance rates have to be changed by Act of Parliament; and, with so many other demands pressing on heavily taxed resources, governments inevitably tend to leave the rates unaltered until pressure for an increase becomes uncomfortably strong.

The new social-insurance scheme was fully launched in the summer of 1948, when the post-war monetary inflation was well under way. By the summer of 1955 the average man's money earnings in industry had increased by somewhat over 50 per cent., and the rates of insurance and assistance payments had kept pace with this increase. But whereas the rise in prices and incomes had been continuous, the raising of social payments was a discontinuous process. Apart from some partial changes in 1951, insurance benefits were raised only in 1952 and again in 1955. Assistance rates, on the other hand, which can be raised by administrative action and must be kept in line with subsistence costs, were increased in 1950, 1951, 1952 and 1955.

The changes were made in order to maintain the real purchasing power of social payments in a period of rising costs. Though these payments are not related to earnings, the result was in fact to restore them at successive intervals to a fairly constant relationship with the average man's industrial wage. If the standard of national assistance (including an average allowance for rent) is compared with the industrial wage, it is seen that the tacit British view of the income required for life at the minimum ranges from just over half-pay for a couple with two children to somewhat over third-pay for a childless couple (e.g. pensioners).

From the outset, however, and contrary to the Beveridge proposals, insurance and family allowance rates were fixed, and remained below, the level of subsistence so defined.[1] For them the implicit standard is set at about 42 per cent. of the average wage for a couple with two children and at 30 per cent. for a childless couple. But it was only in 1948, 1952 and 1955 (when the rates were raised)

[1] Except for employment injury payments, the flat rates of which were deliberately kept well above other insurance benefits. (1) Injury benefits during incapacity for work are about a quarter above the assistance standard. (2) Permanent pensions, not reduced for earnings, in effect represent an addition to the average wage (1955) of about a tenth at the most usual rate for 30 per cent. "disablement", rising to about a third of the wage for 100 per cent. "disablement" (e.g. total blindness or loss of both feet). (3) For the man both disabled and unable to work (owing to his disablement or some subsequent illness), various supplements to the pension (including sickness benefit) raise the income provided, at the highest rate of disablement, in effect almost to two-thirds (married man) and almost to three-quarters (married man with two children) of the average wage.

War pensions (not here discussed), on which industrial injury payments are modelled, make similar but more generous provision, with additions for military rank. The value of war and employment injury pensions is increased by their exemption from income tax.

that even this low standard was attained. In the intervening years the value of the benefits was depreciated by inflation. In the spring of 1952, for instance, the married man, when sick, received less than third-pay if he had two children and less than quarter-pay if he had no children.

In 1954 insurance benefits fell a quarter short of what was needed for subsistence according to the national assistance standard. It was plainly necessary to raise them substantially, and this involved no financial difficulty except for retirement pensions. Demand for the benefits payable during working life, like the working population itself, was not expected to increase very markedly during the years ahead—unless mass unemployment were to return. To raise their rates to subsistence level would involve only a moderate and quite feasible increase in insurance contributions.

Adherence to the Beveridge plan in respect of working-age benefits would have been much easier had Britain adhered to another, less palatable, feature of that plan—payment of pensions well below subsistence rates (though on a rising scale) during the first twenty years of the Welfare State. This had been proposed in order to give Britain the time thought necessary (by such economists as Keynes) to build up resources sufficiently after the war to be able to afford universal subsistence pensions for a steadily increasing army of old folk. Opinion after the war, however, had insisted on pensions immediately at the same rates as working-age benefits, and this added greatly to the financial difficulties of the system.[1]

Looking a quarter of a century beyond 1954, the number of old people in a nearly static population is expected to increase by about $1\frac{2}{3}$ per cent. annually. On the long view Britain has ample economic capacity to carry such an increase in elderly dependants, which is not likely to affect seriously the existing balance between earners and non-earners of all sorts (children, housewives, unemployed and retired taken all together). But the number of old persons drawing retirement pensions is likely to increase by at least $3\frac{1}{3}$ per cent. annually because of the extension of pension rights to formerly uninsured classes. In the strained circumstances of the early 1950's this more immediate prospect seemed to present a fearsome problem in public finance.

In 1954 all changes in social security were held up while the first five-yearly statutory review of the system, and various special inquiries into pensions, were being held. Since the Beveridge report

[1] Another departure from the Beveridge plan is the low rate of family allowances (8s. in 1955). On the other hand, school meals and welfare milk, averaged over all children, represent an addition in kind to family incomes of about 3s. a child weekly. Nevertheless, the insurance standard of payment for a child is more generous than the family allowance, and the assistance standard is more generous still. Family allowances therefore have to be supplemented (in addition to provision for the excluded first child) when a family is supported by insurance or assistance.

was written, against a background of pre-war conditions, the nature of the pension problem had been appreciably modified by the steady expansion of occupational superannuation schemes, which that report had virtually disregarded. At least one man in every three at work in 1954 would be entitled on retirement to a pension derived from his employment, and the further spread of superannuation cover was continuing. The inquiries recommended measures for accelerating the growth of private pension schemes and proposed, though not unanimously, that minimum retirement ages in both public and private schemes should be raised by stages from 65 to 68 (men) and from 60 to 63 (women). No immediate action was taken on these controversial proposals. Coming just before the election of 1955, they received no adequate discussion. The Government of the day decided to make no changes at all in the structure of social security, but to incur the considerable expense of raising all payments—including pensions—sufficiently to restore the purchasing power and the relationship with wages they were intended to command when the system was inaugurated.

The pattern of social-security provision is thus somewhat different from that suggested by the Beveridge report. People are not expected to live on insurance payments alone, but insurance rates are sufficient if they can be moderately supplemented from other sources. Thanks mainly to the absence of prolonged unemployment, a large majority of beneficiaries can provide this supplementation from savings, superannuation, or (much more frequently than before the war) from wages continued during short spells of sickness. The minority without such resources—the main group comprising up to a quarter of all retirement pensioners—gets supplementation, up to subsistence level, from the Assistance Board. The Board's main work, indeed, has become, not helping the utterly destitute, but supplementing insurance payments for those lacking other means. Although there have been wide departures from the Beveridge plan, payments conditional on a means test account for little more than a sixth of the social-security budget, against a third in 1938; and comparative surveys by the International Labour Office put Britain among half a dozen countries leading the world in social-security provision.

The remaining social payments are mostly educational—public grants to universities and scholarships and other direct financial aid to scholars. Apart from free primary and secondary education, together with free transport for children beyond "walking distance" from school, the Welfare State gives financial aid according to need "for the purpose of enabling pupils to take advantage without hardship to themselves and their parents of any educational facilities available to them". Local education authorities are expected to provide clothing for any child who is "unable by reason of the inadequacy of his clothing to take full advantage of the education provided"; to defray any expenses needed to enable pupils "to take part in any school activities"; to pay part or all of the expenses of children sent with an education authority's agreement to a fee-charging school or college, as boarders or otherwise; and to provide maintenance allowances where needed to help children to remain at secondary schools beyond the compulsory age, and scholarships for those winning places in universities and other higher institutions. The Government, too, provides university scholarships and other higher education awards, also graded according to the family's financial capacity. The transformation of standards all this represents is indicated by several facts. In 1953 5·4 per cent. of local-authority expenditure on schools (excluding meals and medical services) went on aid to pupils, against 2 per cent. in 1938. Ministry of Education expenditure on scholarships was 41 times greater than in 1938, and 70 per cent. of 81,500 full-time university students were financially assisted (including private grants) against perhaps 40 per cent. of 50,000 students in 1938.

(f) Education

Public education belongs to the social services (shown in Tables II and III) which require direct State use of economic resources. The Welfare State aims at developing the educational system into a "classless" service for the whole community, good enough and varied enough for nearly all to prefer it to private facilities. (The bulk of schools associated with churches are within the public system; and, to a limited extent, independent private—so-called "public" schools are used for secondary education of selected public scholars). The change of spirit marked by the all-party Education Act of 1944 is exemplified by its "optimal" definition of the parent's duty—to cause his child "to receive efficient full-time education suitable to his age, ability, and aptitude". Hitherto, since 1876, the parent's duty had been the "minimal" one of securing for his child "efficient elementary instruction in reading, writing, and arithmetic".

Between the wars this narrower view of the content of education fell increasingly short of what the schools were striving to do. Nevertheless it still reflected the main emphasis of the system— nine years of compulsory schooling (between ages five and fourteen) which might be of an "elementary" type throughout; diversion into secondary schools (mainly of a "grammar" type), after six elementary years, only of the brighter or better-off minority of children; and a narrow ladder leading higher to universities and colleges. Compulsory schooling now runs up to fifteen. The aim now is, after six years of primary (infant and junior) instruction, to secure for all children at least four years of senior education in secondary schools so varied as to meet the needs and circumstances (rural, urban, industrial; grammar, modern, technical; aesthetic, practical, intellectual) of every sort of child.

The Act aims eventually at extending compulsory schooling until sixteen; at requiring compulsory attendance (equivalent to one day a week) at "county colleges" for young folk aged 16-18 not remaining in secondary schools; and at further enlarging every sort of facility for part-time "further" education of juveniles and adults. The essential change is the conception of secondary education as the right of every child. This implies a transformation of many existing secondary schools and a massive creation of new facilities. The Act inaugurated a period of exciting experimentation in new teaching methods, great activity in school building, and much raising of standards, chiefly in newly equipped areas. For it requires no less than that the schools of each area shall be "sufficient in number, character, and equipment to afford for all pupils opportunities for education offering such variety of instruction and training as may be desirable in view of their different ages, abilities, and aptitudes, and of the different periods for which they may be expected to remain at school".

The implications of the Act afford work for a generation. Some of its more immediate hopes were frustrated, temporarily at least, by difficulties not foreseen in 1944. In spite of the raised leaving-age, up to 1948 there were fewer children at school than in 1938. Then the swollen generation born just before and just after the end of the war began flowing into the schools. In four years the school population of England and Wales increased by 600,000, and a further increase of 800,000 is expected by 1959. Thereafter the wave will begin flowing out, but even in 1965 there are likely to be 6,200,000 children in public primary and secondary schools—a million more than in 1948. Saturation will be reached in primary schools in 1954-7, in secondary schools in 1959-63.

After 1948 all other educational aims were gradually pushed into the background by the sheer need to provide school places and teachers for the great wave of additional children; and the problem was aggravated by the marked preference given to house building over school building. County colleges and a leaving age of sixteen became aspirations for the future, as did adequate provision of nursery facilities and of special schools for backward or physically handicapped children. Although large numbers of existing schools were admittedly obsolescent,[1] improvements and repairs to them were tightly restricted and their replacement was completely stopped. After 1951 the trend towards smaller classes could not be

[1] Many were "no better than slums that should either be pulled down immediately or undergo drastic repair, even at considerable cost" (Select Committee on Estimates, 1953).

maintained. In 1953 almost half the primary- and secondary-school population was being taught in overcrowded classes.[1] By 1954 schools were in many places bursting at the seams, with classes overflowing into church halls, disused warehouses and other improvised premises. And the danger was looming ahead that secondary-school facilities would be seriously inadequate to meet the coming years of strain. It looked as if the public educational system would be hard put to it, until the ebb of pupils set in after 1960, just to "mark time" and maintain the standards already achieved.

(g) Health and Welfare

In public provision of medical care the universalist approach achieved more immediately spectacular results. The aims of the National Health Service, launched in 1948, were defined in a policy statement issued by the all-party Churchill Coalition Government in 1944:

> "A comprehensive health service . . . to ensure that in future every man and woman and child can rely on getting all the advice and treatment and care which they may need in matters of personal health; that what they get shall be the best medical and other facilities available; that their getting these shall not depend on whether they can pay for them, or on any other factor irrelevant to the real need. . . . Just as people are accustomed to look to public organization for essential facilities like a clean and safe water supply or good highways, accepting these as things which the community combines to provide for the benefit of the individual without distinction of section or group, so they should now be able to look for proper facilities for the care of their personal health to a publicly organized service available to all who want to use it."

The situation the new service was to alter was fairly described as "a complicated patchwork pattern of health resources". For there were very wide discrepancies in quantity and quality of health facilities between the best and the worst placed areas and classes, because so much provision was left to the market or to voluntary effort. Personal doctoring for over half the population was a matter for private arrangement, since the public Health Insurance scheme (unlike schemes elsewhere in Europe) included only manual and lower salaried workers, not their wives and children nor any of the self-employed. Local authorities had developed a network of services for protecting maternal and infant health, for home and hospital midwifery, and for medical supervision of school children

---

[1] Exceeding 40 children (primary) or 30 (secondary).

(including some treatment of "minor ailments"); but these services varied widely in content since many were not obligatory. Home nursing was a private, partly charitable service. Apart from municipal services for optical care of schoolchildren and for (rather rudimentary) dental care of schoolchildren and expectant mothers, health insurance gave some help towards opticians' bills for a quarter of the population and towards dentists' bills for nearly a third.

Through the Poor Law the very poor, on proof of destitution, could get "medical relief" at home or institutional care in local infirmaries. Local authorities also supplied the bulk of hospital care for infectious diseases, tuberculosis, maternity and mental patients. After 1929 the more progressive authorities were developing general hospitals outside the Poor Law code, taking patients from wider sections of the community and charging them according to means. But the bulk of general hospitals were charitable institutions. Their doctors gave unpaid service to "public" patients, from whom the hospitals collected donations according to their means. Health Insurance supplied no help at all towards the cost of hospital care, though unofficial contributory schemes attached to voluntary hospitals, singly or in groups, afforded nearly half the population a certain amount of hospital care, without however giving them any clear right to such care. Voluntary hospital doctors (who included most of the more eminent specialists and consultants) earned their fees mainly from middle- and upper-class patients—excluded from the contributory schemes—whom they treated in private clinics or in voluntary hospital "pay bed" blocks.

The hospitals were "many people's business but nobody's full responsibility". The different hospitals of an area frequently failed to agree on any rational division of the work to be done and had no plans for concerted development of facilities. Voluntary hospitals were in debt and depended increasingly on public grants and patients' payments. Their patients were demanding a right to treatment, their doctors salaries for unpaid services. Municipal hospitals were still mainly dominated by the unhappy Poor Law tradition in which they had originated. By 1940, when under the impact of air raids the Government had requisitioned all hospitals and organized them into a planned system, it was obvious that there could be no return after the war to the old separatist ways.

The British Medical Association had campaigned for a decade before the war for extending health insurance into a service providing all necessary medical care (at home or hospital) alike for workers then insured, for their families, and for all others of "like economic status". The B.M.A. service would have included 90 per cent. of the population, but necessarily involved creating some mechanism whereby the 10 per cent. with higher incomes could be identified and excluded, as compulsory private patients. The new compulsory-insurance scheme for money payments could not supply that mechanism, since it was to include everyone, without income limit; and the B.M.A. had no practicable alternative machinery of exclusion to suggest. Though it fought hard for its 90 per cent. health service (for "all who need it"), excluding the upper tenth ("both willing or able" to pay private fees), against the proposed 100 per cent. service (for "all who want it"), it was a foregone conclusion that the Government should prevail. The new health service is in fact used by 95 per cent. of patients, so that private medicine retains an uncertain foothold.

The long dispute with the B.M.A. delayed preparations until the post-war Labour Government was elected and applied the all-party plan with some characteristic alterations. As agreed, family doctors and dentists, along with opticians and pharmacists, remained independent contractors. The Government pays doctors a fixed annual fee for each patient for whom they assume responsibility; while dentists, opticians and pharmacists receive a fee for each article or item of service supplied. But dentistry, dentures and spectacles were offered free to all adults as well as to all children, whereas the Coalition Government had been contemplating an extension to all adults of the part-payment system partially applied in the old health-insurance scheme.

All other important facilities (such as maintenance in hospital and various appliances), for which the Beveridge report and the Coalition had been inclined to favour at least a nominal charge, were also offered free. And, with the medical profession's support, all hospitals were nationalized and organized into large regional systems, whereas the Coalition had hoped to impose local planning upon them without radically altering their divided ownership. The remaining municipal services (chiefly for mothers and children and for home care) were made obligatory and extended to include home nursing, domestic help during maternity and sickness, and (above all) a complete ambulance service free for all, not only in emergency, but for general transport of patients deemed unfit to make "medically necessary" journeys by ordinary transport.

Designed to increase the consumption of medical care, the service succeeded beyond expectation. In 1950, its peak year, public health services of all sorts claimed 3·8 per cent. of the nation's resources, against 1·3 per cent. in 1938. Much of this great increase was merely a substitution of public for former private outlay; and some of it was attributable, not to additional services rendered, but to inflated rewards for certain groups such as dentists and medical specialists. Nevertheless, there was a real increase in the use of almost all facilities, much of it very necessary. Every child, housewife and old person now has a personal doctor. There have been great improvements in the distribution of specialist services and diagnostic aids, in the equipment and physical comforts of hospitals, and in the organization of hospital medical work (including a more constructive approach to the problems of elderly and chronic patients). Fear of the cost of a major operation has gone; old folk who obtained useless spectacles by inheritance or from chain stores now get proper glasses from opticians; the deaf have been equipped with efficient hearing aids.

By removing the restraints hitherto imposed by the market, however, the service gave free rein to the growth of appetites for health care. The public appetite was stimulated not just for medical and dental advice and treatment, but for all the comforts, conveniences and trappings associated therewith. Professional appetites were stimulated too—for the best possible equipment for every purpose, for X-ray photos, comfortable working conditions (including television in nurses' homes), and high standards of earnings and superannuation. Finding funds and spending them became divided responsibilities: hospital managements incurred bills for the Government to pay; one set of people decided the use to be made of ambulances which another set had to supply; the family doctor was not even told the annual cost of the drugs and dressings he was prescribing for treatment or placation of his patients.

It was easy enough for the Government to proclaim[1] that "the wealth or poverty of an individual becomes irrelevant to health care, as it should be. Bills are paid collectively instead of individually. The clubbing together of all citizens to meet the cost of medical care provides free service for any citizen at the moment when he needs it. There need be no more bargaining over fees, or arguments about insurance status. . . . There is no charge for any advice, treatment, drug, appliance or service which is medically necessary. . . . Provided special transport is necessary for medical reasons, the [ambulance] service can be used without payment." The dental services "will give the patient, free of charge, every form of treatment and appliance necessary for dental fitness". But in a field with few accepted standards for quality or cost of *necessary* service *efficiently* provided, it proved more difficult to distinguish what was really "necessary" from what was merely "desirable" or was just "fancied" for no very good reason at all.

Early carefree spending by hospitals was soon restrained by severe—and arbitrary—control of their budgets in detail. While impelling them to a more economical use of resources, this also endangered that freedom to experiment and initiate changes without bureaucratic hampering which is vital to medical progress. Since family doctors were not paid "piece rates", their own earnings could not get out of control. But their prescribing of medicaments

[1] In its popular booklet, *The National Health Service* (1949).

rapidly soared to previously unknown dimensions. In health insurance, prescribing had been stringently controlled, chiefly by making the doctors and pharmacists of each area collectively responsible for not spending beyond their area's quota of the scheme's (arbitrarily limited) drug fund. The new scheme sets no predetermined limit on prescribing. The far milder checks it attempts to impose broke down under the sheer volume of prescriptions flowing in for the authorities to count, check, price and pay.

In the first two years of the service over a quarter of the whole population went to the optician, and more than one in four each got two pairs of spectacles (for reading and for ordinary use). Demand began to fall after mid-1950, as the "backlog" of formerly unsatisfied need was being worked off. The similar boom in dentistry, however, showed no sign of passing. By 1950 the service seemed to have induced a decided change in British habits, with about one adult in five attending the dentist each year, against probably less than one in ten previously. But two-thirds of outlay on the general dental service was going on dentures and only 3 per cent. on the care of children's teeth. Britain has far too few dentists to meet all needs. It had been intended to secure priority of care for children and juveniles, stressing conservation rather than replacement of teeth, in order to reduce the future dental problem to manageable proportions. High earnings in the general service drew away many of the far too few dentists in the "priority" service for children which local authorities were trying to develop; and in the general service the needs of children were swamped by the demands of adults. The new system aggravated the already grave neglect of the rising generation's teeth.

The "open-ended" expenditure of these uncontrolled sectors of the health service could not be ignored. Apart from a general cutting of payments (the rates for which had assumed a much lower level of demand), control has so far been attempted mainly by requiring part-payment by patients, the charges being paid by national assistance for those lacking sufficient means. The Labour Government introduced cost-sharing for adults' spectacles and dentures in 1951. The Conservative Government followed in 1952 with a shilling charge for each prescription (then costing 4s. on average), £1 for every sort of adult dental care, and part-payment for various appliances (including wigs and surgical boots, but not hearing aids or artificial limbs).

These changes still left 95 per cent. of the cost of the service to be met by the State; but in three years they helped bring the optical and dental services down from 15 to 6 per cent. of public outlay on the service, and they reduced public outlay on prescriptions without appreciably affecting their volume. Demand for spectacles settled down at just over 4,000,000 patients a year, against 5,500,000 in

1950; and only one person in nine found that he really needed two pairs of glasses. The municipal children's dental service began to recover, and by 1953 children increased from 8 to 24 per cent. of patients treated in the general service, and juveniles from 9 to 15 per cent. In 1953 adults were using the service with much the same frequency as before for conservative treatment—indeed with greater frequency among adults under thirty-five—but demand for dentures was halved. Much of the "backlog" demand for dentures had passed, patients now had good reason to take care of appliances and not to seek their replacement unnecessarily, and more repairing and adjusting of dentures (as against replacement) was going on.

The remaining "State consumption" social services are mostly for social casualties rather than for ordinary citizens; for placing workers in jobs and training them in necessary skills; and for controlling and improving the physical environment, by town planning, land drainage, etc. Social casualties were formerly left either to the Poor Law (except for the blind and to some extent the tuberculous) or to voluntary effort. The Welfare State places a general duty on the larger local authorities, in which they seek the help of voluntary organizations, to look after the general welfare—as distinct from cash assistance or medical care—of all handicapped groups.

These include orphans and other children deprived of normal homes ("child care", included with education in Table II); infirm, impecunious or neglected old folk; unmarried mothers, and children who must be cared for while their mothers are out at work; homeless and "problem" families; the blind, the tuberculous and the physically handicapped of every description. The large Poor Law "workhouses" and orphanages are being superseded by small homes and hostels, ranging in type from the public boarding-house to the public nursing home and the residential school. Following the Scottish tradition, children are now placed as far as possible with foster parents rather than in institutions. Visiting, cheap meals and other services are arranged for old folk living alone. The Government maintains a register of disabled workers, obliging most employers to engage a prescribed quota of registered men; and it subsidizes special employment schemes for the severely disabled. All these welfare services, though greatly expanded since the war, meet only a fraction of genuine needs. Blind welfare and child care are perhaps the most thoroughly developed.

III. The "Beveridge Revolution"

The foregoing picture delineates a Welfare State in circumstances of strain. In "peaceful" 1950 social policy was doing more things imperfectly than it might have done really well, had social outlay been more firmly concentrated where it could do most good. In the "cold"—or "lukewarm"—war conditions of 1952-4, social priorities had become somewhat more clearly defined, various secondary aims had been deferred until better times—but the Welfare State had to arm itself for defence.

All through it was subject to the steady pressure of monetary inflation, of which the heavy burden of taxes was itself an important cause. During the war the British people had been willing to bear even heavier taxation without constantly pressing for higher money incomes and without preferring additional leisure to additional work, but such responses could not be kept up year after year in time of peace. By 1954 it seemed increasingly hard to reconcile the war budget with the social aspirations of the Welfare State, or to reconcile the combined claims of both with a lightening of taxation such as could facilitate the rapid economic advance on which Britain's future welfare depends.

The vagaries and naïvetés in some aspects of the British attempt at a universalist social policy should not be allowed to obscure the lasting significance of what is being endeavoured. Negatively the "Beveridge revolution" was a popular protest against the underlying assumptions of past social policy. Positively it was a somewhat confused assertion of social ideals that are gradually becoming accepted in most advanced nations. The main Victorian assumption was that normal men should fend for themselves, clubbing together for facilities they could not separately obtain. In misfortune, charitable aid was to be preferred to public assistance. As a last resort the State must indeed save people from starving to death, but only the abnormally unfortunate or feckless need be reduced to such a plight if the masses would learn to be thrifty and industrious and the wealthy to be charitable.

The Poor Law service, from which most modern social services grew, was designed to force the masses to help themselves, or seek private charity, rather than face the social humiliations (including loss of civic rights and separation from one's family) deliberately imposed in poor relief. The network of social facilities which developed under the Poor Law code, all technically denied to any who could not prove themselves to be "paupers", increasingly abandoned their early deterrent severity, but they never lost their flavour of social disgrace and cheeseparing parsimony. The emotional wounds of the Poor Law had gone too deep. When war came in 1939, the "lunatic poor", "medical relief", the tracing of "chargeable" relatives of old folk and hospital patients, even the occasional segregation at meal-time of "necessitous" children granted free school dinners—the whole apparatus and terminology of the Poor Law were still prominent in the social scene. Vivid memories remained of "test and task work", and of 1931, when local

Poor Law authorities took over management of Government relief for more than a million of the unemployed. No fewer than a million aged pensioners who had quietly refused to ask for poor relief flocked to the Assistance Board in 1940, and qualified for help, when relief was offered for them outside the Poor Law under the new name of "supplementary pensions".

The Victorian Poor Law did its work well. Charity flourished and played a great part in creating Britain's modern hospital system, which was still dominated by charity in 1939. But the charitable attitude—the tacit expectation of gratitude for favours bestowed and the unvoiced assumption that the feelings and convenience of recipients were unimportant—came to be nearly as much resented (especially in medical care) as was the Poor Law "taint" itself. The demand for social benefits as a right was, historically, very largely the demand of self-respecting men for respect from those who served them in illness or misfortune. In the nineteenth century the more determined and prosperous working men, with very little help from their employers, created their own system of rights through mutual insurance, as a means of securing by pre-payment medical care and income when needed. Their friendly societies and benefit clubs were the model for the social-insurance scheme of 1911—a compulsory friendly society for the entire body of manual workers, which in essence (despite subsequent extensions) it remained until its supersession in 1948.

Compulsory workmen's insurance belonged to a second phase of social policy, in which it was realized that unemployment and insecurity of income were not mainly personal faults of the worker but risks inherent in the structure of society. Public social services, it was now felt, were required not just for the near-destitute, but for the basic needs of the mass of working-class folk. It was tacitly assumed that these newer, non-pauper services need provide only for the elementary minimum of schooling, doctoring, feeding, accommodation and welfare required for maintaining "the health and working capacity" of the lower classes. Social services were seen chiefly as a means of transferring income from the higher to the lower ranks of society—a necessary public burden rather than a matter for pride.[1] And it was taken for granted that no one who could afford anything better would want to use the public services. Social insurance, hospital contributory schemes and various other services deliberately excluded the middle classes by income limits; municipal dwellings were by law confined to "the working classes"; and a like effect was achieved in public schools, maternity clinics and most other services by low standards and restricted budgeting.

[1] In fact the "working classes" (with weekly incomes of £5 or less) before the war paid sufficient in taxes to cover nine-tenths of the cost of social services chiefly benefiting them.

The "Beveridge revolution" was a protest against second-class services for impliedly second-class citizens, no less than against the haphazards and indignities of the older pauper or charitable services. Positively it called for community provision for generally shared social needs simply on the basis of common citizenship. In social security this required no more than making the middle classes join with the workers in a scheme to secure the right, when earnings fail, to a minimum of income sufficient for elementary everyday needs—a minimum to which every enterprising man will seek to add what he can.

But in respect of medical care, education, welfare and much else it was the workers who were to join the middle classes in enjoying a "classless" common good standard of service, given not merely efficiently but conveniently and courteously—just as they had already joined the middle classes in matters of dress, leisure and numerous other former marks of class distinction. The aim was not minimum provision at all (as in social security) but something nearer to an optimum—a standard of service that few could hope or wish to better by making private arrangements. This upgrading of the "public consumption" services from a "tolerable minimum" to a "common good" standard contributed greatly to raising the whole level of the claims of the social budget on national resources.[1] The services have to be not only good enough but varied enough to meet the far from uniform needs of the wider, more variegated, citizen body now to be more fully served. The need for diversity of provision implies, especially for schools, hospitals and hostels of all sorts, a massive and inevitably prolonged renovation or replacement of Britain's heavy heritage of obsolescent social-service buildings, held to be adequate in the days of minimum thinking.[2]

"Consumption" services for use by all citizens make a man's need for a service—need for a hearing aid, for medical treatment

---

[1] Three examples must suffice. (1) In primary schools built at different periods the square feet of floor space per child amounted, in the days of minimum thinking, to 13 (nineteenth century), 15 (1902-12), 18½ (1912-14), and 22 (1918-37). When the needs of the schoolchild began to be taken really seriously, "good standard" thinking at the Ministry of Education raised requirements to 31½ square feet (1937-9). Schools built in 1945-9 averaged about 60 square feet. Thereafter common sense and improved design brought the average down to about 40 square feet, and showed that any increase beyond that point had no educational value but was sheer waste of resources. (2) Three official committees, reporting successively in 1929, 1943, and 1948, argued that an adequate home midwifery service should not require the urban midwife to manage more than, respectively, 100, 66, and 55 confinements a year. (3) Hospital meals are generous. Before the war they were quite commonly plain and "basic", the patient's relatives being expected to bring in such "extras" as sugar, jam, biscuits, fruit, eggs and tomatoes.

[2] Even Britain's prisons, all but three of which are antiquated nineteenth-century structures, cannot afford that diversity of specialized institutions which is needed for the varied treatment of different types of offenders contemplated by the enlightened Criminal Justice Act of 1948.

or domestic help in illness, for a house or schooling for his children—
the sole condition of his obtaining it. He does not have in addition
to prove that he cannot afford to buy the service in the private
market. This ignoring of financial capacity as a *prior qualification* for
using a service is a necessary consequence of the citizenship basis of
the "consumption" services, which declare (for instance) that a
child's education shall not be "*determined* . . . by the financial
circumstances of his parent", and that patients' access to necessary
medical facilities "shall not *depend* on whether they can pay for
them".

But it was characteristic of British opinion immediately after the
war that this principle of universal *access* to social services, regardless
of financial means, was too easily assumed to entail the further
principle that the whole cost of services given must be charged to
public funds and none to actual users. That is, it was assumed that
users must be able to obtain service at "zero cost" (i.e. with 100 per
cent. subsidy) rather than by any system of cost-sharing adjusting
the degree of subsidy to users' varying financial resources. (As has
been shown, the "free" principle was also extensively applied in the
social-subsidy services). Yet the use of a financial test to *exclude*
certain classes of users altogether (as in the Poor Law or in lower-
income-group insurance) is entirely different from its use to decide
how much any individual user shall himself pay towards the cost of
a service granted simply because he needs it. It is the former, not
the latter, usage which is incompatible with a universalist social
policy.

The demand for "free" benefit as a right, regardless of financial
capacity, was sound enough when the benefit demanded was a
minimum income for men unable to support themselves by working;
and it was not unreasonable when applied more generally to services
confined to a relatively poor class of citizens. In services used by fully
employed, not workless, citizens whose means vary as widely as
their needs, Britain has been discovering since 1948 that the extent
to which users can be charged according to means for services
rendered is a matter of expediency, not of dogma. In some services,
indeed, cost-sharing according to means by the better placed users—
or adjustment of subsidy or financial aid according to financial
need—is the only way of securing the use of limited public resources
to the greatest advantage. As the Welfare State advances, it is likely
that cost-sharing by users will be extended rather than reduced in
scope.

Universalist social services may incidentally transfer income from
the better off to the less well off. But they are maintained fundamentally for the general convenience of society rather than for
"vertical" redistribution of income, which is now chiefly effected
by taxation. The kind of redistribution achieved by the social

services is rather between such groups as well and ill, working and unemployed, young and old, non-parents and parents, private and public tenants, beer drinkers and milk drinkers. During their lives most families belong successively to many of these "paying" and "receiving" groups. Thus to a large extent the Welfare State compels the citizen in effect to redistribute his own spending—to defer part of his earnings until retirement, to set aside funds for medical care and much else he may one day need. The State does this, on behalf of the community, because it believes that otherwise far too many would be badly educated or badly housed, and far too few would have the foresight to save for ill health and old age. Many, indeed, could not afford to do so, especially in times of monetary inflation. At least as many more, if left to their own devices, would not in fact do so, preferring to spend their money differently. How far it is wise for the State to go in overriding the individual's own preferences in the spending of his own income is a central—and an unsettled—question of policy.

In most advanced countries an evolution of social policy broadly resembling British experience can be traced. The differences in detail are, however, very wide. Few other countries had anything quite so embittering as the doctrinaire Victorian Poor Law tradition, so that few today share the popular British horror of "means tests" or the same insistence on "free" service in preference to cost-sharing. Victorian Britain also afforded the classic Marxist illustration of the degradation of all human relations between employers and workmen to the merely economic connexions required by a free labour market. Elsewhere, social services were frequently pioneered, not by the State or by unaided workers' clubs, but by paternalistic employers (who regarded their workers as something more than "hands" to be hired and fired at will) or by joint employer-worker organizations covering whole industries.[1] Some countries developed social services chiefly for particular occupational groups or for industrial workers as a class, leaving out independent craftsmen, shopkeepers and the farming population; others included the latter from the outset as a matter of course. (The contrast here between France and Denmark is instructive.) In some countries voluntary mutual-aid schemes were so well developed that the State has preferred to support, supplement and complete them (e.g. by making a minimum degree of participation compulsory) rather than supersede them by direct publicly organized services. And in most non-British countries State-aided tenants' or owner-occupiers' co-operative societies or joint employer-worker associations, rather than the municipalities, play the leading part in housing.

[1] Examples are the German sickness funds upon which Bismarck founded his pioneering compulsory insurance scheme, and the similar pioneering contribution of the family allowance funds in France.

But the final outcome everywhere is a similar trend towards a universalist approach in social policy. This reflects the now general understanding of the generally shared risks and needs inherent in the nature of modern society. Six main issues may be mentioned.

(1) In modern society virtually all income is in money, not in kind; most citizens earn income by working for employers, not for themselves; almost all produce for a (possibly world-wide) market. All this makes insecurity of income a social risk. The individual deprived of earnings by economic fluctuations, illness or old age cannot rely on support by his family or neighbours as he could in the more self-sufficing rural economies of the past.

(2) In industrialized societies the national need for a literate and technically trained working population soon made compulsory public education indispensable. Today concentrated ownership of economic resources, combined with tight restriction of opportunities for emigration, has converted education into the main ladder of social promotion for those not possessing capital resources —hence the steady pressure for the fullest possible education for every child.

(3) Compulsory education could not be made effective without forbidding child labour. This, reinforced by constantly rising standards of child care imposed by society, converted the child into a costly burden for parents. In the days of subsistence agriculture and domestic industry the family had commonly been a group simultaneously of producers and consumers. Now it is typically a group of consumers (varying in number) supported by a single male earner. Wages, being rewards for services rendered, cannot vary with the number of a man's dependants. Disregarded by the labour market, the dependent family was in effect given no secure place in modern society. Inevitably, family income had to be adjusted to family size, by adding to the breadwinner's unvarying work-income a social income varying with the number of his children. Measures of income redistribution in favour of the family—social payments, subsidies and tax remissions—whereby society shares with parents the everyday costs of child-rearing, are now becoming general in most countries.[1] But they were not widely introduced until parents had reacted to the situation by limiting their families to a somewhat dangerous extent.

(4) The modern transformation of survival chances in any event requires small families.[2] Reduced mortality and reduced fertility

[1] See United Nations Department of Social Affairs: *Economic Measures in Favour of the Family* (1952).

[2] With present low mortality-rates families of Victorian sizes would double Britain's population in less than 30 years.

have together set in motion a demographic revolution from which the Western nations will emerge before the end of the century with nearly static populations containing a permanently greater proportion of old people than ever before. Economic progress and the demographic revolution are aspects of a single process which makes it both more necessary and more possible to secure a reasonable standard of living for those who (at earlier ages than hitherto) expect to retire from work. At the same time monetary inflation, the endemic plague of the Western world since 1914, strengthens the demand for State provision of pensions, since only State action is likely to secure a system of retirement benefits protected against erosion by monetary depreciation.

(5) The twentieth-century scientific and "industrial" revolution in medicine, while greatly enhancing the potential efficacy of medical care, requires so high a rate of investment in medical facilities as to put the cost of medical care increasingly beyond the more slowly changing spending propensity of the private consumer. (Costs in American private-enterprise medicine seem to have risen as much as in Britain's socialized system.)

(6) At least in the earlier-industrialized nations, the great expansive phase of uncontrolled town building multiplied cheap and densely packed dwellings for the new urban masses without ever catching up with their needs. The problem was aggravated by the interruptions of building due to two world wars and the great depression. Much of industrialized Europe is left with a heritage of towns conspicuous for their economic and social inefficiency, containing a mouldering mass of obsolete housing the replacement of which—over and above "normal" replacements and extensions of the stock of dwellings—presents a major task for the decades ahead. The general spread of rent control (always tending to keep rents far behind rising incomes and building costs) and of legal security of occupation for tenants has further increased the incapacity of private enterprise to supply dwellings of required quality at suitably low cost. Throughout western and northern Europe, though not usually in the same ways as in Britain, the provision of low-cost housing is more and more becoming a responsibility of the State and of State-aided non-profit-making agencies. "Everywhere . . . the building of dwellings by capitalists with a view to letting them at a profit is on the decline".[1]

Thus it is circumstances themselves, in ways which transcend political, religious and class differences, that have written the main headings of the social agenda for the second half of the twentieth century in the more advanced nations of the world. The whole of that time will be needed for the full working and implications of the

[1] United Nations Economic Commission for Europe: *Methods and Techniques of Financing Housing in Europe* (1952).

universalist approach to be put to the test of experience and for its lasting significance to be assessed.

Note:—Gross national income (or output) is the total money value of all the nation's economic activities, *including* maintenance and replacement of capital goods. Measured at "factor cost" that value represents the true price of all goods and services, disregarding their artificial raising by indirect taxation (as on tobacco) or lowering by subsidies (as on milk), the effects of which are included in the value measured at "market prices". Factor-cost measurement gives a true indication of the amount of real economic resources appropriated by State "consumption" services. But it would be misleading to use factor-cost national output as a yardstick for assessing all forms of State outlay (whether of the "consumption" or the "transfer" type) when combined in a single total. For that purpose the market-price yardstick is less misleading.

The tables are derived from the official blue book, *National Income and Expenditure, 1946-53,* modified and extended by personal estimates. They combine current outlay by local authorities (which excludes capital spending) with revenue outlay of central authorities, which contains some capital payments (chiefly war-damage compensation, included in "war outlay").

The widest possible definition of "social outlay" has been used. Some experts would omit from a social budget such minor items as medical research (included in health care), public libraries, galleries and museums (education), employment services, environmental services connected with housing, and grants to universities and similar educational institutions. Omission of these would alter the total picture very little. "Health care" includes school medical services and the formerly separate war-pensioners' medical services, as well as the national health service. "Education" excludes school medical services, school meals (treated as a nutrition subsidy) and financial aid to scholars (treated as a social payment).

BOOKS SUGGESTED FOR FURTHER READING

François Lafitte, *Britain's Way to Social Security* (Pilot Press, London, 1945).

Ronald Mendelsohn, *Social Security in the British Commonwealth* (Athlone Press, 1954).

Pensions in the United States—Report to Congressional Joint Committee on the Economic Report (U.S. Government Printing Office, 1953).

Building America's Health—Report of President's Commission on the Health Needs of the Nation (U.S. Government Printing Office, 1953).

Freedom and Welfare (Joint publication of the Scandinavian Governments, London, 1955).

International Survey of Social Security (1950) and *Objectives and Advanced Standards of Social Security* (1952) (International Labour Office, Geneva).

SECTION FIVE

Law

by Professor A. L. Goodhart

On december 12, 1919, the governing body of the Commissariat of Justice of the Soviet Republic issued a decree in which law was defined as "A system (set of rules) for social relationships, which corresponds to the interests of the dominant class and is safeguarded by the organized force of that class". This was based on the Marxist doctrine that law always represents the interests of the strongest party. But if law was purely a class interest, what role could it play in the classless society established in Russia? The logical answer was that law would disappear, and this was the view accepted by the legal philosophers Stuchka and Pashukanis. The latter wrote in his *Theory Of Law And Marxism*: "The dying out of the categories of bourgeois law will in these conditions signify the dying out of law in general: that is to say, the gradual disappearance of the juridic element in human relations."

When the Soviet system of government achieved stability it became clear, however, that a body of law was essential if the State were to function in an orderly manner. The Pashukanis doctrine fell into disfavour, and he himself attempted to repudiate it in 1930. It was too late. In 1932 Mr. A. Y. Vyshinsky, who played so important a role at the United Nations, criticized him in terms that were more trenchant than those commonly employed by Western jurists engaged in an ideological controversy. After describing Pashukanis and his followers as a "gang of thieves, betrayers and traitors [who had] crept into certain of our institutes and made a mockery of our science", he said:

> The most important task confronting all scientific workers in the field of the science of law and State at the present time is the final extirpation—the complete and conclusive liquidation—of all the remnants of these *provocateur* fabrications: that is to say, the complete and final purging of the Augean stables of our legal science from the mud and all the filth of 'hostile' theories, from all the trash which unfortunately has accumulated among us over the years.

In due course Professor Pashukanis seems to have been liquidated, for nothing has been heard of him since.

The bitter attacks made on Pashukanis and the strenuous efforts to repudiate the doctrines which he had taught showed the importance which the rulers of the U.S.S.R. attributed to a proper interpretation of the concept of law. It is clear that they did not think that this was merely an exercise in semantics or a purely academic discussion: it was a recognition on their part that words may rule the world. This is hardly surprising, for it cannot be denied that the ideas which men hold concerning the nature of government are of fundamental importance in political life, and that words may be such ideas stated in epitome. It was that most astute of politicians, the Emperor Augustus, who said that all men may be governed by the tactful use of words.

Although I agree with Mr. Vyshinsky concerning the importance of a correct definition of law, I believe that the definition which he himself advocated is misleading and out of date. After stating that "Law was never an expression of social solidarity. It was always an expression of dominance—an expression of struggle and contradictions", he defined it in these terms:

> Law is the aggregate of rules of conduct—or norms: yet not of norms alone, but also of customs and rules of community living confirmed by State authority and coercively protected by that authority.

He assumed that law can exist only by the authority of the State, and that it must depend on the State power for its enforcement and efficacy. This, as I shall suggest later in this essay, follows the Austinian doctrine that law is the command of the sovereign, and is enforced by the sanction attached to it. This conception of law has an ancestry of more than three centuries, for, as Professor Patterson of Columbia University has said, "it took definite form with the rise of the modern European State and is intimately related to theories of the State, of sovereignty and government". It has given support to the belief in the all-powerful and omnipotent national State, and to it may be attributed some of the evils which the world has suffered during the past half-century. It is therefore of importance to determine whether it is possible at the present time to substitute for this idea of law one which can give us better hope for the future. But before undertaking such a difficult task it is necessary to say something concerning the three terms *society*, *State* and *law* because we cannot understand the history of their interrelation unless we attempt to clarify our ideas concerning their nature.

Society is defined in the Oxford Dictionary as "an association of persons united by a common aim or interest or principle". To form a society in the true sense it is not sufficient, however, to have a common interest, even though this may induce the persons affected by it to act in the same way. Thus all the passengers in a train going to London have a common interest in completing the journey, and all have acted in the same way by boarding the train, but they do not form a society as they are not acting together for the purpose of achieving their common purpose. It is this purposeful relationship which distinguishes a society from other associations, such as an audience at a theatre or a crowd at a football game. Every society which is not purely ephemeral in character must have a clear and definite skeleton of rules, as the relationship between the members can only be expressed in this way. It is therefore correct to say that a society is based on a body of rules controlling the actions of those persons, called the members, who are associated together, either voluntarily or involuntarily, for the purpose of achieving a specific end. These rules are the laws of the society: they are obligatory on the members because if they are disregarded then the society must cease to exist. This is as true of a small debating society in a country village as it is of the greatest of all modern societies—the national State. The distinguishing mark of every society is to be found not in its size or in its system of government, although some form of government, however rudimentary, is always essential, but in its purpose. Aristotle emphasized this when he pointed out that the comic chorus was distinguished from the tragic chorus by its "constitution", although the actors in the two choruses might be the same. The laws of every society must, therefore, be directed to a particular purpose; they must contain a provision, either express or implied, concerning the membership of the society; and they must establish a system of government. It is impossible to think of any society, whatever its nature or purpose, which is not based on these three fundamental provisions. The rules of the society may provide for a sanction in case they are not obeyed by some of the members; but this is not essential, as in many societies all the members recognize that if the rules are not regarded as obligatory then the society will inevitably come to an end. It is only for the recalcitrant few that a sanction is necessary in a properly organized society.

The most important society of all at the present time is the national State. It has achieved such dominance that we are inclined to think that it is unique in character, and that therefore the State system of government and the State law must differ in nature from other systems and other laws, but there is no justification for this view. Thus it has been said that the State differs from all other societies in that it has a monopoly of physical force at its command, but experience has shown that the force at the disposal of the State may be inferior to that which a particular political party in the State controls. If it is said that this monopoly must exist in theory even if it does not exist in fact, then the answer is that in political science a theory is meaningless if it is in conflict with the facts.

It is respect for authority and not physical force which is the essential element in a State. Again it has been said that a State differs from all other societies in its structure as it must have a sovereign and subjects. This theory, because of its apparent simplicity, has a superficial attraction when applied to a unitary State such as Great Britain in which it is possible to ascribe sovereignty to the Queen-in-Parliament; but in a federal State, such as the United States, it is impossible to find a sovereign unless sovereignty is ascribed either to the written Constitution, which is absurd, as a document obviously cannot exercise power itself, or to the people as a whole, which is one of the most dangerous fallacies of modern political thought. The people, as an unorganized body, obviously cannot act coherently, and so the demagogue is free to claim that he is speaking in the name of the sovereign people.

If, then, the distinction between the State and other societies cannot be found in the material element of force or in the system of government, how can it be determined? The answer is that the essence of the State, as in the case of all other societies, lies in its purpose, and it is here that the line of demarcation can be drawn. The primary, and essential, purpose of a State is the maintenance of internal peace within a particular territory. It is to this end that the basic provisions of the law are directed: it is the establishment of the "King's peace" which is the first function of the courts. The truth of this conception of the State is shown by the fact that when a State can no longer maintain internal peace then it has come to an end. A new State, reconstituted under a different constitution, will take its place, and internal peace will be re-established. It would, of course, be nonsense to suggest that this maintenance of peace is ever the sole purpose of the State, as it is obvious that even the most primitive organization must have wider ends in view, but it is the one inevitable one. As Aristotle has said, the State is established so as to make life possible, but its ultimate aim is to make life good.

To maintain order and to achieve internal peace it is essential that the laws of the State have a certain degree of rigidity. It is a platitude to say that law is the skeleton of the body politic which will become flaccid if the bones on which it depends are too soft and pliant. Law must, therefore, have a high degree of strength and permanence if it is to function properly. If it were to alter immediately with every social or economic change it would lose that quality of certainty which is essential to its nature.

A body of law which could claim rigidity as its sole distinction would, however, have little chance of lengthy existence. Anything which is too inflexible is likely to break when a sudden force is brought against it. Law, if it is to survive, must, therefore, attempt to achieve other purposes in addition to that of peace, even if this means the sacrifice of a limited degree of certainty. Of all other ends to which law has been directed, the most important in the whole of legal history has always been justice. It is no coincidence that in every legal system the words "law" and "justice" tend to be bracketed together. We speak interchangeably of the "Courts of Law" and the "Courts of Justice", although we know that the two concepts are not identical. All attempts to define justice in precise terms have failed, but it is generally accepted that the essence of justice is "to render to each man what is his due". So general a statement will, of course, be of little practical value in enabling us to solve any particular problem, as it leaves unanswered the main question, "What is his due?", but it does express an ideal which is of fundamental importance in the life of every country.

The problem of justice affects the law in two different ways which are not always clearly differentiated. In the first place we are concerned with justice in the administration of law. This is frequently said to mean that the law will be applied to every man without fear or favour. There are few people who would deny that today justice, in this sense, is substantially administered in every English court; for personal prejudice, which can never be completely excluded, plays only a very small part. It has, however, been argued in the past that the administration of justice favoured the wealthy, as they could incur the heavy costs involved in many legal proceedings— which, whatever might be true in theory, in fact excluded the poorer members of the community. "The law", it has been said, "like the Ritz Hotel, is open to the rich and to the poor alike". Today, it is argued, the roles have been reversed, as the Legal Aid Scheme enables the poor man, without cost or risk to himself, to bring a legal claim against an opponent who will find himself the loser, whatever the result of the action may be.

These problems of justice in the administration of law are, however, of only minor importance, and are capable, in large part, of solution. It is when we turn to justice in the substantive law itself that the insoluble problems arise. A just law must seek to adjust the competing interests of innumerable persons in a fair manner, but no general rule can ever do more than achieve an approximation of justice. Moreover, a law which provides substantial justice when it is enacted may, under the changing circumstances of a new era, arrive at the opposite result. Justice, it has been said, wears a bandage over her eyes, as she cannot bear to see some of the things that are done in her name.

The conflict between certainty and justice must be a never-ending one. Certainty wishes to maintain a rule, even though the conditions under which it was first adopted are no longer the same. Justice, on the other hand, demands that the rule should alter with every change in the circumstances. A study of legal history shows that this conflict is one in which complete victory is never won by one side or the other: the forces are so equally balanced that neither can defeat the other. During some periods, which may extend over centuries, the emphasis has been on certainty and rigidity, although there must be some change in the law even during these periods; change is accepted, however, with hesitancy and with doubt. These periods of legal rigidity usually come immediately after times of revolution when men find that their strongest desire is for peace and stability. On the other hand, periods of legal reform seem to come when this stability has been established, and when the need for certainty is therefore less immediate. Under such conditions it is possible to place the major emphasis on justice. Reform in the law is rarely revolutionary in character, because, while violence can destroy law, it cannot create an atmosphere in which the delicate and perplexing work of legal construction can be successfully undertaken. It is, therefore, during periods of strength and self-confidence that the law can best hope for its necessary amendment.

The history of English law in modern times strikingly illustrates the conflict between these opposing tendencies. After the turbulence of the Civil War in the seventeenth century and the political uncertainties at the beginning of the eighteenth, we find a strong desire throughout the rest of the century for intellectual peace. The Age of Reason was eminently a reasonable one, more prepared to explain than to reform. This attitude found a ready welcome in all legal circles. During the whole of the eighteenth century there is little legislative activity of any importance. The desire is for established rules; and the common law, which had proved so powerful a weapon against Stuart attempts at tyranny, receives an almost religious reverence. Even the innovations which the great Chief Justice Lord Mansfield introduced into the law at this time tended to be additions to, rather than alterations in, the common law. More typical of the opinions of the age were the famous *Commentaries on the Laws of England* published by Sir William Blackstone in 1765-9. The enthusiasm with which these were received was not due solely to the genius which he showed in introducing order and form into the chaos of the law, but was based in large degree on the fact that he was expressing in eloquent language views that were in accord with the general ideas of the time. For Blackstone the common law was, with one or two doubtful lapses, "the perfection of reason". Any alterations to that "venerable edifice of antiquity" were dangerous, "for, to say the truth, almost all the perplexed questions, almost all the niceties, intricacies, and delays (which have some times disgraced the English, as well as other courts of justice), owe their original not to the common law itself, but to innovations that have been made in it by acts of parliament" (Introduction, § 1, p. 10). He felt that even when time had so changed conditions that it was impossible to determine on what ground a particular rule of the common law was founded, nevertheless it was unwise to make any alterations. He said (§ 3, p. 70):

> It hath been an antient observation in the laws of England, that whenever a standing rule of law, of which the reason perhaps could not be remembered or discerned, hath been wantonly broken in upon by statutes or new resolutions, the wisdom of the rule hath in the end appeared from the inconveniencies that have followed the innovation.

So blind an acceptance of the past must be regarded almost with admiration, for it would be impossible to find a more perfect illustration of the desire for certainty and rigidity in the law, although similar attacks on legal "innovations" are not unknown, even today.

It is not surprising that this exaggerated emphasis on rigidity should have given rise to some reaction, but it could hardly have been expected that it would be so violent and so successful. When Blackstone delivered his lectures at Oxford, a young student of genius attended them: Jeremy Bentham has told us that they first inspired in him his desire for reform, for he immediately discerned the fallacies in the pious platitudes of the complacent jurist. The first blow was struck in 1776 in the *Fragment on Government or a Comment on the Commentaries*, when "men at large were invited to break loose from the trammels of authority and ancestor wisdom in the field of law". In the place of authority Bentham sought for the first time in legal history to apply "the scientific method", to use the modern phrase, in the analysis of law. As Isaac Newton, in the belief of his contemporaries, had found the key to all the physical sciences, so Bentham believed that he had found the key to the social sciences in the doctrine of utility. Every law should be measured by the test of the greatest good to the greatest number, and if it failed to pass then it should be discarded. The enthusiasm of the lawyers for the past infuriated Bentham: "barristers", he wrote, "are so called (a man of spleen might say) from barring against reforms the extremes of the law". The common law, which Blackstone had described as "the perfection of reason", was called dog-law. "Do you know how to make it? Just as a man makes laws for his dog. When your dog does anything you want to break him of, you wait until he does it, and then beat him. This is the way you make laws for your dog, and this is the way judges make laws for you and me."

In his zeal for reform Bentham undoubtedly was unfair to judge-made law. He failed to realize that judges must play an important part in developing the law, and that any attempt to reduce them to mere automata must fail. Even the best-drawn statute may leave gaps which must be filled by the process of judicial interpretation, and new situations which the legislator has not foreseen are certain to arise, for no one can be omniscient. In such circumstances the courts must make law, whether they wish to or not. Bentham over-rated the value of codification—a word which he invented. By disregarding the essential traditional element in law he convinced himself that substantially the same code could be applied in England, Spain, Egypt and China. Unfortunately his many offers to prepare the necessary codes were never accepted.

Bentham's enthusiasm for statute law persuaded him that all law must be the command, direct or indirect, of the sovereign power in the State, which in Great Britain was the King-in-Parliament, and that that sovereign must be uncontrolled by the law. This conception of law was accepted by Bentham's disciple John Austin, and through him has dominated juristic thought in England for more than a century. Unfortunately they failed to realize that this interpretation could be used to justify all absolutism, for under this theory there must always be in every State a body able and entitled to act in an arbitrary manner because its power cannot be limited by the law. According to this doctrine the idea that the State can itself be bound by the law is a chimera. It is true that the minor officials can be legally controlled, but those in the seats of power are absolute. A State whose sovereign consists of a number of persons is likely to act in a less arbitrary manner than one in which sover-eignty is exercised by an individual, but this is immaterial from the theoretical standpoint. It is hardly surprising that Bentham was not concerned with the implication of this theory, for his eyes were directed solely to the reform of the law. This could only be accomplished through Parliament, and therefore the more power that body was conceived to have, the more hope was there that the evils of the common law would be destroyed. Nor did it ever occur to Bentham that a body, such as the British Parliament, could act in a tyrannical manner, especially as the reform of Parliament could at that time be reasonably foreseen.

The struggle over Parliamentary reform and the Napoleonic wars prevented any steps being taken to implement Bentham's recommendations. When he died in 1832 it must have seemed to him that his life-work had proved ineffective, and that he was only one more prophet crying in the wilderness. But with the end of the external and internal conflicts which had occupied the country for over two centuries, a period of tranquillity began, which ushered in the most striking measures of legal reform ever known in legal history. For fifty years the ideal of justice replaced the emphasis on certainty, and the fear of change was forgotten in the excitement created by the belief in human progress. It has been the practice to regard the Victorian era as one of caution and conservatism, but from the legal standpoint it was so progressive, especially in its early years, that it might almost be described as revolutionary. The utilitarian doctrine, whatever might be its defects as a comprehensive philosophy, proved the most powerful weapon ever given into the hands of the reformers. When subjected to the test of utility there was not a single branch of the law which did not prove defective. It would require a volume to describe the changes that were introduced in this tremendous half-century, but brief reference can be made to five major reforms.

The machinery of the law was so completely altered between 1832 and 1882 that the books of practice which were of authority in 1832 are completely meaningless today. Not a single page, or even a single paragraph, has remained unchanged. The venerable system of pleading, which placed the major emphasis on form rather than on substance, was swept away, with the result that some critics today claim that the present rules are too formless in nature. The structure of the courts, which had stood for over seven hundred years, was pulled down, and a new High Court of Judicature was erected in its place. The gulf between the common law and equity was bridged, even if the distinction between the two systems was not destroyed.

The law of evidence, in both the civil and the criminal courts, was basically altered. Today it is difficult to realize that before 1850 any party to an action, or anyone who had a financial interest in its result, was prohibited from giving evidence on the ground that such evidence might be perjured. In *The Pickwick Papers* Dickens demonstrated the absurdity of this rule because when Mrs. Bardell sued the unfortunate Mr. Pickwick for breach of promise of marriage neither of them was allowed to give evidence. Experience has shown that the abolition of this rule has placed the conduct of the modern trials on a rational foundation, although no one would deny that there is a certain amount of embroidery in the evidence given by the parties, especially in running-down cases.

The criminal law, which at the beginning of the nineteenth century was the harshest in any civilized State, has now become almost the most lenient; nevertheless Great Britain has the reputation of being the most law-abiding of the larger nations of the world. Before 1832 more than two hundred crimes were punishable with death: today there are only two. All cruel forms of punishment have been abolished, and transportation has, of course, disappeared.

Before 1857 there was, properly speaking, no law of divorce, for a marriage could only be terminated by a private Act of Parliament. The provision of divorce under a general law introduced a social change which, whether we approve of it or not, has had a profound effect on family life. Of equal importance have been the various

Married Women's Property Acts which gave financial independence to women at a time when they began to take a more prominent place in industry and commerce.

From the legal and the economic standpoints almost the most important legal innovation was the creation of business companies under the various Companies Acts, beginning in 1844. The great economic development during the latter half of the nineteenth century would not have been possible if it had not been for these new legal persons which today control more than two-thirds of the wealth of this country.

Perhaps the most bitterly fought innovation in the law was that which concerned the trade unions. Their history has been a dramatic one, for they began under the threat of being regarded as criminal conspiracies, while today they hold a favoured position in the law which enables them to commit certain torts with complete immunity. It was not until 1871 that the law gave them adequate recognition.

These fundamental changes continued to be introduced into the law long after there had been a reaction against the more exaggerated doctrines of the utilitarian school. The legal historians, of whom Sir Henry Maine was the most distinguished, emphasized the traditional element in all legal systems. They disputed the view that law was nothing more than a command enforced by a sovereign authority, and they showed that this theory would not have been understood by the men of the Middle Ages. Their belief in the gradual and inevitable development of the law in accord with the national spirit helped to bring about the slowing-down, if not the total elimination, of reform at the turn of the century. Surprising support was given to the historical school by the doctrine of evolution, which some legal philosophers regarded as proof of the belief that conscious attempts to improve the law itself, or to introduce improvements in the body politic by means of law, were both unnecessary and unavailing, as the future existence of the State depended on the survival of the fittest. It followed, according to this view, that as little restraint as possible should be placed on the strong, for they were the natural leaders. Laissez-faire, they held, was as justifiable in the law as it was in economics. It was unfortunate if the weak went to the wall, but this was necessary in the interest of the State as a whole. So callous a doctrine could only play a minor role, but its pseudo-scientific foundation gave it a certain amount of influence. It was used as a check on those who were inclined to think that they would be able to achieve any reform they regarded as desirable merely by changing the law.

The two world wars and the intermediate years have brought about great social and economic changes in this country, but their effect on the law itself has been much less striking. Two things have been primarily responsible for this peaceful revolution—the income-tax and the death-duties. Both of these are of long standing, and their astonishing increase since 1914 has not affected their legal nature: they are, therefore, of little interest to the legal philosopher *qua* legal philosopher, however absorbing they may be to him as an ordinary citizen. Nor has the development of the Welfare State been much affected by legal thought, nor, in turn, has it had much influence on new legal ideas.

What about the future? Although some useful reforms have been introduced into the law in recent years these have been of only a minor character. It would be too much to expect that during a time of crisis any major legal changes would be considered. With the return of stability it is probable that we shall enter on a new period of legal reconstruction. It will hardly be comparable to that of the nineteenth century because one need not be an excessive optimist to say that there is not the same urgent need for change today as there was then, for the whole legal system has been transformed in the past century. There will, however, be plenty of work to be done by some future Bentham.

Like the poor, the problem of legal administration will always be with us. It is improbable that the recommendations made by the Committee on Supreme Court Practice and Procedure (popularly known as the Evershed Committee), even if they are accepted, will be able to achieve a material reduction in the cost of litigation. Although it is probably true that the quality of English justice is second to none, it is equally true that it is too expensive for the average man. It has been said with some justification that only the very wealthy or the very poor can afford to litigate in this country. This is one of the reasons for the rapid growth of arbitration in recent years. This might be welcomed, for there is much to be said for domestic tribunals which the parties have chosen for themselves, if it were not an indication that the courts have failed to meet the public demand for justice at a reasonable price. It is also an indication that a less formal administration of justice might better accord with the spirit of the present day: litigants and witnesses sometimes feel that they are entitled to more consideration in the courts than they receive. Nor is it certain that the circuit system, in spite of its ancient history and its dramatic appeal, ought not to be reconsidered, especially in its relation to civil litigation.

The second, and far more difficult, problem is concerned with administrative law. We are slowly beginning to realize that all law is not found in the courts of law. Dicey's definition of law as the rules enforced by the courts has long been out of date, even if it ever was true. With the vast extension of administrative tribunals in recent years we are faced with a new body of legal rules which lie entirely outside the jurisdiction of the ordinary law courts, but which are as truly law as the long-established rules of the common law. There is a growing demand today that the chaos of administrative law should be reduced to order in this country as it has been to a large degree in France. This will be no easy task owing to the rule of ministerial responsibility, because if the minister must accept responsibility for the acts of his officials then he must have the final authority over them which cannot be delegated to any other body.

The third problem is concerned with the codification and reform of the criminal law. There are a number of valid reasons which can be advanced to justify the failure to codify the civil law in England, but there can be no such excuse for the present state of the criminal law. Here, if anywhere, there ought to be clarity and certainty, but no one who has attempted to distinguish between larceny, fraud, embezzlement, receiving, and other forms of dishonesty will be prepared to ascribe these qualities to this branch of the law. There ought to be no difficulty in dealing with this problem because other countries have found an answer to it. Far more difficult in our present state of knowledge is the whole question of criminal punishment which in the past has been regarded by some of the judges and other authorities as nothing more than a simple exercise in the application of common sense. Today there are some persons who deny that punishment as such is ever justified, but in recent years there has been a reaction against this view. Perhaps the most hopeful sign for the future is the growing conviction that no *a priori* theories have any value in this field, and that any advance we can make must be along scientific lines.

Less obvious, but equally interesting, are the problems in the civil law. In the law of tort there are two conflicting theories: the one holds that tortious liability should be governed by the principle "no liability without fault", while the other supports the view that liability should be determined by a consideration of allocation of risk. Perhaps it will be found that the correct answer is to discard all general theories in this wide and divergent branch of the law, and to seek for rules which are reasonable having regard to the particular circumstances. In the law of contract the conception of a contract as a bargain freely entered into by both parties who have agreed concerning its terms has become outmoded in large part owing to the centralization of power in the hands of large industrial units and of trade unions. In recent years the courts have hesitated to hold a man bound by unreasonable terms which he could not, owing to the force of circumstances, refuse to accept, but no adequate solution has as yet been found.

These are only some of the problems which will have to be considered in the future, but when they will be raised and how they will be solved depends in large part on the ancient conflict between the demand for certainty and the demand for justice. Which will gain the upper hand during the coming years no one can foretell with any confidence, because the answer depends finally on world conditions. Until tranquillity has been restored there can be little prospect of legal reform on any major scale.

One last question of transcendent importance therefore remains to be considered. Can we reasonably hope that in world affairs the rule of law will in the future take the place of force? Put in another way, this raises the question whether we can establish a true society of nations, bound together by obligatory rules of conduct.

If we accept Mr. Vyshinsky's command definition of law as the rules established by the State and enforced by the State then clearly there can be little hope for any juridical development in the field of world affairs unless a super-State is created which has the power to enforce its commands on the subordinate national States. According to this view the present national States can only be legally bound to each other if there is some superior power which is capable of enforcing its rules by applying a sanction in case there is a breach of them. This doctrine was probably accepted by the majority of the jurists during the nineteenth century when the command interpretation of law held the field. To them the idea of a law which was not enforced by a specific sanction was a contradiction in terms. International law, therefore, was not law in the true sense, and it could not legally bind the various nations. Every State must be a sovereign State because no law could limit its powers. It may be said that the facts seemed to justify this pessimistic view because the majority of States seemed to abide by the rules of international law only in so far as it suited their interests. A rule which can be disregarded at will obviously has not got that compulsive nature which is an essential element in all law. Without a sanction, it was said, there could be no compulsion to obedience.

"Without a sanction there can be no compulsion to obedience." Is this statement true? There is, perhaps, no more important question in all political philosophy than this, because our whole conception of the State and of constitutional law depends on the answer to it. It is here, I believe, that we can find the distinction between the theory of a totalitarian and of a constitutional system of government.

At first sight there is much to be said for Mr. Vyshinsky's definition, because undoubtedly the rules established by the State are law and they are almost invariably enforced by a sanction. No reasonable person can deny that there is a legal system in force in the U.S.S.R. which, for all we know, may be as effective as the legal system in Great Britain or in the United States. This is self-evident, because no society can exist which does not have rules of conduct which are binding on its members. A State, like any other society, must have a governing body capable of speaking in the name of the State if it is to function at all. We must remember that when we speak of a State we are speaking of an ideal concept which can act only through human beings as its agents, and that what they say only binds the State in so far as they are acting as its agents. Even the most complete autocrat distinguishes between the acts which he does in his personal capacity and those which he does in the name of the State. When Louis XIV said that *"L'Etat c'est moi"* he did not mean that all his acts were acts of State. In so far as those who hold the supreme power in the State act in the name of the State and by its authority, then the rules they establish are binding on the members of the State, and are properly described as State law. They fall within the command definition of law.

But does this mean that there is no State law other than this? Is Mr. Vyshinsky's definition complete, or does it exclude a part of State law which is of peculiar importance? In other words, does it exclude the constitutional rules on which the existence of the State itself is based? The obvious answer for those who accept the command interpretation of law must be that the constitution lies outside the field of law because the State cannot command its own existence. Under this doctrine there must be in every State a person or body of persons who hold the supreme power to command the law, but cannot themselves be bound by the law. In short, there can be no legal control on those who exercise the supreme power. We have all seen how this theory works in a totalitarian State in which the will of a Mussolini, a Hitler or a Stalin can be exercised without any legal limitation. This is perfectly logical because as no one but the supreme leader can command the law therefore he cannot be subject to it. This is equally true where the supreme power is vested in a few men who are regarded as being above the law because they command it.

I believe that this conception of the State, which has had such a disastrous effect in recent years, is based on a fundamental fallacy. It is untrue that law is always a command or requires a sanction for its validity. Its compulsive character usually is based on other and far more effective grounds. It is the recognition of obligation and not the fear of an evil which gives to law its conative quality—it is the sense of *oughtness* which distinguishes law from purely voluntary rules. Legal history has shown that a sanction is applied to a rule because it is recognized as being obligatory: the rule is not obligatory merely because a sanction is applied to it. The sanction is only part of the law-enforcement machinery: it is not an essential part of the law itself. As Sir Frederick Pollock has said: "Law is enforced by the State because it is law; it is not law merely because the State enforces it."

If law is based on obligation and not on command then there is no difficulty in recognizing that the State itself can be subject to law, and that those who exercise its power can be controlled by legal rules in the performance of their functions. It is here that the essence of constitutional rule lies because if those in power cannot be controlled by the law then there is no distinction between constitutional and arbitrary government. This is not a new idea, because Aristotle in his *Politics* pointed out that the law binds the magistrates as well as the ordinary citizens of the State, but this truth has been forgotten in modern times owing to the exaggerated importance that has been ascribed to the nation State. To suggest that its powers could be limited by law was almost treasonable, although it ought to be obvious that the idea of freedom under the law depends on the recognition of such a limitation.

In a State with a written constitution this conception of law as obligation can be readily accepted. It is clear that such a constitution is not commanded by anyone: its existence depends on the recognition on the part of the people that it is obligatory. Nor is there any ultimate sanction for its enforcement, because if those in power—the legislature, the executive, or the judiciary—refuse to obey the provisions of the constitution no penalty can be enforced against them. There have been instances in some countries in which the executive has refused to enforce a particular judgement of the courts; but nothing could be done about it as the physical power lay in the hands of the executive, although no one doubted that in such circumstances the executive had acted unconstitutionally and in breach of the law. Such refusals are, however, exceedingly rare, because the officers of the State, in whatever capacity they may be acting, realize that they are under an obligation to obey the law of the constitution.

In a State, such as Great Britain, which has an unwritten constitution it is more difficult to see the fallacy in the command interpretation of law, as at first sight there seem to be no legal limitations on the power of Parliament concerning the legislation it may enact. Thus it may be true to say that in theory the Queen-in-Parliament might commit political suicide by providing that all power should be transferred to an individual or a group of individuals—which would mean the creation of a totalitarian State. But—and this is an essential But—until such a step is taken the present constitutional rules are binding on all public officers. Thus if the members of the House of Lords and the members of the House of Commons were to meet in a single body and purported to legislate in such a manner no court in Great Britain would recognize their action because it would be unconstitutional. It is, of course, true that the British constitution can be altered by an ordinary act of legislation, but until this is done the present system is binding law. It is binding law, not because it has been commanded or because a sanction is attached to it, but because it is regarded as obligatory by the Sovereign, by Parliament, by the courts and by the ordinary members of the State. It is for this reason that the 50,000,000 people in this country obey the statutes enacted by the 650 members sitting in Westminster. We must remember that Parliament would be impotent if the obligatory nature of its Acts were not recognized by the courts or by the executive. Again the courts would be impotent if the executive refused to recognize the obligatory nature of their judgements. The executive, if sufficiently powerful, could overthrow the legislature and the courts, but if it did so it would be governing by arbitrary force and not by law. To deny that the provisions of the constitution are law in the true sense because their compulsive nature is based on the recognition of obligation and not on force is to contradict the most important fact in the English polity, and to render meaningless most of English history.

This brings me to the most interesting problem in political science today: Why is a law recognized as being obligatory? The answer at first sight seems to be so obvious that it may seem to some to be hardly worth stating: we recognize law as obligatory, it is said, because we fear an evil if we disobey it. The apparent simplicity of this answer conceals its inadequacy. By explaining obligation in terms of fear we fail to distinguish between obedience to law and obedience to arbitrary command. In both these instances we get obedience, but there may be all the difference in the world between them. If a gangster points a gun at me and orders me to raise my hands above my head I, as a reasonable being, will obey his order, but this obedience is of an entirely different nature from the obedience which I give to an order addressed to me by a police officer acting in the course of his duty. It is strange that this distinction, which political philosophy finds it so difficult to analyse and explain, should often be unconsciously recognized by untutored men who are prepared to die in the defence of law against arbitrary power.

What then are the grounds on which this sense of obligation is based? I am not suggesting that the ones I am about to mention will furnish a complete list, but I believe that they have proved to be the most important ones.

Perhaps the oldest and most powerful ground is that of tradition or custom. We all tend to regard a rule as obligatory merely because it has been followed for a considerable length of time. Anyone who has ever been concerned with the care of young children will recognize the powerful effect of this idea, whether we term it an instinct or not; Sir James Frazer and Professor Malinowski have shown how grave an error it is to regard primitive men as lawless; for them a traditional rule of conduct may be more obligatory than is a statute for their modern descendants. Few men today would lie down and die because they had violated an Act of Parliament, but such conduct was not unknown at the dawn of civilization. No one who has had anything to do with an institution such as a University can fail to recognize the sense of obligation which tradition can impose. It is a feeling which may be almost unconscious, but it gains added force from the fact that it may be emotional rather than purely rational.

The second ground is respect for authority. A rule is regarded as obligatory because it has been laid down by one to whom obedience is due. This obedience may be entirely divorced from force or sanction, for it may be owed to one who is old and weak. We find this in the father-son relationship; there is hardly any civilization, apart from the most primitive one, in which the son does not recognize the authority of his father. Again, when the State first begins to emerge, it is the Hero-King to whose laws obedience is due, in some cases long after he is dead. The living ruler may be powerless to alter the rules which tradition ascribes to his great ancestor. It would be a mistake to underrate today the force of this respect for authority: the power of the modern dictator has in large part been founded on it. In a more legitimate way Walter Bagehot in his classic work, *The English Constitution*, emphasized how great was the almost mystical authority of the Crown in the field of law enforcement in this country.

The third powerful influence in creating a sense of obligation has always been found in religion. Perhaps the most apposite illustration of this can be seen in the doctrine of the Divine Right of Kings. Throughout history there has been a belief that a subject is bound by his religion to obey the Royal commands because the King represents the authority of God. Perhaps this particular sense of obligation has played a smaller part in English history than it has in the history of many other countries, but it has nevertheless been a powerful one.

The fourth ground on which a sense of obligation is founded is that of reason or self-interest. The rational man realizes that if he does not accept the obligation of a rule, then there is no reason why others should recognize such an obligation. He knows that the effectiveness of law must, in the last analysis, be based on the obedience which is given to it, and that if he fails to obey the rule then others may take a similar step. We regard as irrational the man who complains that other persons are breaking the law when he himself has failed to show respect for it. It is for this reason that a spirit of lawlessness, even in a minor branch of the law, is so dangerous, for it may spread like a disease throughout the body politic.

Finally, the ground of obligation may be found in our sense of morality. This is of peculiar importance because it is not only a major reason for obedience to State law, but it also affects the substance of the particular laws which constitute the whole legal system. Some legal philosophers have argued that it is necessary in the interest of clear thinking to establish an absolute divorce between law and morality, but I believe that this dichotomy will result in a misleading picture. State law and moral law are obviously separate concepts, but they tend always to be married to each other and to support each other. A divorce between them may lead to social disaster.

By moral law I mean those rules of conduct which are based on the relationship of man to man. Law is always a relationship, and it is therefore possible to distinguish between the different types of law according to the relationship which they represent. In the case of religious law it is obvious that the relationship is between God and man, and it is therefore correct to say that religious law consists of those obligatory rules of conduct which are recognized as being owed primarily to the Divinity. Religious law may, of course, also prescribe a duty to others, but the primary duty in every case is always to God. In the case of State law the primary relationship is that of man to the artificial person known as the State. State law recognizes that it is the duty of every person, subject to the State, to obey the rules prescribed by the duly authorized officers of the State. Thus every person is under a duty to the State to obey the law of contract just as he is under the more obvious duty to obey the criminal law. Here again the primary duty to the State will give rise to subsidiary duties to others. In moral law the relationship is between man and man, and it prescribes the duty which the one owes to the other. The same wrongful act may constitute a violation of all three types of law. Thus if X steals Y's property he is breaking a law of the Christian religion because the Ten Commandments provide "Thou shalt not steal". In doing so he has violated his duty to God. He is also breaking the State law against larceny, and he is therefore violating his duty to the State. Finally he is breaking the moral law by violating the obligation which he owes to all men not to steal from any of them. It is not possible to discuss here the extremely difficult question whether there are any absolute principles of morality: all that it is necessary to say is that in every civilized community men recognize that their relationship to each other is governed by certain obligatory rules of conduct.

If the nature of the duty owed under moral law differs from that owed under State law, how then can it be said that moral law is a ground of obligation for State law? I think that the answer is that the members of any society, and especially of the State, are under a moral duty to obey the rules of the society, not only to the society itself but also to the other members. We may fail to recognize this by personifying the society, but as a society constitutes a relationship between the various members it follows that they must owe a moral duty to each other. I believe that the strength of the English legal system is due in part to a recognition of this essential truth, although the recognition may not always be a conscious one. The English feel that they are entitled to protest against a breach of the law even if it does not affect them personally. It is interesting to note that it is still the theory of the English criminal law that a prosecution is brought by an individual, and that that individual need not be the person who has been injured by the crime. Of even greater importance is the feeling that it is the moral duty of everyone to protest against such a breach, because each member owes a duty to the others to protect their rights. Unless this duty is recognized, a nation, however advanced in civilization, may succumb to tyranny and arbitrary rule because no individual by himself is strong enough to fight against disregard of the law by those in control of the machinery of the State. It is not a coincidence that the English people, who have most clearly recognized this duty, have also best succeeded in defending their liberty. It is correct therefore to say that the moral law is one of the foundation stones of the civil law because every member of the State is under a moral duty not only to obey the law himself, but also to see that it is obeyed for the protection of others.

Although the command definition of law has played a great role in legal history during the past centuries, and has been one of the most powerful forces in the establishment of the modern theory of the State, it has been steadily receding in popularity in recent years. It has been gradually realized that law cannot be explained, much less justified, merely in terms of force, because that is what command and sanction represent. Nor can that interpretation be historically supported, for it fails to explain the medieval polity. Feudalism, which it is so hard for us to comprehend if we think in terms of command, becomes rational if we think in terms of obligation. There was obviously no superior commander who could establish rules binding both on the King, as feudal lord, and on his subjects: nevertheless both the King and his subjects recognized that there were obligations legal in nature which bound both of them. Professor McIlwain has summed-up the medieval point of view in a well-known passage:

> We think of law primarily as a command, they did not. As a consequence we fix our main attention upon the penalty imposed by the maker of the law for a breach of it and this we term its 'sanction'. To the medieval mind, on the contrary, law is primarily reason, and its promulgation is less essential. In fact for most 'laws' there was scarcely any definite 'sanction' whatever, but they were none the less laws.

The medieval interpretation of law may have placed too great an emphasis on reason, forgetting that there are other equally important grounds on which the obligation of obedience may be based, but it did not make the modern error of exaggerating the part played by force. Perhaps today, when we have seen the evils of force disguised as law exercised by selfish men uncontrolled themselves by the law, we may hope that a synthesis of these competing ideas may give us a concept of law on which a better civilization can be built.

By thinking of law in terms of obligation and not of command we will emphasize the most important truth that the State itself can be controlled by law: the inevitability of the all-powerful nation-State will no longer be accepted as an axiom. We shall also be able to stress the difference between a totalitarian State in which there is a body of men who are able to act outside the law, and a State governed by a law which is of universal authority. It is not over-optimistic to hope that this conception of law may in time spread to those countries which now accept Mr. Vyshinsky's doctrine of force, because law is a powerful missionary. In its time the Roman law gave to the world its doctrine of legal order: perhaps in time to come the common law may give to all nations its ideal of freedom under the law.

It is in the obligation conception of law that we may also hope to find a means of finally replacing international anarchy by international law. It will make clear the all-essential point that international law need not wait for the creation of a super-State, or even for the establishment of efficient sanctioning machinery before it can claim to be law in the true sense. It is the spirit—the sense of obligation—and not the machinery that has been lacking in the past. We have glibly spoken of a Society of Nations, but we have forgotten that such a society cannot exist unless the members of it recognize that they are under an obligation, moral as well as legal, to obey its rules. Here again law may finally triumph over force.

BOOKS SUGGESTED FOR FURTHER READING

Aristotle, *Politics*.

J. L. Brierly, *The Law of Nations* (Oxford, 1955).

A. V. Dicey, *Law of the Constitution* (Macmillan, 1939).

H. Kelsen, *General Theory of Law and State* (Harvard, 1945).

G. W. Paton, *Text-book of Jurisprudence* (Oxford, 1951).

R. Pound, *Interpretations of Legal History* (Cambridge, 1923).

INDEX

ACKNOWLEDGEMENTS

WE THANK the following for permission to include quotations in the article on "Writing":

Harcourt, Brace and Company for the lines on page 341 from "Your Teeth Are Ivory Towers" (*The Collected Poems of William Empson*).

New Directions for the lines on page 337 from "The Winter's Tale" (*The Collected Poems of Dylan Thomas*). Copyright 1953 by Dylan Thomas.

Mr. Robert Graves and Messrs A. P. Watt & Son for the lines on page 335 from "The Fallen Tower of Siloam" (*Collected Poems* by Robert Graves).

The Macmillan Company for the lines on page 338 from "A Prayer for My Daughter" (*Collected Poems of W. B. Yeats*).

The quotation by Rodin appearing on pages 301–3 of the "Sculpture" is from *Rodin, The Man—His Ideas—His Works* by Camille Mauclair (tr. C. Black; Duckworth, 1905).

Figure 4 on page 250 of the article on "Genetics" is a copy of Abbildung 39 from W. Beerman, *"Chromomerenkonstanz und spezifische Modifikationen U.S.W."* from *Chromosoma* (Bd. V., pp. 139–98), 1952, reprinted by permission of Springer-Verlag, Berlin, Gottingen, Heidelberg.

ABOUT THE AUTHORS

ALAN PRYCE-JONES is editor of *The Times Literary Supplement* of London, one of the most authoritative media of comment, criticism, and scholarship in the world. He has called upon the following distinguished authorities to contribute to *The New Outline of Modern Knowledge:*

LORD AMULREE, M.D., F.R.C.P., is a physician at University College Hospital, London, President of the Medical Society for the Care of the Elderly, and author of *Adding Life to Years.*

SIR LEIGH ASHTON, until 1955 Director and Secretary of the Victoria and Albert Museum in London, is the author of several books on Chinese art and sculpture.

THOMAS BALOGH, D.Pol., is a Fellow of Balliol College, Oxford, and has been a visiting professor of Economics at the Universities of Wisconsin, Minnesota, and Delhi. He is the author of *Studies in Financial Organization* and *The Dollar Crisis.*

J. H. M. BEATTIE, University Lecturer in Social Anthropology at Oxford, has had extensive field experience in Africa and was a member of the Colonial Administrative Service.

LORD BOYD-ORR, F.R.S., has been Director-General of the United Nations Food and Agriculture Organization and was awarded the Nobel Peace Prize in 1949. He is the author of *The National Food Supply, Food and the People,* and other books on nutrition.

G. S. FRASER is a contributor to *The Times Literary Supplement* and *The New Statesman and Nation.* He is the author of *The Modern Writer and His World* and several volumes of poems.

A. L. GOODHART, Q.C., D.C.L., has been professor of jurisprudence at Cambridge, Oxford, and Yale and is Master of University College, Oxford. Author of many books in the field of law, he has also served as president of the International Association of University Professors.

HARMAN GRISEWOOD was Controller of the B.B.C.'s Third Programme and since 1952 has been Director of the Spoken Word for the B.B.C. He is the author of *Broadcasting and Society.*

R. F. Harrod, author of many books, including *The Life of John Maynard Keynes,* served during the war as a statistical advisor to Lord Cherwell and Winston Churchill. He is Nuffield Reader in International Economics at Christ Church, Oxford.

Rev. Denis J. B. Hawkins, Ph.D., D.D., is the author of *Causality and Implication, Criticism of Experience,* and *Essentials of Theism.*

Christopher Hollis, formerly Conservative M. P. for Devizes, has written many books, including *Rise and Fall of the Ex-Socialist Government, Can Parliament Survive?* and *Breakdown of Money.*

John Holloway, D.Phil., D.Litt., is lecturer in English at Cambridge and the author of *Language and Intelligence, The Victorian Sage,* and numerous articles.

Robin Ironside, a painter as well as an art scholar, has been assistant director of the Tate Gallery, London, and is the author of *The Pre-Raphaelites, British Painting Since 1939,* and *The Burning Glass.*

Sir Harold Spencer Jones, F.R.S., served as the Astronomer Royal from 1933 to 1955. He is the author of *General Astronomy, Worlds without End,* and *Life on Other Worlds.*

François Lafitte is a journalist specializing in social problems and the author of *Britain's Way to Social Security.*

Wilfred Mellers, Staff Tutor in Music at the University of Birmingham, is a contributor to *The New Oxford History of Music* and the author of *Studies in Contemporary Music* and *Music and Society.*

J. G. Porter, Ph.D., is connected with the Royal Greenwich Observatory, broadcasts frequently for the B.B.C. on astronomy, and is the author of *The Night Sky* and *Comets and Meteor Streams.*

J. B. Rhine is Director of the Parapsychology Laboratory at Duke University, editor of the *Journal of Parapsychology,* and author of *Extra-Sensory Perception* and *New Frontiers of the Mind.*

J. M. Richards has been Joint Editor of *The Architectural Review* since 1946 and is the author of *Introduction to Modern Architecture.*

Henry Seligman was a member of the six-man team that built Canada's first atomic reactor. He is director of the Isotope Division at the Harwell Atomic Energy Research Establishment.

E. W. F. Tomlin is the author of *The Approach to Metaphysics, The Great Philosophers, Simone Weil, Living and Knowing,* and many articles.

T. E. Utley has been a member of the editorial staffs of the *Sunday Times, Observer,* and *Spectator.* He is the author of *Essays in Conservatism* and *Modern Political Thought.*

C. H. Waddington, F.R.S., is Buchanan Professor of Animal Genetics at the University of Edinburgh and the author of *Introduction to Modern Genetics, Organizers and Genes,* and *The Scientific Attitude.*

Sir Mortimer Wheeler, president of the Society of Antiquaries, has directed many archaeological expeditions and is the author of several books, including *London in Roman Times* and *Five Thousand Years of Pakistan.*

R. C. Zaehner is Spalding Professor of Eastern Religions and Ethics at Oxford and the author of *Zurvan, a Zoroastrian Dilemma.*

O. L. Zangwill, Professor of Experimental Psychology at Cambridge, is the author of *An Introduction to Modern Psychology.*